DRUGS AND SOCIETY

Weldon Witters, Ph.D.
Department of Zoological and Biological Sciences
Ohio University
Athens, Ohio

Peter Venturelli, Ph.D.
Department of Sociology
Valparaiso University
Valparaiso, Indiana

Glen Hanson, Ph.D., D.D.S.
Department of Pharmacology and Toxicology
University of Utah
Salt Lake City, Utah

Jones and Bartlett Publishers

Boston ■ London

Editorial, Sales, and Customer Service Offices

Jones and Bartlett Publishers
20 Park Plaza
Boston, MA 02116

Jones and Bartlett Publishers International
PO Box 1498
London W6 7RS
England

Library of Congress Cataloging-in-Publication Data

Witters, Weldon L.
    Drugs and society / Weldon L. Witters, Peter J. Venturelli, Glen
R. Hanson.—3rd ed.
      p.   cm.
    Includes bibliographical references and index.
    ISBN 0-86720-317-X
    1. Drugs. 2. Drugs—Toxicology. 3. Drug abuse. I. Venturelli,
Peter J., 1949–   . II. Hanson, Glen R.   III. Title.
RM301.W58 1992
615′.1—dc20   92-1413
                                            CIP

Production Service: The Book Company
Copyeditor: Sue Freese
Typesetting: Modern Graphics
Design: Melinda Grosser for *silk*
Cover design: Ad Cetera
Cover Printer: Henry N. Sawyer
Printing and Binding: Courier Westford

Color plates from *Drugs of Abuse*, U.S. Department of Justice,
Drug Enforcement Administration

Printed in the United States of America
96 95 94 93 92   10 9 8 7 6 5 4 3 2 1

Contents

CHAPTER 3

Drugs, Regulations, and the Law 56

CHAPTER 4

How and Why Drugs Work 92

C H A P T E R   9

Stimulants 246

C H A P T E R   1 0

Tobacco 286

C H A P T E R   1 1

Hallucinogens 318

C H A P T E R   1 2

Marijuana 354

CHAPTER 13

Nonprescription (OTC) Drugs 378

CHAPTER 14

Drugs and Psychiatric Disorders 402

CHAPTER 15

Drug Education, Prevention, and Treatment 422

A P P E N D I X   A

Chemical Structures 457

A P P E N D I X   B

Schedule Classifications of Common Drugs of Abuse 465

A P P E N D I X   C

Common Drugs Interactions 467

A P P E N D I X   D

First Aid in Drug Abuse-Related Emergencies 469

Preface

Drug misuse clearly has become a major social problem in the United States. Approximately 28 million Americans used illicit drugs in 1990 (Jarvik, 1990) and currently 5 to 6 million people in the U.S. are dependent on illegal substances: these figures do not even include the misuse of, or addiction to, legal drugs such as amphetamines and sedative medications, which have been prescribed for patients by health professionals (Holloway, 1991). In addition, 59 million or more people in this country regularly abuse alcohol and nicotine. The impact of such drug abuse on individual lives, health costs, and social consequences is staggering.

Despite evidence that drug abuse problems continue to plague our society, hopeful trends have emerged during the past few years. Household and "treatment center" surveys have demonstrated significant declines in the use of, and dependence on substances of abuse. While such declining trends suggest that efforts to prevent and treat drug addiction have been somewhat successful, it is clear that much more can and should be done.

Although at this time it is impossible to determine the precise causes for the recent drug abuse trends, certainly drug education has been a major factor contributing to the decline. There is little doubt that drug dependence is more likely to occur in those who are ignorant about drugs in general, or drugs with addicting properties in particular.

With the epidemic misuse of drugs in our society, this text has been written to provide the latest information on the topic. The first edition of *Drugs and Society* primarily emphasized biological and historical information about drugs and drug use. The information in the second edition was broadened to include some additional social scientific aspects of drug use and misuse. This new third edition was written in order to answer the questions of why drugs are misused and how drugs pharmacologically affect the body. This edition is essentially a new text. We have provided the latest information on the pharmacological, sociological, and psychological perspectives of commonly abused drugs and have supplemented the text with examples, case histories, and exercises to help students assimilate the material. The text originally published as Witters' *Drugs and Society* has been extensively rewritten by Professor Venturelli and Dr. Hanson. Venturelli has written Chapters 1, 2, 7, 10, 12 and 15 and has had primary responsibility for authoring the instructor's manual together with the computerized test bank. Hanson has written Chapters 3, 4, 5, 6, 8, 9, 11, 13, 14 and the appendices.[1] In this third edition, over 50 percent of the material in each of the chapters has been completely revised. The extensive revision reflects recent changes in our understanding of the phar-

---

[1]The original author, Professor Weldon Witters, passed away while the second edition of this text was in print. We have retained his name in this third edition due to his previous contributions and to show our appreciation for his creation of *Drugs and Society* one last time before Venturelli and Hanson assume full authorship in future editions of this text.

macology of drug use and misuse and the fact that abuse is no longer viewed as merely a physiological or psychological problem. Today's use and misuse of drugs go beyond body and mind reactions. Drug problems involve families, places of employment, neighborhoods, communities, educational and religious institutions, local, regional, national and even international social, political, and economic boundaries. These issues are dealt with in the third edition of *Drugs and Society*.

Because of the current awareness that drug abuse is a broad issue involving many factors, the extensive revision of this text speaks to numerous perspectives and a variety of disciplines dealing with drug abuse problems. Thus, nursing, physical education and other health sciences, psychology, social work, and sociology students will find that the text provides useful information and perspectives to help understand the following aspects of drug abuse: (1) why and how drug abuse occurs, (2) the results of drug abuse, (3) how to prevent drug abuse and, (4) how drugs can be used properly.

PERSPECTIVE AND SEQUENCE

Due to the pervasive nature of drug abuse in our society, this text has integrated material from three authors who represent distinct but essential perspectives on this problem. The current two authors (see footnote 1) are respected experts in their fields, have taught thousands of students in drug-related classes at their respective universities, are actively involved in drug abuse research, and represent the disciplines of sociology, psychology, and pharmacology. The authors have published many articles on drug-abuse topics in national and international journals, have been members of national and local committees that deal with drug abuse problems, and have served as consultants to law enforcement agencies for drug abuse-related issues. The material for the text was derived from: teaching and consulting experiences; international, national, and local seminars and conferences on substance abuse; personal research; and the most recent literature on relevant drug abuse topics.

The material in the text encompasses both social-psychological and biomedical views. *Drugs and Society* begins in Chapter 1 by distinguishing between drug use and abuse and examining how and why people use and abuse drugs. In this chapter basic drug-related terminology is introduced and the overall historical and current patterns of drug abuse in the U.S. are presented. Chapter 2 evaluates the major theories that explain why people misuse drugs: these include sociological, psychological, and physiological explanations and the significance of the association between mental disorders and drug abuse. The next three chapters have been substantially revised for this edition. Chapter 3 reviews the historical evolution of drug use and regulation so that students can appreciate how and why drugs are classified and controlled today. Such knowledge helps students to understand the differences between drug use, misuse, and abuse and their consequences. Chapter 4 instructs students about the factors that determine how drugs affect the body. This chapter details the physiological and psychological variables that determine how and why people respond to drugs used for therapeutic and recreational purposes. Because the addicting properties of most, if not all, substances of abuse are due to the effects of drugs on the reward centers of the brain, Chapter 5 helps the student understand the basic biochemical operations of the nervous and endocrine systems and explains how psychoactive drugs and anabolic steroids alter such functions.

Chapters 6 through 12 deal with specific drug groups that are commonly abused in this country. Those familiar with previous editions of *Drugs and Society* will notice a new, more logical organization in this section of the book. Those drugs that depress brain activity are discussed in Chapters 6 (sedative/hypnotic agents), 7 (alcohol), and 8 (narcotics and pain relievers). The drugs that stimulate brain activity are covered in Chapters 9 (amphetamines, cocaine, and caffeine), and 10 (tobacco; nicotine). The last main category of substances of abuse is the hallucinogens: such drugs alter the senses and create dreamlike experiences. These substances are discussed in Chapters 11 (hallucinogens in general such as LSD, mescaline, and PCP) and 12 (marijuana). Although most drugs that are abused cause more than one effect (for example, cocaine can be a stimulant and a hallucinogen), the classification we have chosen for this text is frequently used by experts and pharmacologists in the drug abuse field and is based on the drug effect that is most likely to predominate following abuse. All of the chapters in this section are similarly organized. They discuss the historical origins and evolution of the agents so students can better understand society's attitudes toward, and regulation of, these drugs. Previous and current clinical uses of these drugs are discussed to help students appreciate distinctions between therapeutic use and abuse. Next, the patterns of abuse of these substances and special features which contribute to their abuse potential are discussed. Finally, nonmedicinal and medicinal therapies for drug-related dependence, withdrawal, and abstinence are presented.

Chapter 13 discusses nonprescription (over-the-counter) drugs that are frequently used. As with illicit drugs of abuse, nonprescription drugs are often administered by uninformed consumers without medical supervision and can also cause significant health problems and dependence when not used properly. Because of these similarities, the discussion of nonprescription drugs in this chapter will help students appreciate the pervasive nature of abuse problems and distinguish between beneficial use and adverse abuse of drugs.

Chapter 14 treats the topic of drug therapy for psychiatric disorders. On the surface this chapter may appear out of context in a textbook that principally focuses on drug abuse; however, as students read this chapter it becomes clear why a discussion of mental illness is consistent with the objectives of this text. All drugs of abuse can change the functions of the brain regions that regulate mental states and thereby induce conditions that mimic psychiatric illness. Consequently, Chapter 14 provides students with unique perspectives of drugs of abuse by discussing the cause of and treatment for psychiatric disorders.

Chapter 15 of *Drugs and Society* acquaints students with the treatment, rehabilitation, and prevention of the major drugs of abuse. This final chapter describes the principal sociological, psychological, and pharmacological strategies used to treat and prevent substance abuse and details their advantages and disadvantages. The discussion in this chapter helps students to understand better why drug abuse occurs, how society currently deals with this problem on an individual and group basis and the likelihood of rehabilitation of persons dependent on these substances.

The appendices have been revised and expanded for the third edition to better complement the material and are included both at the end of some chapters and at the end of the book. For example, a table of all commonly abused drugs, their principal actions and regulations is found in an appendix after Chapter 1. A detailed table is included which lists all of the principal drug abuse legislation in a Chapter 3 appendix. A table of common drug interactions can be found at the end of Chapter 4. Another appendix shows the structures of the major drugs and chemicals discussed in the text (it is located at the end of the book). Finally, descriptions of first aid strategies for treating overdoses with substances of abuse have been added as an appendix at the end of the book.

LEARNING AIDS

Each chapter in this third edition of *Drugs and Society* includes improved learning aids for students. These aids were added to help students understand new terminology and concepts as well as encourage students to think about the application of the information in practical settings. In addition, throughout the book the students will find many real-life examples of drug effects or drug principles to help them appreciate the relevance of the concepts presented. The specific learning aids include: (1) highlighted definitions of terminology as well as a complete glossary at the end of the book; (2) outlines at the beginning of each chapter to help students gain an overview of the chapters' contents; (3) a list of "Learning Objectives" to help students focus on major concepts being taught; (4) summary statements at the end of each chapter which correlate with the learning objectives mentioned above; (5) a "Did You Know That" section at the beginning of each chapter, which lists interesting facts presented in the text;

(6) "Think About It" questions included in each of the chapters' subsections to encourage students to discuss, ponder, and analyze their own feelings and biases about the information presented in the book; (7) box inserts called "For You to Consider . . ." or "Let's Get the Facts . . ." which contain quotations, interviews, and actual clinical examples of principles discussed; (8) well organized and concise tables and figures frequently included throughout the book in order to present the latest information to students in an easily understood format; and, (9) new photographs and drawings added to help illustrate important concepts. Because of these many new features we believe the third edition text of *Drugs and Society* is much more "user friendly" than previous editions of this text and will substantially enhance student learning and interest.

EXPANDED INSTRUCTOR'S AIDS

For the instructor adopting this third edition for classroom use, a heavily revised instructor's manual containing over 1,000 test questions is available. In addition, a computerized test bank, written and supervised exclusively by Venturelli and Hanson, and 40 overhead acetate transparency masters are also available to the instructors.

CONCLUSION

The third edition of *Drugs and Society* is a much improved text intended to help college and university students from a wide range of disciplines gain a fundamental understanding of drug-related problems in our society. In this book we have included the most current views on drug abuse and have attempted not to moralize about issues but to present substantiated information in an easily understood fashion. Extensive, updated references have been listed after each chapter to assist students who want to pursue topics introduced in this text. It is the objective of the authors that students be able to apply basic understanding gained from the study of this text to their personal and professional lives in order to deal with drug abuse problems. In addition, the information presented in this book should help students to use drugs in ways that favorably treat illness and improve the quality of life.

ACKNOWLEDGEMENTS

The numerous improvements that have made this edition of *Drugs and Society* a leading college text in the field of drug use and abuse could not have occurred without the hard work and dedication of numerous people.

First, we gratefully acknowledge the efforts of Joseph Burns, vice-president at Jones and Bartlett Publishers, for his professional direction throughout the revision process. His ability to identify the best developmental specialists in textbook publishing was essential. Notwithstanding, another vice-president, James Keating, was responsible for giving this book life and maintaining it in print during the first and second editions. Also at Jones and Bartlett, the production specialists, Joni McDonald and Paula Carroll are to be applauded for their invaluable assistance and expertise. Likewise, we thank Heather Stratton at Jones and Bartlett for her ability to maintain communication between the authors and the dozens of experts working on this text.

Outside professionals included Maxine Effenson Chuck, an invaluable editor who compelled the authors to burn more of the midnight oil than they had ever anticipated with an endless flow of queries and rewrites. Susan Freese, our copy editor, was responsible for reducing the "fat" of our original sentences and converting unnecessary verbiage into useful information.

At our respective institutions the authors wish to thank a multitude of people who are too numerous to list individually but have given us invaluable assistance for meeting publication deadlines. At Valparaiso University, student aids Heather Falke, Ericka Shrontz, and Dan Woodman top the list and this includes our conscientious permissions editor, Kimberly Hroma. At the University of Utah, we thank the secretarial staff for their support and flawless transcriptions.

Last, and most of all, Drs. Venturelli and

Hanson want to especially thank their wives, Shalini and Margaret, for their patience and encouragement while the authors labored for months in order to extensively revise and complete this timely textbook.

R E F E R E N C E S

Holloway, M. [March, 1991] "Rx for Addiction." *Scientific American,* 95–103.

Jarvik, M. [1990] "The Drug Dilemma: Manipulating the Demand." *Science* 250: 387–392.

DRUGS AND SOCIETY

Drug Use:
An Introduction

CHAPTER OUTLINE

Commonly Used Terms ▪ Drugs ▪ Psychoactive Drugs ▪ "Gateway" Drugs ▪ Medicine ▪ Prescription Drugs ▪ Over-the-Counter Drugs ▪ Drug Misuse ▪ Drug Abuse ▪ Licit versus Illicit Drugs / **Drug Use and Abuse: A Historical Perspective** / **How Widespread Is Drug Abuse?** / **Who Are Potential Drug Abusers?** / **Drug Use or Abuse: Where Do We Draw the Line?** / **Is There a Link between Drug Abuse and Mental Illness?** / **Are Drug Users Socialized Differently?** / **What Is the Frequency of Drug Use?** ▪ Statistics of Drug Use ▪ Main Findings from the 1988 National Household Survey on Drug Abuse / **The Role of the Mass Media in Drug Advertising** / **Appendix: Drugs of Use and Abuse**

LEARNING OBJECTIVES

On completing this chapter, you will be able to:

1. Cite two reasons why it is important to understand drug use and abuse in today's world.
2. Define the following: *drugs; psychoactive drugs; "gateway" drugs; medicine; prescription drugs; over-the-counter drugs; licit drugs;* and *illicit drugs.*
3. Identify the difference between drug *misuse* and *abuse.*
4. Explain when drugs were

first used and under what circumstances.
5. Cite five reasons why people continue to use drugs.
6. Discuss how widespread drug use is and who is likely to be a potential drug abuser.
7. Cite the best way to distinguish between drug use and abuse. (What key factor has to be taken into account in order to determine use or abuse?)
8. Summarize the link between drug abuse and mental illness.

9. List the major characteristics that drug abusers have in common.
10. Explain the four different uses of drugs.
11. Identify what age group has the highest incidence of drug use, according to the National Household Survey on Drug Abuse, conducted in 1988.
12. Evaluate the role that the mass media plays in promoting or discouraging drug use.

Photo: Ewing Galloway, N.Y.

DID YOU KNOW THAT . . .

- Drug addiction is an "equal-opportunity" affliction, found in all races, religions, and social classes.
- Alcohol addiction is the drug problem that affects the greatest number of people.
- Illegal drug trade—a $70- to $90-billion-a-year industry—ranks second in yearly earnings to Exxon and just above General Motors and Mobil Oil.
- All drugs with abuse potential alter brain activity.
- Excessive use of drugs creates imbalances in the brain transmitters, which can either mimic or aggravate existing mental illness.
- Children who feel that their parents are emotionally distant from them are more likely to become drug addicted.
- It is rare to find abusers of cocaine, heroin, or virtually any addictive drug who did not start with some combination of alcohol, tobacco, and marijuana.
- About 7% of the U.S. population is addicted to drugs or alcohol.
- A National Institute on Drug Abuse study found that persons in the 18- to 25-year-old age group were by far the heaviest users of drugs.
- One-third of all adults have used or are using CNS depressants.
- Most heavy users of drugs are multiple drug users; that is, they simultaneously use more than one psychoactive substance.
- Studies show that the majority of young drug users come from homes where drugs are used extensively.

Despite the fact that drug use dates back thousands of years, the use *and* abuse of drugs today is more prevalent and widespread throughout the world than ever before. Understanding drug use and abuse is important for two reasons. First of all, the use and abuse of drugs is a national and, for the most part, international problem. What's more, drugs can easily invade and unravel the very fabric of values and attitudes that hold society together. Drugs can drastically alter individual social behavior, destroy family life, uproot neighborhoods and communities, and, on a broader scale, disrupt the day-to-day functioning of society.

As the title of this book suggests, the broad focus of our study is on drug use in society. In a more specific manner, however, we will address the following questions:

1. What drugs are used and abused?
2. What are the compositions of different drugs, and how do they affect the body?
3. Who uses and abuses various types of drugs?
4. When and how are drugs used and abused?
5. What are the reasons for the use and abuse of drugs?

In this introductory chapter, we will begin by defining key drug terms that are frequently used. Next, the history of drug use and abuse will be explored, considering the widespread use of drugs in contemporary society. We will return to this subject later in the chapter with a review of the results from the National Household Survey on Drug Abuse (1988). Other topics in this chapter include the characteristics of potential drug abusers, the differences between *use* and *abuse*, links between drug abuse and mental illness, the socialization of drug users, and the role of the mass media in drug advertising.

COMMONLY USED TERMS

A **drug** is any substance that modifies biological, psychological, or social behavior. Such modification can enhance, inhibit, or distort the functioning of the body.

---
drugs
any substances that modify biological, psychological, or social behavior
---

There are a number of different types of drugs commonly abused:

1. *Narcotics*—opium, morphine, codeine, and heroin
2. *Depressants, such as sedatives and hypnotics*—barbiturates, benzodiazepines (e.g. Valium), methaqualone (Quaalude), and alcohol
3. *Stimulants*—cocaine, amphetamines, and caffeine as well as coffee, tea, and tobacco
4. *Hallucinogens*—LSD (lysergic acid diethylamide), mescaline, and peyote
5. *Cannabis*—marijuana and hashish
6. *Organic solvents*—inhalants, such as gasoline, airplane glue, and paint thinner, as well as foods, herbs, and vitamins

Appendix 1-1 lists some commonly abused drugs in society, outlining the following information: medical uses; trade names; slang terms;

physical or psychological dependence; tolerance duration; usual methods of administration; possible effects; effects of overdose; and withdrawal syndromes.

---

psychoactive drugs
substances that alter consciousness or perception

Psychoactive drugs affect the central nervous system and alter consciousness or perception. Because of their effects on the brain, these drugs can be used to treat mental illness. Some are abused because of their addictive properties.

"gateway" drugs
drugs that lead to the use and abuse of more powerfully addictive drugs

---

The term *gateway* suggests a path leading to something else. **"Gateway" drugs** are those used initially before proceeding to other more serious drugs. Alcohol, tobacco, and marijuana are examples of drugs that lead to the use and abuse of more powerfully addictive drugs.

---

medicine
drug compounds used to prevent or treat the symptoms of illness

---

Medicines are used to prevent or treat the symptoms of illness. When a drug is prescribed by a physician, it sometimes is referred to as *medicine*.

---

prescription drugs
drugs prescribed by a physician

Drugs prescribed by a physician are known as **prescription drugs**. Common examples include drugs prescribed to eliminate drowsiness or induce sleep, stimulation, or relaxation. Prescription drugs are generally more potent than over-the-counter (OTC) drugs (see following). The sales of prescription drugs outnumber those of OTC drugs, and the use and abuse of prescription drugs tend to be greater than OTC drug use and abuse.

---

over-the-counter (OTC) drugs
nonprescription drugs

Use of prescription drugs can only be authorized by licensed medical practitioners. **Over-the-counter (OTC) drugs**, which are *nonprescription* drugs, are sold without a prescription. In 1989, OTC drugs had annual sales of $9.7 billion. Currently, hundreds of ingredients are approved by the Food and Drug Administration (FDA) for inclusion in about 300,000 OTC preparations. Because people can purchase OTC drugs at will, without first seeking any medical advice, these drugs are commonly misused or abused. Laxatives are a good example. Also, OTC drugs are not necessarily safe. In one study, for example, 15% of patients using OTC ibuprofen suffered kidney damage. Fortunately, the damage was reversible when the drug use was stopped.

---

drug misuse
the unintentional or inappropriate use of prescribed or OTC drugs

---

Drug misuse is the unintentional or inappropriate use of prescribed or OTC drugs. Misuse includes but is not limited to:

1. Taking more drugs than prescribed
2. Using OTC or psychoactive drugs in excess without medical supervision
3. Mixing drugs with alcohol

For You to Consider...

Drug Quiz

A test of what people knew about illicit drugs and their effects would have been a brief exercise a decade ago. Now, the list of questions is uncomfortably long, the answers more disturbing than ever. How much do you know?

1. Name the major drug problem among teenagers today.
2. How fast can a child become an alcoholic?
3. Why are grade school children drawn to wine coolers?
4. Are some drugs gateways that may lead to further substance abuse?

5. How does today's marijuana compare with the marijuana of a generation ago?
6. Does the use of marijuana cause damage to the brain?
7. Do marijuana and cigarettes inflict about the same lung damage?
8. How did "crack" get its name?
9. How long does alcohol stay in the bloodstream after a round of heavy drinking?
10. How long do traces of marijuana remain in the body after it has been smoked?
11. What does "crack" look like?
12. What is "crank"?
13. How long does a "crack" high last?
14. How does marijuana affect mood?

15. How many children ages 12 to 17 say they have tried hallucinogens like LSD, PCP, peyote, or mescaline at least once?
16. Can geneticists figure out which people are likeliest to become addicts?
17. What is the price of a single dose of "crack"?
18. Blotter paper is associated with which drug?
19. Which drug temporarily gives its user abnormal physical strength?
20. What is "Ecstasy"?

Answers in Appendix 1-2, page 23.

Source: V. Sussman, "How to Beat Drugs," *U.S. News and World Report,* 11 Sept. 1989, 69–72.

4. Using old medicines for self-treatment of new symptoms of an illness or ailment
5. Discontinuing certain prescribed drugs against a physician's recommendation
6. Administering prescription drugs to other family members without medical consultation

---

drug abuse
the willful misuse of either legal or illegal drugs for recreation or convenience; also known as chemical or substance abuse

---

Drug abuse, also known as *chemical* or *substance abuse*, is the willful misuse of either legal or illegal drugs for recreation or convenience. This also includes the use of such substances as paint thinner and airplane glue, which are inhaled and can alter mood, perception, or motor activity.

---

licit versus illicit drugs
licit refers to legalized drugs or substances, such as coffee, alcohol, and tobacco; *illicit* refers to illegal drugs, such as marijuana, cocaine, and heroin

---

Psychoactive drugs are classified as either **licit** (legal) or **illicit** (illegal). Coffee, tea, cocoa, alcohol, tobacco, and OTC drugs are licit, or legal substances, and, when used in moderation, are usually socially acceptable. Marijuana, cocaine, and LSD are examples of illicit drugs.

Researchers have made some interesting findings regarding legal and illegal drug use:

1. The use of such legal substances as alcoholic beverages and tobacco is considerably more common than is the use of illegal drugs such as marijuana, heroin, and LSD. Other legal drugs such as depressants and stimulants, though less

popular than alcohol and tobacco, are still more widely used than the illegal heroin and LSD.

2. The popular use of those legal drugs, particularly alcohol and tobacco, has caused far more deaths, sickness, violent crimes, economic loss, and other social problems than the use of illegal drugs.

3. Societal reaction to various drugs changes with time and place. Opium is today an illegal drug and widely condemned as a *panopathogen* (a cause of all ills), but in the last two centuries it was a legal drug and popularly praised as a *panacea* (a cure of all ills). In contrast, cigarette smoking is legal in all countries today, but in the seventeenth century it was illegal in most countries and the smoker was harshly punished in some. For example, the penalty for cigarette smoking was having the nose cut off in Russia, lips sliced off in Hindustan [India], and head chopped off in China (Thio 1983, 332–333).

Think About It...

1. What would you do if you found yourself at a party where nearly everyone started using marijuana? How would you react if it were cocaine instead?

2. What would you do if your date started smoking a cigarette, knowing that you are against cigarette smoking?

3. What would you do if you knew someone sneaked some amphetamines into the party punch? Would you tell the chaperon or host? Would you warn your close friends? Would you warn any other people? Why or why not?

DRUG USE AND ABUSE: A HISTORICAL PERSPECTIVE

Many people think that problems with drugs are unique to this era. However, drug use and abuse has always been part of human society. For example, the Grecian oracles of Delphi used drugs, Homer's Cup of Helen induced sleep and provided freedom from care, and the mandrake root mentioned in *Genesis* supplied hallucinogenic belladonna compounds. In *Genesis* 30:14–16, the mandrake is mentioned in association with love-making:

> In the time of wheat harvest Reuben went out and found some mandrakes in the open country and brought them to his mother Leah. Then Rachel asked Leah for some of her son's mandrakes, but Leah said, "Is it so small a thing to have taken away my husband, that you should take my son's mandrakes as well?" But Rachel said, "Very well, let him sleep with you tonight in exchange for your son's mandrakes." So when Jacob came in from the country in the evening, Leah went out to meet him and said, "You are to sleep with me tonight; I have hired you with my son's mandrakes." That night he slept with her.

Ancient literature is filled with references to the use of mushrooms, datura, hemp, marijuana, opium poppies, and so on. Under the influence of some of these drugs, many people experienced extreme ecstasy or sheer terror. Some old pictures of demons and devils look very much like those described by modern drug users during so-called "bummers," or bad "trips." The belief that witches could fly may also have been drug induced because many natural preparations used in so-called witches' brews induced the sensation of dissociation from the body, as in flying or floating.

There are some indications that, as far back as 2240 B.C., attempts to regulate drug use were made. For instance, in that year, problem drinking was addressed in the code of Hammaurabi and is described as "a problem of men with too much leisure time and lazy dispositions." Nearly every culture has, as part of its historical record, laws controlling the use of a wide range of drugs.

Why are people so attracted to drugs? Like the ancient Assyrians, who sucked on opium lozenges, and the Romans, who ate hashish sweets some 2,000 years ago, many users claim to be bored, in pain, frustrated, unable to enjoy life, or alienated. They turn to drugs in the hope of finding oblivion, peace, "togetherness," or euphoria. The fact that few drugs cause all the effects for which they are taken doesn't seem to be a deterrent. People continue to take drugs for a number of reasons:

A drinking party *Photo:* North Wind Picture Archives

Drinking companions *Photo:* North Wind Picture Archives

1. They may be searching for pleasure, and drugs may make them feel good.
2. Drugs may relieve stress or tension or provide a temporary escape for people with anxiety.
3. Peer pressure is strong, especially for young people. The use of drugs has become a rite of passage in some levels of society.
4. In some cases, drugs may enhance religious or mystical experiences. A few cultures teach children how to use specific drugs for this purpose.

Boiling and testing opium in China *Photo:* North Wind Picture Archives

5. Drugs can relieve pain and symptoms of illness.

Since historically, people have been unsuccessful in eliminating the fascination with drugs, it is important that we come to understand it. To reach such an understanding, we will address why people are attracted to drugs, how different types of drugs affect the body and the mind, and what forms of treatment are available for eliminating abuse.

HOW WIDESPREAD IS DRUG ABUSE?

As mentioned above, drug use today is more acute and widespread than in any previous age. The evidence for this is that drug busts are an everyday occurrence in the United States. On any given day, you can scan most major national and international newspapers and undoubtedly run across stories about illegal drug manufacturing, distribution, or use.

Substance abuse is not confined to any specific social or socioeconomic groups. Many of us, for example, are a little dismayed when we discover that certain individuals we admire—such as celebrities, politicians, athletes, clergy, and academics—admit to or are apprehended for abusing illicit drugs. We are also taken aback when we hear that cigarettes, alcohol, and marijuana abuse are commonplace in some junior high and even grade schools. Further, most of us know of at least one close friend or family member who abuses drugs.

No one is immune. Research shows that drug consumption cuts across income, social class, and age groups (see Table 1-1). Drugs are as seductive to the poor as they are to the wealthy, to the highly educated and the school dropout, to the young and the old.

Think About It...

1. Oppose the statement that, since drugs have been used and abused throughout history, there is nothing wrong with getting "high" at parties or with close friends.
2. Roleplay a scenario showing how peers can pressure one another into trying marijuana for the first time.
3. Debate the pros and cons of using drugs to relieve pain experienced by a terminally ill cancer patient.

TABLE 1-1 Trend data from NIDA's National Household Survey, prevalence of any illicit drug use, 1979–1988

These data indicate a downward trend in illicit drug use. This trend continued through 1991.

	1979	1982	1985	1988
Use in Past Month				
All ages 12+	13.7%	12.2%	12.1%	7.3%
12–17	17.6	12.7	14.9	9.2
18–25	37.1	30.4	25.7	17.8
26–34	18.5	19.2	21.1	13.0
35+	2.5	3.4	3.9	2.1
Use in Past Year				
All ages 12+	19.5	18.7	19.6	14.1
12–17	26.0	22.0	23.7	16.8
18–25	49.4	43.4	42.6	32.0
26–34	26.9	29.5	32.0	22.6
35+	4.4	5.6	6.6	5.8
Use in Lifetime				
All ages 12+	33.3	32.3	36.9	36.6
12–17	34.3	27.6	29.5	24.7
18–25	69.9	65.3	64.3	58.9
26–34	51.5	57.7	62.2	64.2
35+	13.6	13.2	20.4	23.0

Source: National Institute on Drug Abuse, *NIDA Notes* 5, no. 1 (Winter 1989/1990): 4.

Note: These figures include use of marijuana, cocaine, hallucinogens, inhalants (except in 1982), heroin, and nonmedical use of sedatives, tranquilizers, stimulants, and analgesics. Data on inhalant use were not collected in 1982, which may lower overall prevalence figures for that year, especially for 12- to 17-year-olds.

WHO ARE POTENTIAL DRUG ABUSERS?

Is it the person from the ghetto, the Vietnam veteran, the youngster from an emotionally turbulent family, or the homeless person in a large city who is the most likely drug abuser? What setting most encourages drug abuse: the physician's office, the suburban home, the business office, the assembly line, the construction site, or the nursing home for the elderly?

The answer is that *all* of these places foster drug addiction. Addicts and drug abusers are found among homemakers and automobile assembly-line workers, in the operating rooms and nursing stations of hospitals, among businesspeople enjoying three-martini lunches, in the religious community and the legal profession, and in the suburbs and the ghettos.

The pervasiveness of drug use is not discriminating. Addiction is found among all races, religions, and social levels. Drug abuse is a so-called **"equal-opportunity" affliction.** For example, the drug dependency that affects the greatest number of people, alcohol addiction, is prevalent among professionals as well as nonprofessionals.

"equal-opportunity" affliction
refers to the fact that drug abuse is found among all races, religions, and social levels

---

DRUG USE OR ABUSE: WHERE DO WE DRAW THE LINE?

Drug use may be viewed from the different perspectives of the users rather than by the pattern of drug taking. For example, a patient who is suffering severe pain due to injuries received in an automobile accident may require high doses of a narcotic, such as morphine or Demerol, to control her discomfort. She may be able to function at home and work while taking this drug. If deprived of the narcotic, she would experience excruciating pain and debilitation. While the patient is in pain, there's no reason for her not to have the drug. However, once the healing has occurred and the pain has been relieved, the drug use should cease. If the patient continues using the narcotic because it provides a sense of well-being or has become a habit, the pattern of drug intake would then be considered abuse. Thus, it is not necessarily the amount of drug that is taken or the frequency of dosing that determines abuse (although those that abuse drugs do usually consume frequent high doses). Rather, it is the *motive* for taking the drug that is the principal factor in determining abuse.

Social activities often involve the use of licit drugs. *Photos: upper right*, Rob Crandall/
Stock, Boston; *upper left*, © Topham/The Image Works; *lower*, Spencer Grant, Stock, Boston

Let's Get the Facts

Officials: Drug Use Figures Still Too High

WASHINGTON (AP)—A new survey shows fewer high school students and young adults are using illicit drugs, but federal health and drug officials say the numbers are still too high.

"One out of two (high school) students still uses an illegal drug before he graduates; one out of 10 uses cocaine," said national drug policy director William Bennett. "Those numbers are unacceptably high."

The survey released Monday is an annual effort by the University of Michigan and funded by the National Institute on Drug Abuse to track the use of drugs by high school seniors, college students and other young adults.

It shows a decrease in overall illegal drug use over the past decade and in 1989 by all three groups.

High school seniors and college students today are half as likely to try an illegal drug as they were in 1980, according to the survey.

Despite the good news, said Health and Human Services Secretary Louis Sullivan, "We must not allow our efforts to slacken."

The decline in alcohol use has been more modest and cigarette smoking is about as widespread today among seniors as it was a decade ago. Nearly 19 percent of seniors are daily smokers and 60 percent have used alcohol within the past 30 days.

Survey officials acknowledge the limitation, but said the data suggest drug use among dropouts may also be declining.

Among specific drugs:

● Marijuana: Casual use—within the last 30 days—among seniors is down from a peak of 37 percent in 1979 to 17 percent in 1989, and for college students, it has dropped from 34 percent in 1980 to 16 percent last year.

● Cocaine: 2.8 percent of seniors are casual cocaine users, down from a peak of 6.7 percent in 1985, and among college students the drop is

larger. But for the smokable form of the drug known as crack, casual and daily use has stayed about the same for seniors since 1987 when it was first included in the survey.

● Ice: Also known as crystal methamphetamine, "ice" was included for the first time in the survey because of increasing concerns about the drug. About 1.2 percent of the seniors surveyed said they had used it at least once in the past year.

● Ecstasy: The drug MDMA, known as "Ecstasy," also was included for the first time, and was tried by 3.8 percent of the college students surveyed and 3.3 percent of the high school graduates not in college.

● Steroids: About 3 percent of high school seniors said they had used anabolic steroids, which are a controlled substance used to build muscles.

Source: Associated Press, *Vidette Messenger* [Valparaiso, IN], 14 Feb. 1990, 5B.

This subtle distinction can make identifying drug abuse difficult. Namely, someone has to determine the real reason a drug is being used and then decide whether it is legitimate. What guidelines should be followed in making such a determination?

In general, *drug abuse* has been described as "a pattern of drug use that is not approved by society or the medical community." Such a broad definition is of limited use because there are different opinions as to what is socially and medically acceptable. Often, even physicians cannot decide among themselves what constitutes legitimate use of a drug. For example, MDMA ("Ecstasy") is a drug currently prohibited for therapeutic use, but

in 1985, when the Drug Enforcement Administration (DEA) was deciding its status, some 35 to 200 physicians (mostly psychiatrists) were using it in their practice. These clinicians claimed that MDMA relaxed inhibitions and enhanced communications and was useful as a psychotherapeutic adjunct to assist in dealing with psychiatric patients (Schecter 1989). From the perspective of these physicians, Ecstasy was a useful medicinal tool. However, the DEA did not agree and made Ecstasy a Schedule I drug (see Chapter 3). This classification excludes any legitimate use of a drug in therapeutics; consequently, according to this ruling, anyone taking Ecstasy is guilty of drug abuse.

"HE'S THE TYPICAL AMERICAN MOUSE— LIKES A DRINK BEFORE DINNER, SMOKES A LITTLE, WATCHES TV..."

Source: ® Sidney Harris, *American Scientist* magazine. Used with permission.

Other special interest groups take a more liberal view. They consider drug abuse a statutory problem and describe it as "the use of drugs in an illegal manner." According to such a limited definition, excessive use of alcohol by anyone over 21 years of age would not be considered a form of drug abuse, in spite of the consequences. Obviously, such a narrow view of drug abuse is not very useful in trying to deal with the consequences of extreme inappropriate drug use, such as alcoholism.

If the problem of drug abuse is to be understood and solutions are to be found, it is important to identify what causes this problem. When a drug is being abused, it is not legitimately therapeutic; that is, it does not improve the user's physical or mental health. If such drug use is not for therapeutic purposes, what is the motive for using it?

There are many possible answers to this question. Most drug abusers perceive some psychological advantage when using these compounds (at least initially). For many, the psychological lift is significant enough that they are willing to risk social exclusion, arrest, incarceration, and fines to have their drug. The psychological effects that these drugs cause may entail an array of diverse feelings. Different types of drugs have different psychological impacts. The type of drug an individual selects to abuse may ultimately reflect his own mental state.

That is, for people who experience chronic depression, have a sense of inferiority, and do not enjoy life, a stimulant such as cocaine or amphetamines might be selected; these drugs cause excitation, euphoria, a sense of superiority, and confidence accompanied by energy. On the other hand, people who are in a chronic state of stress and anxiety and are not able to deal with the pressures of life may choose a depressant such as alcohol or barbiturates; these agents sedate, relax, provide relief from tension and anxiety, and even have some amnesic properties allowing users to forget their problems. People who have an artistic flare and find the world drab and uninteresting may select a hallucinogenic drug such as LSD to heighten their senses and cause dreamlike experiences.

As individuals rely more on drugs to correct

what they either consciously or unconsciously perceive as psychological deficiencies, they become psychologically dependent and are considered to be abusing drugs.

IS THERE A LINK BETWEEN DRUG ABUSE AND MENTAL ILLNESS?

In this section, we will discuss drug abuse from a biological and pharmacological perspective, and in the next section, we will discuss drug abuse from a social science perspective. While the two perspectives are quite distinct, we hope that, when both viewpoints are taken together, they will provide a more comprehensive picture of the reasons certain people are more likely to use and abuse drugs.

All drugs with abuse potential alter brain activity; specifically, they change the activity of chemical messengers in the central nervous system (CNS) called *neurotransmitters* (see Chapter 5). Most mental illnesses have also been linked to disruption of these very same transmitter systems. Because of similarities, we can better understand how excessive use of drugs of abuse create imbalances in the brain transmitters that can either mimic or aggravate existing mental illness.

According to Mello and Griffiths (1987, 1511–1514), drug abuse or dependence is itself classified as a form of mental illness. High doses of cocaine or amphetamines cause psychotic paranoia, similar to that associated with schizophrenia. (*Schizophrenia* is defined as "a group of psychotic reactions characterized by withdrawal from reality.") When a patient with a history of schizophrenia takes either of these drugs, there is an increased likelihood of a *psychotic episode* (Kosten 1989, 379–389), an occurrence in which an individual either partially or completely withdraws from reality. CNS depressants such as alcohol and barbiturates cause severe symptoms of depression that may lead to fantasies about suicide. Mentally ill patients with existing mood disorders are very susceptible to the mood suppression caused by these depressants. Psychedelics such as LSD can cause hallucinations or delusions associated with some forms of un-

controlled psychosis. The correlation between mental illness and drugs of abuse is noteworthy and leads to important conclusions concerning these drugs.

First, by understanding how drugs of abuse alter the drug abuser's mental state, it is possible to gain insight into the mechanisms responsible for related mental illness. Thus, drugs that cause schizophrenia, such as cocaine and amphetamines, have been found to dramatically increase the activity of the neurotransmitter dopamine in the limbic part of the brain (see Chapter 6). This correlates with the finding that schizophrenia is also associated with increased limbic dopamine activity.

Second, as we examine the similarities between drug abuse and mental illness, useful therapeutic strategies can be developed for both problems. For example, all of the antipsychotic medications used to combat and treat schizophrenia block the activity of the neurotransmitter dopamine. It follows that similar drugs would be useful in treating psychotic behavior caused by high doses of cocaine; in fact, these dopamine-blocking drugs are very effective in the treating of cocaine- and amphetamine-related psychosis. The converse is also true: By understanding the consequences of taking high doses of cocaine and amphetamines, it may be possible to develop more effective treatment for psychotic disorders such as schizophrenia. Consequently, by studying abuse of these stimulants, models of schizophrenia can be created in laboratory animals. The goal is to identify better means of treating this severely debilitating disorder.

Third, because mental illnesses and drugs of abuse affect the same part of the brain, some people use illicit drugs to self-medicate their mental disorders. Consequently, one study found that 50% to 73% of a sample of cocaine abusers had a history of psychiatric problems independent of their drug abuse problem; the mental illnesses consisted of major depression, anxiety disorders, and antisocial personalities (Rounsaville 1991, 43–51).

Psychiatric patients are most likely to self-medicate cocaine to relieve the symptoms associated with major depressive disorders (Kosten 1989). The CNS effects of cocaine resemble the actions of traditionally used antidepressants. Thus, one of the most effective ways of treating cocaine addiction is to substitute the commonly used antidepressant drug desipramine for cocaine; this helps to relieve cocaine craving and assists in eliminating the dependency.

ARE DRUG USERS SOCIALIZED DIFFERENTLY?

Social scientists, primarily sociologists and social psychologists, believe that most social development patterns are closely linked to drug use. Based on the age at which an adolescent starts to consume alcohol, predictions can be made about his or her sexual behavior, academic performance, and other behaviors, such as lying, cheating, fighting, and marijuana use. The same predictions can be made when the adolescent begins using marijuana. The early use of alcohol and/or marijuana represents a move toward less conventional behavior, greater susceptibility to peer influence, increased delinquency, and lower achievement in school. In general, drug abusers have 13 characteristics in common:

1. Their drug use usually follows clear-cut developmental steps and sequences. Use of legal drugs, such as alcohol and cigarettes, almost always precedes use of illegal drugs.
2. Use of certain drugs, particularly marijuana, is linked to the **amotivational syndrome**, which causes a general change in personality. This change is characterized by apathy, a lack of interest in pursuing and accomplishing goals, and a noticeable overall lack of ambition.*

---

amotivational syndrome
personality change due to drug use; characterized by apathy, a lack of interest in pursuing and accomplishing goals, and an overall lack of ambition

---

*Some argue that a general lack of ambition precedes rather than results from drug use. In other words, the amotivational syndrome often attributed to a person's heavy marijuana use is probably already part of his or her personality, regardless of drug use. Our opinion is that continued use of marijuana is likely to heighten this syndrome.

3. Immaturity and maladjustment usually precede the use of marijuana and other illicit drugs.
4. Those more likely to try illicit drugs usually have a history of poor school performance and classroom disobedience.
5. Delinquent or deviant activities usually precede involvement with illicit drugs.
6. A set of values and attitudes that facilitates the development of deviant behavior exists before the person tries illicit drugs.
7. A social setting where drug use is common, such as communities and neighborhoods where "crack" houses and drug-using gangs dominate, are likely to reinforce and increase the predisposition to drug use.
8. Drug-induced behaviors and drug-related attitudes of peers are usually among the strongest predictors of subsequent drug involvement.
9. Children who feel their parents are distant from their emotional needs are more likely to become drug addicted.
10. The older people are when they start using drugs, the greater the probability of stopping drug use. The period of greatest risk of initiation into illicit drug use is usually over by the early twenties.
11. The family structure has changed. More than half the women in the United States work outside the home. How this affects the quality of child care and nurturing is difficult to assess. Also, a higher percentage of children are being raised in single-parent households due to separation and divorce. Mobility obstructs a sense of permanency, and it contributes to a lack of self-esteem. Often, children are moved from one location to another, and their community can easily become nothing more than a group of strangers. There may be little pride in home or community and no commitment to society.
12. Among minority members, a major factor involved in drug dependence is a feeling of powerlessness due to discrimination based on race, gender, social standing, or other attributes. Groups subject to discrimination have a disproportionately high rate of unem-

Let's Get the Facts

Study Finds Higher Drug Use among Adolescents Whose Parents Divorce

Children who are adolescents when their parents divorce have more extensive drug use and more drug-related health, legal, and other problems than their peers, according to a recent study by NIDA grantee Dr. Richard Needle. The study has linked the extent of teens' drug use to their age at the time of their parents' divorce.

Dr. Needle, who performed the research at the University of Minnesota, found that teenagers whose parents divorce use more drugs and experience more drug-related problems than two other groups of adolescents: those who were 10 or younger when their parents divorced, and those whose parents remained married.

The research "contributes to our understanding of the crucial and changing roles the family plays in explaining adolescents' drug-using behavior," says Dr. Needle, who is serving a 2-year appointment as a senior staff fellow in NIDA's Community Research Branch.

The study also has important implications for drug abuse prevention efforts, says Dr. Meyer Glantz, of NIDA's Prevention Research Branch. "This study says that not everybody is at the same risk for drug use," says Dr. Glantz. "People at greater risk can be identified, and programs should be developed to meet their special needs."

Dr. Needle's 5-year study, which began in 1982, followed 508 randomly selected families with children ages 11,

12, or 13, who were participants in a large health maintenance organization. Over the course of the study, 67 families experienced disruption, including separation, divorce, and remarriage.

The study found that drug use among all adolescents increased over time. However, drug use was higher among adolescents whose parents had divorced, either when their children were preteens or teenagers. Drug use was highest for those teens whose parents divorced during their children's adolescent years. The latter group also reported more adverse consequences related to drug use, such as physical problems, family disputes, and arrests.

Dr. Needle found distinct gender differences in the way divorce affected adolescent drug use, whether the divorce occurred during the offspring's childhood or adolescent years. Males whose parents divorced reported more drug use and drug-related problems than females. Females whose caretaking parent remarried reported increased drug use after the remarriage. By contrast, males whose caretaking parent remarried reported a decrease in drug-related problems following the remarriage.

Dr. Needle cautions that the findings may be of limited applicability,

since most of the families were White and had middle to high income levels. He also urges that the findings not be interpreted simplistically. "These data should not be interpreted as an argument for the nuclear family," Dr. Needle says.

The findings, says Dr. Glantz, indicate the complex ways in which factors such as divorce and remarriage can influence drug-using behavior, particularly when the disruptions occur during adolescence.

Reference

Needle, Richard H.; Su, Susan S.; and Doherty, William J. Divorce, remarriage, and adolescent substance use: A prospective longitudinal study. *Journal of Marriage and the Family* 52:157–169, 1990.

Source: National Institute on Drug Abuse, *NIDA NOTES,* 5, no. 3 (Summer 1990): 10.

ployment and below-average income. The Carnegie Council on Children estimated that 19 million children grow up in poverty every year and feel powerless in their situation. The adults they have as role models are unemployed and powerless. There are higher rates of delinquency and drug addiction in such settings.

13. Abusers that become highly involved in selling drugs begin by witnessing that drug trafficking is a lucrative business, especially in run-down neighborhoods. In some communities, selling drugs is the only available alternative to real economic success (Blum and Richards 1979).

T h i n k   A b o u t   I t . . .

1. Interview a drug counselor. Ask him or her what three things are likely to cause drug use.
2. Invite a former drug addict to speak to your class.
3. Observe a heavy cigarette smoker for several days, and report your findings to the class.
4. Why are people from divorced homes more likely to use illicit drugs?

WHAT IS THE FREQUENCY OF DRUG USE?

Sociologist Erich Goode lists four different uses of drugs:

1. *Medical use*—prescription drugs and OTC drugs used to relieve or treat mental or physical symptoms
2. *Legal recreational use*—examples are cigarettes and liquor
3. *Illegal instrumental use*—taking a prescription drug without a prescription so as to accomplish a task or goal, such as taking nonprescribed amphetamines in order to drive through the night
4. *Illegal recreational use*—examples include using marijuana or cocaine to get "high" (Goode 1990, 95)

Why has there been such an increase in drug use? There are several possible answers, none of which by itself offers a satisfactory solution. One interesting perspective is that practically all of us are drug *users*, and what constitutes drug *abuse* is just a matter of degree. Another explanation is that more varieties of both licit and illicit drugs are available today. Evidence for this is found in numerous citations. One source estimates that 70% of all currently marketed drugs were either unknown or unavailable 15 years ago (Lipton and Lee 1988, 136). Another source, *Drug Use Around the World* (Kusinitz 1988), asserts that, "in the modern age, increased sophistication has brought with it techniques of drug production and distribution that have resulted in worldwide epidemic of abuse" (p. 149). Finally, other reliable estimates report that as much as one-third of the American population over age 12 has tried an illegal substance (Goode 1990, 97).

STATISTICS OF DRUG USE

An incredible amount of money is spent each year for legal chemicals that alter consciousness, awareness, or mood. There are four classes of these legal chemicals:

1. *Social drugs*—$58.9 billion for alcohol; $25.2 billion for cigarettes (add another $1.4 billion for cigars, chewing, pipe, and roll-your-own tobacco, and snuff tobacco); $5.7 billion for coffee, tea, and cocoa
2. *Prescription or ethical drugs*—$16.7 billion
3. *Over-the-counter (OTC) or patent drugs*—$9.7 billion, including cough and cold items, external and internal analgesics, antacids, laxatives, antidiarrheals, and sleep aids/sedatives
4. *Miscellaneous drugs* (such as aerosols, nutmeg, morning glory seeds, and others)—amount unknown

Studies from the Social Research Group of George Washington University; the Institute for Research in Social Behavior in Berkeley, California; and others provide detailed, in-depth data showing that drug use is universal. A major purpose of these studies was to determine the level of psychoactive drug use in the population aged 18 through 74, excluding those persons hospitalized or in the armed forces. Data were collected to identify persons using specific categories of drugs: caffeine, sleeping pills, nicotine, alcohol, and other psychoactive drugs. These studies show that people in the 18- to 25-year-old age group are by far the heaviest users and experimenters (see Table 1-1).

Over 80% of respondents in the studies report that they drank coffee during the previous year, and over 50% said that they drank tea. Another finding from these data shows that nearly one-third of the population drinks more than five cups of caffeine-containing beverages each day. In 1989, 295 billion doses of caffeine were consumed in the United States. These figures exclude caffeine sources such as chocolate, cocoa, cola drinks, No Doz, and other OTC products with caffeine, such as Excedrin, Anacin, and others.

The number of cigarettes smoked in the United States in 1987 was approximately 550 billion (Forster, Jacobs, and Siegel 1989). Almost 22 gal-

For You to Consider...

Symptoms of Drug and Alcohol Abuse

Profile of the Child Least Likely to Use Drugs

1. Child comes from a strong family.
2. Family has a clearly stated policy toward drug use.
3. Child has strong religious convictions.
4. Child is an independent thinker, not easily swayed by peer pressure.
5. Parents know the child's friends and the friends' parents.
6. Child often invites friends into the house and their behavior is open, not secretive.
7. Child is busy, productive, and pursues many interests.
8. Child has a good secure feeling of self.
9. Parents are comfortable with their own use of alcohol, drugs, and pills and set a good example in using these and are comfortable in discussing their use.
10. Parents set a good example in handling crisis situations.

Symptoms of Possible Drug Use

EDITOR'S NOTE: A child should display more than merely one of the symptoms below when experimenting with drugs. Please remember that any number of the symptoms could also be the result of a physical impairment or disorder.

1. Abrupt change in behavior. Ex.— from very active to passive, loss of interest in previously pursued activities such as sports or hobbies.
2. Diminished drive and ambition.
3. Moodiness.
4. Shortened attention span.
5. Impaired communication such as slurred speech, jumbled thinking.
6. Significant change in quality of school work.
7. Deteriorating judgment and loss of short-term memory.
8. Distinct lessening of family closeness and warmth.
9. Sudden carelessness of appearance.
10. Inappropriate overreaction to even mild criticism.
11. Secretiveness about whereabouts and personal possessions.
12. Friends who avoid introduction or appearance in the child's home.
13. Use of words that have odd, underworld connotations.
14. Secretiveness and/or desperation for money.
15. Rapid weight loss or appetite loss.
16. "Drifting off" beyond normal daydreaming.
17. Extreme behavioral changes such as hallucination, violence, unconsciousness, etc., could indicate a dangerous situation is close at hand needing fast medical attention.
18. Unprescribed or unidentifiable pills.
19. Strange "contraptions" or hidden articles.
20. Articles missing from the house. Child could be stealing to receive money to pay for drugs.

Source: L.A.W. Publications, *Let's All Work to Fight Drug Abuse,* new ed. (Addison, TX: C & L Printing Company, Inc., 1985), p. 38. Used with permission of the publisher.

lons of beer were consumed by each man, woman, and child, as were more than 2 gallons of wine and more than 2.8 gallons of distilled spirits. Studies show that many people have used marijuana at least once in their lives: about 17% of youth (4 million), 56% of young adults (17 million), and 31% of adults (45 million) (NIDA 1988).

The average household owns about 35 drugs, of which one out of five is a prescription drug and the other four are over-the-counter drugs (NIDA 1988). Of the many prescriptions written by physicians, approximately one-fourth modify moods and behaviors in one way or another. Surveys report that over 50% of adults in the United States have, at some time in their lives, taken a psychoactive drug (one that affects mood or consciousness). Over one-third of adults have used or are using depressants or sedatives.

An NIDA study indicates drug-use trends based on gender. Men are most likely to use stimulants in their thirties, depressants in their forties and fifties, and sedatives from age 60 on. Women, however, are most likely to use stimulants from ages 21 through age 39 and depressants more frequently in their thirties. Women's use of sedatives is similar to the pattern of use by men, with the frequency of use increasing with age. Women tend to use pills to cope with problems, whereas men tend to use alcohol. In addition, persons over 35 are more likely to take pills, whereas younger people prefer alcohol. Among those using pills, younger persons and men are more likely to use stimulants than older persons and women, who take sedatives (Chambers and Griffey 1975).

The actual figures for use of all psychoactive drugs are probably 35% higher than reported. This discrepancy exists partly because a large number of people get psychoactive drugs on the "black market" and from friends and relatives who have legitimate prescriptions. An estimated 70% of all psychoactive prescription drugs used by people under 30 are obtained without the user having a prescription. Pharmacists' records show that about 480 million psychoactive drug prescriptions were written in 1985, with the rate of increase estimated at about 7% per year. Figures such as these show that it may be more difficult to find persons who do not use psychoactive drugs than who do.

MAIN FINDINGS FROM THE 1988 NATIONAL HOUSEHOLD SURVEY ON DRUG ABUSE

The National Household Survey on Drug Abuse (NIDA, 1988) is a recent series of a survey estimating drug use in the United States. As shown in Table 1-2, all interviewees were divided into three age groups: youth (ages 12–17), young adults (ages 18–25), and older adults (ages 26 and over). The results of this comprehensive survey show that a whopping 72.4 million Americans age 12 or older (37% of the population) have tried some illegal drug at least once in their lives.

Of the legal drugs, alcohol use is highest (young adults, 90.3%), followed by cigarette use (same age group, 75%). Marijuana remains the most commonly used illegal drug. One-third of all Americans age 12 years and older have used marijuana at least once in their lives.

While 1988 lifetime drug use rates were high, all three age groups indicated a decrease in the use of most drugs from previous years. This declining trend continued through 1991. In analyzing an earlier version of the National Household Survey and the Johnston et al. (1985) survey, Stephens made the following conclusions regarding drug use, which are still relevant:

1. Other than alcohol and cigarettes, marijuana is clearly the most abused (that is, used outside of a medical context) psychoactive drug in American society.
2. Many Americans, particularly those in the age group 18 to 25 years, have used psychoactive drugs. Almost a third of young adults report having used cocaine or a psychotherapeutic drug at least once.
3. Although it is true that many Americans have used psychoactive drugs, most of this use appears experimental or occasional recreational use.
4. Nevertheless, there are many Americans who use drugs heavily. This is especially true for marijuana use.
5. Most heavy users of drugs are multiple drug users—that is, they concurrently and simultaneously use more than one psychoactive substance.
6. The highest prevalence rates for drug abuse were observed in the late 1970s and

TABLE 1-2 Lifetime prevalence of drug use: 1972–1988 (use in lifetime)

Drug (number interviewed)	1972 (880)	1974 (952)	1976 (986)	1977 (1,272)	1979 (2,165)	1982 (1,581)	1985 (2,246)	1988 (3,095)
Youth (age 12–17)								
Marijuana & hashish	14.0	23.0	22.4	28.0	30.9	26.7	23.6	17.4***
Inhalants	6.4	8.5	8.1	9.0	9.8	—	9.2	8.8
Hallucinogens	4.8	6.0	5.1	4.6	7.1	5.2	3.3	3.5
Cocaine	1.5	3.6	3.4	4.0	5.4	6.5	4.9	3.4*
Heroin	0.6	1.0	0.5	1.1	0.5	•	•	0.6
Nonmedical use of any psychotherapeutic	—	—	—	—	7.3	10.3	12.1	7.7***
Stimulants	4.0	5.0	4.4	5.2	3.4	6.7	5.6	4.2
Sedatives	3.0	5.0	2.8	3.1	3.2	5.8	4.1	2.4*
Tranquilizers	3.0	3.0	3.3	3.8	4.1	4.9	4.8	2.0***
Analgesics	—	—	—	—	3.2	4.2	5.8	4.2
Cigarettes	—	52.0	46.5	47.3	54.1	49.5	45.2	42.3
Alcohol	—	54.0	53.6	52.6	70.3	65.2	55.5	50.2*
Young Adults (age 18–25)								
Marijuana & hashish	47.9	52.7	52.9	59.9	68.2	64.1	60.3	56.4
Inhalants	—	9.2	9.0	11.2	16.5	—	12.4	12.5
Hallucinogens	—	16.6	17.3	19.8	25.1	21.1	11.3	13.8
Cocaine	9.1	12.7	13.4	19.1	27.5	28.3	25.2	19.7**
Heroin	4.6	4.5	3.9	3.6	3.5	1.2	1.2	0.4*
Nonmedical use of any psychotherapeutic	—	—	—	—	29.5	28.4	26.0	17.6***
Stimulants	12.0	17.0	16.6	21.2	18.2	18.0	17.1	11.3***
Sedatives	10.0	15.0	11.9	18.4	17.0	18.7	11.0	5.5***
Tranquilizers	7.0	10.0	9.1	13.4	15.8	15.1	12.0	7.8**
Analgesics	—	—	—	—	11.8	12.1	11.3	9.4
Cigarettes	—	68.8	70.1	67.6	82.8	76.9	75.6	75.0
Alcohol	—	81.6	83.6	84.2	95.3	94.6	92.6	90.3
Older Adults (age 26+)								
Marijuana & hashish	7.4	9.9	12.9	15.3	19.6	23.0	27.2	30.7*
Inhalants	—	1.2	1.9	1.8	3.9	—	5.0	3.9
Hallucinogens	—	1.3	1.6	2.6	4.5	6.4	6.2	6.6

•Low precision; no estimate reported.

*Difference between 1985 and 1988 statistically significant at the .05 level.

***Difference between 1985 and 1988 statistically significant at the .001 level.

(continued)

TABLE 1-2 Lifetime prevalence of drug use: 1972–1988 (use in lifetime)

Drug (number interviewed)	1972 (880)	1974 (952)	1976 (986)	1977 (1,272)	1979 (2,165)	1982 (1,581)	1985 (2,246)	1988 (3,095)
Cocaine	1.6	0.9	1.6	2.6	4.3	8.5	9.5	9.9
Heroin	•	0.5	0.5	0.8	1.0	1.1	1.1	1.1
Nonmedical use of any psychotherapeutic	—	—	—	—	9.2	8.8	13.8	11.3*
Stimulants	3.0	3.0	5.6	4.7	5.8	6.2	7.9	6.6
Sedatives	2.0	2.0	2.4	2.8	3.5	4.8	5.2	3.3**
Tranquilizers	5.0	2.0	2.7	2.6	3.1	3.6	7.2	4.6***
Analgesics	—	—	—	—	2.7	3.2	5.6	4.5
Cigarettes	—	65.4	64.5	67.0	83.0	78.7	80.5	79.6
Alcohol	—	73.2	74.7	77.9	91.5	88.2	89.4	88.6

Source: National Institute on Drug Abuse, *National Household Survey on Drug Abuse* (Washington, DC: NIDA, 1988).
•Low precision; no estimate reported.
*Difference between 1985 and 1988 statistically significant at the .05 level.
**Difference between 1985 and 1988 statistically significant at the .01 level.
***Difference between 1985 and 1988 statistically significant at the .001 level.

early 1980s. Since then there has been a continuing and at times rather significant drop in drug use (Stephens 1987, 49–50).

Even though drug use is lower than it was several years ago, it is still prevalent among young adults.

THE ROLE OF THE MASS MEDIA IN DRUG ADVERTISING

This introductory chapter would be incomplete without considering an important medium that has become increasingly responsible for disseminating information about drugs and drug use.

Print and electronic media comprise what is known as the *mass media.* Included in the *print* media are newspapers, books, and magazines; radio, television, movies, and records form the *electronic* media. Although over 70% of the adult population are regular newspaper readers, television remains the most influential medium. Almost 93 million American homes have television

sets; 59% have more than one set, and 96% have color sets.

In the United States, the number of hours spent watching television is staggering. Statistics indicate that the average household spends 49 hours and 49 minutes per week watching television (Nielsen 1986). This is over 7 hours per day!

Advertisers invest huge amounts of money in television commercials because of the popularity of the medium. Radio, newspapers, and magazines are also saturated with advertisements for OTC drugs, constantly offering relief from whatever illness you may have. There are pills for inducing sleep and staying awake, as well as for treating indigestion, headache, backache, tension, constipation, and the like. Mood, level of consciousness, and physical discomfort can be significantly altered by using these medicinal compounds.

Furthermore, experts warn that drug advertising will increase geometrically. A few years ago, the FDA lifted a two-year ban on consumer advertising of prescription drugs (Wang 1985).

In their attempt to sell drugs, product advertisers use the authority of a physician or health expert or the seemingly sincere testimony of a mesmerized product user. Adults are strongly affected by testimonial advertising because these drug commercials can appear authentic and convincing to large numbers of viewers, listeners, or readers. The constant barrage of commercials, including many for OTC drugs, relay the message that, if you are experiencing some symptoms, drug taking is acceptable. As a result, adults and eventually children are led to believe that drugs are necessary to maintain well-being.

Studies have shown that the majority of young drug users come from homes in which drugs are used extensively (Goode 1972; Coombs 1988). Thus, besides the persuasive effects of the mass media, children also frequently witness drug use at home. For instance, in the morning, parents may consume large quantities of coffee to wake up and other forms of medication throughout the day: tablets for an upset stomach, vitamins for stress, or aspirin for a headache. Finally, before retiring, the grown-ups may take a "little night cap" or a sleeping pill to relax. Pills alone are taken in almost unbelievable volume.

Think About It . . .

1. As an individual or class project, cut out magazine advertisements depicting drug use. What are the ads trying to convey? How are they trying to convince the audience to use their products?
2. Photocopy drug advertisements from magazines 20 years ago. Compare these ads to the current ads. What differences exist?
3. With several classmates or as a class project, count the number of medicines in each of your medicine cabinets at home and compare results with others. What conclusions can be drawn about your attitudes toward legalized drug use, as well as your parents' attitudes?
4. Interview people who use drugs frequently and also people who never or rarely use drugs. What differences exist between the two sets of people?

KEY TERMS

drug
psychoactive drug
"gateway" drugs
medicine

prescription drugs
over-the-counter (OTC) drugs
drug misuse
drug abuse

licit versus illicit drugs
"equal-opportunity" affliction
amotivational syndrome

SUMMARY

1. There are two reasons why it is important to understand the use and abuse of drugs in today's world: (a) Drug use is both a national and international problem; and (b) drug abuse by citizens can severely affect the stability of society.

2. Definitions: *drugs*—any substances that modify biological, psychological, and social behavior; *psychoactive drugs*—drugs that alter consciousness or perception; *"gateway" drugs*—alcohol, tobacco, and marijuana, drugs that lead to the use and abuse of more powerfully addictive drugs such as cocaine and heroin; *medicine*—drugs prescribed by a physician to prevent or treat the symptoms of an illness; *prescription drugs*—drugs that are usually more potent than OTC drugs; *over-the-counter drugs*—drugs sold without a

prescription; *licit drugs*—drugs legally bought or sold; and *illicit drugs*—drugs that are legally prohibited, such as marijuana, heroin, and cocaine.

3. The difference between drug *misuse* and *abuse* is that *misuse* refers to the unintentional or inappropriate use of prescribed drugs while *abuse* refers to the willful misuse of either legal or illegal drugs for recreation or convenience.

4. Attempts to regulate drug use date to the code of Hammurabi (2240 B.C.) and is even mentioned in the book of *Genesis*. Drugs have always been used for the same purposes they are today.

5. People continue to use drugs for five reasons: (a) to achieve pleasure; (b) to relieve stress or tension; (c) peer pressure; (d) to enhance religious or mystical experiences; and (e) to relieve pain and symptoms of illness.

6. No one is immune to drug use and abuse. It penetrates all income, social-class, and age groups.

7. The motive for taking drugs is the best way to distinguish between drug use and abuse.

8. The link between drug abuse and mental illness is that most forms of mental illness and drug abuse disrupt the activity of the chemical messengers in the central nervous system (CNS), called *neurotransmitters*.

9. Drug abusers have the following common characteristics: (a) legal drug use has preceded illegal drug use; (b) the amotivational syndrome, which is characterized by apathy, lack of interest in pursuing goals; (c) a history of poor school performance and classroom disobedience; (d) a history of delinquent behavior; (e) use of drugs in a social setting where drug abuse is common; (f) involvement in peer groups where drug use occurs frequently; (g) parents who are usually distant from their children's emotional needs; (h) the age of onset of drug taking correlates with the ability to stop (i.e., the older the adolescent at onset, the greater the probability of stopping drug use); (i) possibly living in single-parent homes and high rates of mobility; (j) racial, gender, and social-class discrimination and prejudice among minorities; and finally, (k) the view of selling drugs as being a lucrative business venture, for those involved in selling.

10. Drugs are used in the following ways: (a) as medicine; (b) for legal recreational use; (c) for illegal instrumental use; and (d) for illegal recreational use.

11. The 1988 National Household Survey on Drug Abuse found that, of the three age groups studied—youth (ages 12–17), young adults (ages 18–25), and older adults (ages 26 and over)—young adults were by far the heaviest drug users and experimenters.

12. The mass media disseminates an enormous amount of information about drug use and convinces people to treat medical symptoms with drugs.

A P P E N D I X E S

1-1: DRUGS OF USE AND ABUSE

The table that follows on pages 24–27 provides detailed information about the drugs listed. Note that the heading *CSA Schedules* refers to categorization under the Controlled Substances Act (CSA). The roman numeral(s) to the right of each drug name specifies each as a Schedule I, II, III, IV, or V drug. See Chapter 3, Appendix, for more information on scheduling.

1-2: DRUG QUIZ ANSWERS

1. Alcohol.
2. As quickly as six months. An early start on drinking and an immature brain and body make youngsters vulnerable.
3. Because they look and taste much like soda. (Girls especially like them because they don't look or taste like beer.) But wine coolers average 6% alcohol content, compared with 4% for beer and 10% to 14% for wine. Wine typically is served in smaller amounts, so a 12-ounce cooler delivers more alcohol than a glass of wine.
4. Yes. Researchers say it is rare to find abusers of cocaine, heroin, or virtually any addictive drug who did not start with some combination of alcohol, tobacco, and marijuana.
5. It is much more potent. The National Institute on Drug Abuse reports that the amount of THC,

APPENDIX 1-1   Drugs of use and abuse

Drugs/ CSA Schedules		Medical Uses	Trade or Other Names	Slang Names
Narcotics				
Opium	II III V	Analgesic, antidiarrheal	Dover's Powder, Paregoric, Parepectolin	Opium
Morphine	II III	Analgesic, antitussive	Morphine, MS-Contin, Roxanol, Roxanol-SR	M, Morpho, Morph, Tab, White, Stuff, Miss, Emma, Monkey
Codeine	II III V	Analgesic, antitussive	Tylenol w/Codeine, Empirin w/Codeine, Robitussan A-C, Fiorinal w/Codeine	School Boy
Heroin	I	None	Diacetylmorphine	Horse, Smack, H, Stuff, Junk
Hydromorphone	II	Analgesic	Dilaudid	Little D, Lords
Meperidine (Pethidine)	II	Analgesic	Demerol, Mepergan	Isonipecaine, Dolantol
Methadone	II	Analgesic	Dolophine, Methadone, Methadose	Dollies, Dolls, Amidone
Other Narcotics	I II III IV V	Analgesic, antidiarrheal, antitussive	Numorphan, Percodan, Percocet, Tylox, Tussionex, Fentanyl, Darvon, Lomotil, Talwin[2]	T. and Blue's, Designer Drugs, (Fentanyl Derivatives), China White
Depressants				
Chloral Hydrate	IV	Hypnotic	Noctec	—
Barbiturates	II III IV	Anesthetic, anticonvulsant, sedative, hypnotic, veterinary euthanasia agent	Amytal, Butisol, Fiorinal, Lotusate, Nembutal, Seconal, Tuinal, Phenobarbital	Yellows, Yellow Jackets, Barbs, Reds, Redbirds, Tooies, Phennies
Benzodiazepines	IV	Antianxiety, anticonvulsant, sedative, hypnotic	Ativan, Dalmane, Diazepam, Librium, Xanax, Serax, Valium, Tranxene, Verstran, Versed, Halcion, Paxipam, Restoril	Downers, Goof Balls, Sleeping Pills, Candy
Methaqualone	I	Sedative, hypnotic	Quaalude	Lude, Quay, Quad, Mandrex
Glutethimide	III	Sedative, hypnotic	Doriden	—
Other Depressants	III IV	Antianxiety, sedative, hypnotic	Equanil, Miltown, Noludar, Placidyl, Valmid	Tranquilizers, Muscle Relaxants, Sleeping Pills

Source: Adapted from U.S. Department of Justice/Drug Enforcement Administration, *Drugs of Abuse, 1989 Edition* (Washington, D.C.: Government Printing Office, 1989) and "Let's All Work to Fight Drug Abuse" (Dallas, TX: L.A.W. Publications, 1991).

[1]Designated as a narcotic under CSA (Controlled Substances Act).

[2]Not designated as a narcotic under CSA.

Dependence		Tolerance	Duration (hours)	Administration Methods	Possible Effects	Effects of Overdose	Withdrawal Syndrome
Physical—Psychological							
High	High	Yes	3–6	Oral, smoked			
High	High	Yes	3–6	Oral, smoked, injected			
Moderate	Moderate	Yes	3–6	Oral, injected	Euphoria, drowsiness, respiratory depression, constricted pupils, nausea	Slow and shallow breathing, clammy skin, convulsions, coma, possible death	Watery eyes, runny nose, yawning, loss of appetite, irritability, tremors, panic, cramps, nausea, chills and sweating
High	High	Yes	3–6	Injected, sniffed smoked			
High	High	Yes	3–6	Oral, injected			
High	High	Yes	3–6	Oral, injected			
High	High-Low	Yes	12–24	Oral, injected			
High-Low	High-Low	Yes	Variable	Oral, injected			
Moderate	Moderate	Yes	5–8	Oral			
High-Mod.	High-Mod.	Yes	1–16	Oral			
Low	Low	Yes	4–8	Oral	Slurred speech, disorientation, drunken behavior without odor of alcohol	Shallow respiration, clammy skin, dilated pupils, weak and rapid pulse, coma, possible death	Anxiety, insomnia, tremors, delirium, convulsions, possible death
High	High	Yes	4–8	Oral			
High	Moderate	Yes	4–8	Oral			
Moderate	Moderate	Yes	4–8	Oral			

(continued)

APPENDIX 1-1 *(continued)*

Drugs/ CSA Schedules		Medical Uses	Trade or Other Names	Slang Names
Stimulants				
Cocaine[1]	II	Local anesthetic		Bump, Toot, C, Coke, Flake, Snow, Candy, Crack
Amphetamines	II	Attention deficit disorders, narcolepsy, weight control	Biphetamine, Desoxyn, Dexedrine	Pep Pills, Bennies, Uppers, Truck Drivers, Dexies, Black Beauties, Speed
Phenmetrazine	II	Weight control	Preludin	Uppers, Peaches, Hearts
Methylphenidate	II	Attention deficit disorders, narcolepsy	Ritalin	Speed, Meth, Crystal, Crank, Go Fast
Other Stimulants	III IV	Weight control	Adipex, Cylert, Didrex, Ionamin, Melfiat, Plegine, Sanorex, Tenuate, Tepanil, Prelu-2	—
Hallucinogens				
LSD	I	None		Acid, Microdot, Cubes
Mescaline and Peyote	I	None		Mesc Buttons, Cactus
Amphetamine Variants	I	None	2,5-DMA, PMA, STP, MDA, MDMA, TMA, DOM, DOB	Ecstasy, Designer Drugs
Phencyclidine	II	None	PCP	PCP, Angel Dust, Hog, Peace Pill
Phencyclidine Analogues	I	None	PCE, PCPy, TCP	—
Other Hallucinogens	I	None	Bufotenine, Ibogaine, DMT, DET, Psilocybin, Psilocyn	Sacred Mushrooms, Magic Mushrooms, Mushrooms
Cannabis				
Marijuana	I	None		Pot, Grass, Reefer, Roach, Maui Wowie, Joint, Weed, Loco Weed, Mary Jane
Tetrahydrocannabinol	I II	Cancer chemotherapy antinauseant	THC, Marinol	THC
Hashish	I	None		Hash
Hashish Oil	I	None		Hash Oil
Inhalants		None	Gasoline, Airplane Glue, Veg. Spray, Hairspray, Deodorants, Spray Paint, Liquid Paper, Paint Thinner, Rubber Cement	Sniffing, Glue Sniffing, Snorting

Dependence Physical—Psychological		Tolerance	Duration (hours)	Administration Methods	Possible Effects	Effects of Overdose	Withdrawal Syndrome
Possible	High	Yes	1–2	Sniffed, smoked, injected	Increased alertness, excitation, euphoria, increased pulse rate & blood pressure, insomnia, loss of appetite	Agitation, increase in body temperature, hallucinations, convulsions, possible death	Apathy, long periods of sleep, irritability, depression, disorientation
Possible	High	Yes	2–4	Oral, injected			
Possible	High	Yes	2–4	Oral, injected			
Possible	Moderate	Yes	2–4	Oral, injected			
Possible	High	Yes	2–4	Oral, injected			
None	Unknown	Yes	8–12	Oral	Illusions and hallucinations, poor perception of time and distance	Longer, more intense "trip" episodes, psychosis, possible death	Withdrawal syndrome not reported
None	Unknown	Yes	8–12	Oral			
Unknown	Unknown	Yes	Variable	Oral, injected			
Unknown	High	Yes	Days	Smoked, oral, injected			
Unknown	High	Yes	Days	Smoked, oral, injected			
None	Unknown	Possible	Variable	Smoked, oral, injected, sniffed			
Unknown	Moderate	Yes	2–4	Smoked, oral	Euphoria, relaxed inhibitions, increased appetite, disoriented behavior	Fatigue, paranoia, possible psychosis	Insomnia, hyperactivity, and decreased appetite occasionally reported
				Smoked, oral			
Unknown	Moderate	Yes	2–4	Smoked, oral			
				Smoked, oral			
Unknown	Moderate	Yes	2–4				
Unknown	Moderate	Yes	2–4				
None	Unknown	Yes	30 min.	Sniffed	Euphoria, headaches, nausea, fainting, stupor, rapid heartbeat	Damage to lungs, liver, kidneys, bone marrow, suffocation, choking, anemia, possible stroke, sudden death	Insomnia, increased appetite, depression, irritability, headache

the active ingredient in marijuana, averaged 1% by weight in 1970. Today's dope averages 3% to 3.5%. Sinsemilla, an increasingly popular type of marijuana, averages 6.5% THC and may contain as much as 10% to 15%.

6. Animal studies demonstrate that ingesting the daily equivalent of a joint or two for several years destroys brain cells.

7. Researchers say one to three joints daily produces lung damage and cancer risks comparable with smoking five times as many cigarettes.

8. From the crackling made by the crystals of cocaine when smoked.

9. Alcohol leaves the body in 24 hours or less.

10. Traces of THC show up in the urine 10 to 35 days after marijuana is smoked.

11. Soaplike shavings or broken chalk.

12. It is the street term for *methamphetamine*, a class of stimulants also called "speed."

13. Six to eight minutes.

14. Whatever a person's conscious or unconscious emotional state, marijuana magnifies it. After the initial effect, however, it acts as a depressant.

15. According to the federal 1988 National Household Survey on Drug Abuse, 704,000 youngsters have tried hallucinogens at least once.

16. No method can reliably predict who will become chemically dependent.

17. Generally $2 to $5 in major urban centers but $25 and up in smaller cities, depending on supply and demand.

18. "Acid," or LSD.

19. Known as "angel dust," PCP has pain-killing properties that make users extraordinarily difficult to restrain physically.

20. Also known as XTC or "Adam" (from its chemical acronym MDMA), "Ecstasy" is a hallucinogen currently popular with college students. It appears to cause brain damage.

Source: V. Sussman, "How to Beat Drugs," *U.S. News and World Report,* 11 Sept. 1989, 69–72.

R E F E R E N C E S

Associated Press. "Officials: Drug Use Figures Still Too High." *Vidette Messenger* [Valparaiso, IN], 14 Feb. 1990, 5B.

Blum, R. H., and L. Richards. "Youthful Drug Use." In *Handbook on Drug Abuse,* edited by R. L. DuPont, A. Goldstein and J. O'Donnell, 257–269. Washington, D.C.: NIDA, 1979.

Chambers, C. C., and M. S. Griffey. "Use of Legal Substances within the General Population: The Sex and Age Variables." *Addictive Diseases* 2 (1975): 7–19.

Coombs, R. H., ed. *The Family Context of Adolescent Drug Use.* New York: Haworth, 1988.

Forster, C. D., N. R. Jacobs, and M. A. Siegel, eds. *Drugs and Alcohol—America's Anguish.* Wylie, TX: Information Plus, 1989.

Goode, E. *Deviant Behavior.* 3rd ed. New Jersey: Prentice Hall, 1990.

———. *Drugs in American Society.* New York: Knopf, 1972.

Gossop, M. *Living with Drugs.* 2nd ed. Aldershot, England: Wildwood House/Gower House, 1987.

Johnston, L. D., P. M. O'Malley, and J. G. Bachman. *Use of Licit and Illicit Drugs by America's High School Students: 1973–1984.* Washington, D.C.: National Institute on Drug Abuse, 1985.

Kosten, T. R. "Pharmacotherapeutic Intervention of Cocaine Abuse: Matching Patients to Treatments." *The Journal of Nervous and Mental Disease* 177 (1989): 379–389.

Kusinitz, M. "Drug Use Around the World." In *Encyclopedia of Psychoactive Drugs,* edited by S. Snyder, series 2. New York: Chelsea House, 1988.

"Let's All Work to Fight Drug Abuse." Dallas, TX: L.A.W. Publications, 1985, 1991.

Lipton, M. A., and H. J. Lee. *Psychopharmacology: A Generation of Progress.* New York: Raven, 1988.

Mello, N., and R. Griffiths. "Alcoholism and Drug Abuse: An Overview." In *Psychopharmacology: The Third Generation of Progress,* edited by H. Meltzer. New York: Raven, 1987.

National Institute on Drug Abuse. "Study Finds Higher Drug Use among Adolescent Whose Parents Divorce." *NIDA Notes* 5, no. 3 (Summer 1990): 10.

———. *NIDA Notes* 5, no. 1 (Winter 1989/1990): 4.

———. *National Household Survey on Drug Abuse.* Washington, D.C.: National Institute on Drug Abuse, 1988.

Nielsen Company. *Television: 1986 Nielsen Report.* Nielsen, Northbrook, IL, 1986.

Rounsaville, B. "Psychiatric Diagnosis of Treatment-Seeking Cocaine Abusers." *General Psychiatry* 48 (1991): 43–51.

Schecter, M. "Serotonergic-Dopaminergic Meditation of 3,4-Methytenedioxy-Methamphetamine [MDMA, Ecstasy]." *Pharmacology Biochemistry and Behavior* 31 (1989): 817–824.

Stephens, R. C. *Mind-Altering Drugs: Use, Abuse, and Treatment.* Law and Criminal Justice Series. Beverly Hills, CA: Sage, 1987.

Sussman, V. "How to Beat Drugs." *U.S. News and World Report,* 11 Sept. 1989, 69–72.

Thio, A. *Deviant Behavior.* 2nd ed. Boston: Houghton Mifflin, 1983.

Wang, P. "A New Way to Drugs." *Time,* 30 December 1985, 33–34.

Explaining Drug Use and Abuse

CHAPTER OUTLINE

The Biological Basis of Drug Abuse / **Social Structure and Social Process Theories** ▪ Social Disorganization and Social Strain Theories ▪ Subculture Theory: Social and Cultural Support / **Social Process Theories: Focusing on the Individual** ▪ Social Learning Theory ▪ The Reward System ▪ Control Theories ▪ Labeling Theory / **A Changing World** / **Current Social Change in Most Societies** / **Drug Abuse among Adolescents** ▪ The Adolescent Subculture ▪ Drugs and Peers ▪ Types of Adolescents Likely to Abuse Drugs / **Drug Abuse among Adults** ▪ The Subculture of Medical Professionals ▪ The Subculture of Athletes ▪ The Subculture of the Elderly ▪ Other Understudied Subcultural Groups

LEARNING OBJECTIVES

On completing this chapter, you will be able to:

1. List and briefly describe the following theories: social disorganization and strain; subculture; social learning; and labeling. What questions does each theory ask?
2. Explain how social disorganization theory, which focuses on how rapid social change outpaces our ability to adjust, accounts for drug use and abuse.

3. Explain how subculture theory accounts for a tendency among the elderly to become drug users and/or abusers.
4. Explain how social learning theory accounts for psychoactive drug use in society.
5. List and describe three factors in the learning process that Howard Becker believes first-time users go through before they become attached to using illicit psychoactive drugs.

6. Explain how control theory accounts for drug abuse. (Distinguish between internal versus external control.)
7. Define the following concepts: primary and secondary deviance; master status; and retrospective interpretation.
8. Explain how, according to labeling theory, the concepts in objective 7 lead to acquisition of a drug-abuser label.

Photo: Jean-Claude Lejeune/Stock, Boston

DID YOU KNOW THAT . . .

- Most drug use is learned from others.
- Whenever drug use becomes consistent and habitual, it usually occurs in the peer-group setting with people we like.
- General drug use has decreased in the last several years; however, the percentage of high school seniors who try drugs at least once remains high.
- According to a recent survey, 91% of high school seniors have tried alcohol, and 64% have tried cigarettes.
- Drugs are sometimes used to compensate for a lack of self-confidence.
- Health care professionals abuse narcotics at a rate 40 times greater than the general public.
- Nineteen percent of the current work force 18 and older uses marijuana, and 6.6% uses cocaine.
- Research indicates that athletes are more likely to abuse amphetamines, anabolic steroids, and several types of pain killers.
- In most cases, drug misuse by the elderly involves inappropriate use of legally prescribed drugs or overuse of OTC medications.
- Biological factors may contribute to drug abuse.
- No single theory can explain why most people use drugs.
- Some theories suggest that rapid social change leads to drug use.
- People who perceive themselves as drug users are more likely to develop serious drug abuse problems.

Why do people use drugs? In this chapter, we will disclose some people's motivations and the circumstances that may lead them to use drugs. Namely: Why is the use of drugs so widespread? Who is using drugs? What are some explanations for drug use?

To answer these questions, we will present a biological perspective on drug abuse. Then we will consider several scientific explanations from a social psychological perspective. The theories presented are mainline sociological and psychological explanations of drug use authored by classic, neoclassic, and contemporary theoreticians who are nationally and internationally renowned. Drug use among various age groups and professionals will be examined, as well.

THE BIOLOGICAL BASIS OF DRUG ABUSE

The reasons for drug abuse are complex and varied, with many contributing factors. And only recently have biological explanations been seriously considered as contributing to the problem. For example, it has been suggested that, in some people, the central nervous system (CNS) reward sensors are more sensitive to drugs that are abused, making the drug experience more pleasant and more alluring for these individuals (Jarvik 1990). (The **CNS** is defined as "one of the major divisions of the nervous system, composed of the brain and spinal cord.) In contrast, others find the effects of drugs of abuse very unpleasant; such people are not likely to be attracted to these drugs (Farrar and Kearns 1989).

CNS (central nervous system)
one of the major divisions of the nervous system, composed of the brain and spinal cord

A likely, though not totally proven, reason for these opposite responses to abused drugs is the difference in the way the neurotransmitters of the brain react. **Neurotransmitters** are biochemical messengers, which cause an impulse from one neuron to be transferred to the next. Perhaps for the individual particularly susceptible to drug

neurotransmitters
biochemical messengers, which cause the impulse from one neuron to be transferred to the next

abuse, these drugs enhance the **dopamine system,** the transmitter system thought to mediate the rewarding aspects of most drugs of abuse (see Chapter 5). In those not so inclined, these drugs do little to diminish the activity of this transmitter system (Jarvik 1990, 367).

dopamine system
the transmitter system believed to mediate the rewarding aspects of most drugs of abuse

At this time, the biological theories of abuse liability are just hypotheses. As yet, it is impossible to prove that these hypotheses hold for human subjects. However, if certain biological conditions predispose some people to abusing drugs, these traits could be genetically transmitted, such that some family members would be at a greater risk for drug abuse. Genetic factors definitely play a role in some addictions, such as alcoholism (Pickens and Svikis 1988). It is not yet clear what contribution genetic factors have in determining susceptibility to other drugs of abuse.

One genetic consideration relevant to drug abuse has been discussed above. Another explanation is that many abusers have underlying mental illnesses; this suggests that the use of illicit drugs is an attempt to self-medicate a psychological disorder (as discussed in Chapter 1). It is well documented that some, if not most, forms of mental illnesses are genetically transmitted, particularly affective diseases, such as severe depression. Because depression may encourage use of illicit stimulants, it might appear that there is a genetic predisposition to abuse these drugs when, in fact, the inherited trait causes a mental condition, which secondarily leads to the use of the illicit drugs.

Such confounding issues make it difficult to identify specific biological factors that increase the risk of drug abuse. However, with greater understanding of the mechanisms by which the drugs of abuse exert their effects, these biological contributions will be explained and hopefully lead to improved therapeutics in both the prevention and resolution of drug abuse problems.

SOCIAL STRUCTURE AND SOCIAL PROCESS THEORIES

Numerous social psychological theories have been offered for explaining drug use and abuse. Keep in mind that no one theory can explain why people use drugs. People differ immensely from one another and, as a result, take drugs for very different reasons. Because of these varied human characteristics, many theories appear vastly different from one another and sometimes even contradictory. There are two reasons for this:

1. The explanations are derived from different perspectives of social psychology.
2. The differences result from trying simultaneously to account for individual qualities, unique situations, and circumstances regarding why drugs are used.

Social structure and social process are the two types of theories that are discussed in this and the next section. The social structure theories presented in this section are (1) social disorganization, (2) social strain, and (3) subculture theories. These theories assert that people do not simply behave on their own but that social behavior results from how subcultures, groups, and society are organized.

SOCIAL DISORGANIZATION AND SOCIAL STRAIN THEORIES

The focus of these theories is on how the organization of a society, group, or subculture is responsible for drug abuse by its members. The belief is that it is not the society, group, or subculture that is causing the behavior—in this case, drug use—but that the organization itself or the lack of an organization determines the resulting behavior.

Social disorganization and social strain theories identify the different kinds of social change that are disruptive and how, in a general sense, people are affected by such change. Social disorganization theory asks: What in the social order causes people to deviate? Social strain theory asks: Can the way in which a society is organized cause social deviance? This theory believes that frustration results from being unable to achieve desired goals. This perceived shortcoming compels an individual to deviate in order to achieve desired needs.

Overall, social disorganization theory describes a situation where, because of rapid social change, previously affiliated individuals no longer find themselves integrated into a community's social, commercial, religious, and economic institutions. When this occurs, community members that were once affiliated become disaffiliated and lack effective attachment to the social order. As a result, these disaffiliated people begin to gravitate toward deviant behavior.

In order to develop trusting relationships, stability and continuity are essential for proper socialization. As will be discussed later in this chapter, if identity transformation occurs during the teen years, when drugs are first introduced, a stable environment is very important. Yet in a technological society, destabilizing and disorienting forces often result because technology causes rapid social change.

While most people have little or no difficulty when confronted with rapid social change, others

For You to Consider...

These excerpts, gathered from interviews, reflect social disorganization and strain theory.

These days, everything is rush, rush, rush. There are just not enough hours in the day. I set aside weekends in order to relax. Alcohol and marijuana allow me to relax from the rest of the week.

I am into my own life because everyone is doing this. I see nearly everyone doing well around here. It's only those who are too stupid to succeed who are poor. I have had a rough time making it lately. Cocaine and speed help, but I know it's not the answer to all my problems. For now, drugs help me to put up with all the shit going on in my life.

Source: Interview 1 with a 22-year-old part-time, female college student at a state-supported liberal arts college in the Southeast; conducted April 10, 1986, by Peter Venturelli. Interview 2 with a 25-year-old male residing in the Southeast and receiving various forms of welfare; conducted March 10, 1985, by Peter Venturelli.

perceive this change as beyond their control. For example, consider an immigrant who experienced a nervous breakdown because he was unable to cope with the new society. The following interview shows how such confusion and lack of control lead to drug use, which is viewed as an attractive alternative to coping with confusion and stress:

Interviewee: The world is all messed up.
Interviewer: Why? In what way?
Interviewee: Nobody gives a damn anymore about anyone else.
Interviewer: Why do you think this is so?
Interviewee: It seems like life just seems to go on and on. . . . I know that when I am under the influence, life is more mellow. I feel great! When I am "high," I feel relaxed and can take things in better. Before I came to Chalmers College [a pseudonym], I felt home life was one great big mess; now that I am here, this college is also a big pile of crap. I guess this is why I like smoking dope. When I am "high," I can forget my problems. My surroundings are friendlier; I

am even more pleasant! Do you know what I mean?*

In conclusion, social disorganization and strain theory says that the reason people use and abuse drugs is found in larger society, namely, in the way it is organized, experienced, and perceived.

SUBCULTURE THEORY: SOCIAL AND CULTURAL SUPPORT

Subculture theory explains drug use as being caused by peer pressure. Subculture theory asks: How does deviance result from peer-group influence? Psychologically, in all groups, there are members who are very well liked and, as a result, are perceived as role models by those who wish to be popular. Drug use that results from peer pressure demonstrates the extent to which the more popular peer-group members are able to influence and pressure others to use or abuse drugs (Bandura 1969; Rotter 1972).

In sociology, individual popularity is referred to as **status**. This notion of individual prestige and status is the key to understanding how members of peer groups may be persuaded to experiment with drugs. In groups where drugs are consumed, the amount of peer influence depends on the prestige level of certain key individuals. The most popular group members are the most successful in influencing newcomers to the group. Moreover, in groups where drugs are extensively used, the more avid users maintain a keen interest in inducing others to join them. Why? Leaders find that having followers is very self-gratifying.

---

status
refers to individual popularity and social position in the eyes of others

---

Within a peer group, drug use can also be an attempt to solve problems collectively. In the book

*Interview with a 19-year-old male marijuana user attending a small, private, liberal arts college in the Southeast. Conducted by Peter Venturelli, February 12, 1984.

Delinquent Boys: The Culture of the Gang (1955), Cohen pioneered a study that showed for the first time that delinquent behavior is a collective attempt to gain status within the peer group. Unable to achieve respect within the larger society, certain youths find that being able to commit delinquent acts without detection is admirable in the eyes of other members who belong to the same peer group. Thus, Cohen believes, delinquent behavior is a subcultural solution for avoiding status frustration.

While Cohen is primarily discussing juvenile delinquency, his notion that delinquent behavior is a subcultural solution may have other applications. In particular, it suggests that the underlying cause for drug use in groups results from sharing common feelings of alienation and estrangement from society. From this perspective, using drugs as an escape is a collective response to a society that appears distant, uncaring, and unattainable.

Consider the elderly who are looked upon as a separate subculture, with distinct health characteristics. Elderly people are often perceived as either being on the verge of contracting an illness or being chronically ill; this perception is perpetuated by the medical profession, family members, and advertisers. Pharmaceutical companies, for example, in their over-the-counter (OTC) drug advertising, stress that their products will most definitely relieve constipation, arthritic pain, nervous tension, and vitamin deficiency. In turn, because the elderly are portrayed as potentially ill, they—like everyone else—are influenced to believe that life would be more enjoyable if they would take certain drugs.

It has been confirmed that often, the older a person becomes, the greater the probability that he or she will become dependent on drugs. For this subculture, prescription and OTC drugs are often necessary for maintaining so-called normal health.

SOCIAL PROCESS THEORIES: FOCUSING ON THE INDIVIDUAL

The social process theories presented in this section include social learning, control, and labeling theories. The basis of these theories is that the individual is either coerced by extraneous factors or is socialized by others to seek drugs.

SOCIAL LEARNING THEORY

Social learning theory explains drug use as a form of learned behavior. Conventional learning occurs through imitation, trial and error, improvisation, rewarding appropriate behavior, and cognitive mental processes. Social learning theory focuses directly on how drug use and abuse is acquired through interaction with others who use and abuse drugs.

The theory emphasizes the pervasive influence of **primary groups**, which are groups that share a high amount of intimacy and spontaneity and whose members are bonded emotionally. Families and residents of a close-knit urban neighborhood are examples of primary groups. In con-

For You to Consider...

This excerpt from an interview reflects social and cultural support theory.

> I first started messing around with alcohol in high school. In order to be part of the crowd, we would sneak out during lunchtime at school and get "high." About six months after we started drinking, we moved on to other drugs. . . . Everyone in high school belongs to a clique, and my clique was heavy into drugs. We had a lot of fun being "high" throughout the day. We would party constantly. Basically, in college, it's the same thing.

Source: Interview with a 19-year-old male student at a small, private, liberal arts college in the Southeast; conducted on February 9, 1985, by Peter Venturelli.

primary groups
close-knit groups that share a high amount of intimacy, spontaneity, and emotional bonding

trast, **secondary groups** are groups that share segmented relationships where interaction is based on prescribed role patterns. An example of a secondary group would be the relationship between you and a sales clerk in a grocery store or among a group of employees scattered throughout a corporation.

---

secondary groups
groups that share more distant and segmented relationships

Learning theory addresses a type of interaction that is *highly specific*. This type of interaction involves learning specific motives, techniques, and appropriate meanings that are commonly attached to a particular type of drug.

As the sociologist Becker points out in his well-known article "Becoming a Marijuana User," the novice who is perceived as a first-time user has to learn the technique:

> I was smoking like I did an ordinary cigarette. He said, "No, don't do it like that." He said, "Suck it, you know, draw in and hold it in your lungs till you . . . for a period of time."
>
> I said, "Is there any limit of time to hold it?"
>
> He said, "No, just till you feel that you want to let it out, let it out." So I did that three or four times (Becker 1966, 47).

Learning to perceive the effects of the drug is the second major outcome in the process of becoming a regular user. Here, the ability to feel the authentic effects of the drug is being learned. The more experienced drug users in the group impart their knowledge to naive or first-time users. The coaching information they provide describes how to recognize the euphoric effects of the drug, as illustrated in another excerpt:

> I just sat there waiting for something to happen, but I really didn't know what to expect. After the fifth "hit" [a hit consists of deeply inhaling a marijuana cigarette as it is being passed around and shared in a group], I was just about ready to give up ever getting "high."

Then suddenly, my best buddy looked deeply into my eyes and said, "Aren't you 'high' yet?" Instead of just answering the question, I immediately repeated the same words the exact way he asked me. In a flash, we both simultaneously burst out laughing. This uncontrollable laughter went on for what appeared to be over five minutes. Then he said, "You silly ass, it's not like an alcohol 'high,' it's a 'high high.' Don't you feel it? It's a totally different kind of 'high.' "

At that very moment, I knew I was definitely "high" on the stuff. If this friend would not have said this to me, I probably would have continued thinking that getting "high" on the hash was impossible for me.*

After learning the technique and how to perceive the effects of the drug, Becker informs us that members in groups teach first-time users how to enjoy the experience:

> Because they [first-time users] think they're going to keep going up, up, up till they lose their minds or begin doing weird things or something. You have to like reassure them, explain to them that they're not really flipping or anything, that they're gonna be all right. You have to just talk them out of being afraid. Keep talking to them, reassuring, telling them it's all right. And come on with your own story, you know: "The same thing happened to me. You'll get to like that after awhile." Keep coming on like that; pretty soon you talk them out of being scared . . . that gives them more confidence (Becker 1966, 55).

Once drug use has begun, continuing the behavior involves the following learned sequence: (1) where and from whom the drug can be purchased, (2) how to maintain the secrecy of use from authority figures and casual aquaintances, and (3) justification for continual use.

THE REWARD SYSTEM

Once the drug use pattern has been established, what part of the learning process sustains drug-

---

*Interview with a 17-year-old male attending a small, private, liberal arts college in the Southeast. Conducted by Peter Venturelli, May 15, 1984.

taking behavior? Sutherland (1947, 5–9), a pioneering criminologist in the field of sociology, believes that the mastery of criminal behavior depends on the frequency, duration, priority, and intensity of contact with others who are involved in similar behavior. This theory can also be applied to drug-taking behavior.

Through Becker's learning theory, we saw that motives, techniques of how to use the drug, and appropriate meanings are taught to others. Sutherland's principles of social learning to drug use, which he calls *differential association theory*, focus on how other members of social groups reward criminal behavior and under what conditions this deviance is perceived as important and pleasurable.

Becker's and Sutherland's theories explain why adolescents use psychoactive drugs. Essentially, both theories say that the use of drugs is learned during intimate interaction with others who serve as a primary group.

Learning theory also explains how adults and the elderly acquire a favorable attitude toward drug-taking behavior. Through advertising, both the pharmaceutical industry and medical specialist are instructing, persuading, and instilling the necessary motives, techniques, and appropriate meanings for using drugs. When drug advertisements and medical experts authoritatively recommend a particular drug, in effect, they are persuading viewers or listeners that taking a particular drug will make them feel better.

CONTROL THEORIES

Control theories place importance on positive socialization. **Socialization** is defined as "the process by which individuals learn and internalize the attitudes, values, and behaviors needed to become participating members of conventional society." Generally, control theorists believe that human

socialization
the process by which individuals learn and internalize the attitudes, values, and behaviors needed to become participating members of conventional society

beings can easily become deviant if left without social controls. Thus, theorists who specialize in control theory emphasize the necessity of maintaining bonds to family, school, peers, and other social, political, and religious organizations.

In the 1950s and 1960s, criminologist Walter C. Reckless (1961) developed containment theory. According to this theory, the socialization process results in the creation of strong or weak internal and external control systems.

Internal control is determined by the degree of self-control, high or low frustration tolerance, positive or negative self-perception, successful or unsuccessful goal achievement, and either resistance to or adherence to deviant behavior. Internal controls consist of the motives, drives, disappointments, frustrations, rebellions, and feelings of inferiority that could encourage a person to engage in deviant behavior. Environmental pressures, such as social conditions, may limit the accomplishment of goal-striving behavior; such conditions include poverty, minority-group status, inferior education, and lack of employment.

The external, or outer, control system consists of effective or ineffective supervision and disci-

For You to Consider...

This excerpt from an interview reflects social control theory.

I guess you could call me more of a loner type. I belong to groups, but I am never really involved much in them. I have just a few really close friends and these friends are also like me—mostly nonjoiners.

Here I am in my early thirties, and I still enjoy getting "high." When I was in my early twenties, I thought that once my friends would eventually leave and get married or move away, I would quit using drugs. Now that most of these friends are no longer here, I still get "high," mostly on my own.

Source: Interview with a 32-year-old male, middle-management employee residing in the Midwest; conducted on December 9, 1986, by Peter Venturelli.

pline, consistent or inconsistent moral training, positive or negative acceptance, identity, and self-worth. Examples are latchkey children who become delinquent and alcoholic parents who are inconsistent with discipline. Attractions and temptations in society are also influential, as in the case of an impoverished young man who perceives instant wealth by becoming a drug dealer. This is another example of breakdown in social control.

In applying this theory to the use or abuse of drugs, we could say that, if an individual has a weak external control system, the internal control system must take over to handle external pressures. Similarly, if an individual's external control system is strong from positive socialization based on discipline, moral training, and development of positive feelings of self-worth, then this individual's internal control system will not be seriously challenged. If, however, either the internal or external control system is mismatched—in that one happens to be weak and the other strong—the possibility of drug abuse increases.

If an individual's external and internal controls are both weak, he or she is most likely to use and abuse drugs. Table 2-1 shows the likelihood of drug use resulting from either strong or weak internal and external control systems. It indicates that, if both internal and external controls are strong, the use and abuse of drugs is not likely to occur. However, if the internal and external systems are both weak, drug use is most likely to occur (providing, of course, that drugs are available and presented by trusted friends).

Travis Hirschi (1971, 85, 159), a much respected sociologist and social control theorist, believes that delinquent behavior tends to occur whenever people lack (1) attachment to others;

(2) commitment to goals; (3) involvement in conventional activity; and (4) belief in the common value system. If a child or adolescent is unable to become circumscribed within the family setting, school, and the nondelinquent peers, then the drift to delinquent behavior is inevitable.

We can apply Hirschi's theories to drug use as follows:

1. Drug users are less likely than nonusers to be closely tied to their parents.
2. Good students are less likely to use drugs.
3. Drug users are less likely to participate in social clubs and organizations and engage in team sport activities.
4. Drug users are very likely to have friends whose activities are congruent with their own attitudes.

The social control theories of Reckless and Hirschi can be compared. Reckless's version of control theory says that people with weak personalities (those who lack self-control or exhibit low frustration tolerance and live in neighborhoods saturated with drug-using groups) are likely to use and abuse drugs. Similarly, older adults who lack self-control and who have been reared in families where OTC drugs were liberally used are more likely to become drug users.

In comparing Hirschi's version of control theory with Reckless's theory, we find two differences and two similarities. Specifically, the theories differ in that Hirschi places less importance on describing internal control functions. Moreover, Hirschi holds the quality and extent of attachment, commitment, and involvement with family, school, and the peer group responsible for conformity.

The theories are similar in that both suggest

TABLE 2-1 Likelihood of drug use

Internal Control	External Control	
	Strong	Weak/Nonexistent
Strong	Least likely (almost never)	Less likely (probably never)
Weak	More likely (probably will)	Most likely (almost certain)

that control is either internally or externally enforced by family, school, and peer-group expectations. In addition, individuals who are either (1) not equipped with an internal system of self-control reflecting the values and beliefs of conventional society or (2) personally alienated from major social institutions such as family, school, and church may deviate without feeling guilty for their actions.

Control theory shows how attachments to conventional groups prevent deviance and asks: How does the amount of group conformity preclude deviant behavior?

LABELING THEORY

Labeling theory suggests that the image we have of ourselves is largely controlled by other members of society. It implies that we have a minimal amount of control over the image we desire to portray. Instead, members of society have a lot of power in redefining or recasting our image. The image we hold of ourselves is really in the hands of the people we admire and look up to. The key ingredient here is how we are perceived by society. If its members define our actions negatively, then the definitions become facts of reality.

Decades before this theory was formulated, Charles H. Cooley, a pioneering theorist and social philosopher, suggested that how we evaluate ourselves largely results from communication with significant others. In other words, the basis of how we view ourselves is largely determined by the opinions of people who are important to us, like parents and teachers. According to Cooley, the self is "a system of ideas drawn from communicative life, that the mind cherishes as its own" (Cooley 1902, 179).

Cooley believes that the self develops through social interaction. His theory of the "looking-glass self" states that, from social interaction, other people evaluate and react to our verbal and nonverbal (body language) behavior. The specific situation that occurs when individuals reflect on social behavior while engaged in day-to-day conversations is known as the *reflective process*. The cartoon on page 40 illustrates this process.

Additional substance has been added to la-

For You to Consider...

This excerpt from an interview reflects labeling theory.

I guess I didn't care anymore after my mom called me a "dope fiend" over and over again. She found some pills and my favorite hash pipe one day in one of my jacket pockets and confronted me with all sorts of foul accusations.

Most of my friends knew I was into drugs, so it was no big deal when my mom found out.

Even the dean of students here at Chalmers [a pseudonym] knows that I deal in drugs. He just never mentioned it again after the first time he called me in about my dealing. I think he's afraid of my dad who is very active on the board of trustees here.

Source: Interview with a 20-year-old male college student at a small, private, liberal arts college in the Southeast; conducted April 10, 1983, by Peter Venturelli.

beling theory by Edwin Lemert (1951, 133–141), who distinguishes between two types of deviance: primary and secondary deviance. **Primary deviance** is inconsequential deviance, which occurs without having a lasting impression on the perpetrator. Generally, most first-time violations of law, for example, are primary deviations. Whether the suspected or accused individual has committed the deviant act does not matter. What matters is whether the individual identifies with the deviant behavior.

primary deviance
deviant behavior with which the perpetrator does not identify

Secondary deviance develops when the individual begins to identify and perceive himself or herself as deviant. The moment this occurs, deviance shifts from being primary to secondary. Many adolescents casually experiment with drugs. If, however, they begin to perceive themselves as

This is an illustration of the reflective process that often occurs in daily conversations when we think that our unspoken thoughts are undetectable and hidden. In reality, however, these innermost thoughts are clearly conveyed through body language and nonverbal gestures.

drug users, then this behavior is virtually impossible to eradicate. The same holds true with OTC drug abuse. The moment an individual believes that he or she feels better by using a particular drug, the greater the likelihood that he or she will use the drug consistently.

secondary deviance
type of deviant behavior that develops when the perpetrator views himself or herself as deviant

Howard Becker (1973) believes that, while most people occupy multiple status positions (such as male or female, senior citizen or adolescent, student, father, employee, etc.), certain negative status positions (such as alcoholic, mental patient, criminal, drug addict, etc.) are so powerful that they dominate others. For example, if people who are important to Jack call him a "druggie," this becomes a powerful label that will take precedence over any other status positions Jack may occupy. This label becomes Jack's **master status**—that of

an addicted drug user. Even if Jack is also an above-average biology major, an excellent drummer, and a very likeable individual, those factors become secondary. Further, once a powerful label is attached, it becomes much easier for the individual to uphold the image dictated by members of society. Master-status labels distort an individual's public image in that other people expect consistency in role performance.

master status
the overriding status in the eyes of others that identifies an individual, e.g. doctor, lawyer, alcoholic, HIV positive

Once a negative master status has been attached to an individual's public image, labeling theorist Schur asserts that retrospective interpretation occurs. **Retrospective interpretation** is a form of "reconstitution of individual character or identity" (1971, 52). This largely involves redefining a person's image within a particular social group.

retrospective interpretation
the social psychological process of redefining a person's reputation within a particular group

Finally, William I. Thomas's (1923, 203–222) contribution to labeling theory can be summarized in the theorem that "If men define situations as real, they are real in their consequences." In other words, if the collective definition of a situation is subjectively perceived in a certain direction by other members of society, the perception becomes fact. Thus, according to this theory, when someone is perceived as a drug user, the perception functions as a label of that person's character and shapes his or her self-perception. There is considerable evidence of the importance we attach to the images we portray, as expressed in terms of grooming, demeanor, manners, styles of clothing, and material goods consumed.

After having read about some of the main contributors to labeling theory, we can summarize by saying that the labels we use to describe people have a way of influencing their self-perceptions. In returning to our example, even if Jack does not initially believe he is an addict but instead an occasional user, the idea that his friends perceive him as a drug abuser will cause Jack to be uneasy whenever he is in their company. These uneasy feelings will interfere with Jack's ability to convey a nondrug-using image. At first Jack may deny the charge. Then he may poke fun at what others think of him. But eventually, Jack will begin to perceive himself more in line with the consistent perceptions of his accusers. This final perception occurs gradually. If he is unsuccessful in eradicating the addict image, Jack will reluctantly concur with the label that has been pinned on him or leave the group so that he can once again become acceptable in the eyes of other people.

Labeling theory does not explain why deviant behavior occurs in the first place, but it does explain how you can come to identify yourself as a deviant because of other people's perceptions. Labeling theory asks: How does a person begin to perceive himself or herself as deviant? No one theory is best in all cases. It depends on the individ-

Let's Get the Facts

Families with Little or No Drug Use

Information on the reduction and prevention of drug misuse and abuse can be obtained from studies of those families who rarely or never use drugs. In comparison to drug-using families, the nonusing or low-use families show the following characteristics:

1. Children perceive more love from both parents, particularly the father.
2. There is less difference between how parents would ideally like their children to be versus how they actually perceive them.
3. Children are seen as more assertive, although a basic firmness in childrearing is maintained.
4. Parents and their children's friends are compatible.
5. Parents have more influence on their children than do peers, and emphasize discipline, self-control, and family tradition.
6. Less approval of drug use is expressed by both parents and peers.
7. There is more spontaneous agreement observed in family problem solving.
8. Family members function more democratically or quasi-democratically, with shared authority and better communication.

Source: From *Drug Abuse from the Family Perspective* (Washington, D.C.: National Institute on Drug Abuse, 1980), p. 26.

ual, his or her circumstances for taking the drug, and the type of drug being used.

Think About It...

1. Of the two social structure theories (social disorganization/social strain and subculture theories), which best explains drug use? Why?
2. Of the three social process theories (social learning, control, and labeling theories), which best explains drug use? Why?
3. If a member of your family or your best friend had a drug problem, which theory or theories would best help you understand his or her problem? Why?

A CHANGING WORLD

Historical records document drug use as far back as 2240 B.C., when Hammaurabi, the Babylonian king and lawgiver, addressed the problems associated with drinking alcohol. Further, as noted in Chapter 1, virtually every culture has had problems with drug use and abuse. Based on this information, we can conclude that drug use and abuse is a very old problem. Some may wonder why we want to study this age old problem.

We offer five reasons why drug use and abuse is an even more serious issue than it was in the past and thus worthy of study:

1. From 1960 to the present, drug use has become a widespread phenomenon. Before the sixties, drug use was a serious problem only within certain isolated populations. Today, however, it affects nearly every social group.

2. Today, drugs are much more potent than they were years ago. For example, in 1960, the average THC content of marijuana was 1% to 2%. (THC is the ingredient responsible for making a person "high.") Today, marijuana contains 4.1% THC. To a large extent, the increase of THC content is due to improved cultivation techniques (Mijuriya and Aldrich 1988).

3. Whether they are legal or not, drugs have become commonplace, and their sale is a multibillion-dollar-a-year business.

4. Drug use endangers the future of a society by physically harming its youth and potentially destroying the lives of many young men and women. When "gateway" drugs such as alcohol and tobacco are used at an early age, there is a strong possibility that the user will progress to other drugs, such as marijuana, cocaine, and amphetamines. Early drug use will likely lead to a lifelong habit, which has serious implications for the future.

5. The possibility of serious accidents caused by drug users is probably more real today. For instance, the operation of sophisticated technology and electronic equipment requires that workers and professionals be free

of the effects of mind-altering drugs. Just imagine if several computer programmers responsible for supervising air traffic control were occasional cocaine users or if technicians at a major X-ray diagnostic and cancer treatment center smoked marijuana during their lunchbreaks. Simply stated, in this era, we rely more on others in order to achieve social, economic, and political goals. Can we trust them?

Think About It...

1. Of the five reasons cited above, which is the best explanation for why drug abuse is more serious today than in the past? Why?

For You to Consider...

Drugs and Job Performance

While nearly every occupation has its share of workers who use illicit psychoactive drugs on the job, think of how you might be affected if the people performing the jobs listed below were under the influence of alcohol, marijuana, or cocaine.

    Physicians
    Dentists
    Nurses
    Lab technicians
    Electrical, mechanical, civil, and construction
        engineers
    Vehicle operators
    Health and building inspectors
    Ambulance drivers
    Airline pilots, ground crew, and traffic controllers
    Stockbrokers and investment bankers
    Lawyers, judges, and criminal justice personnel
    Nuclear power plant operators
    Presidents, prime ministers, and other heads of state
    Legislators
    Ministers and priests
    Firefighters and police officers

For You to Consider...

"You Wasn't In Unless You Were Getting High"

The following excerpt describes the impact of peer pressure on a youth who uses heroin to be "hip."

Cats on the block had been using it for years and they had been trying to get me to use it but I backed off. A couple of my partners went down and they pulled a stick-up and they had plenty of money, so they came back after buying dope for everybody. We seen the availability of it and they seemed to know what they were talking about. It was a thing where heroin was always talked about. We all went off in a vacant building, must have been about a dozen of us. We just lined up, rolled up our sleeves and started pushing the dope, you know, everybody got a shot.

We was sitting around with friends of ours. We all grew up together and they were into it before we were. We wanted to know what kind of feeling that was, the way we watched them high. And they looked like they felt so good. So I stayed for awhile and tried it.

When we used to play hooky, we used to have hooky parties, and the older crowd of dudes used to try to come to the party to mess with the women. Then they'd sneak off in the bathroom and start shooting heroin. And they'd come out and say, "Hey, take [snort] a couple of blows, I think you'll like it." And we'd do, just being naive and wanting to hang out, we did it. At first I really didn't like it. I don't know what it was that continued me with it because it made me more sick than pleasing.

Using heroin in those days was a fad. You wasn't cool unless you used it and, you know, you want to be like everybody else, you want to be like your big brother, gang fightin'. You want to be hip, and you wasn't in the crowd unless you were getting high.

Source: Reprinted with the permission of Lexington Books, an imprint of Macmillan, Inc., from Life with Heroin: Voices from the Inner City by Bill Hanson, George Beschner, James M. Walters, and Elliott Bovelle. Copyright © 1985 by Lexington Books.

2. Can you name other occupational groups not listed in the box on job performance whose drug use could pose a serious danger to society?

CURRENT SOCIAL CHANGE IN MOST SOCIETIES

Does social change per se cause people to use and abuse drugs? In response to this question, *social change*—defined as "any measurable change caused by technological advancement that affects cultural values and attitudes"—does not by itself cause widespread drug use. In most cases, social change materialistically advances a culture by profoundly affecting how things are accomplished. At the same time, however, rapid social change disrupts day-to-day behavior preserved by tradition, which has a tendency to fragment such conventional social groups as families, communities, and neighborhoods. By *conventional behavior*, we mean behavior that is largely dictated by custom and tradition and thus evaporates under rapid social change.

Is there any link between social change and drug use? Although no direct link exists, there is plenty of proof that certain dramatic changes occur in the organization of society and may eventually lead certain groups to use and abuse drugs. Figure 2-1 illustrates how the number of lifecycle stages increases, depending on the level of technological development. Overall, this implies that, as societies advance from preindustrial to industrial to postindustrial, there is a greater likelihood that new subcultures will develop (see Fischer 1976, for similar thinking). In contrast to industrial and postindustrial societies, preindustrial societies do not have so many separate and distinct periods and cycles of social development. What is implied here is that the greater the number of distinct lifecycles, the greater the fragmentation between the members of different stages of development. Further, fragmentation encapsulates group members, promoting the bond among members of the same

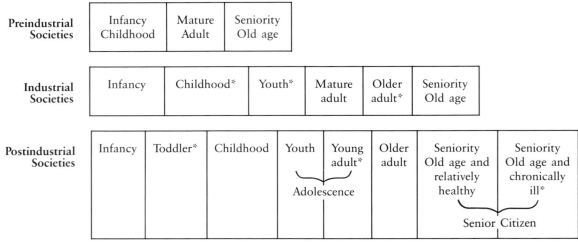

*Represents a newly developed and separate stage of identification and expression.

FIGURE 2-1   Levels of technological development and corresponding subcultures

group but discouraging contact with other groups. An example would be the number of hippie subcultures that developed during the 1960s (Yinger 1982). Two other groups that will be elaborated on later are teen-agers and the elderly, both of which have become increasingly alienated from other age groups in society.

Simply stated, today's social institutions no longer influence people as much as they did in the past. As a consequence, people are free to explore different means of expression and types of recreation. For most groups, this is a liberating experience, leading to new and exciting outcomes. For other groups, the freedom to explore involves drug use and abuse.

The social and moral qualities that characterize each subculture are similar to generational differences in that they result from having been exposed to a specific set of circumstances and events. How and in what manner members of a particular generation respond is unique to that generation. An example would be the use of alcohol and marijuana that often coincides with many adolescent subcultures emphasizing rock music, chic clothing, and a "hang loose and enjoy" philosophy. Frequently, such drug use begins during the youth period (age 12 to 17 years), peaks in the

young adult period (age 18 to 25), and rapidly diminishes in adulthood (age 26 and beyond).

While general drug use has decreased in the last several years (as shown in Chapter 1), the percentage of high school seniors who have used drugs at least once remains high (see Table 2-2). These data were collected in a 1989 survey of more than 17,000 high school seniors from public and private schools, conducted for the National Insti-

TABLE 2-2   1989 survey of high school seniors

Type of Drug	Percentage of Students Who Have Ever Used It
Alcohol	90.7
Cigarettes	63.7
Marijuana/Hashish	43.7
Stimulants	19.1
Inhalants	17.6
"Crack"	10.3
Hallucinogens	9.4

Source: NIDA 1989.

tute on Drug Abuse by the University of Michigan Institute for Social Research (NIDA, 1989). In the next several sections, we will discuss why drug use and abuse is so prevalent among adolescents and young adults.

DRUG ABUSE AMONG ADOLESCENTS

THE ADOLESCENT SUBCULTURE

Most early drug use begins during adolescence. Sources from the Department of Health and Human Services (Beschner and Friedman 1986) indicate that "almost all young people in the United States are exposed to illicit drugs, and a high percentage experiment with them during early adolescence." By seventh grade, about half of all students feel pressure to try marijuana (Borton 1983). To set behavioral standards, young people look to one another for guidance. Their role models are often pop singers, young TV and movie actors and actresses, and other unconventional types who advocate attitudes and lifestyles that are unique to their subculture.

Coleman (1974, 108–125) believes that the adolescent period emphasizes (1) looking inward, (2) psychic attachment to one another, (3) a drive toward autonomy, and (4) an enthusiasm for unconventional behavior. In summary:

1. Adolescents prefer to be in each other's company. One important reason for this preference is an inextricable linkage between bonds of friendship and group identity. Quite often, younger and older generation members are perceived as "outsiders" or "out-group members."
2. Youth culture also displays a strong preference for autonomy. Rock music and videos and MTV, for example, are characterized by themes that either challenge or shun traditional values.
3. Finally, youth who are in the middle- and late-adolescent period have more of an interest in change than adults. In part, adolescents have less vested interest in conforming to conventional standards while adults find

that conformity has either become a habit or is rewarding by itself. Further, adolescents tend to challenge convention simply because it does not reward their spontaneity toward life. Their desire to resist or subvert traditional values results from the burden of attempting to adjust to an authoritarian and demanding society.

While everyone—old and young alike—experiences a society that is demanding and appears authoritarian, the extent and pressure to conform is more strongly felt and perceived as a threat by the young. Instead of dealing with the demand for social conformity, some young people turn to drugs to bolster their own identities and rebel or to lessen the stress they feel (Coleman 1974). Another explanation is that many middle-class adolescents raised in an affluent society do not embrace the same type of economic goals as their parents. They question the values of the compulsive work ethic and the "treadmill" existence, and they wonder why they should be motivated to succeed in the first place (Inciardi 1987; Yinger 1982). Although many youth passively conform to the system, they lack real motivation. This lack of internal commitment can be consciously expressed through drug use.

DRUGS AND PEERS

Peer groups encourage exploration and experimentation with many aspects of life—such as sex and drugs—that would not be tolerated if adults were present. Research shows that illicit drug use results from peer-group influence (MacDonald et al. 1987; Matchett 1971) and that acquaintances, not friends, first introduce adolescents to drugs (Blum 1974). Other research found that, while 49% of adolescent drug users bought drugs from close friends, almost an equal amount, 48%, purchased their drugs from other similar-aged adolescents who were not friends (Tec 1974, 99–106).

Regardless of how illicit drugs are obtained, whenever drug use becomes consistent and eventually habitual, it usually occurs in the peer-group setting (Mead 1974; Wilson 1975). We also can be quite certain that most families do not advocate

For You to Consider...

Danger Signals of Drug Abuse

Many people are prescribed drugs that affect their moods. Using these drugs wisely can be important for physical and emotional health. But sometimes it is difficult to decide when using drugs to handle stress becomes inappropriate. It is important that your use of drugs does not result in catastrophe. Here are some danger signals that can help you evaluate your own way of using drugs.

1. Do those close to you often ask about your drug use? Have they noticed any changes in your moods or behavior?
2. Are you defensive if a friend or relative mentions your drug or alcohol use?
3. Are you sometimes embarrassed or frightened by your behavior under the influence of drugs or alcohol?
4. Have you ever gone to see a new doctor because your regular physician would not prescribe the drug you wanted?
5. When you are under pressure or feel anxious, do you automatically take a depressant or drink or both?
6. Do you take drugs more often or for purposes other than those recommended by your doctor?
7. Do you mix drugs and alcohol?
8. Do you drink or take drugs regularly to help you sleep?
9. Do you have to take a pill to get going in the morning?
10. Do you think you have a drug problem?

If you have answered yes to a number of these questions, you may be abusing drugs or alcohol. There are places to go for help at the local level. One such place might be a drug-abuse program in your community, listed in the Yellow Pages under "Drug Abuse." Other resources include community crisis centers, telephone hotlines, and the Mental Health Association.

Source: From *Drug Abuse from the Family Perspective* (Washington, D.C.: National Institute on Drug Abuse, 1980), p. 24.

---

the use of illicit psychoactive drugs. Unsupervised, fun-loving peers are the logical source of such illicit activity.

Adolescence is often a period of stressful development, fraught with significant insecurities, ranging from physical and psychological growth to the shift from family to peer-group loyalty. During these periods, the adolescent is confronted with new roles and experiences: dating, meeting new friends, and working part time. These new roles may lead to an identity confusion brought on by physiological, psychological, and sociological factors. Often, during this confusing period of development, when insecurity and mental confusion abound, psychoactive drugs such as alcohol, marijuana, and cocaine are available. An outside factor may add to the turmoil that the adolescent is experiencing. Namely, society stereotypes adolescence as a time of immaturity, role confusion, laziness, recklessness, and a lack of self-discipline.

These expectations by themselves will impact the adolescent and his or her self-perception.

Drugs offer the possibility of suspending reality, a tempting alternative when considering the scenario presented. In other words, for certain types of adolescents, relief is often found in doing drugs, a remedy that not only postpones facing reality but also offers fun and excitement.

TYPES OF ADOLESCENTS LIKELY TO ABUSE DRUGS

Recent research indicates that a great deal of variety exists within adolescent subculture (Lefrancois 1981). Some adolescents will never use drugs, while others will become habitual drug abusers. How can we distinguish what types of adolescents will abuse drugs?

The amount of agreement on the priority of values and corresponding acceptable standards of behavior between adolescents and parents varies enormously. Although some adolescents are in complete harmony with their parents, many others are at the opposite end of the spectrum. In light of variation, the following groups can be distinguished:

1. The first group is in complete conformity with the values and general attitudes of their parents. They study hard in school, comply with the values held by conventional society, and maintain social relationships with similar nondelinquent adolescents. In most cases, adolescents who belong to this group never use drugs.

2. The second group concurs with their parents' values and beliefs but stand apart somewhat from purely conventional society. These adolescents have their own role models, often found in music, films, and fashion, where different lifestyles are promoted. Some value and attitude conflict surfaces during adolescence, but it is largely intermittent and rarely serious. If drugs are used, the duration is short; usually, this behavior ceases after a few years.

3. The third group experiences a much more turbulent period of stress and conflict with representative authority figures, mostly parents and teachers. As a result of this stormy period, long-lasting and intimate attachments with family members and people of the opposite sex are virtually nonexistent. Adolescents in this group have a history of conflict with parents that peaks during this period. They seek out teen-age friends of the same sex who are in similar circumstances. Drug use begins with alcohol or marijuana and tends to escalate to other types of drugs, such as cocaine, PCP, and amphetamines. Encounters with law enforcement officials regarding either drug use and/or milder forms of juvenile delinquency like truancy, vandalism, and petty theft are common.

4. Members of this fourth group are the most alienated. They are in constant conflict with adults; they are disruptive in school and perform poorly; and they are prone to chronic drug use, dealing drugs, drinking excessive amounts of liquor, running away from home, stealing, and repeated truancy. These adolescents believe in what Sykes and Matza (1957) call "a billiard ball conception of self," where life is viewed as either bad luck or good luck that is solely determined by fate.

Generally, drug abuse is more common in the third and fourth groups because of poor family relationships, deep feelings of alienation, and the inability to achieve goals.

Think About It...

1. Give two reasons why, despite all that is known about their harmful effects, adolescents continue to abuse drugs.
2. What aspect of social change do you think can lead to drug use? Why?
3. Assume that you had to speak to a group of teen-age drug abusers. What would you say to them about drug use?

DRUG ABUSE AMONG ADULTS
THE SUBCULTURE OF MEDICAL PROFESSIONALS

Physicians, dentists, nurses, and pharmacists are perceived by society as medical specialists who either prescribe or administer drugs to treat symptoms of illness and disease. It is astounding how many of these professionals also use and abuse drugs.

A study indicates that, out of 500 physicians and 504 medical students in Massachusetts, 59% of the doctors and 78% of the students said they had used psychoactive substances (Clark and Springen 1986). All were under the age of 40. Marijuana and cocaine were used primarily for recreational purposes.

Another study by the American Medical Association estimates that 500 doctors are lost from the medical profession each year because of alcoholism. While that may not sound like a significant number, realize that it is the equivalent of the annual graduating classes from five large medical schools. This figure does not include those doctors lost because of use of narcotics and other drugs, which is also substantial. Physicians have one of the highest addiction rates of the professionals addicted to drugs other than alcohol. This is partly due to their access to narcotics and other potent drugs along with the stress of the medical profession (Hall, Stickney, and Popkin 1978, 787–793).

Contradicting this are the latest findings by Baldwin et al. (1991) and Hughes et al. (1991), based on research done by Medora (Medora, in press). These studies report that medical students and resident physicians have lower rates of illicit substance abuse (i.e., amphetamines, cocaine, heroin, marijuana, and LSD) than their peers in the general population. Yet, another report on general health care professionals indicates that they abuse narcotics at a rate 40 times greater than the general public. The primary reason given for this alarming abuse is the availability of drugs. According to another report, nurses and other medical support personnel who are employed in hospitals are becoming increasingly aware that a certain minority of fellow workers occasionally use mind-altering drugs such as morphine, methadone, Demerol, Percodan, and Percocet. Long working hours and physical and emotional stress are two of the primary reasons hospital personnel cite for their occasional drug use. Health care professionals tend to believe that the harmful effects of drug use and addiction happen only to people who lack knowledge about drug use. Further, because of daily dispensation of drugs to patients, health care professionals are much more likely to become desensitized to the importance of maintaining strict attitudes in prescribing drugs to themselves and others.

There is more consistent evidence that the nursing profession has had comparable problems with certain kinds of addictions, particularly depressants, narcotics (to a lesser extent than physicians), and stimulants. The American Nurses Association estimates that 6% to 8% of all nurses have a drug abuse problem; another source indicates that one in seven nurses will abuse drugs, and of these, one in five will become addicted (Green 1989). Finally, a 1984 nationwide survey of State Boards of Nursing showed that 67% of the 1,520 nurses brought before the boards had abused drugs or alcohol (Green 1984). This is particularly disturbing because drug abuse is reported to these boards only when the problem has become severe; thus, this group of nurses represents "the tip of the iceberg."

A minority of nurses even pilfer drugs from patients, while others conceal drug use by altering drug inventories.

It is no surprise that drug abuse by medical professionals most frequently occurs in hospitals, nursing homes, and clinics. In these environments, drugs are easily stolen or reported missing.

Due to evidence over the past 10 years or so that medical personnel are potential drug abusers, most hospitals have formally adopted procedures for monitoring drug inventories and dispensation of psychoactive drugs.

THE SUBCULTURE OF ATHLETES

Drugs for relieving pain and healing injuries have been used by athletes for decades. Today, however, athletes are using drugs for improving athletic performance and/or for recreational purposes. *Ergogenic agents* is the term used to describe specific drugs used to improve athletic performance. The practice of using drugs for this purpose is known as *"doping."*

One of many revelations made about drug use in recent years comes from retired pitcher Dock Ellis, who is now a drug counselor in Los Angeles. Ellis reported that, as a baseball Pirate, he pitched his 1970 no-hitter against San Diego while under the influence of LSD (Kaplan 1984, 37).

What athletes are most likely to use and eventually abuse drugs? One study indicates serious tendencies toward abuse in athletes who are (1) from poor families where marital discord was prominent; (2) hyperactive; (3) abusers of cigarettes or marijuana at an early age; and (4) from families where parents abused alcohol or drugs.

In response to the use and abuse of psychoac-

Canadian sprinter Ben Johnson at the Summer Olympics in Seoul, Korea. His gold medal was taken away because of steroid use. *Photo:* © Daemmerich/The Image Works

tive and performance-enhancing drugs, the International Olympic Committee has prohibited the use of the following substances (Dugal 1980, 41):

Anabolic steroids—synthetic male hormones
Miscellaneous central nervous system stimulants—like amiphenazole and strychnine
Narcotic analgesics—codeine, heroin, and morphine
Psychomotor stimulants—amphetamines and cocaine
Sympathomimetic amines—ephedrine and related compounds

Research shows that athletes are more likely to abuse amphetamines, anabolic steroids, and several types of pain killers. Amphetamines are often used with cocaine in order to increase psychomotor activity. Steroids are taken by athletes interested in building muscle tissue.

It is estimated that as many as 40% of athletes in baseball, basketball, and football use drugs. Sports teams today are thus much more likely to be actively involved in drug testing, counseling, and rehabilitation programs to purge drugs from professional athletics.

Why do athletes abuse drugs? Some observers think that it is partly due to player lifestyles. Athletes have a lot of money to spend and long hours

Many professional football players, such as Lyle Alzedo, have been associated with the use of anabolic steroids and other performance-enhancing drugs. *Photo:* Peter Read Miller, Sports Illustrated

Let's Get the Facts

Current Marijuana and Cocaine Use among Employed Adults by Type of Employment

The following list summarizes findings of a survey conducted by George Washington University and the National Institute on Drug Abuse of 3,000 adults, of whom 1,716 were employed in jobs outside the home and the remainder were students, homemakers, or retirees.

1. Most youths do not cease drug use when they begin working.
2. Eighteen percent of the total sample reported past-year marijuana use, and 6% reported past-year cocaine use.
3. Significant differences were found among occupational categories in marijuana use; no differences found in current cocaine use.
4. Age was the most significant predictor of marijuana and cocaine use. Younger employees (18–24 years old) were more likely to report drug use than older employees (25 years plus).
5. Marijuana and cocaine use were significantly higher among male than female employees.

With regard to marijuana and cocaine use among younger employees 18 to 34 years old:

6. Employees with less than a high school education had higher rates

Job Category	Marijuana Use Current (%)	Cocaine Use Current (%)
Professional/Managerial (n = 546)	7	1
Business/Farm owner (n = 77)	13	2
Sales/Manufacturers representative (n = 99)	15	3
Clerical (n = 212)	7	1
Skilled trade (n = 251)	16	3
Semi-skilled trade (n = 19)	12	1
Laborer (n = 36)	10	5
Service worker (n = 170)	12	4
Other (n = 68)	24	2
	Chi sq = 19.5 $p < .05$	Chi sq = 6.6 NS

of marijuana and cocaine use than employees with higher levels of education. Current marijuana use ranged from 35% for employees who had not finished high school to 16% for employees who had attended or graduated from college.

7. Within the 18-to-34-year-old subgroup, there were no significant differences in marijuana and cocaine use rates across five educational categories (18–24; 25–34; 35–44; 45–54; 55 +).

Source: R. F. Cook, and ISA Associates, "Drug Use among Working Adults: Prevalence Rates and Estimation Methods," in *Drugs in the Workplace: Research and Evaluation Data,* edited by S. W. Gust and J. M. Walsh, 17–23, NIDA Research Monograph 91 (Rockville, MD: National Institute on Drug Abuse, 1989).

to fill as they travel from city to city. They tend to move in the "fast track," where drugs offer quick pleasure and are easy to obtain with little risk. Athletes often find it hard to believe that drugs can hurt them; they think that using such substances is okay as long as you are careful about overdoing it. Unfortunately, the euphoria that results from taking some drugs may become habit forming quickly. Hence, some people become psychologically dependent on it in a short time. Carl Eller, a former Minnesota Vikings star who admitted to cocaine use after a lengthy NFL career, says that his first exposure to the drug came at a party with friends. Members of the "in crowd" are often eager to impress athletes by offering them a "fast-track" drug.

Some drug therapists say that athletes who have shown star potential have often been treated specially all their lives. In turn, they sometimes think they should have special privileges and make their own rules. The adjacent box tells the story of an outstanding basketball star, Gary McClain, who admitted he was high on cocaine when he won the NCAA title and also when he met former President Reagan afterward.

THE SUBCULTURE OF THE ELDERLY

While only a very small percentage of the elderly (people 65 years old and over) ever use illegal drugs, they consume nearly 25% of all the legally prescribed and OTC drugs sold annually in the United States (Besteman 1979, 7–8). A small percentage of the elderly are drug abusers; however, their drug use is often unrecognized by society.

In the vast majority of cases, drug misuse among the elderly involves the inappropriate use of legally prescribed or overuse of OTC medications. Specifically, drugs are either overused or underused, or old medicines are taken to relieve new symptoms. Further, findings from several studies indicate that a small proportion of the elderly obtain multiple prescriptions for drugs, hoard drugs for nonprescribed use, and occasionally share drugs (Petersen 1977, 127–151).

What unique factors are responsible for drug misuse among the elderly?

1. Elderly people who suffer pain may need to relieve physical deterioration, such as a weak heart, an ineffective immune system, intestinal disorders, chronic arthritic or rheumatic pain, as well as reduced liver and kidney function.
2. The elderly often lack family support. Depressants such as sedatives are prescribed by physicians to help lonely people cope during their remaining years.
3. As people become older, they have more difficulty sleeping for long periods of time. This is ironic because while the elderly person has more time to rest and sleep, the aging body requires less of it. Physicians who constantly hear complaints from the elderly regarding their inability to sleep often prescribe benzodiazepine and barbiturate hypnotics.
4. Physicians tend to satisfy complaints by the elderly regarding pain and discomfort with OTC drug recommendations or prescriptions that may relieve physical or psychological symptoms.
5. Faced with many drugs on the market, the elderly tend to become *polydrug users* (people taking multiple drugs). This may lead to problems because elderly people sometimes mismanage drugs due to confusion, inconsistency, or vision impairment. They frequently end up taking the wrong drugs at the wrong times.
6. Finally, an increase in alcohol abuse has been reported among the elderly. Approximately 20% to 30% of the elderly population in the United States abuses alcohol (Petersen 1977, 138–139).

COMPARISONS BETWEEN ADOLESCENTS AND THE ELDERLY   Some interesting similarities exist between elderly and adolescent drug abusers. Both adolescent and elderly people are attracted to drugs because they are undergoing substantial role changes. Both groups are, for the most part, unemployed; they lack income and self-reliance; and from society's viewpoint, they possess limited amounts of social status. While adolescents have

For You to Consider...

Case Study: The Gary McClain Case

I was standing in the Rose Garden, wired on cocaine. Nothing new about my being that way. . . . I'd even played wired in some games, including our semifinal win over Memphis State in the NCAA Final Four in Lexington, Ky., five days earlier. And now that we were the best, the team that had just upset Georgetown for the 1985 national championship, it was business as usual for me. President Reagan was welcoming my teammates and me at the White House and giving his speech about how inspirational our victory was. And the cocaine had me floating in my own private world.

I was wide awake even though it had been an exhausting few days. We had been allowed to go home after the victory celebration in Philadelphia. But as soon as I walked through the door of my parents' home in Hempstead, N.Y., someone from the school called to tell me to come back. The President would see us. I had to return to Villanova to join my teammates for the bus ride to Washington.

But I didn't want to see the President yet. Are you kidding? I wanted to see my home boys. I wanted to hang out. I wanted to get high, to mess around with them, to laugh and hear them tell me what it was like to watch me on TV. We were national champions. We could do just about what we wanted. And I wanted to do cocaine.

And I did. I did lots of it, all night, even though I knew I had to get going soon. I did it in the car with the friends who drove me at two in the morning from Long Island to Villanova. And I did it by myself in the bathroom of the team bus that left Villanova at seven, headed for the White House. I used up half of the gram one of my friends gave me for the bus ride.

When we reached the White House, I began freaking out. All those paranoid thoughts going through my mind. What if they send a dog on the bus, where I'd left the rest of the coke under my pocket? Oh, my god, there's a little wooden archway I have to pass through. Could be a cocaine detector. All these guys are walking around with earphones. Must be the CIA. And I thought they were looking at me, speaking into their radios, "Gary McClain is high. Let's get him." I was scared and confused, just as I was so many times while my addiction to drugs dragged me lower and lower.

I was the first player President Reagan mentioned by name. He used a quote of mine in his speech, something about how hard we had worked to achieve our goal of a national championship. But I wasn't concentrating on what he was saying. I was standing a couple of feet behind him, looking in his hair, thinking, this guy has more dandruff than your average man. Thinking thoughts like, I could push him in the head, just a little tap, and make news across the world. That's how high I was. I was looking at Reagan, thinking this guy is the smoothest con artist in the world. He's reading from a piece of paper, and America thinks he is so cool.

Actually I wasn't such a bad con artist myself. I had spent years lying so I wouldn't get in trouble for doing drugs. I had manipulated people around me, schemed and scammed when I needed to. And now I was high in the White House. After Reagan finished his talk and took off, the team had a big press conference on the North Lawn. Coach Mass, Rollie Massimino, was talking. The question just flew out from a reporter: What are your feelings on drugs? What advice would you give to young people about them? Coach Mass said his advice would be simple, just to "stay away from them." And all the while with me there freaking. A teammate was standing behind me. He knew I did a lot of coke so he gave me a little nudge. Sort of a little joke.

It wasn't funny though. Looking back, things had gotten scary. I was trying to put on this image of Gary McClain, champion, when I was really Gary McClain, drug addict. It would be this way until I reached my alltime low and finally went for help. It might still be this way right now except for my mother, who offered her support and love when I went away to a rehabilitation center. I'm lucky to be clean. Lucky to have real friends who stood by me when others turned their backs. Lucky to be alive. . . .

Source: Reprinted courtesy of *Sports Illustrated* from the October 12, 1987 issue. Copyright © 1987 Time Inc. "The Downfall of a Champion" by Gary McLain as told to Jeffrey Marx. All Rights Reserved.

to cope with the psychological stress of immaturity and a lack of self-confidence, the elderly grapple with the stress that comes from physical deterioration, loneliness, and boredom. Thus, adolescents and the elderly both experience a sense of alienation and isolation. The two groups face significant adjustment problems that can be temporarily anesthetized with drugs.

OTHER UNDERSTUDIED SUBCULTURAL GROUPS

Women, children of alcoholics, Hispanics, the multidisabled, "gay" people, and the homeless are understudied groups that are susceptible to drug use and abuse. Women often have problems with polydrug abuse, or abuse several drugs concurrently. Women, in contrast to men, have a greater tendency to become addicted to tobacco, stimulants, and sedatives. Approximately 60% of women drink alcohol, and they represent one-third of all alcoholics in the United States (Engs 1990, 5).

Alcohol abuse is prevalent throughout U.S. society. More and more evidence indicates that alcoholism runs in families. Lex (1988) found that approximately 28 million Americans have one or more alcoholic parent(s). Among Hispanics, Mexicans, Puerto Ricans, and Cubans, males are the heaviest drinkers. Approximately 14% of Mexican-American and Puerto Rican men are classified as "heavy drinkers," those who are daily consumers of alcohol to the point of mild to heavy intoxication.

The drug-abuse problems of the multidisabled and the homeless are also underreported. People who suffer from alcoholism and are disabled are viewed as multidisabled by the National Council on Alcoholism (NCA). Approximately 10% of all Americans are either physically or mentally disabled, and it is believed that a high percentage are substance abusers.

It is difficult to estimate the total number of homeless people in the United States; figures range from 250,000 to 3 million (Lubran 1987, 4–6). Researchers knowledgeable about the homeless estimate that a majority have problems with alcohol abuse.

Finally, little research has focused on drug use among "gay" people. Based on what little research there is, high percentages of gay people abuse alcohol and marijuana. The consumption of alcohol is part of the socializing common at nightspots such as bars, discos, and restaurants. The gay subculture thrives on social gatherings and meeting places where either drugs or alcohol are often a part of the scene.

Think About It...

1. Imagine an interview with an athlete who uses drugs to enhance his or her physical performance. What questions would you ask?
2. Why do you think steroid users ignore information about the harmful effects of using such drugs?
3. What would you do about an elderly grandparent who abused alcohol? Why?
4. Do you believe alcoholism runs in families? Why?

KEY TERMS

CNS (central nervous system)	primary groups	secondary deviance
neurotransmitters	secondary groups	master status
dopamine system	socialization	retrospective interpretation
status	primary deviance	

S U M M A R Y

1. *Social disorganization* and *social strain* theories focus on how the organization of a society, group, or subculture is responsible for drug abuse among its members. Social disorganization theory asks: What in the social order causes people to deviate? Social strain theory asks: Can the organization of society cause social deviance? *Subculture theory* views peer pressure as a motivating factor for drug use. *Social learning theory* explains drug use as learned behavior. *Labeling theory* attempts to explain how a person can come to identify himself or herself as deviant because of other people's perceptions.

2. Social disorganization theory emphasizes that rapid social change can cause people to become disaffiliated from conventional society; as a result, some of these people may turn to drug use.

3. Subculture theory can be applied to drug use and abuse by the elderly. Generally, society stereotypes the elderly as being in need of drugs; what's more, advertising emphasizes that OTC drugs are necessary for maintaining normal health.

4. Social learning theory focuses on how others teach illicit drug use, particularly on how motives to use drugs are taught.

5. Sociologist Howard Becker believes that first-time drug users become attached to drugs because of the following three factors: (1) They learn the techniques of drug use; (2) they learn to perceive the pleasurable effects of drugs; and (3) they learn to enjoy the drug experience.

6. Control theory suggests that drug use results from a lack of social control, namely, a lack of attachment to norm-abiding groups and a lack of internal and external social controls. (Internal control is self-control, and external control is effective supervision.)

7. *Primary deviance* is deviant behavior that the perpetrator does not identify with; hence, it is inconsequential deviant behavior. *Example:* "I just tried cocaine once. I'll never do it again; it's not for me." *Secondary deviance* is deviance that one readily identifies with. *Example:* "Maybe I am good at stealing, like my friends tell me." *Master status* refers to a primary status that upholds numerous other statuses, such as male or female, corporate executive, and full-time student. *Example:* "Did you know that my neighbor is a heroin addict?" *Retrospective interpretation* refers to redefining a person's image within a particular group. *Example:* "My roommate is an alcoholic; I never would have thought that of him. Now I know why he always wants to go to parties and stay late into the night."

8. The concepts *primary* and *secondary deviance, master status,* and *retrospective interpretation* all relate to labeling theory. They help explain how a person can perceive himself or herself as being deviant and how others make this judgment, as well. During the onset of primary deviance, the accused perpetrator of deviant behavior is not perceived as truly deviant. Circumstantial causes are often attributed to his or her behavior. In a more advanced phase of deviant identity, secondary deviance results when the accused begins to identify with the deviant behavior. Master status is when an individual's deviant reputation predominates in the eyes of others. Retrospective interpretation involves redefining past behavior in light of the deviant image.

R E F E R E N C E S

Baldwin, D. C., Jr., P. H. Hughes, S. E. Conrad, C. L. Storr, and D. V. Sheehan. "Substance Abuse among Senior Medical Students." *Journal of the American Medical Association* 265 (1991): 2074–2078.

Bandura, A. *Principles of Behavior Modification.* New York: Holt, Rinehart and Winston, 1969.

Becker, H. S. *Outsiders: Studies in the Sociology of Deviance.* New York: Free Press, 1966.

Beschner, G., and A. Friedman. *Teen Drug Use.* Lexington, MA: D. C. Heath, 1986.

Besteman, K. J. Elder Ed.—*Using Your Medicines Wisely—A Guide for the Elderly.* National Institute on Drug Abuse. Washington, D.C.: USGPO, 1979.

Blum, R. H. *Students and Drugs.* San Francisco: Jossey-Bass, 1974.

Borton, T. "Pressure to Try Drugs and Alcohol Starts in Early Grades." *Weekly Reader,* 25 April 1983.

Clark, M., and K. Springen. "Docs and Drugs: Physicians Heal Thyself." *Newsweek,* 6 Oct. 1986, 28.

Cohen, A. K. *Delinquent Boys: The Culture of*

the Gang. Glencoe, IL: Free Press, 1955.

Coleman, J. S. Youth: Transition to Adulthood. Chicago: University of Chicago Press, 1974.

Cook, R. F., and ISA Associates. "Drug Use among Working Adults: Prevalence Rates and Estimation Methods." In Drugs in the Workplace: Research and Evaluation Data, edited by S. W. Gust and J. M. Walsh, 17–23. NIDA Research Monograph, 91. Rockville, MD: NIDA, 1989.

Cooley, C. H. Human Nature and the Social Order. New York: Scribner's, 1902.

Dugal, Robert. "Screening: The Scientific Deterrent to Athletic Drug Abuse." Laboratory Management 41 (1980): 41–48.

Engs, R. C., ed. "College Women." In Women: Alcohol and Other Drugs, edited by R. C. Engs. Dubuque, IA: Kendall/Hunt, 1990.

Farrar, H., and G. Kearns. "Cocaine: Clinical Pharmacology and Toxicology." The Journal of Pediatrics 115 (1989): 665–675.

Fischer, C. S. The Urban Experience. New York: Harcourt Brace Jovanovich, 1955.

Fischer, R. "A Cartography of the Ecstatic and Meditative States." Science 174 (1971): 894–904.

Green, P. "The Chemically Dependent Nurse." In Nursing Clinics of North America: Nursing Interventions for the Addicted Patients, vol. 24, 81–94. Philadelphia, PA: Saunders, 1989.

———. "The Impaired Nurse: Chemical Dependency." Journal of Emergency Nursing 10, no. 1 (1984): 23–29.

Hall, R. C. W., S. K. Stickney, and M. K. Popkin. "Physician Drug Abuser." Journal of Nervous and Mental Disease 166 (1978): 787–793.

Hirschi, T. Causes of Delinquency. 2nd ed. Los Angeles: University of California Press, 1971.

Hughes, P. H., S. E. Conrad, D. C. Baldwin Jr., C. L. Storr, and D. V. Sheehan.

"Resident Physician Substance Use in the United States." Journal of the American Medical Association 265 (1991): 2069–2073.

Inciardi, J. A. Criminal Justice, 2nd ed. Chicago, IL: Harcourt Brace Jovanovich, 1987.

Jarvik, M. "The Drug Dilemma: Manipulating the Demand." Science 250 (1990): 387–392.

Kaplan, J. "Taking Steps to Solve the Drug Dilemma." Sports Illustrated, 28 May 1984, 36–45.

Lefranciois, G. R. Adolescents. 2nd ed. Belmont, CA: Wadsworth, 1981.

Lemert, E. M. Social Psychology: A Systematic Approach to the Theory of Sociopathic Behavior. New York: McGraw-Hill, 1951.

Lex, B. "Prepared Statement: Causes and Consequences of Alcohol Abuse." In Hearings Before the Committee on Governmental Affairs, U.S. Senate, Part 1. Washington, D.C.: U.S. Government Printing Office, 1988.

Lubran, B. G. "Alcohol-Related Problems among the Homeless." Alcohol and Health Research World 11 (1987): 4–6, 73.

MacDonald, A. P., P. R. Walls, and R. LeBlanc. "College Female Drug Users." Adolescence 8 (1987): 189–196.

Matchett, W. F. "Who Uses Drugs? A Study in a Suburban Public High School." Journal of School Health 41 (1971): 90–93.

Mead, G. H. Mind, Self, and Society. Chicago, IL: University of Chicago Press, 1974.

Medora, R. S. "Impaired Health Care Professionals—A Perspective." Drug Use in America: Social, Cultural and Political Perspectives, edited by P. J. Venturelli. Boston, MA: Jones and Bartlett, 1992.

Mijuriya, T. H., and M. R. Aldrich. "Cannabis 1988: Old Drug, New Dangers—The Potency Question." Journal of Psychoactive Drugs 20 (1988): 47–55.

NIDA and NIAA. Highlights from the 1987 National Drug and Alcoholism Treatment

Survey (NDATS). Rockville, MD: NIDA/NIAA, 1989.

Petersen, D. M., and F. J. Whittington. "Drug Use among the Elderly: A Review." Journal of Psychedelic Drugs 9 (1977): 25–37.

Peterson, R. C., ed. "Marijuana and Mental Health." In Marijuana Research Findings: 1980. National Institute on Drug Abuse Research Monograph 31, 1–53. Washington, D.C.: Department of Health and Human Services, 1980.

Pickens, R. W., and D. S. Svikis. "Biological Vulnerability in Drug Abuse." NIDA Research Monograph, no. 88. Washington, D.C.: NIDA, 1988.

Reckless, W. C. "A New Theory of Delinquency." Federal Probation 25 (1961): 42–46.

Resteman, K. J. Elder ed.: Using Your Medicines Wisely—A Guide for the Elderly. Washington, D.C.: U.S. Government Printing Office, 1979.

Rotter, J. B. "General Expectancies for Internal Versus External Control of Reinforcement." In Application of a Social Learning Theory of Personality, edited by J. B. Rotter and E. J. Phaves. New York: Holt, Rinehart and Winston, 1972.

Schur, E. M. Labeling Deviant Behavior. New York: Harper and Row, 1971.

Sutherland, E. Principles of Criminology, Fourth edition. Philadelphia, PA: J. B. Lippincott, 1947.

Sykes, G. M., and D. Matza. "Techniques of Neutralization." American Sociological Review 22 (1957): 664–670.

Tec, N. Grass Is Green in Suburbia. Roslyn Heights, New York: Libra, 1974.

Thomas, W. I. with D. S. Thomas. The Child in America. New York: Knopf, 1923.

Wilson, M., and S. Wilson. Drugs in American Life. New York: H. W. Wilson, 1975.

Yinger, M. J. Countercultures: The Promise and the Peril of a World Turned Upside Down. New York: Free Press, 1982.

Drugs, Regulations, and the Law

CHAPTER OUTLINE

LEARNING OBJECTIVES

On completing this chapter, you will be able to:

1. Identify the major criteria that determine how society regulates drugs.
2. Describe how patent medicines influenced the early development of drug regulation in the United States.
3. Describe the similarities between opium and cocaine and the roles each has played in the formation of drug legislation.
4. Explain the significance of the Pure Food and Drug Act of 1906 and why it was important in regulating drugs of abuse.

5. Identify the changes in drug regulation that occurred because of the 1938 Federal Food, Drug, and Cosmetic Act.
6. Explain the significance of the Durham-Humphrey Amendment of 1951.
7. Describe the changes in drug regulation that occurred due to the Kefauver-Harris Amendments of 1962.
8. Identify and explain the stages of testing for an investigational new drug (IND).
9. Discuss the special provisions (exceptions) made by the Food and Drug Administration (FDA) for drug marketing.

10. Outline the procedures used by the FDA to regulate nonprescription drugs.
11. Explain the FDA's *switching policy* and its significance to the over-the-counter (OTC) market.
12. List the principal factors that influence the formation of laws regulating drug abuse.
13. Identify and explain the Harrison Act of 1912.
14. Outline the major approaches used to reduce substance abuse.
15. Identify the principal defenses used in drug-related criminal proceedings.
16. Identify the major costs to society of drug abuse.

Photo: Rob Crandall/Stock, Boston

There is a tendency to assume that social sanctions and laws regarding drugs have always had aims similar to those we observe today in the United States. In fact, drug regulations and laws, as we know them in the United States and other industrialized countries, have developed only recently, often seemingly by a process of trial and error. Yet by contrasting conditions in industrialized and less developed countries, we see that not every society follows American ways of regulating or outlawing drugs. Some seem more repressive, some seem more permissive, and some have been a source for raising and importing drugs that other countries have forbidden.

In fact, as we look at developing societies now in the stage of industrialization that our grandparents experienced in America years ago, we might gain insight into how attitudes on drug regulation developed here. We might also appreciate some of the dilemmas that seem so puzzling to us today.

In this chapter, we will examine the development of drug regulation in the United States as it applies both to manufacturing drugs and controlling their use and abuse. Although it would seem that the regulation of drug manufacturing versus that of drug abuse would be at opposite ends of the spectrum, in fact, the two have evolved from the same process.

CULTURAL ATTITUDES TOWARD DRUG ABUSE

The current attitudes of U.S. culture toward behavior-altering substances are based upon the evolved Western concepts of self-determination and respect for others' rights. It is felt that to lose control of body or mind is wrong. When such behavior is private and out of sight, it might be tolerated. But when it becomes public, habitual, or highly visible, there may be disapproval along with fear that uncontrolled behavior will be socially unproductive and a burden to others. Such disapproval may become stronger when the behavior violates codes of conduct or decency, and disapproval may be nearly unanimous if the resulting behavior harms other people physically. Even so, these American attitudes are relatively new. For example, it is easy to find movies of the fifties and sixties that show drunken behavior as merely ridiculous or even harmless fun; however, today, such antics would be angrily disapproved of by a vast majority.

What we expect of government regulation regarding drugs and behavior-altering substances has also changed recently. A hundred years ago, most people expected the government to protect citizens' rights to produce and privately patent new foods and substances; they did not expect or desire the government to regulate product quality or claims. Instead, the public relied on private morals and common-sense knowledge to obtain quality and protection in an era of simple technology. Unfortunately, U.S. society had to learn by tragic experience that its trust was not well placed; many unscrupulous entrepreneurs were willing to risk the safety and welfare of the public in order to maximize profits and acquire wealth. In fact, most medicines of these earlier times were not only ineffective but often dangerous.

What lessons have we learned from these painful experiences? Due to the high-technology, rapid advancements society has made, we must turn to highly trained experts and government "watchdog" agencies for consumer information and protection. Out of this changing environment have evolved two major guidelines for controlling drug development and marketing:

1. *Society has the right to protect itself from the damaging impact of drug use.* This concept is closely aligned with the emotional and highly visible issue of drug abuse, but as we have become more scientifically enlightened, it has extended to include other more subtle drug side effects, as well. For example, at the turn of the century, there was great public alarm about the addicting properties of drugs like opium and cocaine but little concern about the cancer-producing drugs of the time. The reason: The impact of addiction, which was easily observed and widespread, was an obvious social threat. Cancer, however, was rarely diagnosed; poorly understood by physicians, let alone the public; and not perceived as a significant threat when it came to drug safety.

   Today, we are still concerned about drug addiction, but approximately 25% of the deaths in the United States are caused by cancer. Obviously, our current awareness and understanding of cancer is much greater; consequently, today's society does not tolerate the marketing of drugs that have been shown to be carcinogenic (cancer causing). With greater understanding about drugs and how they affect us, contemporary society makes greater safety demands on the drugs available for consumption.

2. *Society has the right to demand effective drugs.* The concept of "you get what you pay for" is rooted in this expectation. If drug manufacturers promise that their products relieve pain, these drugs should be analgesics; if they promise that their products relieve depression, they should be antidepressants; if they promise that their products relieve stuffy noses, they should be decongestants.

The public, through regulatory agencies and statutory enactments, has attempted to require that drug manufacturers produce *safe* and *effective* pharmaceutical products. In addition, society has used similar strategies to protect itself from the problems associated with the specific drug side effect of dependence or addiction, which is associated with drug abuse.

THE EVOLUTION OF DRUG REGULATION

We tend to take for granted that public agencies of developed countries insist that drugs be safe and effective and require that drugs with abuse potential be either tightly regulated or outlawed entirely. But in fact, governments have only started doing this in very recent times. Although controversy continues as to how restrictive laws that regulate drug use and marketing should be, few would argue that we should return to the "good old days" of unregulated laissez-faire policies, when patients took all the risks. Those were the days of patent medicines, nostrums, elixirs, restoratives, rejuvenators, and panacea medicines, which were sold freely and without question to a naive public.

THE GREAT AMERICAN FRAUD: PATENT MEDICINES

In the late 1800s and early 1900s, the sales of uncontrolled medicines flourished and became widespread. Many of these products were called **patent medicines**, which signified that the ingredients were secret, not that they were patented. The law of the day seemed to be more concerned with someone's recipe being stolen than with preventing harm to the naive consumer. Toxic ingredients in these medicines included acetanilid in Bromo-Seltzer and Orangeine and prussic (hydrocyanic) acid in Shiloh's Consumption Cure.

patent medicines
unregulated proprietary medicines often associated with fraudulent therapy

The patent medicines, or at least those that were later analyzed, appear to have been composed

FIGURE 3-1 A poster of one of the patent medicines that contained liberal doses of opium and a high concentration of alcohol. Wistar's medicine was widely used around the turn of the century to treat tuberculosis ("consumption"), which was responsible for over 25% of all adult deaths in the United States. The federal government finally forced the remedy off the market by 1920.

largely of either colored water or alcohol, with an occasional added ingredient such as opium or cocaine. Hostetter's Stomach Bitters, with 44% alcohol, could easily have been classified as liquor. Sale of Peruna (28% alcohol) was prohibited to Native Americans because of its high alcoholic content! Birney's Catarrh Cure contained 4% cocaine. Wistar's Balsam of Wild Cherry (see Figure 3-1), Dr. King's Discovery for Consumption, Mrs. Winslow's Soothing Syrup, and several others contained opiates as well as alcohol.

The medical profession of the mid- and late-nineteenth century was ill prepared to do battle with the ever-present manufacturers or distributors of patent medicines. Qualified physicians during this time were rare. Much more common were medical practitioners with poor training and little understanding. In fact, many of these early physicians practiced a brand of medicine that was generally as useless and frequently more life threatening than the patent medicines themselves.

In 1905, *Collier's Magazine* ran a series of articles called the "Great American Fraud," which warned of the abuse of patent medicines. This brought the problem to the attention of the public (Adams 1905). *Collier's* coined the phrase "dope fiend" from *dope*, an African word meaning "intoxicating substance." The American Medical Association (AMA) joined in and widely distributed reprints of the *Collier's* story to inform the public about the dangers of these medicines, even though the AMA itself accepted advertisements for patent medicines that physicians knew were addicting. The publicity caused mounting pressure on Congress and on President Roosevelt to do something about these fraudulent products. In 1905, the president proposed that a law be enacted to regulate interstate commerce of misbranded and adulterated foods, drinks, and drugs. This received further impetus when Upton Sinclair's book *The Jungle* was published in 1906—a nauseatingly realistic exposé describing in detail the filth, disease, and putrefaction in the Chicago stockyards.

Not all patent medicines were ineffective, watered-down concoctions without pharmacological activity. In fact, some of these so-called curatives were all too active and contained potent, dangerous, and addicting drugs. Two substances

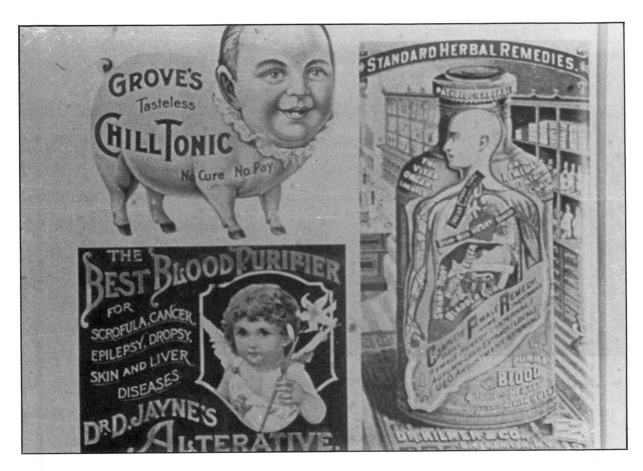

Patent medicines

helped to shape attitudes that would form the basis of regulatory policies for years to come: the opium derivatives (narcotic drugs, such as heroin and morphine) and cocaine.

STAGES IN RECOGNIZING A HEALTH HAZARD: THE CASE OF OPIUM

People today do not realize how recently it was common to eat or smoke opium in the United States and throughout Europe. The opium "eaters" were typically middle-class Caucasians who had become hooked on opiates in patent medicines. Because of the state of the art of medicine in the 1800s, the opiates provided an important

form of relief from pain. Physicians at the time believed an opiate dependency was better than alcoholism and encouraged substitution of one drug for the other. For example, the famous English physician Thomas Sydenhaum enthusiastically advocated the use of laudanum, a concoction of opium dissolved in sherry-flavored cinnamon, cloves, and saffron. The most common uses of laudanum and other opium products were to treat pain and diarrhea and to promote a sense of relaxation and well-being. Many famous people of the nineteenth century, including writers like Samuel Taylor Coleridge, became addicted to laudanum (Scott 1969).

Although such concoctions were used freely, physicians were aware of opium's dangerous properties; they maintained that the benefits of use far outweighed the dangers. One such clinician was George Wood, a professor of medicine at the University of Pennsylvania. In 1868, he wrote that opium addiction could result in "total loss of self-respect, and indifference to the opinions of the community." In addition, he stated that, for the truly addicted, "everything is sacrificed to the insatiable demands of the vice." In spite of these condemnations, like his fellow physicians, Wood believed that opium addiction was only marginally dangerous and less of a threat than alcohol addiction.

In the late 1850s and early 1860s, techniques for subcutaneous injection of morphia (an opium derivative related to morphine) became widely available. Prior to this time, opium was only taken by mouth, which was less effective and less addicting. With the advent of injected morphia, the addiction problems became much more severe and generalized (Morgan 1981). Some people became addicted to morphine as a result of the use of this drug during the Civil War to treat dysentery, pain, and fatigue and took the habit home when the war was over. At this time, dependence on opium or morphine was considered undesirable and not respectable, but because the drugs were legal (and uncontrolled) and their moderate use did not appear to disrupt the life of the user, addiction caused no serious social concern. The only restriction on importation was a tax, passed in 1842, on all opiates brought into the United States.

Although public concern would probably have developed sooner or later because of the growing extent of opiate addiction among the while middle class, the first restrictions centered on opium smoking among Chinese immigrants. Tens of thousands of Chinese laborers were brought to the United States in the 1850s and 1860s to work on the railroad construction throughout the West. They brought with them their custom of smoking opium for relaxation. Labor contractors actually offered an allowance of half a pound of smoking opium a month as a bonus to recruit Chinese immigrant laborers. This policy continued until an economic depression affected areas with large concentrations of Chinese immigrants. Unemployed American workers (there were no unemployment

checks or welfare benefits then) unfairly blamed the Chinese laborers as the cause of their economic problems. The Chinese-run *opium dens* became a convenient scapegoat. White women and girls supposedly were induced to visit the opium dens, whereupon they would become depraved "dope fiends."

It was possible in many states to buy smoking-grade opium in pharmacies and even in general stores. The state of Nevada, in 1877, was the first to prohibit retail sales of smoking opium. Twenty states—mostly in the West, with substantial immigrant Chinese population—passed statutes to prohibit operation of opium dens or the smoking and possession of opium. The actual importation and selling of opium remained legal until 1887, when importation of opium by Chinese (but not by Americans!) was forbidden. The effect of this restriction was to encourage smuggling by organized groups. The tariff was increased further in 1890 and then halved in 1897 to discourage the smuggling and illegal manufacture by Chinese. In 1909, the Smoking Opium Exclusion Act banned the importation of smoking-grade opium, again as a response to inflammatory anti-Chinese publicity about American girls and boys who were lured into addiction and "doomed, hopelessly doomed, beyond the shadow of redemption" (Austin 1978). This hysterical attack on smoking opium is difficult to reconcile with the extensive use of laudanum and injected morphine by middle-class Americans at that time. In 1914, the tax was increased to $400 per pound on opium prepared in the United States, and the Harrison Act, also passed in 1914, increased penalties for illegal use of opiates even further.

With increased concern about the growing problem of opium addiction, attempts were made to treat and cure severe dependence. One of the most notable was proposed by German physician Eduard Levinstein in 1878. He recommended that the addicted patient be isolated for one to two weeks in a room devoid of any means of committing suicide. The patient would be constantly attended, and withdrawal symptoms would be treated with hot baths, bicarbonate of soda, chloral hydrate (a CNS depressant; see Chapter 6), and unlimited quantities of brandy and champagne (apparently a rich person's cure). Levinstein believed that, once a cure had been achieved, there would be no relapse. He also felt that, if governments would rigidly regulate morphia and only permit physicians access to the drug, addiction would become a rare occurrence. Unfortunately, while Levinstein's approach was well intended (and actually incorporated some concepts that are still used today to treat drug dependence), it was relatively ineffective; there was only a 25% success rate.

CHANGING ATTITUDES: THE DANGERS OF COCAINE

The idea of weaning addicts from drug dependence by substituting another drug became popular as the incidence of opium addiction became more alarming. One drug commonly used to relieve opium users of their narcotic habit was the potent stimulant cocaine (Morgan 1981). Cocaine was first refined from the Peruvian coca plant in 1860 by Albert Niemann. Although the powers of the coca plant had been known in Europe as early

"THE GENERIC NAME FOR MEPROSUTRICIN? SNAKE-SKIN OIL."

Source: ® Sidney Harris, *American Scientist* magazine. Used with permission.

as the sixteenth century, the properties of its active ingredient, cocaine, had not been studied. Once purified, many individuals became intrigued with its powerful effects on the nervous system. The famous psychiatrist Sigmund Freud was particularly interested in this potent stimulant as an antidepressant and as a hopefully harmless replacement for opium addiction, but he soon became disillusioned by the harmful effects of cocaine.

The American experience with cocaine in some ways mirrored that of Freud. Because of its numbing effects, cocaine was first used in America as a local anesthetic for eye surgery and then as a nerve tonic. Like Freud, the American people at first embraced this new miracle drug with great enthusiasm. It was included in tonics—the best known of which was called Coca-Cola—as well as in wines and an array of patent medicines promoted as cures for coughing to hemorrhoids (see Chapter 7 for more details) (Wallace et al. 1981). Exaggerated claims were the rule of the day (Morgan 1981). One advocate declared that cocaine "would supply the place of food, and make the coward brave and the silent eloquent." Actually, the continual use of this drug made the unsuspecting addicted, a lesson that the American people painfully learned and are learning again.

It was against this backdrop of ineffectual patent medicines and growing awareness of the dangers of addiction to opium and cocaine that legislation was first passed to provide safer and more effective pharmaceutical products to the public while restricting access to addicting substances.

For You to Consider...

"Wonder Drugs" That Fooled Even the Great Doctors

Some of the world's most famous doctors were fooled for a time by the untested but apparently beneficial effects of drugs that are now, a century later, notorious for their dangers to health and society.

Opium and morphine, which helped numb the pain for so many wounded in the American Civil War, were both candidates for the "wonder drug" that might help stressed and nervous people become calm and focused, according to George Wood, a prestigious University of Pennsylvania professor. In the years after the Civil War, Wood minimized the known addictive dangers of opium and wrote the most glowing medical endorsements for it. He said that opium produced "a universal feeling of delicious ease and comfort," as well as "an exaltation of our better mental qualities, a warmer glow of benevolence, a disposition to do great things, . . . a higher devotional spirit." He announced that opium raised "the intellectual and imaginative faculties to the highest point." The prestige of such a famous doctor's endorsement went a long way in blinding Americans to the dangers of opium, which were becoming increasingly obvious over the years.

The next "wonder drug," cocaine, received a similar rave review from an even more famous physician, psychiatrist Sigmund Freud. He saw this stimulant as a cure for depression and as a relatively harmless substitute for opium addiction. In 1884, Freud described his medicinal use of cocaine: "I have been working with a miracle drug. I have had dazzling success in the treatment of a case of gastric catarrh. . . . I take very small doses of it regularly against depression and against indigestion, and with the most brilliant success." Freud wrote a treatise on cocaine entitled *"Uber Coca"* ("about coca"), which he described as "a song of praise for this magical substance."

Freud's enthusiasm for the substance diminished somewhat when he began to appreciate the dangers of this drug. He used cocaine as a substitute to help wean his friend, Fleischl, from morphine addiction (Aldrich and Barker 1976). Following administration of large doses of the powerful stimulant, Freud spent a frightful night nursing Fleischl through an episode of cocaine-induced psychosis. In the end, Fleischl's opium addiction was relieved, but an addiction to cocaine took its place. After this experience, Freud turned against the use of all drugs (Holmstedt 1967).

THE ROAD TO REGULATION AND THE FDA

The decline of patent medicines started with the 1906 Pure Food and Drug Act, which required manufacturers to indicate the amounts of alcohol, morphine, opium, cocaine, heroin, and marijuana extract on the label of each container. It became obvious at this time that many of the medicinal products on the market labeled as nonaddictive were in fact potent drugs "in sheep's labeling" and could cause severe dependence. However, most government interest centered on regulation of the food industry, not drugs. Federal drug regulation was based on the free-market philosophy that consumers could select for themselves; it was decided that they should have information on possible dependence-producing drugs to ensure that they understood the risks associated with using these products. The Pure Food and Drug Act made misrepresentation illegal, so that a potentially addicting patent drug could not be advertised as non–habit forming. This marked the beginning of new involvement by governmental agencies in drug manufacturing. (See Table 3-1 for a summary of federal regulation of drug marketing.)

The Pure Food and Drug Act was modified, although not in a consumer-protective manner, by the Sherley Amendment in 1912. The distributor of a cancer "remedy" was indicted for falsely claiming on the label that the contents were effective. The case was decided in the Supreme Court in 1911. Justice Holmes, writing for the majority opinion, said that, based on the 1906 act, the company had not violated any law because legally all it was required to do was accurately state the contents, their strength and quality. The accuracy of the therapeutic claims made by drug manufacturers was not controlled. Congress took the hint and passed the Sherley Amendment to add to the existing law the requirement that labels should not contain "any statement . . . regarding the curative or therapeutic effect . . . which is false and fraudulent." However, the government had to prove fraud, which turned out to be difficult (and in fact is still problematic). This amendment did

TABLE 3-1 Milestones in federal regulations that control drug marketing

Date	Name of Legislation	Cause	Content
1906	Pure Food and Drug	Concern about addiction to patent medicines.	Potentially addicting patent medicines required to be labeled.
1912	Sherley Amendment	An ineffective cancer remedy.	Drug labels could not contain false or fraudulent claims.
1938	Federal Food, Drug, and Cosmetic Act	Forty people killed by a sulfa product dissolved in diethylene glycol.	Defined what was meant by term *drugs;* required new drugs be safe; labels to list ingredients and quantity and explain correct use; created prescription and OTC drugs.
1951	Durham-Humphrey Amendment	Concern about public use of OTC drugs.	Established criteria for prescription and nonprescription drugs.
1962	Kefauver-Harris Amendment	Thalidomide tragedy.	Established testing procedure for new drugs; required drug companies to demonstrate safety and effectiveness.

not improve drug products. It only encouraged pharmaceutical companies to be more vague in their advertisements (Temin 1980).

PRESCRIPTION VERSUS OTC DRUGS

The distinction between prescription and over-the-counter (OTC) drugs is relatively new to the pharmaceutical industry. All nonnarcotic drugs were available OTC prior to World War II. It was not until a drug company unwittingly produced a toxic product that killed over 40 people that the Food and Drug Administration (FDA) was given control over drug safety in the 1938 Federal Food, Drug, and Cosmetic Act. The bill had been debated for several years in Congress and showed no promise of passage. Then a pharmaceutical company decided to sell a liquid form of a sulfa drug (the first antibiotic) and found that the drug would dissolve well in a chemical solvent, diethylene glycol (presently used in antifreeze products). The company marketed the antibiotic as Elixir Sulfanilamide without testing the solvent for toxicity. Under the 1906 Pure Food and Drug Act, the company could not be prosecuted for the toxicity of this form of drug or for not testing the formulation of the drug on animals first. They could only be prosecuted for mislabeling the product on the technicality that *elixir* refers to a solution in alcohol, not a solution in diethylene glycol. Again, it was apparent that the laws in place provided woefully inadequate protection for the public.

The 1938 act differed from the 1906 law in several ways. It was organized according to the regulated commodity (food, drug, or cosmetic), rather than by the type of violation. It defined drugs to include products that affected bodily structure or function even in the absence of disease. Companies had to file applications with the government for all new drugs showing that they were *safe* (not effective, just safe!) for use as described. And the drug label had to include all ingredients and the quantity of each, as well as instructions regarding correct use of the drug and warnings about its dangers.

Prior to passage of the 1938 act, you could go to a doctor and get a prescription for any nonnarcotic drug or go to the pharmacy directly if you had already decided what was needed. The effect of the labeling requirement in the 1938 act was to allow drug companies to create a class of drugs that could not be sold legally without a prescription. Although not for certain, it has been suggested that the actions by the FDA were motivated by the frequent public misuse of two classes of drugs developed prior to passage of the 1938 law: sulfa antibiotics and barbiturates. People often took too little of the antibiotics to cure an infection and too much of the barbiturates and became addicted.

The 1938 Food, Drug, and Cosmetic Act allowed the manufacturer to determine whether a drug was to be labeled prescription or nonprescription. The same drug could be sold as prescription by one company and as an OTC by another! After the Durham-Humphrey Amendment was passed in 1951, almost all new drugs were placed in the prescription-only class. The drugs that were patented and marketed after World War II included the potent new antibiotics and the phenothiazine tranquilizers such as Thorazine. The FDA and the drug firms thought these were potentially too dangerous to sell OTC. The Durham-Humphrey Amendment established the criteria, which are still used today, for determining if a drug should be classified as prescription or nonprescription. Basically, if a drug does not fall into one of the following three categories, it is considered nonprescription:

1. The drug is habit-forming.
2. The drug is not safe for self-medication because of its toxicity.
3. The drug is a new drug that has not been shown to be completely safe.

Senator Kefauver's hearings, which began in 1959, initially were concerned with the enormous profit margins earned by drug companies because of the lack of competition in the market for new, patented drugs. Testimony by physicians revealed that an average doctor in clinical practice often was not able to evaluate accurately the efficacy of the drugs he or she prescribed. The 1938 law did not give the FDA authority to supervise clinical testing of drugs; consequently, the effectiveness of drugs being sold to the public was not being determined. Both the Kefauver and Harris

Amendments in the House showed no likely signs of becoming law until the **thalidomide** tragedy occurred.

Thalidomide was used in Europe and distributed on a small scale in the United States as a sedative for pregnant women. There are two approximately 24-hour intervals early in pregnancy when thalidomide can alter the development of the arms and legs of an embryo. If a woman takes thalidomide on one or both of these days, the infant could be born with abnormally developed arms and/or legs (called **phocomelia**, from the Greek words for *flippers*, or "seal-shaped limbs").

Although standard testing probably would not have detected this congenital effect of thalidomide and the tragedy would likely have occurred anyway, these pathetic infants stimulated passage of the 1962 Kefauver and Harris Amendments. They strengthened the government's regulation of both the introduction of new drugs and the production and sale of existing drugs. The amendment required, for the first time, that drug manufacturers demonstrate the efficacy as well as the safety of their drug products. The FDA was also empowered to withdraw approval of a drug that was already being marketed. Drug companies' testing procedures had to be approved before they could

Characteristic limb deformities caused by thalidomide. *Photo:* Taussing, H.B. 1962. Study of German outbreak of phocomelia: Thalidomide syndrome. *Journal of American Medical Association*, 180:1106–1114. Copyright 1962, American Medical Association. Used by permission.

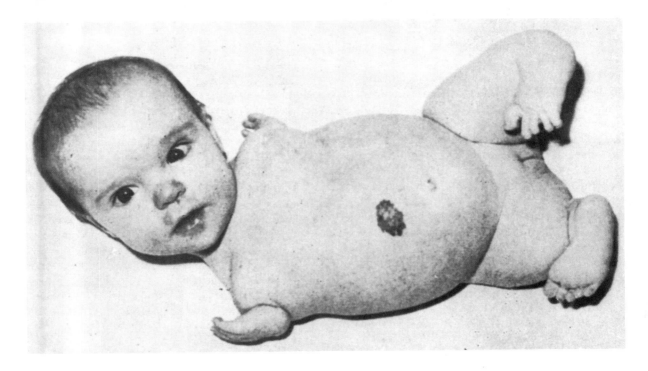

start testing new drugs, and they had to adhere to standards of good manufacturing practice.

THE RISING DEMAND FOR EFFECTIVENESS IN MEDICINAL DRUGS

To evaluate the effectiveness of the over 4,000 drug products that were introduced between 1938 and 1962, the FDA contracted the Drug Efficacy Study with the National Research Council. This investigation started in 1966 and ran for three years. The council was asked to rate drugs as either effective or ineffective, but they ended up with six classifications: (1) effective, (2) effective but less so than another, (3) probably effective, (4) possibly effective, (5) ineffective as a fixed combination, and (6) ineffective. Although the study was supposed to be based on scientific evidence, this often was not available, and so conclusions were sometimes founded on the clinical experience of the physicians on each panel; this was not always reliable information. It is ironic that the study was initiated because physicians in practice were admittedly unable to make decisions about the clinical worth of drugs without the benefit of research, yet many of the drugs being evaluated were reviewed by physicians.

A legal challenge resulted when the FDA took an "ineffective in a fixed combination" drug off the market and the manufacturer sued. This finally forced the FDA to define what constituted an adequate and well-controlled investigation. Adequate, documented clinical experience was no longer satisfactory proof that a drug was safe and effective. Each new drug application now had to include information about the drug's performance in comparison to that of a carefully defined control group. The drug could be compared with (1) a placebo, (2) another drug known to be active based on previous studies, (3) the established results of no treatment, or (4) historical data on the course of the illness without the use of the drug in question. In addition, a drug marketed before 1962 could no longer be "grandfathered in." If the company could not prove the drug had the qualifications to pass the post-1962 tests for a new drug,

it was considered a new, unapproved drug and could not legally be sold.

Think About It...

1. Do you feel it is more important for the government to assure that drugs are safe or effective? Why?
2. Why has the federal government been so reluctant to become involved in regulating drugs?
3. Of the federal legislation passed to regulate drugs, which do you feel was the most important and why?

REGULATING THE DEVELOPMENT OF NEW DRUGS

The amended Federal Food, Drug, and Cosmetic Act in force today requires that all new drugs be registered with the FDA. Because of the rules and regulations described above, all pharmaceutical companies must follow a series of steps when seeking permission to market a new drug.

REGULATORY STEPS FOR NEW PRESCRIPTION DRUGS

STEP 1: ANIMAL TESTING A chemical must be identified as having potential value in the treatment of a particular condition or disease. The company interested in marketing the chemical as a drug must run a series of tests on at least three species of animal. Careful records must be kept of side effects, absorption, distribution, metabolism, excretion, and the dosages of the drug necessary to produce the various effects. **Carcinogenic, mutagenic**, and **teratogenic** variables are tested. The dose-response curve must be determined along with potency, and then the risk benefit of the substance must be calculated (see Chapter 4). If the company still believes there is a market for the substance, it will forward the data to the FDA to obtain an investigational new drug (IND) number for further tests.

carcinogenic
able to cause cancer

mutagenic
able to cause mutation (alter genes)

teratogenic
able to cause abnormal development of the fetus

STEP 2: HUMAN TESTING Animal tests provide some information, but ultimately, tests must be done on the species for which the potential drug is intended, the human. These tests usually follow three phrases. Phase 1 is called the *initial clinical stage*. Small numbers of volunteers, both healthy people and patients in free clinics, are used to establish drug safety and dose range for effective treatment and to examine side effects. Formerly, much of this research was done on prison inmates, but because of bad publicity and the possibility of coercion, fewer prisoners are used today. Medical students, paid college student volunteers, and volunteers being treated at free clinics are more often used. All the data are collected, analyzed, and sent to the FDA for approval before beginning the next phase of human subject testing.

Phase 2 testing is called the *clinical pharmacological evaluation stage*. The effects of the drug are tested to eliminate investigator bias and to determine side effects and the effectiveness of the treatment. Because the safety of the new drug has not been thoroughly established, only a few patients with the medical problem the drug is intended to treat are used for these studies. Statistical evaluation of all this information is done before proceeding with phase 3 testing.

Phase 3 is the *extended clinical evaluation*. By this time, the pharmaceutical company has a good idea of drug effectiveness as well as dangers. The drug can be offered to a wider group of participating clinics and physicians, who cooperate in administration of the potential drug—when medically appropriate—to thousands of volunteer patients.

This stage makes the drug available on a wide experimental basis. Sometimes, by this point, there has been publicity about the new drug, and people with the particular disease for which the drug was developed may actively seek out physicians licensed to experiment with it. People not familiar with the sad consequences of taking inadequately tested drugs may protest at how long the drug-testing process takes.

During phase 3 testing, safety checks are made and any side effects are noted that might show up as more people are exposed to the drug. After the testing program is over, careful analysis is made of the effectiveness, side effects, and recommended dosage. The information is sent to the FDA for final evaluation. The amount of information at this point usually comprises many thousands of pages of data and analysis, and the FDA must sift through it and decide whether the risks of using the drug justify its potential benefits. The FDA usually calls for additional tests before deciding the drug is safe and effective and granting permission to market it.

STEP 3: PERMISSION TO MARKET At this point, the FDA can allow the drug to be marketed under its patented name. It may cost $125 to $200 million and take 5 to 10 years to develop a new drug in the United States (Roney 1991). The situation is similar elsewhere, although in some European countries, the clinical evaluations are less stringent and require less time. Once the drug is marketed, it continues to be closely scrutinized for adverse effects. Compared to the United States, the European approach makes it easier to recall a drug after having been approved for marketing, if unexpected adverse effects develop. In some cases, negative effects may not show up for a long time. For example, it was determined in 1970 that diethylstilbestrol (DES), when given to pregnant women to prevent miscarriage, causes an increased risk of a rare type of vaginal cancer in their daughters when these children entered their teens and young-adult years. The FDA subsequently removed from the market the form of DES that had been used to treat pregnant women. As described above, the thalidomide tragedy resulted in passage of the law that gave the FDA this authority.

EXCEPTIONS: SPECIAL DRUG-MARKETING LAWS
There is continual concern that the process used by the FDA to evaluate prospective drugs is laborious and excessively lengthy. Recently, an amendment was passed to allow the early marketing of drugs with obvious therapeutic action. The so-called "fast-track" rule has been applied to testing of certain drugs used for the treatment of rare cancers, AZT (zidovudine) for the treatment of AIDS, and other similar drugs. As a result, they have reached the market after a much reduced testing program.

A second amendment, the Orphan Drug Law, allows drug companies to receive tax advantages if they develop drugs that are not very profitable because they are only useful in treating small numbers of patients, such as those who suffer from rare diseases. A rare disease is defined as one that affects less than 200,000 persons in the United States or one for which the cost of developing a drug is not likely to be recovered by marketing it (*Drug Facts and Comparisons* 1991).

THE REGULATION
OF NONPRESCRIPTION DRUGS

As already mentioned, the Durham-Humphrey Amendment to the Food, Drug, and Cosmetic Act made a distinction between prescription and nonprescription (OTC) drugs and required the FDA to regulate OTC marketing. In 1972, the FDA initiated a program to evaluate the effectiveness and safety of the nonprescription drugs on the market and to ensure that they included appropriate labeling (for more details, see Chapter 13). Each so-called active ingredient in the OTC medications was assigned to one of 27 categories and reviewed by a panel of drug experts, including physicians, pharmacologists, and pharmacists. Based on the recommendations of these panels, the ingredients were placed in one of the following three categories:

I—Generally recognized as safe and effective for the claimed therapeutic indication

II—Not generally recognized as safe and effective or unacceptable indications

III—Insufficient data available to permit final classification

Over 300 individuals participated as panel members in these reviews. Between 1972 and 1981, they made initial determinations on over 700 ingredients in more than 300,000 OTC drug products and submitted more than 60 reports to the FDA.

The second phase of the OTC drug review consisted of an evaluation by the FDA of the panels' findings. The FDA submitted a tentative adoption of the panels' recommendations (after revision, if necessary), following public comment and scrutiny. After a period of time and careful consideration of new information, the agency issued a final ruling and classification of the ingredients under consideration.

THE EFFECTS OF THE OTC REVIEW ON TODAY'S MEDICATIONS   The review process for OTC ingredients has had a significant impact on the public's attitude about OTC products and their use (both good and bad) in self-medication. It was apparent from the review process that many OTC drug ingredients did not satisfy the requirements for safety and effectiveness. In fact, in 1990 alone, the FDA banned 223 uses of nonprescription drug ingredients, ruling that the ingredients were ineffective against problems ranging from acne to swimmer's ear. Consequently, it is almost certain that, in the future, there will be fewer active ingredients in OTC medicines, but these drugs will be safer and more effective than ever before. In addition, with heightened public awareness, greater demand has been brought to bear on the FDA to make better drugs available to the public for self-medication. In response to these pressures, the FDA has adopted a **switching policy**, which allows it to review prescription drugs and evaluate their suitability as OTC products. The following criteria must be satisfied if a drug is to be switched:

---

switching policy
an FDA policy allowing the change of suitable prescription drugs to OTC status

1. The drug has been marketed by prescription for at least three years.
2. Use of the drug has been relatively high during the time it was available as a prescription drug.
3. Adverse drug reactions are not alarming, and the frequency of side effects has not increased during the time the drug was available to the public.

Since this policy was instituted, approximately 40 to 50 drugs have been switched to OTC status, and many more are being considered. A total of 170 ingredients are likely to be considered for switching from 1992 to 1997.

In general, this switching policy has been well received by the public. In fact, 65% of the switched ingredients have ranked first or second in their drug categories within the first five years of being switched (Siegelman 1990). The medical community and the FDA are generally positive about OTC switches, as well. There are some concerns, however.

William E. Gilbertson, director of the FDA's division of OTC drug evaluation, feels that the agency needs to proceed cautiously with switches and place greater emphasis on adequate labeling to assure that consumers have adequate information to use OTC products safely and effectively. "Most assuredly, making more drugs available will put an added burden on consumers in terms of benefit/risk decisions. In that regard, the ways we disseminate OTC information will be important" (Siegelman 1990).

THE REGULATION OF DRUG ADVERTISING

Much of the public's knowledge and impressions about drugs, especially those available OTC, come from advertisements. It is difficult to ascertain the amount of money currently spent by the pharmaceutical industry to promote its products. Because of the intense competition between OTC drugs, it is likely that up to 15% to 20% of the dollar sales for these products is spent on advertising to the general public. For prescription drugs, it is likely that the costs of advertising and drug promotion approach $2 to $3 billion annually.

There is no doubt that these promotional efforts by pharmaceutical manufacturers have tremendous impact on the drug-purchasing habits of the general public and health professionals. Not surprisingly, drug use based on misleading or false advertising claims rather than facts can result in unsatisfactory drug therapy and, in some situations, can be dangerous. Regulations governing the advertising of nonprescription drugs are set and enforced by the Federal Trade Commission (FTC). These rules are less stringent than those for prescription medicines.

PRESCRIPTION ADVERTISING The economics of prescription drugs is unique because a second party, the health professional, dictates what the consumer, the patient, will purchase. Although there have been recent efforts by pharmaceutical companies to advertise medications directly to the public, the vast majority of prescription drug promotion is directed at the health professional and controlled by the FDA. The approaches employed by manufacturers to encourage health professionals to prescribe their products include advertising in prestigious medical journals, direct-mail advertising, and some radio and television advertising. All printed and audio materials distributed by drug salespeople are controlled by advertising regulations from the FDA. Perhaps the most effective sales approach is having drug representatives personally visit health professionals; this tactic is harder to regulate.

Unfortunately, many health professionals rely on drug company salespeople for the so-called latest scientific information concerning drugs and their effects. While these representatives of the drug industry can provide an important informational service, it is essential that health professionals remember that these people make a living by selling their products, and often their information is slanted accordingly.

Many people in and out of the medical community have questioned the ethics of drug advertising in the United States and are concerned about the negative impact that deceptive promotion has upon target populations. One of the biggest problems in dealing with false advertising is defining such deception. Probably the best guideline for such a definition is summarized in the Wheeler-Lea Amendment to the Federal Trade Commission Act:

> The term *false advertisement* means an advertisement, other than labeling, which is misleading in a material respect; and in determining whether any advertisement is misleading, there shall be taken into account not only representations . . . but the extent to which the advertisement fails to reveal facts.

Tough questions are being asked as to how much control should be exerted over the pharmaceutical industry to protect the public without excessively infringing on the rights of these companies to promote their goods. The solutions to these problems will not be simple; however, efforts to keep drug advertisements accurate, in good taste, and informative are worthwhile and will be necessary if the public is expected to make rational decisions about drug use.

FEDERAL REGULATION AND QUALITY ASSURANCE

No matter what policy is adopted by the FDA and other drug-regulating agencies, there will always be those who criticize their efforts and complain that they do not do enough or even too much. The FDA has been blamed for being excessively careful and requiring too much testing before new drugs are approved for marketing; on the other hand, when new drugs are released and cause serious side effects, the FDA is condemned for being sloppy in their control of drug marketing.

What is the proper balance, and what do we, as consumers, have the right to expect from government? These are questions each of us should ask, and we have a right to share our answers with government representatives.

On the other hand, regardless of our individual feelings, it is important to understand that the current (and likely future) federal regulations do not assure drug safety or effectiveness for everyone. Too many individual variables alter the way each of us responds to drugs, making such universal assurances impossible. Federal agencies can only deal with general policies and make general

decisions. For example, what if the FDA determines that a given drug is reasonably safe in 95% of the population and effective in 70%? Are these acceptable figures, or should a drug be safe in 99% and effective in 90% before it is suitable for general marketing? What of the 5% or 1% of the population who will be adversely affected by this drug? What rights do they have to be protected?

There are no simple answers to these questions. Federal policies are compromises that assume that the clinician who prescribes the drug and/or the patient who buys and consumes it will be able to identify when use of that drug is inappropriate or threatening. Unfortunately, sometimes drug prescribing and drug consuming are done carelessly and unnecessary side effects occur or the drug does not work. The questions surface again: Are federal drug agencies doing all they can to protect the public? Should the laws be changed?

It is always difficult to predict the future, especially when it depends on fickle politicians and erratic public opinion. Nevertheless, with the dramatic increase in new and better drugs being available to the public, it is not likely that federal or state agencies will diminish their role in regulating drug use. Now more than ever, the public demands safer and more effective drugs. This public attitude will likely translate into even greater involvement by regulatory agencies in issues of drug development, assessment, and marketing.

Another reason for increased regulation in the future is that many of the larger pharmaceutical companies have become incredibly wealthy. Several of the most profitable companies have become subsidiaries of powerful corporations that are driven more by profit margins than philanthropic interests. In such an environment, governmental agencies are essential to assure that the rights of the public are protected. Only a fool would desire to return to the early days of federal policies based on "buyer beware" principles.

Moreover, current demands by the public for greater involvement in therapy suggest that self-medication will become an important factor in dictating future drug policies. In response to such public desires, the FDA is already involved in switching prescription drugs to OTC status, making more effective medications available to the public on demand. Not surprisingly, this policy has been challenged. Some clinicians suggest that making more effective drugs available OTC to a public ignorant about these agents and their side effects can be dangerous. While such concerns slow the change process, as long as medical costs continue to escalate rapidly, the policy of switching drugs from prescription to nonprescription status will almost certainly continue. Ironically, the trend toward self-treatment in some ways is a return to the independent attitudes of the turn of the century.

T h i n k   A b o u t   I t . . .

1. What are some of the potential problems with the current process for evaluating new drugs for marketing?
2. What are the advantages and potential disadvantages of switching prescription drugs to OTC status?
3. Advertisements for drugs have been criticized as being deceptive. If you had the authority, what would you do to correct the problems with drug advertising (consider both prescription and nonprescription types)?

DRUG ABUSE AND THE LAW

The laws that govern the development, distribution, and use of drugs in general and drugs of abuse in particular are intertwined. There are, however, some unique features concerning the manner in which federal agencies deal with the drugs of abuse that warrant special consideration. A summary of drug-abuse laws is shown in Table 3-2, and a section on the development of laws and enforcement agencies appears in Appendix 3-1.

Coffee, tea, tobacco, alcohol, marijuana, hallucinogens, depressants (like barbiturates), and narcotics have been subject to a wide range of controls, from none to rigid. Islamic countries have instituted severe penalties, such as strangulation for smoking tobacco or opium and strict bans on alcohol. In other countries, these substances have been legal or prohibited at the same time or at different times, depending on the situation and the desires of the population. In the past, laws were changed because so many people demanded access to a specific drug of abuse that it would have been impossible to enforce a ban (such as the revocation of Prohibition) or because the government needed tax revenues that could be raised by selling the drug (one of the arguments for legalizing drugs of abuse today).

The negative experiences that Americans had at the turn of the century with addicting substances such as opium led to the Harrison Act of 1914. This was the first legitimate effort by the federal government to regulate and control the production, importation, sale, purchase, and distribution of addicting substances. The Harrison Act served as the foundation and reference for subsequent laws directed at regulating drug abuse issues.

Today, the ways in which law enforcement agencies deal with substance abuse are largely determined by the Comprehensive Drug Abuse Prevention and Control Act of 1970. This act divided substances with abuse potential into categories based on the degree of their abuse potential and their clinical usefulness. The classifications are referred to as *Schedules* and range from I to V. Schedule I substances have high abuse potential and no currently approved medicinal use; they cannot be prescribed by health professionals. Schedule II drugs also have high abuse potential but are approved for medical purposes and can be prescribed, with restrictions. The distinctions between Schedule II through V substances are the likelihood of abuse occurring and the degree to which the drugs are controlled by governmental agencies. The least addictive and least regulated of the substances of abuse are classified as Schedule V (see the chapter Appendix for more details).

FACTORS IN CONTROLLING DRUG ABUSE

Three principal issues influence laws on drug abuse:

1. If a person abuses a drug, should he or she be treated as a criminal or as a sick person inflicted with a disease?
2. How is the user (supposedly the victim) dis-

TABLE 3-2   Federal laws for the control of narcotic and other abused drugs

Date	Name of Legislation	Summary of Coverage and Intent of Legislation
1914	Harrison Act	First federal legislation to regulate and control the production, importation, sale, purchase, and free distribution of opium or drugs derived from opium.
1922	Narcotic Drug Import and Export Act	Intends to eliminate the use of narcotics except for medical and other legitimate purposes.
1924	Heroin Act	Makes it illegal to manufacture heroin.
1937	Marijuana Tax Act	Provides controls over marijuana similar to the Harrison Act over narcotics.
1942	Opium Poppy Control Act	Prohibits growing opium poppies in the United States except under license.
1951	Boggs Amendment to the Harrison Narcotics Act	Establishes severe mandatory penalties for conviction on narcotics charges.
1956	Narcotics Control Act	Intends to impose very severe penalties for those convicted of narcotics or marijuana charges.
1965	Drug Abuse Control Amendments (DACA)	Adopts strict controls over amphetamines, barbiturates, LSD, and similar substances with provisions to add new substances as the need arises.
1966	Narcotic Addict Rehabilitation Act (NARA)	Allows treatment as an alternative to jail.
1968	DACA Amendments	Provides that sentence may be suspended and record be erased if not convicted for another violation for one year.
1970	Comprehensive Drug Abuse Prevention and Control Act	Replaces or updates all other laws concerning narcotics and dangerous drugs.
1972	Drug Abuse Office and Treatment Act	Establishes $1.1 billion over three years to combat drug abuse and start treatment programs.
1973	Methadone Control Act	Places controls on methadone licensing.
1973	Heroin Trafficking Act	Increases penalties for traffickers and makes bail procedures more stringent.
1973	Alcohol, Drug Abuse, and Mental Health Administration (ADAMHA)	Consolidates NIMH, NIAAA, and NIDA under ADAMHA.
1973	Drug Enforcement Administration (DEA)	Bureau of Narcotics and Dangerous Drugs is remodeled to become the DEA.
1974 and 1978	Drug Abuse Prevention, Control, and Treatment Amendments	Extends the 1972 law.
1978	Alcohol and Drug Abuse Education Amendments	Sets up Office of Alcohol and Drug Abuse Education in the Department of Education; more emphasis on drug abuse in rural areas and on coordination at the federal-state level.
1980	Drug Abuse Prevention, Treatment, and Rehabilitation Amendments	Extends prevention education and rehabilitation programs.
1984	Drug Offenders Act	Sets up special program for offenders and organizes treatment.

TABLE 3-2 Federal laws for the control of narcotic and other abused drugs *(continued)*

Date	Name of Legislation	Summary of Coverage and Intent of Legislation
1986	Alcohol and Drug Abuse Amendments of 1986	Continues funding for prevention, education, and treatment programs.
1986	Controlled Substances Analogue Enforcement Act of 1986	Sets up controls for the enforcement of "designer drugs."
1986	Anti-Drug Abuse Act of 1986	Establishes the Office for Substance Abuse Prevention in ADAMHA.
1988	Anti-Drug Act	Establishes the Office of the National Drug Control Policy to oversee all federal policies regarding research about and control of drugs of abuse.

tinguished from the pusher (supposedly the criminal) of an illicit drug, and who should be more harshly punished—the person that creates the demand for the drug or the person who satisfies the demand?

3. Are the law and associated penalties effective deterrents against drug use or abuse, and how is effectiveness determined?

In regard to the first issue, drug abuse may be considered both an illness and a crime. It is an illness, an abnormal functional state, when a person is compelled (either physically or psychologically—see Chapter 4) to continue using the drug. It is a crime when the law, reflecting social opinion, has made abuse of the drug illegal. Health issues are clearly involved because uncontrolled abuse of almost any drug can lead to physical and/or psychological damage. Because the public has to pay for health care costs or societal damage, laws are created and penalties implemented to prevent or correct drug abuse problems. (See Figure 3-2 on federal trafficking penalties.)

Concerning the second issue, drug laws have always been more lenient to the *user* than to the *seller* of a drug of abuse. Actually, it is often hard to separate user from pusher, as most drug abusers engage in both activities. Because huge profits are often involved, some people may not use the drugs they peddle and are only pushers; the law tries to

deter use of drugs by concentrating on these persons but has questionable success. Organized crime is involved in major drug sales, and these "drug rings" have proven hard to destroy.

In regard to the third issue, all available evidence indicates that, in the United States, criminal law has only limited success in deterring drug abuse. Even though there are recent signs that the use of illicit drugs has declined (NIDA 1991), during 1990, approximately 28 million Americans used illicit drugs; marijuana was used by 10% and cocaine by about 4% (Jarvik 1990). It is clear that the drug abuse problem is far from being resolved, and many feel that some changes should be made in how we deal with this problem. There are two basic approaches: (1) that we repeal our present prohibitory laws against controlled substances and legalize drugs and (2) that we strengthen current laws (Jarvik 1990). Interestingly, a Gallup poll reports that between 60% and 80% of the public supports continued prohibition of most drugs of abuse (Gallup and Gallup 1988).

Recent efforts to control illegal drugs have been through **interdiction** of supply. In fact, interdiction has repeatedly received more than 70% of the total congressional appropriations for drug control, despite the fact that this approach has not been particularly effective. While it is true that seizures of large caches of illicit drugs seem to be reported routinely in the national press, there is no indication that the availability of drugs has di-

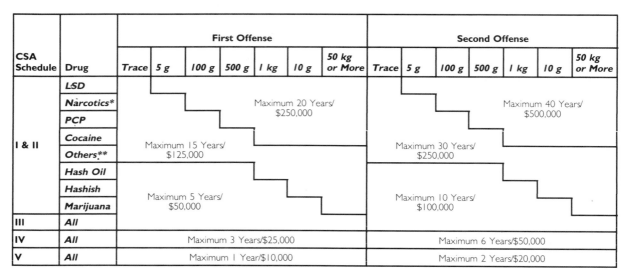

CSA Schedule	Drug	First Offense							Second Offense						
		Trace	5 g	100 g	500 g	1 kg	10 g	50 kg or More	Trace	5 g	100 g	500 g	1 kg	10 g	50 kg or More
I & II	LSD														
	Narcotics*				Maximum 20 Years/ $250,000							Maximum 40 Years/ $500,000			
	PCP														
	Cocaine		Maximum 15 Years/ $125,000							Maximum 30 Years/ $250,000					
	Others**														
	Hash Oil														
	Hashish		Maximum 5 Years/ $50,000							Maximum 10 Years/ $100,000					
	Marijuana														
III	All														
IV	All	Maximum 3 Years/$25,000							Maximum 6 Years/$50,000						
V	All	Maximum 1 Year/$10,000							Maximum 2 Years/$20,000						

*Except coca leaves and derivatives.
**Others—some stimulants, some depressants and some hallucinogens.

FIGURE 3-2   Federal trafficking penalties *Source: Drugs of Abuse,* p. 9. Courtesy of the Drug Enforcement Administration.

minished substantially. One can argue that, as long as a strong demand for these psychoactive agents exists, demand will be satisfied if the price is right. Even if interdiction is successful in reducing the supply of one drug of abuse, if demand persists, it usually will be replaced by another with similar abuse potential (i.e., substitution of amphetamines for cocaine—see Chapter 9).

interdiction
the policy of cutting off or destroying supplies of illicit drugs

Other approaches should be emphasized. Greater emphasis should be placed on eliminating the demand for the drugs of abuse. This objective is not easily achieved. Drug abuse is a complex and very individual problem, with many causes and aggravating factors. Even so, experience has taught us that prevention is a better strategy and, in the long run, less costly than interdiction or the criminal justice system. The following are some suggestions as to how demand can be reduced (Halloway 1991):

1. Reduction of demand by youth must be the top priority of any prevention program if it is to provide a long-term solution. To achieve this requires stabilizing defective family structures, implementing school programs that create an antidrug attitude, establishing a drug-free environment, and promoting resistance training to help youth avoid drug involvement.

2. Replacement therapy has also shown to be a useful approach to weaning the individual dependent on drugs of abuse. The most common example of this strategy is the use of methadone to treat the heroin addict (see Chapter 8). Use of methadone prevents the cravings and severe withdrawal routinely associated with breaking the heroin habit. Unfortunately, most heroin addicts insist that they be maintained on methadone indefinitely. Even though methadone is easier to

control and is less disruptive than heroin, one drug addiction has been substituted for another, which draws criticism.

A second example of the replacement approach is the use of Valium-type (benzodiazepines) drugs to treat the alcoholic (see Chapter 6). The benzodiazepines diminish the severe withdrawal responses (both physical and psychological) that occur in the alcohol-dependent person who has abruptly stopped drinking. The amount of benzodiazepine can be gradually decreased, minimizing withdrawal problems.

A similar approach has been advocated for cocaine addiction (see Chapter 9). The use of antidepressants (particularly desipramine) diminishes the intense cravings that cocaine-dependent persons experience as they try to give up the habit (Gawin et al. 1989).

Replacement therapy certainly is not the entire answer to all drug abuse problems, but it often can provide a window of opportunity for behavioral modification so that a long-term solution to the abuse problem is possible.

3. Attitudes toward drug abuse and its consequence must be changed. The drug-use patterns of many people, both young and old, are strongly influenced by peers. If people believe that drug abuse is glamorous and contributes to acceptance by friends and associates, the incidence of drug abuse will continue to be high. In contrast, if the prevailing message in society is that drug abuse is stupid and not socially acceptable, the incidence will be much less. This message is perhaps being heard: There was a dramatic decline in demand for cocaine in the United States from 1987 to 1990 (see Chapter 9).

CONSTITUTIONAL PROTECTIONS

The most common defense used in drug-related criminal proceedings is the individual liberty guarantee based on the Bill of Rights, the Fourteenth Amendment to the U.S. Constitution, and additional individual liberty guarantees in states' constitutions. The defenses most commonly used in drug cases are:

pharmacological duress ("the drug made me do it")
the right to privacy
the freedom of religion
cruel and unusual punishment
double jeopardy
sanity

The law works for the protection of the individual, and it often works more smoothly for those who can pay for the best legal assistance. It is difficult for the average citizen and criminal justice worker to see a guilty person released on a technicality. Nevertheless, the system is based on the assumption that it is better to err in releasing some violators than to imprison someone who is innocent. The following are the Articles of the Bill of Rights and the Fourteenth Amendment of the Constitution, which have played a major role in criminal defenses for drug prosecutions:

Amendment 1 states that "Congress shall make no law . . . prohibiting the free exercise of religion or abridging the freedom of speech." This has been the basis for allowing the Native American Church to use peyote (see Chapter 11).

Amendment 4 guarantees the right to be secure in your own home, sometimes called the right to privacy, and to have protection against unauthorized search and seizure. This amendment is the basis for many successful drug defenses. Legal authorities cannot search someone's home without just cause but must have a search warrant or other permission to do so. If a person is stopped while driving a car, the car is searched, and a hidden drug is found, this is not admissible as evidence unless the officer can demonstrate that there was a reason, such as unsafe driving, to stop the driver.

Amendment 5 stipulates that a person cannot be charged twice for the same crime and once released, cannot be recharged for the same crime. This is sometimes called the *due process amendment* because it further says that you cannot be deprived of life, liberty, or property without due process of law.

Amendment 8 is the cruel and unusual punishment limitation. Sentences that are clearly out of line with the norm for the times can be successfully appealed.

Amendment 14 provides each person equal protection under the law. This amendment also guarantees due process.

The insanity defense is used in some drug criminal proceedings. The Fifth and Fourteenth Amendments provide due process, but persons are excluded from criminal responsibility if they carried out the act as a result of insanity or the inability to tell right from wrong (i.e., as when under the influence of a drug). The American Psychiatric Association has declared that drug addiction is a nonpsychotic mental disorder, so persons can claim they are not able to control their actions; at the same time, they must show they were insane at the time of the crime, which is difficult. Addicts are often given leniency if they agree to enroll in treatment or rehabilitation programs. If a person commits a serious crime while under the influence of the drug, the defense is much more complex. The claim that crimes were committed under the influence of alcohol, cocaine, amphetamines, or other behavior-altering substances has, on occasions, resulted in diminished sentences for the defendant.

DRUG LAWS AND DETERRENCE

As previously discussed, drug laws do not serve as a satisfactory deterrent against the use of illicit drugs. People have always used and abused drugs and very likely will continue to do so. Despite stricter laws and greater support for law enforcement, four significant reasons remain for the persistent drug-abuse problem:

1. There is always a certain amount of deviant behavior in any society, but the many forms

---

For You to Consider...

Drugs and Prosecution

In 1988, Charles McCovey walked into a video store in Kearns, Utah, gun in hand, with the intent of committing robbery. During the crime, McCovey shot and killed Anna Holmes, the pregnant mother of four. The victim's premature baby was delivered by caesarean section following the homicide and died two years later from complications of the early birth. McCovey was apprehended soon after the crime and was tried for first-degree murder. Witnesses claimed that McCovey senselessly murdered Mrs. Holmes. According to their testimony, the victim did nothing to provoke or oppose the murderer; McCovey unexpectedly turned his gun on Mrs. Holmes and fired.

What appeared to be a tragic case of senseless homicide was complicated by the fact that the suspect was a chronic drug user. In fact, at the time of the crime, he was under the influence of methamphetamine, alcohol, and perhaps cocaine. At the trial, the defense attorney argued that Charles McCovey "did not do anything more than try to commit a robbery"; the firing of the gun was unintentional and caused by the effects of the drugs. The jury believed the defense and convicted McCovey on lesser second-degree murder charges. Instead of the death penalty, McCovey was given two five-years-to-life sentences for aggravated robbery and second-degree murder.

---

of modern communication have heavily stressed drug abuse as a major form of deviant behavior in U.S. society. This probably encourages certain susceptible people to participate in this behavior. An example of this would be the individual who wants to be different and express his or her right to rebel against authority.

2. Publicity surrounding drugs of abuse, especially if they are promoted in a glamorous fashion in the public media, attracts some people. Such presentations inform members of society about new and different

drugs in an enticing manner and encourage experimentation.

3. Many drug warnings may actually work as lures for potential drug users. There is a saying in advertising: "I don't care what you say about me, as long as you keep mentioning my name." Many people hear of something new and want to try it to get a new feeling, to impress peers, to take a risk, and so on.

4. There is an incredible conflict of information on drugs. If the information that is intended to guide and inform the public is not factual and consistent, people become skeptical and pay little attention to warnings (Brecher 1972).

Historically, it appears that misinformation about new psychoactive drugs has influenced many people to try them. If a drug is said to be an aphrodisiac, to give a different and special "high," or to give insight into the meaning of life, many people believe such unsubstantiated claims (often given in the form of testimonials or anecdotal stories) and want to try it. This type of attraction has existed as long as information has been communicated about mind-altering substances. Such claims have been made for opium, methaqualone, ether, nitrous oxide, hashish, peyote, and just about every other substance taken by humans to alter the state of consciousness.

As the amount of addiction increased during the mid-1960s, many ill-conceived programs and laws were instituted as knee-jerk reactions, with little understanding about the underlying reasons for the rise in drug abuse. Restrictive laws rarely work to reduce the use of illicit drugs if the majority of people do not support the laws. Even as laws become more restrictive, there usually is little impact on the level of addiction; in fact, in some cases, addiction problems actually have increased. For example, during the restrictive years of the 1960s and 1980s, drugs were sold everywhere to everyone—in high schools, colleges, and probably in every community. In the 1980s, especially, increasingly large volumes of drugs were sold throughout the United States. Billions of dollars were paid for those drugs. Although no one knows precisely how much money was exchanged, it likely approached $80 to $100 billion a year for all illegal drugs, of which the two biggest categories were an estimated $30 billion for cocaine and $24 billion for marijuana. In fact, it has been claimed that, for some states such as California and Oregon, marijuana is the single largest cash crop.

Because of the large sums of money involved, there was corruption at all levels. Notorious examples include the loss of millions of dollars of contraband heroin and cocaine held as evidence in police vaults in New York City, as well as other cities and towns throughout the country; the indictment of a number of detectives in the homicide division of Miami for selling drugs and taking large bribes; and the claim that there were direct links between drug dealers and the governments of Panama, Colombia, and Bolivia. Some law enforcement agencies have said that drugs are the largest export item from these countries. It is known that Miami has been the key point of entry into the United States for both cocaine and marijuana and that money is "laundered" in businesses set up as fronts. It was reported that the Miami branch of the Federal Reserve Bank of Atlanta was the only branch bank in the U.S. Reserve System to show a cash surplus—$4.74 billion—in 1980.

Because of insufficient numbers of law enforcement personnel and inadequate detention facilities, much drug traffic goes unchecked. In addition, the judiciary system gets so backlogged that many cases never get to court. Plea bargaining is almost the rule in order to clear the court docket. Often dealers and traffickers are back in business the same day they are arrested. This seriously damages the morale of law enforcement people, legislators, and average citizens.

It is estimated that there are nearly 1 million drug-related arrests each year. This is a tremendous cost to society in terms of damaged lives and family relationships; being arrested for drug-related crime seriously jeopardizes your opportunity for a normal life. Drug taking is closely tied to societal problems, and it will remain a problem unless society provides more meaningful experiences to those most susceptible to drug abuse. Improved education and increased support should be given to preteens because that is the age when deviant behavior starts. In cases where drug education programs have been successful in involving students, the amount of drug taking and illegal activity seems to have decreased (see Chapter 15).

THE COSTS OF DRUG ADDICTION TO SOCIETY

Society pays a high price for drug addiction. Many of the costs are immeasurable, for example, broken homes, illness, shortened lives, and loss of good minds to industry and professions. The dollar costs are also great. The **National Institute on Drug Abuse (NIDA)** has estimated that the typical narcotic habit costs the user $100 a day or more to maintain, depending on location, availability of narcotics, and other factors. Assuming that a heroin addict has a $100-a-day habit, this addict would need about $36,000 a year just to maintain the drug supply. It is impossible for most addicts to get this amount of money legally, so many resort to criminal activity to support their habits.

Let's Get the Facts

Desire for Drugs Fuels Crime

A study released by the Department of Justice on August 25, 1991, estimated that approximately 13% of the 219,000 convicted offenders in local jails throughout the United States committed their crimes in order to obtain money to purchase illicit drugs. Of those felons who committed robbery, about one-third were after drug money. This study also found that nearly 25% of the violent criminals and 30% of those committing property crimes were using illicit drugs at the time of their offense. Overall, approximately 23% of these inmates were incarcerated because of illegal drug activities. This figure was substantially higher than the 9% found in 1983, when this study was last conducted (Associated Press release, August 26, 1991).

NIDA
the National Institute on Drug Abuse, the principal federal agency responsible for directing drug abuse–related research

Most crimes related to drugs involve theft of personal property—primarily burglary and shoplifting—and less commonly, assault and robbery (mugging). It is estimated that a heroin addict has to steal three to five times the actual cost of the drugs to maintain the habit. This means that he or she would have to steal about $100,000 a year. A number of addicts resort to pimping and prostitution. No accurate figures are available on the costs of drug-related prostitution, although some law enforcement officials have estimated that prostitutes take in a total of $10 to $20 billion a year. It has also been estimated that nearly one out of every three or four prostitutes in major cities has a serious drug dependency.

Another significant concern is the recent increases in clandestine laboratories throughout the country that are involved in synthesizing or processing illicit drugs. Such laboratories produce amphetaminelike drugs, heroinlike drugs, and **"designer" drugs** and process other drugs of abuse such as cocaine. The **Drug Enforcement Administration (DEA)** reported 184 laboratories seized in 1981 and that increased to 647 in 1987. The reasons for such dramatic increases relate to the enormous profits and relatively low risk associated with these operations. As a rule, clandestine laboratories are fairly mobile, relatively crude (often operating in a kitchen, basement, or garage), and

---

"designer" drugs
illicit drugs that are chemically modified so they are not considered illegal but that retain abusive properties

DEA
the Drug Enforcement Administration, the principal federal agency responsible for enforcing drug abuse regulations

operated by individuals with only elementary chemical skills. Because of a lack of training, the chemical procedures are done crudely, resulting in adulterants and impure products. Such contaminants can be very toxic, causing severe harm or even death to the unsuspecting user (Soine 1989).

The costs to society continue after addicts are caught because it takes from $50 to $100 a day to incarcerate each of them. To support programs like methadone maintenance costs much less. New York officials estimate that methadone maintenance programs cost about $2,000 a year per patient. Some outpatient programs, such as those in Washington, D.C., claim a cost as low as $5 to $10 a day (not counting cost of staff and facilities), which is much less than the cost of incarceration.

A more long-term effect of drug abuse that has substantial impact on society is the medical and psychological care often required by addicts as a consequence of disease resulting from their drug habit. Particularly noteworthy are the communicable diseases spread because of needle sharing within the drug-abusing population, such as AIDS (acquired immune deficiency syndrome) and hepatitis. Because of its poor prognosis, AIDS is the most publicized of these diseases. In the United States, 20% of the nearly 100,000 AIDS cases as of June 1989 were intravenous (IV) drug users. The AIDS virus in this population appears to be transmitted in small amounts of contaminated blood left on shared needles. The likelihood of contracting AIDS in the drug-abusing population correlates with the frequency of injection and the amount of needle sharing (Booth 1989). Care for these AIDS patients lasts from months to years in intensive care units at a cost of billions of dollars to the public. Some social workers have advocated that new, uncontaminated needles be made available to drug addicts free of charge to prevent the spread of AIDS by contaminated needles. Others argue against this approach, complaining that such a policy encourages abuse of drugs through the more dangerous IV route.

Also of great concern is drug abuse by women during pregnancy. There is no longer doubt that some psychoactive drugs can have profound, permanent effects on a developing fetus. The best documented of these is fetal alcohol syndrome

For You to Consider...

The "Frozen Addicts"

In the early 1980s, a different group of young drug addicts began showing up in hospitals around San Francisco. These patients had symptoms associated with Parkinson's disease (slow movement, muscle rigidity, tremors, etc.), which was very unusual because Parkinson's disease almost never occurs before the age of 50 years. The only link between these patients was that all had consumed a new synthetic heroin that had just hit the "streets." After tracking down samples of this substance, it was determined that a contaminant called *MPTP* was present because the individual making the drug had been sloppy in his chemistry. When administered to laboratory animals, MPTP was found to selectively destroy a part of the brain in a fashion very similar to that seen in Parkinson's disease. The brain damage was permanent in all of those who consumed the contaminated narcotic, and these drug abusers became known as the "frozen addicts" (Langston 1985).

(FAS), which can affect the offspring of alcoholic mothers (see Chapter 7). It is likely that use of cocaine and amphetamine-related drugs can also cause irreversible congenital changes when used during pregnancy (see Chapter 9). All too often, the affected offspring of addicted mothers become the responsibility of welfare organizations at great cost to social services programs.

FUTURE CONSIDERATIONS IN DRUG ABUSE REGULATION

In the United States, there presently is a "get tough" attitude about drug abuse. Slogans such as "Just say no" and "War on Drugs" reflect the perspective of a public that has been victimized by escalating crime (many of which are drug related); personally touched by drug tragedies in families, at work, or with associates and friends; and economically drained by dealing with the cost of the problem. It is no wonder that, in 1989 and 1990, drug abuse was viewed as the number-one problem in this country by the majority of its citizens (see Anti-Drug Abuse Act in the chapter Appendix). Consequently, it is likely that, in the near future, politicians and governmental policy makers will devote much of their effort and revenues to dealing with drug abuse-related issues. It is already apparent that much more money will be spent on drug abuse programs in the 1990s than ever before. From 1989 to 1991, the National Institute on Drug Abuse dramatically increased its budget directed at improving education and treatment programs in communities and schools. In addition, new research money was earmarked for identifying the causes of abuse, which will hopefully lead to new therapeutic approaches (Halloway 1991).

An issue that has not been resolved and probably will continue to cause controversy is drug testing. How much of a deterrent is drug testing in the workplace, in athletics, and in schools? What right does the public have to know if people serving them (such as airline pilots, truck drivers, train engineers, etc.) are under the influence of drugs? Is drug testing an infraction of constitutional rights? How reliable is drug testing? What is the likelihood of false-positives (tests that erroneously indicate the presence of a drug)? Does drug testing significantly reduce drug abuse or merely cause users of illicit drugs to find ways to fool the test? These questions will need to be addressed in the years to come.

Most certainly, new laws controlling the use and sales of illicit drugs will be passed. Based on current attitudes, it appears that, in the short term at least, such laws will be more rigid, with harsher penalties for those that deal in illegal drugs. Although there is a segment of the public demanding legalization of some or all drugs of abuse, it is firmly opposed by medical associations and federal agencies and not likely to happen any time soon.

If any of the abused drugs were to be legalized, it most likely would be marijuana. A case could be made that marijuana is less dangerous, both medically and behaviorally, than alcohol or tobacco. Decriminalization of this substance was first recommended by the National Commission on Marijuana and Drug Abuse in 1973. A majority of states have already followed through with laws that make possession of marijuana for personal use a misdemeanor, and Alaska and Oregon have already made marijuana use almost legal under some conditions (Single 1989). But in today's emotional anti–drug abuse climate, it is unlikely that even marijuana will be made legal at the federal level, although its regulations might be eased to reflect the feeling that it is less of a threat than other illicit agents.

Think About It . . .

1. What was the significance of the Harrison Act in regulating substances of abuse?
2. Why do you think that interdiction is rarely effective in controlling drug abuse problems?
3. You are a member of Congress and determined to pass legislation that would help reduce the drug abuse problem in the United States. What would be the objectives and principal features of your legislation? (Remember to consider both the criminal and medical aspects of the drug abuse problem.)

KEY TERMS

patent medicines
thalidomide
phocomelia
carcinogenic

mutagenic
teratogenic
switching policy
interdiction

NIDA
"designer" drugs
DEA

S U M M A R Y

1. Developed societies, such as that found in the United States, have evolved to believe that they have the right to protect themselves from the damaging impact of drug use and abuse. Consequently, governments, including that of the United States, have passed laws and implemented programs to prevent social damage from inappropriate drug use. In addition, such societies have come to expect that drugs be effective; in other words, consumers of drugs have the right to get what they pay for.

2. The patent medicines of the late 1800s and early 1900s demonstrated to the public the problems of insufficient regulation of the drug industry. These products were promoted as cures for every kind of illness, although they were rarely effective treatment for any medical problem. In addition, patent medicines were often poorly made and contained dangerous and sometimes addicting ingredients. Because of these dangers, medical organizations, the government, and the public became convinced that greater drug regulation was necessary. From this change in attitude evolved the legislation that formed the foundation of U.S. drug regulation.

3. Both opium and cocaine have long histories of use and abuse in many societies. Both substances were included in the early patent medicines and extolled as miracle drugs that could cure an array of medical disorders. Both drugs were also found to cause severe dependence when used over the long term and ironically were frequently promoted as cures for

drug addiction. After going through a period of fascination with these drugs in the late 1800s, the American public became aware of their addicting properties and pressured the government into becoming more involved in regulating patent medicines and other drug products. These concerns led to the Pure Food and Drug Act of 1906 and ultimately the Harrison Act of 1914. These experiences helped to shape public and government attitudes toward regulation of all types of drugs but most particularly those with abuse properties, such as opium and cocaine.

4. The 1906 Pure Food and Drug Act was not a strong law, but it required manufacturers to include on labels the amounts of alcohol, morphine, opium, cocaine, heroin, or marijuana extract in each product. This was the first real attempt to make consumers aware of the actual contents in the drug products they were consuming and help them make educated decisions about using these substances. This act also prohibited misrepresentation and marked the beginning of involvement by the government in drug manufacturing and promotion.

5. The 1938 Federal Food, Drug, and Cosmetic Act gave the Food and Drug Administration control over drug safety. This act was passed following a deadly tragedy that killed over 40 people who consumed an antibiotic product containing diethylene glycol as a solvent. The act required drugs to be safe (although not necessarily effective) and that all ingredients, quantities, instructions for use, and

warnings be included on the labels. This legislation allowed drug companies to create the prescription and nonprescription classes of drugs and also served as the basis for most subsequent drug legislation that regulates the distribution and use of both prescription and nonprescription drugs.

6. The 1951 Durham-Humphrey Amendment to the Food, Drug, and Cosmetic Act made a formal distinction between prescription and nonprescription drugs. This amendment required all new drugs to be placed, at least temporarily, in the prescription category. In addition, it established the criteria still used today for determining into which category a drug should be classified.

7. The Kefauver-Harris Amendments of 1962 resulted from the thalidomide incident. Although the objectives of these amendments have little to do with issues directly related to the thalidomide problem in pregnancy, this tragedy convinced the public and government that greater control of the drug industry was necessary. This legislation required manufacturers to demonstrate both efficacy and safety of their products and established the testing procedures that would be necessary before the FDA would approve a drug for marketing.

8. All new drugs to be considered for marketing must be first tested on three species of animals. The margin of safety as well as the properties of the drug are determined. Following these initial tests, if the drug still looks positive, the FDA evaluates the compound and, if favorably reviewed, it is given investigational new drug

(IND) status and authorized to be used for human testing. In phase 1, the *initial clinical phase*, the drug is given to small numbers of healthy volunteers in order to determine side effects and the manner in which the body responds to the drug. Phase 2 is called the *clinical pharmacological evaluation stage* and assesses the clinical effectiveness of the drug in a few patients with the disorder the drug is intended to treat. Phase 3 is the *extended clinical evaluation*. The drug is given to a wide range of volunteer patients with the condition that the drug is to treat. During this phase, thousands of patients receive the drug and its effectiveness and safety are determined. After completing these phases of review, the FDA assesses the data and determines if the drug should be allowed to be marketed for use.

9. There is concern that the process used by the FDA to evaluate drugs is not versatile enough to address all of the public's drug requirements. Attempts have been made to deal with special needs or take care of special groups in society. The "fast-track" rule is an amendment to accelerate the evaluation of new drugs with obvious therapeutic action. Another special provision made by the FDA, the Orphan Drug Law, provides provisions and tax incentives to pharmaceutical companies to develop and test drugs to be used in the treatment of rare diseases.

10. In 1972, the FDA initiated a program to assure that all OTC drugs were safe and effective. Special panels were selected to evaluate the safety and effectiveness of over 700 OTC drug ingredients. Each of these ingredients was classified as follows: category I, those found to be safe and effective and approved for OTC use; category II, those either ineffective or unsafe and removed from OTC medicinal products; and category III, those for which there was insufficient information to make a decision.

11. The FDA is committed to making more effective drugs available OTC in response to public demand for greater self-treatment opportunities and reduced health care costs. The *switching policy* allows the FDA to review prescription drugs and evaluate their suitability as OTC products.

12. Three of the principal factors that influence laws on drug abuse are: (a) Should drug abusers be treated as criminals or patients? (b) How can drug users and drug pushers be distinguished? (c) What types of laws and programs are effective deterrents against drug abuse?

13. The Harrison Act of 1914 was a principal piece of legislation in defining drug abuse and preventing its occurrence. Specifically, the Harrison Act attempted to regulate the production, importation, sale, purchase, and distribution of addicting substances, such as opium.

14. There is controversy as to how to best reduce substance abuse. A principal strategy by governmental agencies to achieve this objective is interdiction; the majority of money used to fight drug abuse is spent on trying to stop and confiscate drug supplies. Experience has proven that it is impossible to eliminate access to drugs of abuse and that interdiction is rarely effective. In order to reduce drug abuse, demand for these substances must be diminished. The youth must be a top priority in any substance abuse program. Young people should be educated that drug abuse is undesirable. Treatment should be provided that enables drug addicts to stop their habits with minimal discomfort. Finally, education should be used to change attitudes toward drug abuse and its consequences. Potential drug abusers need to be convinced that substance abuse is personally and socially damaging and unacceptable.

15. Many felonious crimes are committed by drug abusers, which has resulted in unique legal problems. Defenses in drug-related crimes are often based upon individual liberties guaranteed by the Bill of Rights and the Constitution. These defense strategies include (a) freedom of religion; (b) the right to privacy; (c) due process or the double-jeopardy defense; (d) cruel and unusual punishment; and (e) pleas of temporary insanity induced by drug use.

16. A major reason for concern about drug abuse is that society pays a high price for drug addiction and dependence. Drug addiction disrupts and traumatizes individuals, families, communities, and countries. The costs are measured in billions of dollars used for treating drug emergencies, caring for family members, rehabilitating users, enforcing laws, and paying for the effects of drug-related crimes. Other costs of drug abuse, not less significant but more difficult to quantify, include personal suffering, emotional trauma, and permanent damage done to lives.

A P P E N D I X

3-1: THE DEVELOPMENT AND ADMINISTRATION OF DRUG ABUSE LAWS

THE HISTORY OF DRUG ABUSE LAWS

THE HARRISON NARCOTICS ACT

Several of the important drug laws described below were passed in the United States for such ugly and irrelevant reasons as anti-Chinese sentiment. These had a significant impact on the use of opiates and other drugs legally defined as narcotics. In 1909, Congress passed the Smoking Opium Exclusion Act, which forbade the importation of opium for nonmedical use; however, it permitted the use and manufacture of opium for nonmedical use. By 1914, it was still possible to purchase opiates legally in the form of patent medicines or to smoke opium (provided you were a white American) in some states (28 had state laws against smoking opium).

For some time, the United States had been attempting to improve trade relations with China. The Harrison Narcotics Act was passed as much to impress the Chinese government that the United States was willing to regulate opiate use and help China control its serious opium addiction problem as to address the opiate-addiction problem in the United States. Again, *Collier's* and also *Harper's Magazine* had helped to create public pressure for antidrug legislation by publishing articles about the use of "dope," vividly illustrated with pictures and cartoons of opium dens and drug abuse. In 1914, there were an estimated 200,000 addicted Americans; as many as 1 person in 400 was an opium addict.

The Harrison Act was a tax bill, rather than a drug regulatory bill. It controlled dispensing and dealing in narcotics. All dealers in narcotics—such as physicians, veterinarians, and dentists—were required to register with the Bureau of Internal Revenue, which was to enforce the law. The medical groups were upset and felt that their freedom to prescribe had been compromised.

SUPREME COURT DECISIONS ON NARCOTICS

In 1919, the Supreme Court ruled in the Webb case that it was illegal to give drugs to an addict simply to prevent withdrawal. In the Behrman case in 1922, the Court ruled that it was unlawful to use drugs for a cure program.

THE NARCOTIC DRUGS IMPORT AND EXPORT ACT OF 1922

This legislation limited imports to crude opium and coca leaves for medical purposes. Also called the Jones-Miller Act, it doubled penalties for dealing in narcotics to a $5,000 fine and 10 years in prison. It further specified conviction for mere possession of illegal drugs.

THE HEROIN ACT OF 1924

This law made it illegal to manufacture heroin or to process the drug for any purpose other than government-controlled research.

FEDERAL NARCOTICS HOSPITALS

In 1928, over one-third of all prisoners in the United States were serving sentences for drug-related offenses. Nearly half were convicted for use of two drugs, mescaline and marijuana, which were classified as narcotics at the time. In 1929, the federal government authorized the establishment of two narcotics hospitals, or treatment facilities: one at Lexington, Kentucky, which opened in 1935, and the other at Fort Worth, Texas, which opened in 1938. They were closed in the early 1970s, partly because the associated programs had been shown to be ineffectual. Of the patients addicted to narcotics, over 90% were using the same drug within six months after they were released, and only 5% remained drug free over an extended period of time. With the advent of methadone and outpatient treatment, it was decided that the centers were no longer needed.

THE MARIJUANA TAX ACT

As will be described in the chapter on marijuana (Chapter 12), this plant was the center of controversy in the early 1930s because of the increasing use of it for smoking. In 1937, after a strong publicity campaign by papers and magazines, the Marijuana Tax Act was passed, providing controls over marijuana similar to those of the Harrison Act on narcotics. A tax was levied on all transactions connected with marijuana. The law was never very effective, and gradually, use of marijuana became more widespread. In 1969, the Supreme Court ruled the punishment for nonpayment of the tax was unconstitutional because of self-incrimination. (It was comparable to the leading question: When did you stop beating your wife?) Marijuana was still controlled by federal narcotics laws and was legally (although not pharmacologically) considered a narcotic until 1971.

THE OPIUM POPPY CONTROL ACT

In 1942, this law was passed to license the growing of opium poppies in the United States because supplies from abroad had been cut off by World War II. Opium was necessary for use in medicine. There was also a demand for poppy seeds, which were used in baked goods. There is no opium in the seeds, which are sterilized so they are unable to germinate and produce opium poppies.

THE BOGGS AMENDMENT

This legislation was passed in 1951 as an amendment to the Harrison Narcotics Act; it established minimum mandatory sentences for all narcotic and marijuana offenses. This was the beginning of a new program of hardline control of addictive drugs and of marijuana.

THE NARCOTIC DRUG CONTROL ACT OF 1956 In 1955, a report by a sub-committee of the Senate Judiciary Committee stated that drug addiction was responsible for 50% of crime in urban areas and 25% of all reported crimes. It was also reported that Communist China planned to demoralize the people of the United States by encouraging drug addiction. In view of the subcommittee's report, Congress passed an even tougher law, the Narcotic Drug Control Act of 1956. This act imposed very stiff penalties for narcotics and marijuana use. It prohibited suspended sentences, probation, or parole for all narcotic offenses except a first conviction for possession. Under the law, a convicted seller or distributor of illegal narcotics was to be sentenced to prison. In most federal cases, an individual who possessed over a few ounces of narcotics or marijuana was assumed to be a "pusher" and was treated as such. This law also provided for execution of a "pusher" selling heroin to a person under age 18.

THE SINGLE CONVENTION TREATY This agreement replaced and consolidated parts of eight previous international agreements on narcotics. Sponsored by the United Nations World Health Organization, it became effective in 1964, although the U.S. Senate did not ratify participation until 1967 because it thought parts of the treaty were weaker than an earlier 1953 treaty. This treaty regulated the production, manufacture, import, export, trade, distribution, use, and possession of products from the opium poppy, coca plant, and cannabis plant. It did not regulate depressant, stimulant, and hallucinogenic drugs. Signatory parties were required to phase out quasi-medical use of opium smoking (within 15 years of signing), coca leaf chewing, and the nonmedical use of cannabis (within 25 years of signing). In order to legalize marijuana in the United States, it would be necessary to abrogate this treaty, which could be done by an-nouncing the intent to withdraw from it six months in advance.

THE DRUG ABUSE CONTROL AMENDMENTS (DACA) OF 1965 In the early 1960s, the use of illegal drugs rose sharply, and a shift in the types of drugs being used took place. Large numbers of people were experimenting with drugs that altered mood and state of consciousness. Along with these new drugs came a rash of "bad trips," medical complications, and drug emergency cases. Publicity on adverse reactions caused by these new varieties of "street" drugs roused the public to bring pressure on Congress for controls. By the end of 1965, Congress had passed a new series of laws, the Drug Abuse Control Amendments (DACA).

These laws, which excluded narcotics and marijuana, brought three classes of drugs under federal control: (1) amphetamines, (2) barbiturates, and (3) a group of drugs that had a potential for abuse because of their psychedelic or hallucinogenic effects. For the first time, lysergic acid and lysergic acid amide were placed in a controlled-substance group because LSD could easily be made from them. However, the DACA laws did allow the use of peyote by members of the Native American Church in their religious ceremonies.

Some of the key regulations in the 1965 amendments were:

1. No prescription for these drugs could be filled or refilled after six months from date of issue or refilled more than five times.
2. Manufacturers had to keep records of sales for three years.
3. Penalties for violation of the regulations ranged from up to one year and a $1,000 fine for a first offense to up to three years and a $10,000 fine for a second offense. Penalties were much more severe for selling to anyone under 21 years of age.

In 1968, an amendment to the DACA established that the sentence was to be suspended for a first conviction. If there was no conviction in the one-year probationary interlude, the first conviction was to be erased from the record.

THE NARCOTIC ADDICT REHABILITATION ACT (NARA) This act passed in 1966 and gave states the opportunity to put pressure on addicts to go through treatment programs or go to jail. The law allowed reduction of a sentence if progress could be shown in treatment and rehabilitation.

THE COMPREHENSIVE DRUG ABUSE PREVENTION AND CONTROL ACT OF 1970 This act was passed by Congress in 1971. President Nixon had proposed a broader education, research, and rehabilitation program to be covered by new drug laws, but after a great deal of political hassling, Congress made it primarily a law enforcement bill, with some provision for treatment and education. This act did the following:

1. Expanded community mental health centers and the Public Health Service Hospitals for drug abusers and authorized drug education workshops and material for professional workers and public schools
2. Set up a Commission on Marijuana and Drug Abuse to study these drugs for two years and to submit a report and make recommendations
3. Excluded alcohol and tobacco from the group of drugs under study
4. Determined that there would be no mandatory federal sentence for a first offense of illegal possession of any controlled drugs and decreed that the possible sentences could be a year's imprisonment and/or a $5,000 fine or one year's probation (If probation was not violated, the conviction was erased

from the person's record, first offense only)

5. Determined that any person over 18 selling drugs to anyone under 21 should receive twice the first offense penalty and three times the penalty for a second or subsequent offense

6. Decreed that any individual caught selling as part of a group of five or more (considered a drug ring) may receive a penalty of at least 10 years and not more than a $100,000 fine for the first offense; a second offense had a penalty of not less than 20 years and not more than a $200,000 fine or life imprisonment

7. Divided drugs with actual or relative potential for abuse into five categories called *Schedules*:

    a. Schedule I substances have a high potential for abuse and have no currently accepted medical use in treatment in the United States (currently include heroin, LSD, peyote, MDMA "Ecstasy," marijuana).

    b. Schedule II substances have a high potential for abuse, with severe psychic dependence potential. They have some currently accepted medical uses in the United States, but their availability is tightly restricted. Currently, amphetamines, raw opium, morphine, methadone, cocaine, and pentobarbital are in this category.

    c. Schedule III substances have less potential for abuse than those in groups I or II, and they have current medical use in the United States. They have low to moderate potential for physical addiction but a high potential for psychological dependence. Examples of Schedule III drugs include limited quantities of certain opioid drugs, some depressants such as glutethimide (Doriden), pare-

goric, certain barbiturates (except those listed in another schedule), and recently, the anabolic steroids (testosterone type).

    d. Schedule IV drugs have low potential for abuse relative to drugs in Schedule III, have a currently accepted medical use in the United States, and have a limited potential for psychological or physical addiction compared to Schedule III drugs. Phenobarbital, chloral hydrate, diazepam (Valium) and other benzodiazepines and propoxyphene (Darvon) are in this schedule.

    e. Schedule V substances have a low potential for abuse relative to Schedule IV drugs and have a currently accepted medical use in the United States. Abuse of this class of drugs may lead to limited physical or psychological dependence relative to Schedule IV drugs. Lomotil and small amounts of codeine in cough preparations and analgesics are included in Schedule V.

Prescription orders can be written for drugs in Schedules II through IV only by health professionals who are especially licensed by the Drug Enforcement Administration (DEA). Some Schedule V drugs may be distributed without prescription by a pharmacist, subject to state regulation. See Table 3-3 for regulatory requirements for each level of scheduling.

THE METHADONE CONTROL ACT   In 1972, the Food and Drug Administration released methadone to be used in treatment of opiate addiction. It had only been used experimentally up to that time. Because of poor administration and coordination of some early methadone maintenance programs, abuse of the drug on the street had increased. The Methadone Control Act of 1973 put controls on dispensing and

monitoring methadone to help keep the drug off the streets.

THE HEROIN TRAFFICKING ACT OF 1973   This law tightened penalties for traffickers so that bail making could not be continually abused.

THE ALCOHOL AND DRUG ABUSE EDUCATION AMENDMENTS   In 1978, several amendments set up an Office of Alcohol and Drug Abuse Education in the Office of Education. These laws gave more emphasis to drug abuse in rural areas and helped to coordinate federal, state, and local programs in education and prevention training.

In 1980, the Drug Abuse Prevention, Treatment, and Rehabilitation Amendments updated and funded further efforts in prevention education, as well as new programs in rehabilitation. This law was followed by the Drug Offenders Act of 1984 and the Alcohol and Drug Abuse Amendments of 1986, both of which reorganized rehabilitation programs for both alcohol and drugs of abuse. The Controlled Substances Analogue Enforcement Act of 1986 set guidelines to control the growing problem of designer drugs flooding some markets.

THE DRUG ABUSE OFFICE AND TREATMENT ACTS   Starting with the increased publicity on drug use by servicepersons in Vietnam, new policies were formed to try to control the situation and try new treatment techniques that had never been funded before. In 1972, the Drug Abuse Office and Treatment Act was signed; in 1974 and 1978, amendments were made to improve the law. This law has financially supported treatment slots for addicts, including many for methadone clinics and experimental programs (discussed in Chapter 15).

At the same time, the funds given to the Veterans Administration (VA) hospitals were greatly increased to handle addiction in the military. All military branches became more attentive to drug problems and initiated drug infor-

TABLE 3-3   Regulatory requirements

CSA Schedule	Registration	Recordkeeping	Distribution Restrictions	Dispensing Limits
I	Required	Separate	Order forms	Research use only
II	Required	Separate	Order forms	Rx: written; no refills
III	Required	Readily retrievable	Records required	Rx: written or oral; with medical authorization, refills up to 5 in 6 months
IV	Required	Readily retrievable	Records required	Rx: written or oral; with medical authorization, refills up to 5 in 6 months
V	Required	Readily retrievable	Records required	OTC (Rx drugs limited to M.D.'s order)

Source: Drugs of Abuse, p. 9. Courtesy of the Drug Enforcement Administration.
*Permit for some drugs, declaration for others
**Manufacturer reports required for specific drugs

mation and treatment programs. One significant advance was the recognition of alcoholism as a drug problem. The military had largely ignored alcoholism previously, even though it was visible and common. The VA hospitals began to devote more effort to the specific treatment of alcoholism than to problems caused by all other drugs.

THE ANTI–DRUG ABUSE ACT OF 1988
This legislation was a result of the so-called "War on Drugs" declared by President Reagan and supposedly continued by President Bush. The original act authorized a total of $2.7 billion for federal, state, and local drug law enforcement, school-based drug prevention efforts (from preschool through high school), and drug abuse treatment, with a special emphasis on intravenous drug abusers at high risk for AIDS. It supported new research intended to identify the reasons for drug abuse behavior and more effective ways to treat the drug abuser. The specific result of this act was the creation of the Office of National Drug Control Policy, which

was to oversee all federal policies relating to drug abuse (Schuster 1989). In 1990, the total estimated money directed by this office for drug law enforcement and criminal justice was $6.5 billion (Halloway 1991).

The federal laws controlling drug use and attempting to prevent drug abuse are summarized in Table 3-2. It is certain that new laws will be passed in the future with the intent of solving problems caused by drug abuse.

FEDERAL AGENCIES WITH DRUG ABUSE MISSIONS

DRUG ENFORCEMENT ADMINISTRA-TION (DEA)   Because of the unique problems of drug abuse, Congress, in 1930, authorized the establishment of the Bureau of Narcotics in the Treasury Department to administer the relevant laws. This agency remained in the Treasury Department until 1968, when it became part of a new group in the Justice Department, the Bureau of Narcotics and Dangerous Drugs. Harry Anslinger served as head of the bureau

for over 30 years, from its creation until 1962 when he retired. Anslinger was an agent during Prohibition, and later, as head of the bureau, he played an important role in getting marijuana outlawed by the federal government. In 1973, the Bureau of Narcotics and Dangerous Drugs became the Drug Enforcement Administration (DEA). Today, the DEA has the responsibility of infiltrating and breaking up illegal drug traffic in the United States, as well as controlling the use of Scheduled substances.

SPECIAL ACTION OFFICE FOR DRUG ABUSE PREVENTION (SAODAP)   In 1971, President Nixon set up a temporary agency, SAODAP, to initiate short-term and long-term planning of programs and to coordinate drug programs with the states so that proper funding procedures and policies were followed. This office was in the White House and was intended to advise the president. One of the major reasons for establishing such an office was the initial report of a high heroin addiction

Manufacturing		Import/Export		Manufacturer/Distributor Reports to DEA	
Security	Quotas	Narcotic	Nonnarcotic	Narcotic	Nonnarcotic
Vault/safe	Yes	Permit	Permit	Yes	Yes
Vault/safe	Yes	Permit	Permit	Yes	Yes
Secure storage area	No but some drugs limited by Schedule II	Permit	*	Yes	**
Secure storage area	No but some drugs limited by Schedule II	Permit	Declaration	Manufacturer only	**
Secure storage area	No but some drugs limited by Schedule II	Permit to import; declaration to export	Declaration	Manufacturer only	No

rate in returning Vietnam veterans. This program was supposed to fight actively the increase in addiction in the United States. SAODAP was abolished, as planned, with most of its education, research, treatment, and rehabilitation functions going to a new agency, the National Institute on Drug Abuse (NIDA). An expert on the staff of advisors to the president, the domestic policy staff, assumed the duties of advising the president on drug-related matters and drug-abuse programs. The advisor was to keep track of budgets for drug programs and coordinate policy with law enforcement groups. Under the Reagan administration, further changes were proposed. A pattern of federal policy was established; that is, control and management of drug programs in the United States change with each new "crisis."

ALCOHOL, DRUG ABUSE, AND MENTAL HEALTH ADMINISTRATION (ADAMHA)

In 1973, a new agency was formed after Department of Health, Education, and Welfare Secretary Weinberger stripped the alcohol and drug abuse sections from the National Institute of Mental Health (NIMH). This action formed the National Institute of Alcohol Abuse and Alcoholism (NIAAA) and the NIDA (see previous section). NIAAA, NIDA, and NIMH are currently under the agency ADAMHA. This shuffling and redesign was part of federal attempts to bring the post-Vietnam heroin crisis under control and address the perennial problems of alcoholism and dependence on other drugs. The mission of NIAAA and NIDA was and still is to coordinate both clinical and basic research involved directed at drugs of abuse. During fiscal year 1991, these institutes controlled budgets of $259 (NIDA) and $140 (NIAAA) million (FASEB 1990, 4).

STATE REGULATIONS

There have always been questions regarding the relative responsibilities of state versus federal laws and their respective regulatory agencies. In general, the U.S. form of government has allowed local control to take precedence over national control. Because of this historic attitude, states were the first to pass laws to regulate the abuse or misuse of drugs. Federal laws developed later, after the federal government gained greater jurisdiction over the well-being and lives of the citizens and it became apparent that, due to interstate trafficking, national drug abuse problems could not be effectively dealt with on a state-by-state basis. Some early state laws banned the use of smoking opium, regulated the sale of various psychoactive drug substances, and in a few instances, set up treatment programs. However, these early legislative actions made no effort to prevent drug abuse. Drug abuse was controlled to a great extent by social pressure rather than by law. It was considered morally wrong to be an alcoholic or an addict to opium or some other drug.

The drug laws in 1932 varied considerably from state to state, so the National Conference of Commissioners on Uniform State Laws set up the Uniform Narcotic Drug Act (UNDA), which was later adopted by nearly all states. The UNDA provided for the control of possession, use, and distribution of opiates and cocaine. In 1942, marijuana was included as a narcotic.

In 1967, the Food and Drug Administration proposed the Model Drug Abuse Control Act and urged the states to adopt it on a uniform basis. This law extended controls over depressant, stimulant, and hallucinogenic drugs similar to the 1965 federal law. Many states set up laws based on this model.

The federal Controlled Substances Act of 1970 stimulated the National Conference of Commissioners to propose a new Uniform Controlled Substances Act (UCSA). The UCSA permits enactment of a single state law regulating the illicit possession, use, manufacture, and dispensing of controlled psychoactive substances. At this time, most states have enacted the UCSA or modifications of it.

Today, state law enforcement of drug statutes does not always reflect federal regulations, although for the most part, the two statutory levels are harmonious. For example, marijuana in small amounts for personal use is only considered an act of minor misconduct in Alaska or Oregon but is considered a Schedule I substance by federal regulatory agencies (as of this writing). Consequently, as long as this substance is used inside the state boundaries of Alaska or Oregon for personal use only, there is little likelihood of prosecution. However, the more severe federal laws are invoked whenever use of this illicit substance involves interstate issues (such as being transported across state boundaries).

R E F E R E N C E S

Adams, S. H. "The Great American Fraud." Collier's 36, no. 5 (1905): 17–18; no. 10 (1905): 16–18; and no. 16 (1906): 18–20.

Aldrich, M., and R. Barker. "Historical Aspects of Cocaine Use and Abuse." In *Cocaine: Chemical, Biological, Clinical, Social and Treatment Aspects,* edited by S. Mule. Cleveland, OH: CRC Press, 1976.

Austin, G. A. *Perspectives on the History of Psychoactive Substance Use.* NIDA Research Issues, no. 24. Washington, D.C.: Department of Health, Education, and Welfare, 1978.

Booth, R. et al. *A Tale of Three Cities: Risk Taking among Intravenous Drug Users.* Problems of Drug Dependence, NIDA Research Monograph Series, no. 95. Washington, D.C.: Department of Health, Education, and Welfare, 1989.

Brecher, E. M. *Licit and Illicit Drugs.* Boston: Little, Brown, 1972.

Drug Facts and Comparisons. St. Louis: Lippincott, 1991.

F.A.S.E.B. Newsletter, December 1990, p. 4.

Gallup, G., and A. Gallup. *The Gallup Poll: Public Opinion 1988.* Wilmington, DE: Scholarly Resources, 1988.

Gawin, F., D. Allen, and B. Humbleston. *Archives of General Psychiatry* 46 (1989): 322.

Halloway, M. "Rx for Addiction." *Scientific American,* March 1991, 95–103.

Herbst, A., T. Green, and H. Ulfelder. "Primary Carcinoma of the Vagina: An Analysis of 68 Cases." *American Journal of Obstetrics and Gynecology* 106 (1970): 210–218.

Holmstedt, B. "Historical Survey." In *Ethnopharmacological Search for Psychoactive Drugs,* edited by D. H. Efron. Public Health Service Publication, no. 1645. Washington, D.C.: U.S. Government Printing Office, 1967.

Jarvik, M. "The Drug Dilemma: Manipulating the Demand." *Science* 250 (1990): 387–392.

Langston, J. W. "MPTP and Parkinson's Disease." *Trends in Neuroscience* 8 (1985): 79–83.

Morgan, H. W. "The Therapeutic Revolution." In *Drugs in America, A Social History, 1800–1980.* Syracuse, NY: Syracuse University Press, 1981.

NIDA Notes 6 (Spring 1991): 35.

Roney, J. "Marketing a New Drug." *American Druggist,* March 1991: 74.

Schuster, C. *Implication for Research of the 1988 Anti-Drug Abuse Act.* Problems of Drug Dependence, NIDA Research Monograph Series, no. 95. Washington, D.C.: Department of Health, Education, and Welfare, 1989.

Scott, J. M. *The White Poppy: A History of Opium.* New York: Funk & Wagnalls, 1969.

Siegelman, S. "The Coming Wave of Rx-to-OTC Switches." *American Druggist,* August 1990: 37–42.

Single, E. "The Impact of Marijuana Decriminalization: An Update." *Journal of Public Health Policy* 10 (1989): 456–466.

Soine, W. *Contamination of Clandestinely Prepared Drugs with Synthetic By-Products.* Problems of Drug Dependence, NIDA Research Monographs, no. 95. Washington, D.C.: Department of Health, Education, and Welfare, 1989.

Temin, P. *Taking Your Medicine: Drug Regulation in the United States.* Cambridge, MA: Harvard University Press, 1980.

Wallace, I., D. Wallechinsky, and A. Wallace. "Dr. Freud's Magic Nose Powder." *Parade Magazine,* 20 September 1981.

How and Why Drugs Work

CHAPTER OUTLINE

The Intended and Unintended Effects of Drugs / **The Dose-Response Relationship and the Dimensions of Effective Doses**
▪ Lethality and Effectiveness ▪ Potency versus Toxicity ▪ Margin of Safety ▪ The Therapeutic Index / **Drug Interaction** ▪ Additive Effects ▪ Antagonistic (Inhibitory) Effects ▪ Potentiative (Synergistic) Effects ▪ Dealing with Drug Interaction / **Pharmacokinetic Factors That Influence Drug Effects** ▪ Forms and Methods of Taking Drugs ▪ Distribution of Drugs in the Body ▪ Inactivation and Elimination of Drugs from the Body ▪ Physiological Variables That Modify Drug Effects ▪ Pathological Variables That Modify Drug Effects / **Tolerance to Drugs** ▪ The Rebound Effect ▪ Reverse Tolerance (Sensitization) ▪ Cross-Tolerance / **Physical Dependence** ▪ Cross-Dependence ▪ Psychological Factors ▪ The Placebo Effect / **Psychological Dependence** / **Addiction and Abuse: Who Becomes Drug Dependent?**

LEARNING OBJECTIVES

On completing this chapter, you will be able to:

1. Describe some of the common unintended drug effects.
2. Explain why the same dose of a drug may affect individuals differently.
3. Explain the difference between *potency* and *toxicity*.
4. Describe the concepts *margin of safety* and *therapeutic index* for a drug.
5. Identify and give examples of additive, antagonistic, and potentiation (synergistic) drug interactions.
6. Identify the pharmacokinetic factors that can influence the effects caused by drugs.
7. Cite the physiological and pathological factors that influence drug effects.
8. Describe the significance of fat solubility to a drug's distribution in the body.
9. Explain the significance of the blood-brain barrier to psychoactive drugs.
10. Define *threshold dose*, *plateau effect*, and *cumulative effect*.
11. Discuss the role of the liver in drug metabolism and the consequences of this process.
12. Define *biotransformation*.
13. Explain what factors can cause drug tolerance.
14. Describe the relationship among *tolerance*, *withdrawal*, *rebound*, *physical dependence*, and *psychological dependence*.
15. Discuss the significance of placebos in responding to drugs.

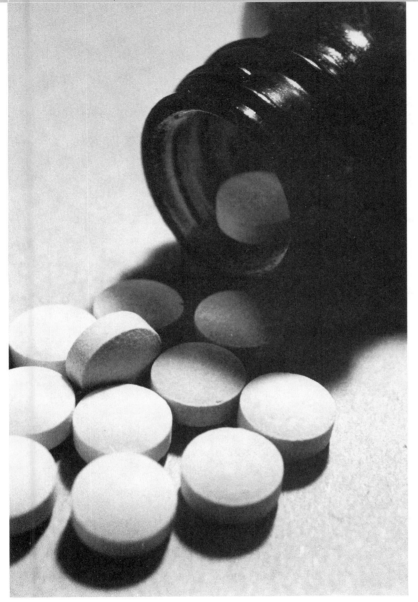

Photo: © Camerique

DID YOU KNOW THAT . . .

- The same dose of a drug does not have the same effect on everyone.
- In high enough doses, almost any drug or substance can be toxic.
- The greater the therapeutic index, the safer the drug.
- Use of some drugs can dramatically enhance the effects of others.
- Computers have become important tools used by pharmacists to track and prevent unwanted drug interactions.
- The form in which a drug is taken can influence the effect it has.
- Many drugs are unable to pass from the blood into the brain.
- Some drugs have a maximum effect, regardless of dose.
- Most drugs cross the placental barrier from the mother to the fetus.
- The liver is the primary organ that metabolizes drugs.
- Physical dependence is characterized by withdrawal effects when use of the drug is stopped.
- Tolerance to one drug can often cause tolerance to other similar drugs; this is called *cross-tolerance*.
- Placebos can have significant effects in relieving symptoms such as pain.
- The body produces endorphins, which have effects like narcotics.
- Psychological dependence on a drug often leads to drug abuse.
- Hereditary factors may predispose some individuals to becoming psychologically dependent on drugs with abuse potential.

It is human nature to believe that somewhere a "perfect pill" exists that will cure us of disease or simply make us feel better. Many misconceptions have arisen because of this belief, leading people to assume that the right pill or right therapy can always be found for any medical problem. All too often, ignorance of drugs and how they work causes unrealistic expectations, which leads to dangerous and even fatal consequences. Given the easy access to high-technology substances that people now have, it is essential that we be well-informed about the many variables that determine the type and intensity of response to each drug we might take. Although it is impossible to predict accurately the effect that a given dose of a drug will have on an individual, certain factors should be considered to help improve the likelihood of a desirable drug response.

In this chapter, we will consider the factors that affect how and why drugs work. We will begin with a review of the general effects of drugs, both intended and unintended. The dose-response relationship will be addressed next, followed by drug interaction. The section on pharmacokinetic factors considers how drugs are introduced, distributed, and eliminated from the body, along with physiological and pathological variables that modify drug effects. The last sections in the chapter consider the concepts of tolerance, physical versus psychological dependence, and addiction.

THE INTENDED AND UNINTENDED EFFECTS OF DRUGS

When physicians prescribe drugs, their objective is usually to cure or relieve symptoms of a disease. However, frequently, drugs cause unintended effects that neither the physician nor the patient bargained for.

The desired responses produced by a drug are called *main effects*, whereas those that are unintended are called *side effects*. The distinction between main and side effects depends on the therapeutic objective. A response that is considered unnecessary or undesirable in one situation may, in fact, be the intended effect in another. For example, antihistamines found in many over-the-counter (OTC) drugs have an intended main effect of relieving allergy symptoms, but they often cause annoying drowsiness as a side effect. However, these same antihistamines are also included in OTC sleep aids, where their sedating action is used with an intended main effect of encouraging sleep in people suffering from insomnia.

Several basic kinds of side effects can result from drug use:

Nausea or vomiting—Almost any drug can cause an upset stomach; in fact, with some medications, such as aspirin, this is a common complaint.

Changes in mental alertness—Some medications can cause sedation and drowsiness (e.g., antihistamines in OTC allergy medications) or nervousness and insomnia (e.g., caffeine in OTC stay-awake products).

Dependence—This phenomenon compels people to continue using a drug because they want to achieve a desired effect or they fear an unpleasant reaction, called **withdrawal**, which occurs when the drug is discontinued. Dependence has been associated with such benign OTC drugs as nasal decongestant sprays and laxatives, as well as more potent drugs such as stimulants (see Chapter 9), narcotics (see Chapter 8), and alcohol (see Chapter 7).

withdrawal
unpleasant effects that occur when use of a drug is stopped

Allergic reactions (hypersensitive reactions or sensitization)—Allergic reactions occur when the body rejects a drug and attempts to destroy and dispose of it. Figure 4-1 shows the sequence of events in *sensitization* when the drug (called the **haptene**) is introduced into the body.

haptene
a chemical that is viewed as foreign by the body and eliminated by an allergic response

Allergic reactions vary considerably but can include:

Skin rashes, swelling, and pain
Hives, itching, and sweating
Angioneurotic edema, an accumulation of fluid in the soft tissue of the face, resulting in swelling of the eyes, cheeks, and lips
Delayed reactions, which occur 7 to 14 days after exposure to the drug and include hives, arthritis, and fever
Damage to internal organs such as the heart and kidneys

This partial list of side effects demonstrates the types of risk involved whenever any drug (prescription, nonprescription, or illicit) is used. Consequently, before taking a drug, whether for therapeutic or recreational use, you should review the potential disadvantages it poses and determine if the benefits justify the risks. For example, it is important to know that morphine is a good drug for relieving severe pain, but it also depresses breathing and retards intestinal activity, causing constipation. Likewise, amphetamines are used to suppress appetite, but they also increase blood pressure and stimulate the heart. Cocaine is a good local anesthetic but can cause tremors or even seizures. The greater the danger of using a drug, the less likely the benefits will warrant its use.

Table 4-1 outlines additional common types of sensitivity reactions.

FIGURE 4-1 The allergenic mechanism, showing how a person becomes sensitized to a foreign substance and how a subsequent immune response occurs if that person is exposed to the same hapten.
Source: T. A. Loomis, *Essentials of Toxicology*, 3rd ed. (Philadelphia: Lea & Febiger, 1978), p. 114. Used with permission of the author and publisher.

Initial Exposure

↓

Hapten (allergenic substance) is introduced and combines with a protein to become an antigen*

↓

The body forms antibodies to bind or isolate the antigens (antibodies are either cellular or humoral proteins) ⟶

↓

The person has now become sensitized

Subsequent Exposure (The Immune Response)

↓

Hapten introduced and combines with a protein to form an antigen

↓

Antibody-antigen reaction occurs

↓

Cell damage due to release of histamines, and so on, causing swelling, fever, tenderness

↓

Shock reaction in severe reactions (anaphylactic shock)

↓

Death may occur

*Some drugs may be antigenic in nature rather than haptens.

TABLE 4-1   Common types of sensitivity reactions

Skin Manifestations	Drugs Involved
Contact dermatitis (skin is itchy, reddened, blistered, and sometimes necrotic)	Mercurials, penicillin, streptomycin, sulfonamides
Urticaria (hives with reddening, swelling)	Penicillin, pollens, salicylates, some foods
Exfoliation (loss of skin with swelling)	Barbiturates, sulfonamides, iodides

Systemic Manifestations	Drugs Involved
Blood abnormalities: 1. Granulocytopenia (depression of granulocyte white cell count)	Arsenicals, gold salts, phenylbutazone
2. Thrombocytopenia (depression of the platelet number)	Arsenicals, quinine, sulfonamides
3. Aplastic anemia (depression of all blood cells)	Chloramphenicol, phenylbutazone, sulfonamides
Anaphylactic shock (flushing, lightheadedness, decrease in blood pressure, airway obstruction)	Iodides, local anesthetics, mercurials, penicillin, pollen extracts, serums, vaccines
Asthma (bronchiolar obstruction)	Pollen extracts, salicylates, serums

Source: T. A. Loomis, *Essentials of Toxicology,* 3rd ed. (Philadelphia: Lea & Febiger, 1978), p. 123. Used with permission of the author and publisher.

THE DOSE-RESPONSE RELATIONSHIP AND THE DIMENSIONS OF EFFECTIVE DOSES

All effects, both desired and unwanted, are related to the amount of drug administered. A small concentration of drug may have one effect, whereas a larger dose may have a greater effect or a different effect entirely. Because there is some correlation between the response to a drug and the concentration of the drug dose, it is possible to calculate *dose-response* curves. Several factors should be considered regarding the correlation between a drug's dose and effects.

Once a dose-response curve for a particular drug has been plotted, it can be used to predict the probable response of an individual to a particular dose of that drug in the future. Like many variables, the dose-response curve follows certain distributive patterns. The dose-response curve of a truly random sample of the population tends to follow the Gaussian, or normal bell-shaped, distribution curve seen in statistics texts. Figure 4-2 shows such a distribution curve, which commonly occurs when calculating a drug response influenced by the size of the dose.

The dose-response curve in Figure 4-2 is based on test results from a large population. If smaller samples are used, the data may not show such an even, symmetrical distribution curve because of individual variability in the population. Thus, Figure 4-2 is for illustrative purposes. If a drug were given to a population, a particular dose of the drug would cause varied responses in that population. In other words, everyone does not respond the same to a given dose of a drug. For example, the same dose of barbiturate might cause sedation in some people but have little effect on others. It is this variability in response that makes it difficult to predict the precise drug effect from a given dose. Consequently, a physician will sometimes give a prescription with the warning that, if any reaction occurs or if the drug does not work, the prescrip-

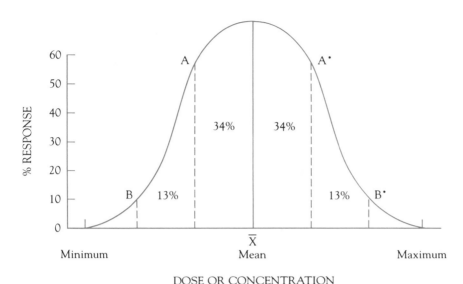

FIGURE 4-2 A theoretical dose-response curve. Gaussian distribution, where X is the mean, or statistical average dose. The area between A and A★ is plus-or-minus one standard deviation around the mean and totals about 68%. The area between B and B★ is plus-or-minus two standard deviations around the mean and totals about 94%. The curve represents the variability of responses in a representative population. *Source:* T. A. Loomis, *Essentials of Toxicology*, 3rd ed. (Philadelphia: Lea & Febiger, 1978), p. 14. Used with permission of the author and publisher.

tion will be changed. Such caution is important because it is very difficult to know precisely how an individual will respond to a drug treatment.

Many factors can modify a response to a drug. One of the most important is **tolerance**, or reduced response over time to the same dosage, an effect that will be examined carefully in a later section. Other factors include different levels of enzymatic activity in the liver (which changes the drug by metabolism), acidity of the urine (which affects rate of drug elimination), ambient temperature, the time of day, and the state of a person's health. It is because of multiple interacting factors such as these that it is difficult to calculate accurately the final drug effect for any given individual.

---

tolerance
changes causing decreased response to a set dose of a drug

One variable factor, not usually considered by the average drug consumer, is the time of day a drug is administered. The body experiences definite rhythmic changes, some of which are understood and some of which are not. For instance, most people cannot metabolize barbiturates and alcohol as rapidly in the early morning as they can in the late afternoon. If you ask someone whether a drink would have more effect in the morning or evening, he or she may intuitively understand that there is a difference but not know the reason why. The "one for the road" taken late at night will produce a longer-lasting rise in blood-alcohol level because of a decreased rate of metabolism than an identical drink taken earlier in the evening.

LETHALITY AND EFFECTIVENESS

Even though the ways in which individuals respond to drugs vary, it is important to compare, as accurately as possible, therapeutic and toxic doses. For new drugs being considered for marketing, this is done by extensive testing on three species of animals before humans are tested. The animal testing is done by administering a wide range of drug dosages and determining the lethal dose. From the results, calculations of the lethal dose (LD) for 50% of the test animals are made.

This dose, also called the *LD-50*, is found by plotting the dose against the percentage of lethality.

Such information is important in assessing the safety, or risk, of new drugs and provides important dosage information that can be used for human testing. Figure 4-3 is a typical graph showing the lethality curves of two drugs given to laboratory animals.

In subsequent animal studies, the pharmacologist will lower the dose while evaluating the therapeutic (intended) response to the drug. Using this approach, the therapeutically effective dose (ED) in 50% of the animals, the *ED-50*, can be determined and compared to the LD-50. This comparison helps to determine the margin of drug safety.

The LD and the ED of any drug may range from 1% (LD-1 or ED-1) to 100%. For alcohol, it is estimated that the LD-1 would be at 0.35% to 0.38% blood alcohol, and the LD-50 would be about 0.50% blood alcohol. These figures mean that, in a test population of 100 persons consuming alcohol until the level in their blood reaches about 0.35%, one of them would die from the effects of the alcohol; at 0.50%, about 50 would die. In most states, 0.10% is the legal intoxication level.

POTENCY VERSUS TOXICITY

Potency relates to the quantity of a drug necessary to cause an effect. The smaller the dose required to achieve a drug action, the greater the drug potency. For example, in Figure 4-3, drug 2 is less potent than drug 1 when considering death as the measured effect. In other words, it takes more of drug 2 to get the same lethal response as from drug

FIGURE 4-3   Dose-response calculations to find the lethal dosages. Note that the lethal dose for 50% (LD-50) is found by extending lines from the 50% lethal point to the dose of the drug. This graph makes it possible to compare the lethality of drugs. In this example, note that drug 1 has an overall lethality greater than drug 2, and the LD-50 of drug 2 is at a much higher dose range. *Source:* T. A. Loomis, *Essentials of Toxicology*, 3rd ed. (Philadelphia: Lea & Febiger, 1978), p. 16. Used with permission of the author and publisher.

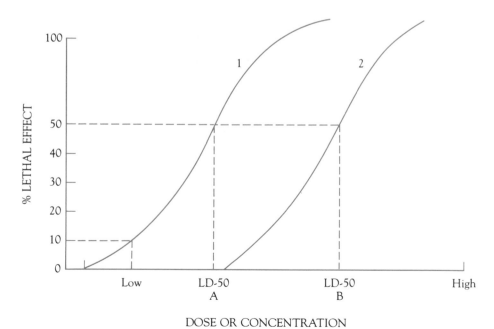

1; some drugs are much more powerful than others, so they must be taken in smaller doses. From the figure, it can be seen that drug 1 reaches the LD-50 with smaller amounts than drug 2. Table 4-2 shows a comparison of LD-50s for single doses of several drugs and chemicals.

potency
the amount of drug necessary to cause an effect

Toxicity refers to the capacity of a drug to upset or even destroy normal body functions. Toxic compounds are often called *poisons*, although almost any compound—including sugar, table salt, aspirin, and vitamin A—can be toxic at sufficiently high doses. If a foreign chemical is introduced into the body's environment, it may disrupt chemical balances. In many instances, the body is able to compensate for this disruption, perhaps by induction of liver enzymes and increased metabolism of the chemical, and little effect is noted. In other cases, the delicate balance is altered and the

person becomes sick or even dies. If the homeostatic balance is already under stress from disease, the introduction of a new chemical may have a much more serious effect than in a healthy person who can adjust to the toxicity of the drug.

toxicity
the capacity of a drug to do damage or cause adverse effects in the body

A drug with high potency often reaches toxic levels at low doses, so the amount given must be carefully measured and monitored; if caution is not taken, serious damage to the body or death can occur (see adjacent box). Potency depends on many factors, such as absorption of the drug, its distribution in the body, individual metabolism, the form of excretion, the rate of elimination, and its activity at the site of action. As mentioned,

TABLE 4-2 Comparison of the LD-50s in rats and mice for various substances

Agent	LD-50 in mg/kg body weight
Ethanol	10,000
Sodium chloride	4,000
Ferrous sulfate	1,500
Morphine	900
Phenobarbital	150
DDT	100
Strychnine	2
Nicotine	1
Tubocurarine	0.5
Botulinus toxin	0.00001

Source: T. A. Loomis, *Essentials of Toxicology*, 3rd ed. (Philadelphia: Lea & Febiger, 1978), p. 18. Used with permission of the author and publisher.

For You to Consider...

Fatal Consequences of Potent Synthetic Narcotics

The issues of potency and toxicity are particularly important when dealing with new drugs of abuse that are being created in clandestine laboratories and then sold on the "streets." Some of these new pharmacological creations are referred to as *"designer" drugs* and are unexpectedly potent. For example, derivatives of the commonly used narcotic pain reliever fentanyl (see Chapter 8) have been reported to be many times more potent than heroin. One such drug, alpha methylfentanyl, has been sold on the "streets" since 1982 as an illicit synthetic heroin. This drug actually has a potency 3,000 to 5,000 times greater than that of heroin, and if mistakenly taken as heroin by a narcotic addict, a lethal dose can easily be administered (Henderson 1988). From 1985 to 1990, such mistakes resulted in scores of fatal narcotic overdoses in the United States.

potency is determined by the amount of drug necessary to cause a given response (which may or may not be a toxic effect). If a drug such as a gas, like ether, is absorbed rapidly from the lungs, it has a rapid onset of action but may not stay in the body long. Injection of the depressant sodium pentothal (a barbiturate) into the blood causes a rapid, potent, sedating effect. However, its action is short because it is metabolized and eliminated quickly. Some drugs stay bound to lipids (fats) or to proteins in the body for long periods of time and are slowly released; they are slow acting but long lasting. In contrast, when water-soluble drugs go through the kidney filtration system, they are removed rapidly. Other drugs break down very slowly and persist in the body; consequently, the dosage given must be low and monitored carefully.

All of these factors can influence potency. A simple classification system is sometimes used to compare the toxic potency of drugs. A drug is:

Extremely toxic if the LD-50 is less than 1 milligram per kilogram of body weight (1 mg/kg)
Highly toxic if the LD-50 is between 1 and 50 mg/kg

Moderately toxic if the LD-50 is between 50 and 100 mg/kg
Slightly toxic if the LD-50 is between 0.5 and 5 grams/kg (g/kg)

Toxicity is not always related to dosage in a simple linear relationship. (Refer to drugs 1 and 2 in Figure 4-4.) A small dose might be potent and lethal while the potency increases at a slow rate (see drug 2 in Figure 4-4); another drug may be less potent but increase in toxicity or potency at a rapid rate with the dose given (see drug 1 in Figure 4-4). Note that, although the LD-50 of drug 2 is greater than that of drug 1, the reverse is true of their LD-5s.

MARGIN OF SAFETY

When developing new therapeutic drugs, it is useful to plot how safe a drug is at various doses. It is important to know how much of a drug can be given without markedly increasing the lethality or the toxicity. The comparison of dosage and lethality is called the **margin of safety**.

The margin of safety is determined by plotting the magnitude of a range of doses, from ineffective

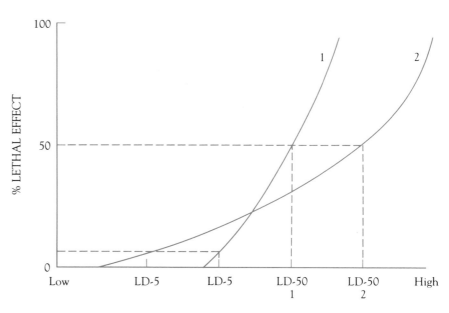

FIGURE 4-4 Dose-response curves for drugs 1 and 2. Note that drug 2 is more potent at a lower dose than drug 1 but less potent at higher doses. *Source:* T. A. Loomis, *Essentials of Toxicology,* 3rd ed. (Philadelphia: Lea & Febiger, 1978), p. 19. Used with permission of the author and publisher.

margin of safety
the range in dose between the amount of drug necessary to cause a therapeutic effect and a toxic effect

therapeutic index
the toxic dose divided by the therapeutic dose; used to calculate margin of safety

to lethal. Figure 4-5 shows a typical plot of drug toxicities. From such a plot, it is easy to compare the margin of safety for each drug. Notice that drug 3 (line has a shallow slope) has a greater margin of safety than the others and that drug 1 (line has a steep slope) has a low margin of safety. It would be more difficult to manage treatment with drug 1 because there is a narrow range in which a dosage can be given without being toxic. Lithium carbonate is an example of this type of drug: A dose that is slightly too low is ineffective in the treatment of manic disorders; however, the effective dose is close to being toxic. The margin of safety is always an important consideration when selecting a drug for treatment.

Pharmacologists have developed the **therapeutic index** as a simple technique to calculate a drug's margin of safety. To find the index, divide the LD-50 dose by the ED-50 dose:

$$\frac{\text{LD-50 dose}}{\text{ED-50 dose}}$$

Figure 4-6 shows how to calculate a therapeutic index and then interpret the safety of a drug from such calculations. First, the drug is tested for LD-50 and ED-50. In this example, the values for LD-50 and ED-50 are 100 and 10 mg, respectively; thus, 100/10 produces a therapeutic index of 10. The higher the therapeutic index, the more desirable the drug because it has a greater margin of safety. Notice that, in Figure 4-6, there is still a lethal effect at the higher ED range. ED-100 may have an LD-5 effect. Normally, one would not use a drug with this level of toxicity or lethality.

There is no such thing as the perfect drug that goes right to the target, has no toxicity, produces no side effects, and can be removed or neutralized when not needed. Unfortunately, most effective drugs are potentially dangerous if the doses are high enough. Pharmacologists refer to a perfect drug as a "magic bullet"; so far, we have no "magic bullets." Even relatively safe drugs available over the counter can cause problems for some prospective users. The possibility that adverse effects will occur should always be considered before using any drug.

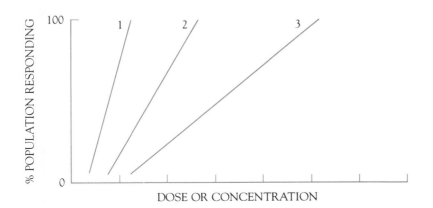

FIGURE 4-5 Dose-response curves for three drugs comparing margin of safety. Note that drug 3 has a greater margin of safety than drug 2 or 1. *Source:* T. A. Loomis, *Essentials of Toxicology*, 3rd ed. (Philadelphia: Lea & Febiger, 1978), p. 20. Used with permission of the author and publisher.

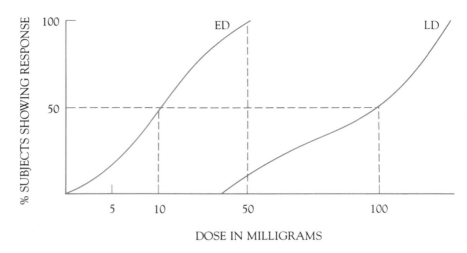

ED = Dose to cause given response   LD = Lethal dose, same compound

FIGURE 4-6 Calculating the therapeutic index (LD-50/ED-50). Note that the ED is the effective dose and the LD is the lethal dose for 50% of the subjects. The therapeutic index is 10 (100/10 = 10). *Source:* T. A. Loomis, *Essentials of Toxicology*, 3rd ed. (Philadelphia: Lea & Febiger, 1978), p. 22. Used with permission of the author and publisher.

DRUG INTERACTION

An important factor that can influence a person's response to a drug is the presence of another drug. Many people, particularly the elderly, consume several drugs at a time without considering the potential consequences. A typical example of multiple drug use is in treatment of the common cold. Because of the many cold-related symptoms, the sufferer may consume an assortment of pain relievers, antihistamines, decongestants, and anticough medications.

Multiple drug use can create a serious medical problem because many drugs influence the actions of other drugs. Even physicians may be baffled by unusual effects when multiple drugs are consumed. Complications can arise that are dangerous, even fatal. The interacting substance may be another drug or it may be some substance in the diet or in the environment, such as a pesticide. Drug interaction is an area where much more research and public education is greatly needed.

Depending on the effect on the body, drug interaction may be categorized into three types:

additive, antagonistic (inhibitory), and *potentiative (synergistic).*

ADDITIVE EFFECTS

Additive interactions are the combined effects of drugs taken concurrently. An example of an additive interaction results from using aspirin and acetaminophen (the active ingredient in Tylenol) at the same time. The pain relief provided is equal to the sum of the two analgesics, which could be achieved by a comparable dose of either drug alone. Thus, if a 300 mg tablet of Bayer aspirin were taken with a 300 mg tablet of Tylenol, the relief would be the same as if two tablets of either Bayer or Tylenol were taken instead.

ANTAGONISTIC (INHIBITORY) EFFECTS

An antagonistic drug effect occurs when one drug cancels or blocks the effect of another. For example, if a person takes antihistamines to reduce nasal congestion, he or she may be able to antagonize some of the drowsiness often caused by these drugs by using a central nervous system (CNS) stimulant like caffeine.

Drug antagonism can be dangerous if not properly monitored. For example, a man was hospitalized for a heart attack. He immediately received barbiturates to calm him down and to induce sleep. In addition, he received an anticoagulant to prevent blood clots that could cause another heart attack, and his blood-clotting time was carefully measured as the dosage of anticoagulant was raised to an effective level. The dose of anticoagulant was larger than usual because the barbiturate caused the enzymes that remove the anticoagulant to metabolize more effectively. When the man returned home, he decided he did not need the barbiturates, and he stopped taking them. Without the inhibiting effect of the barbiturates on the metabolizing enzyme, the dosage of anticoagulant became too high, and the man suffered severe internal bleeding because clots couldn't form properly in response to bruising or tissue trauma.

Another example of an antagonistic interaction is taking tetracycline, an antibiotic, along with milk, antacids, or even in combination with another antibiotic, penicillin. Each of these substances inhibits the action of tetracycline so that the infection being treated with tetracycline is not controlled. Most antagonistic drug interactions are avoidable if physician and patient are well informed.

POTENTIATIVE (SYNERGISTIC) EFFECTS

The third type of drug interaction is known as potentiation, or **synergism**. Potentiation occurs when the effect of a drug is enhanced due to the presence of another drug or substance. This other substance may, in turn, stimulate or inhibit specific enzymes or cause the formation of metabolites that are more potent than the original drug. A common example is the combination of alcohol and Valium. It has been estimated that as many as 3,000 people die each year from mixing alcohol with CNS depressants such as Valium. Alcohol, like barbiturates, is a CNS depressant. When depressants are taken together, CNS functions be-

come impaired and the person becomes groggy. A person in this state may forget he or she has taken the pills and repeat the dose. The combination of these two depressants (or other depressants, such as antihistamines) can depress the CNS to the point where vital functions such as breathing and heartbeat are severely impaired.

synergism
the ability of one drug to enhance the effect of another; potentiation

Although the mechanisms of interaction among CNS depressants are not entirely clear, it is likely that these drugs enhance each others' direct effects on inhibitory chemical messengers in the brain (see Chapter 5). In addition, interference by alcohol with liver-metabolizing enzymes also contributes to the potentiation that occurs between alcohol and some depressants, such as barbiturates (Jaffe 1990).

In one example of potentiation, a housewife living in suburbia awoke with a cold, so she took aspirin and an antihistamine. In order to face coping with young children and the new day, she took a "nerve pill" (sedative); she also took her oral contraceptive and a diet pill. Then she drove her husband to the railroad station, and on the way home, she wrapped her car around a tree. She had been exposed to a combination of drugs that synergistically interacted to depress her central nervous system and cause unconsciousness.

Although drug effects and interactions are not very well understood, it is important to be aware of them. Increasing amounts of evidence indicate that many of the drugs and substances we deliberately consume will interact and produce unexpected and sometimes dangerous effects (see Table 4-3). It is alarming to know that many of the foods we eat and some chemical pollutants also interfere with and modify drug actions. Pesticides, traces of hormones in meat and poultry, traces of metals in fish, nitrites and nitrates from fertilizers, and a wide range of chemicals—some of which are used

TABLE 4-3 Common drug interactions

Substance	Combined with	Interaction Produced
Drug		
Sedatives		
Valium, Librium	Alcohol, barbiturates	Increases effects of both
	Antipsychotic agents	Increases effects of both
Tranquilizers		
Thorazine, Mellaril	Alcohol, barbiturates	Oversedation
	Antihistamine	Increases effects of both
	MAO inhibitors (antidepressants)	Interferes with antidepression
Antibiotics		
tetracycline	Penicillin, milk, dairy products, antacids	Reduces activity
Analgesics		
aspirin	Anticoagulants	Increases blood thinning
Demerol	CNS depressants	Increases sedation
Oral contraceptives	Arthritis medication	May increase metabolism
	Barbiturates, tranquilizers	Lessens hormonal effect
Foods		
Milk and dairy products	Antibiotics like tetracycline	Prevents absorption
Aged cheese, beer, wine, sardines	MAO inhibitors (antidepressants)	Hypertension, stimulation of heart
Soybeans, cabbage, turnips, carrots	Thyroid medication	Blocks drug action
Licorice (large amounts)	Diuretics (Diuril)	Excretion of potassium; may cause heart arrhythmia

Source: Based on Graedon 1976; Martin 1971.
Note: See Appendix C for additional examples of drug interactions.

as food additives—have been shown, under certain conditions, to interact with some drugs.

DEALING WITH DRUG INTERACTION

As the medical community has become aware of the frequent complications arising from multiple drug use, efforts have been made to reduce the incidence as well as the severity of the problem. It is essential that the public be educated about interactions most likely to occur with drugs that are either prescribed or self-administered (e.g., OTC drugs). People need to be aware that OTC drugs are as likely to cause interaction problems as prescription drugs; consequently, drug combinations should be used with caution. If there is

any question concerning the possibility of drug interaction, people should talk to their physicians, pharmacists, or other health care providers. Also, if a patient is being effectively treated by a drug for a medical problem and the drug is suddenly no longer effective or the effects become exaggerated, the possibility of interference by another drug being jointly consumed should be considered.

Computers now play a major role in preventing severe drug interaction. As patients have prescriptions filled, pharmacists enter the type and quantity of each drug being prescribed into the computer under the patient's name. Often, all of the computers associated with the pharmacies in a city or region are networked. Consequently, even if the patient has prescriptions from other physicians that are filled at different pharmacies, potential interaction problems, which could occur with all the drugs the patient has used, can be evaluated via the computer network. Such computer systems have been very effective in identifying possible dangers and preventing interaction problems.

Drug interaction is a major problem in drug-abusing populations, as well. Most abusers are multiple drug *(polydrug)* users with little concern for the dangerous interactions that could occur. It is common for drug abusers to combine multiple CNS depressants to enhance their effects or a depressant with a stimulant to titrate a CNS effect (i.e., determine the smallest amount that can be taken to achieve the desired "high") or to experiment with a combination of stimulants, depressants, and hallucinogens just to see what happens. The effects of such haphazard drug administration are impossible to predict, difficult to treat in emergency situations, and all too frequently fatal.

T h i n k   A b o u t   I t . . .

1. What is the value of comparing drugs and their effects by describing them in terms of lethality, potency, safety margin, and therapeutic index?
2. If your physician or pharmacist is trying to determine the dosage of an antibiotic you will need to fight a kidney infection, what kinds of factors should be considered?
3. You have been taking a CNS depressant to help get you to sleep. The drug worked well for a week but was no longer effective after you caught a cold and started taking an OTC decongestant. What might explain why the decongestant interfered with the effects of the sleep aid?

PHARMACOKINETIC FACTORS THAT INFLUENCE DRUG EFFECTS

It is not easy to predict how any given individual will respond to drug use. Hence, the following major factors should be considered when anticipating drug administration. In determining how

drugs affect the body, pharmacologists generally must answer five questions:

1. How does the drug enter the body? (administration)
2. How does the drug move from the site of administration into the body's system? (absorption)
3. How is the drug distributed to various areas in the body? (distribution)
4. How and where does the drug produce its effects? (action)
5. How is the drug inactivated, metabolized, and/or excreted from the body? (biotransformation and elimination)

These issues relate to the **pharmacokinetics** of a drug and are important considerations when predicting the way the body will respond to it.

---

pharmacokinetics
the study of factors that influence the distribution and concentration of drugs in the body

---

FORMS AND METHODS OF TAKING DRUGS

Drugs come in many forms. The form in which a drug is administered may influence the rate of passage into the bloodstream from the site of administration, which will influence efficacy. The ways that drugs may be compounded and introduced onto or into the body are summarized in Table 4-4.

The means of introducing the drug to the body will also affect how quickly the drug enters the bloodstream and is distributed to the site of action, as well as how much will ultimately reach its target and exert an effect. The principal forms of drug administration include oral ingestion, suppository, inhalation, injection, topical application, and implantation.

ORAL INGESTION   One of the most common and convenient ways of taking a drug is orally. (This is called **enteral** administration; all other means

TABLE 4-4 Drug forms

Category	Types	Description
Solutions	Waters	Volatile oils in water
	Syrups	Sugar + water + flavoring
	Elixirs	Sugar + water + flavoring + alcohol
Suspensions	Emulsions	Fat globules in water
	Magma	Finely ground particles in water
Topicals	Liniments	Drug mixtures in oil, water, or alcohol
	Lotions	Mild liquid preparations
	Ointments	Fatty or oily preparations
Solids	Powders	Fine particles
	Tablets	Compressed powders
	Pills	Powders held together by honey or candy
	Capsules	Drugs in gelatin containers
	—enteric coated	—Protect capsule in stomach
	—sustained release	—Released over a period of time
	—suppositories	—Inserted into anus or vagina

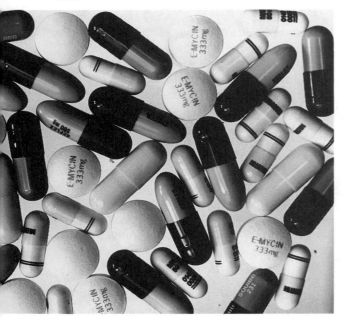

Many OTC decongestants contain drugs that stimulate the cardiovascular system. The FDA requires that statements of caution be included on the labels of such products to warn people with cardiovascular disease of potential problems. *Photo:* © Antman/The Image Works.

are called **parenteral** administration.) This type of administration usually introduces the drug into the body by way of the stomach or intestines.

enteral
refers to drugs taken orally

parenteral
refers to drugs taken by other than oral means

Following oral administration, it is difficult to control the amount of drug that reaches the site of action for three reasons:

1. The drug must enter the bloodstream after passing through the stomach or intestines without being destroyed or changed to an inactive form. Once the drug is in the bloodstream, it must be diffused to the target area and remain there in sufficient concentration to have an effect.
2. Materials in the gut, such as food, may interfere with the passage of some drugs through the gut lining and thus prevent therapeutic action. For example, the antibiotic tetracycline binds to the calcium in

dairy foods; consequently, milk should be avoided prior to taking this drug.

3. The liver might metabolize orally ingested drugs too rapidly, before they are able to have an effect. The liver is the major detoxifying organ in the body, which means it removes chemicals and toxins from the blood and usually changes them into an inactive form that is easy for the body to excrete. This function is essential to survival, but it creates a problem for the pharmacologist developing effective drugs. It is especially problematic in the case of oral administration because the substances absorbed from the digestive tract usually go to the liver before being distributed to the general circulation and their site of action.

SUPPOSITORIES   Another method of administering drugs is as insertion into the body via a suppository. This form of drug, depending on its purpose, is placed either in the rectum or the vagina, from which it is gradually released. Suppositories usually treat localized problems, such as vaginal infections or hemorrhoids; however, they also can be used to administer a drug to the whole body, for example, in the treatment of vomiting. Suppositories are somewhat unpredictable (not to mention uncomfortable), as the absorption of most drugs into the body from the insertion sites is erratic.

INHALATION   Some drugs are administered by inhalation. The lungs have large beds of capillaries, so chemicals capable of crossing membranes can enter the blood quite readily. Ether, chloroform, and nitrous oxide anesthetics are examples of drugs that are therapeutically administered by inhalation. Nicotine from tobacco smoke and even cocaine are drugs of abuse that can be inhaled as smoke. One serious problem with inhalation is the potential for irritation to the mucous membrane lining of the lungs; another is that the drug may have to be continually inhaled to maintain the desired concentration.

INJECTION   Some drugs are given by injection: intravenously (IV), intramuscularly (IM), or sub-

cutaneously (SC). A major advantage of administering drugs by IV is the speed of action; the dosage is delivered rapidly and directly, and often less drug is needed because it reaches the site of action quickly. This method can be very dangerous if the dosage is calculated incorrectly. Additionally, impurities in injected materials may irritate the vein; this is a particular problem in the drug-abusing population, where needle sharing frequently occurs. The injection itself injures the vein by leaving a tiny point of scar tissue where the vein is punctured. If repeated injections are administered into the same site, the elasticity of the vein is gradually reduced, causing the vessel to collapse.

Intramuscular injection can damage the muscle directly if the drug preparation irritates the tissue or indirectly if the nerve controlling the muscle is damaged. If the nerve is destroyed, the muscle will degenerate (atrophy). A subcutaneous injection may kill the skin at the point of injection if a particularly irritating drug is administered. Another danger of drug injections occurs when contaminated needles are shared by drug users. This has become a serious problem in the spread of dangerous infectious diseases such as AIDS (acquired immune deficiency syndrome) and hepatitis.

TOPICAL APPLICATION   Those drugs that readily pass through surface tissue such as the skin, the lining of the nose, and the mouth can be applied topically for systemic (whole-body) effects. Although most drugs do not appreciably diffuse across these tissue barriers into the circulation, there are notable exceptions. For example, an antimotion sickness patch (Transderm Scop) can be placed on the skin behind the ear; the drug passes through the skin and enters the body to prevent motion-related nausea and vomiting. This product has made it possible for many people to enjoy deep-sea fishing while being tossed about on a rough ocean. Another example of a topical drug is the controversial substance (i.e., not FDA approved) DMSO (dimethylsulfoxide), which often is used by athletes or sometimes trainers to treat inflammation of athletic injuries. After applying DMSO to the skin at the site of an injury, the drug quickly passes through the skin into the circulation and within a few minutes is secreted into the saliva, causing a distinctive taste and smell of garlic.

IMPLANTATION   Administrating drugs orally, with suppositories, by inhalation, or via injection is usually satisfactory; however, the concentration of the drug increases rapidly and then declines in the blood, ranging between too much and too little, neither of which is effective. Implantable drug-delivery devices are being used to provide a more constant, steady release of a variety of drugs. With such devices, a person is exposed to lower total doses of drugs and does not have to be concerned about when to take the drug.

An example of an implantable drug delivery system is the subdermal hormonal implant Norplant, a contraceptive made available in the United States in 1990. This contraceptive consists of six silastic capsules, which are placed beneath the skin under the arm. Norplant slowly and consistently releases a progestin-type hormone (levonorgestrel), which reliably prevents pregnancy in more than 99% of the users. The effectiveness of this product continues for approximately five years (*Drug Facts and Comparisons* 1991).

Another type of implantable device, the Ommaya reservoir, is used to treat certain types of brain cancer and infection. A small container is inserted under the skin of the scalp to deliver drugs to the cerebrospinal fluid. The drug reservoir can be refilled with a hypodermic syringe.

A different type of pump has been implanted in the chest wall to deliver heparin, an anticlotting drug, to the bloodstreams of patients with severe clotting problems. Before the development of this pump, people had to be hospitalized when clotting occurred; with the pump, they need to return to the hospital only at four- to eight-week intervals to replenish the pump's supply of heparin (Blackshear 1979).

DISTRIBUTION OF DRUGS IN THE BODY

Following administration (regardless of the mode), most drugs are distributed throughout the body in the blood. The circulatory system consists of many miles of arteries, veins, and capillaries and includes five to six liters of blood. Once a drug enters the bloodstream, by passing across thin capillary walls, it is rapidly diluted and carried to organs and other body structures. It requires approximately one minute for the blood and consequently the drugs that are in it to circulate completely throughout the body.

Another factor affecting the distribution of drugs is their tendency to bind to protein within the blood. Protein binding in the blood hinders the distribution of many drugs because when a drug is bound to these proteins, it can become inactive and will regain its activity only when freed from the protein. The drug-protein complex is usually a large molecule that cannot pass through the walls of the blood vessels; thus, the drug is unable to leave the blood to reach its site of action.

How easily a drug enters the bloodstream depends on its fat solubility. Drugs that are fat soluble (i.e., able to dissolve in oily or fatty solutions) easily pass through the walls of the blood vessels and are rapidly distributed in the blood. The property of fat solubility also determines if drugs can enter cells through their outer fatty membranes or can enter tissues and organs that have a high fatty content, such as the brain. Drugs like pentothal, tetrahydrocannabinol (THC) from marijuana, and methamphetamine are highly fat soluble, so they are distributed rapidly through the body, enter the brain quickly, and act immediately.

Membranes influence drug distribution and consequently drug activity in several ways. Each cell membrane is made up of a double layer of *phospholipid*. These lipid molecules are arranged so that the water-soluble parts point outward toward the exterior and the interior of the cell, and the fat-soluble parts point toward each other. Clusters of protein molecules of various sizes float in the lipid part of the cell membrane. These proteins include *receptors* (explained in Chapter 5) and *pores*. The pores, or transport channels, in the membrane control the entry and exit of molecules into the cells, thus regulating their concentration. Most pores are rather selective; they allow only water and some small molecules or ions through but not drugs. If molecules, such as drugs, are lipid soluble, they pass through the membranes and enter the cell readily. Others with ionic charges may or may not be able to pass, depending on their chemical structures and the type of cell. Because of these features, membranes have both active and passive mechanisms that affect the passage of drugs and other substances.

In summary, the capillaries play a vital role in the movement of drugs through the body. All drugs ultimately circulate in the bloodstream and pass through the capillaries. It is from the capillaries that most drugs migrate to come in contact with organs, tissue membranes, and their ultimate target site. The lipid solubility, protein binding, and ionic state of the drug influence the rate of migration and the concentration of the drug at the site where it exerts its pharmacological action. Figure 4-7 shows the sequence of steps most drugs go through to reach their target areas.

BIOLOGICAL BARRIERS TO DRUGS For the most part, drugs are distributed throughout the body after administration; however, biological barriers can prevent movement of some drugs into organs or across tissues. These barriers may interfere with

drug activity and limit the therapeutic usefulness of a drug if they prevent it from reaching its site of action. Such barriers may also be useful by preventing entry of a drug into a body structure where it can cause problems. Two of the principal biological barriers in the body are the **blood-brain barrier** and the placental barrier.

blood-brain barrier
selective filtering between the cerebral blood vessels and the brain

Because of its continual state of high activity, the brain requires about 20% of the body's blood in order to satisfy its nutrient and oxygen needs. The blood is carried to the nerve cells in a vast network of thin-walled capillaries. Fat-soluble molecules are most likely to pass readily through the capillaries into brain tissue. Many water-soluble

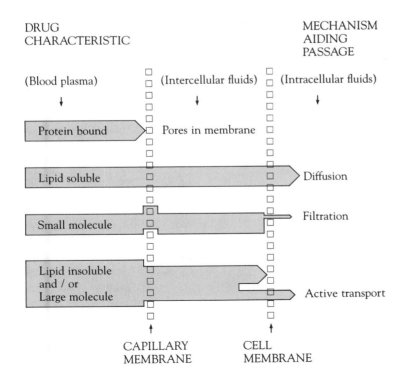

DRUG
CHARACTERISTIC

MECHANISM
AIDING
PASSAGE

(Blood plasma)   (Intercellular fluids)   (Intracellular fluids)

Protein bound   Pores in membrane

Lipid soluble   Diffusion

Small molecule   Filtration

Lipid insoluble and / or Large molecule   Active transport

CAPILLARY
MEMBRANE

CELL
MEMBRANE

FIGURE 4-7 Drug movement across membranes is influenced by protein binding, lipid solubility, size and charge of molecule, presence of active transport systems, diffusion, and other factors. Almost all drugs, with the exception of those that are protein bound, can pass through the capillary wall into the interstitial fluids. Diffusion, filtration, or active transport will help other drug types move through the cell membrane into the intracellular fluid.

molecules, such as glucose, cannot pass through the fatty capillary wall; these molecules require special active transport systems to carry them from the blood to the brain tissue. However, most proteins, ionized molecules, water-soluble substances, and drugs are not affected by these selective transport systems and are able to pass only slowly or not at all from the blood through the capillaries into the brain.

This selective filtering is called the *blood-brain barrier* and apparently provides the brain with a protective mechanism to exclude many substances. But it creates problems when it is desirable to treat the brain with certain drugs. Penicillin, for example, is lipid insoluble (i.e., soluble in water, not fat solutions), so it is not effective in the treatment of infections of brain tissue; consequently, other antibiotics, which are more fat soluble, are used for treating infections of the brain. It is possible to bypass the blood-brain barrier by injecting drugs directly into the cerebrospinal fluid, but this procedure is difficult and dangerous and is not used for routine drug administration.

A second biological barrier, the placenta, prevents the transfer of certain molecules from the mother to the fetus. The capillary beds of the placenta and the mother are in close apposition but do not connect directly, so that the blood supplies do not mix. Because the fetus is not genetically identical to the mother, it has many different proteins that the mother's immune system would not recognize as compatible. If the fetal and maternal blood were to mix, the mother would form antibodies against these foreign proteins and destroy them. Consequently, the placental barrier appears to be a defense system to block the passage of undesirable substances between mother and fetus; however, the placenta does allow the passage of nutrients from the mother and waste materials from the child in order to sustain fetal growth and development.

It appears as though there is some selectivity as to which chemicals pass through this barrier. A principal factor that determines passage of substances is molecular size. Usually, large molecules do not cross the placental barrier, while smaller molecules do. Because most drugs are relatively small molecules, they will usually pass from the maternal circulation into the fetal circulation.

REQUIRED DOSES FOR EFFECTS   Most drugs do not take effect until a certain amount has been administered. The smallest amount of a drug needed to elicit a response is referred to as its **threshold.**

---

threshold
the minimum drug dose necessary to cause an effect

The effectiveness of some drugs may be calculated in a *linear* (straight-line) fashion, which means the more drug taken, the greater the effect. However, many drugs have a maximum effect that they can cause, regardless of dose; this is called the **plateau effect.** OTC medications, in particular, have a limit on their effects. For example, nonprescription analgesics such as aspirin can be effective in treating mild to moderate pain, but regardless of dose, aspirin will not relieve severe pain. Other drugs may cause distinct or opposite effects, depending on the dose. For example, low doses of alcohol may act like a stimulant, whereas high doses usually cause sedation. Scopolamine (a belladonna alkaloid) may produce sedation at low doses and excitation, delirium, and hallucination at high doses.

---

plateau effect
the maximum drug effect, regardless of dose

THE TIME-RESPONSE FACTOR   The time-response factor is the relation between the time that has elapsed since a drug was administered and the onset of the effect. This factor, or response, is often classified as immediate, short-term, or **acute,** referring to the response after a single dose. The response can also be **chronic,** or long-term, usually associated with repeated doses. The intensity and quality of the overall effect may change considerably within a short period of time. For example, the main intoxicating effects of a large dose of alcohol generally peak in less than one hour and then gradually taper off. An initial stimulating effect may later change to sedation. With some drugs, an initial state of tension or anxiety may later change to relaxation and a sense of well-being due to a decrease in drug concentration because of metabolism.

---

acute
immediate or short-term effects after taking a single drug dose

chronic
long-term effects, usually after taking multiple drug doses

The effects of long-term, or chronic, use of some drugs can be quite different from their short-term, or acute, use. The administration of small doses may not produce any apparent, immediate, detrimental effect, but chronic use of the same drug (frequent use over a long time) may cause prolonged effects that are not apparent until years later. Although there is little evidence to show any immediate damage or detrimental response to short-term use of small doses of tobacco, there is evidence that its chronic use has damaging effects on heart and lung functions. Because of these long-term consequences, research on tobacco and its effects often continues for years, making it difficult to link specific diseases or health problems with use of this substance. Thus, the results of tobacco research are often disputed by tobacco manufacturers with vested financial interests in the substance and its public acceptance.

Another important time factor that influences drug responses is the interval between multiple administrations. If sufficient time for drug metabolism and elimination does not occur between doses, a drug can accumulate within the body. This build-up of drug due to relatively short dosing intervals is referred to as a **cumulative effect**. Because of the resulting high concentrations of drug in the body, unexpected prolonged drug effects or toxicity can occur.

---

cumulative effect
the build-up of a drug in the body after multiple doses taken at short intervals

---

INACTIVATION AND ELIMINATION OF DRUGS FROM THE BODY

Immediately following drug administration, the body begins to eliminate the substance in various ways. The time required to remove half of the original amount of drug administered is called the **biological half-life** of the drug. The body will eliminate either the drug directly without altering it chemically or (in most instances) after the drug has been metabolized (chemically altered) or modified. **Metabolism** usually makes it possible for the body to inactivate a drug as well as eliminate it more rapidly. The body has means to metabolize all its naturally occurring information-transferring substances, such as the neurotransmitters (chemical messengers associated with nervous tissues—see Chapter 5) and hormones and deals with drugs in a similar manner—as something to be removed as efficiently as possible. It is important for homeostatic balance to have chemical-initiated signals (associated with nervous or endocrine systems) continue for as short a time as necessary. Rapid clearance of neurotransmitters and hormones is part of the body's fine-tuning process, so that overstimulation or oversuppression of body activities by these regulatory substances does not occur. Pharmacologists must consider how these natural systems will eliminate drugs and what the resulting

---

biological half-life
the time required for the body to eliminate and/or metabolize half of a drug dose

metabolism
chemical alteration of drugs by body processes

---

break-down products will be before drugs can be marketed.

The liver is the major organ that removes drugs and hormones from the body. It is a complex biochemical laboratory with hundreds of enzymes at work in many cells, continuously synthesizing, modifying, and deactivating biochemical substances such as drugs. The healthy liver is capable of metabolizing all of the endogenous substances and many of the foreign chemicals introduced into the body. After the liver metabolizes a drug (the resulting chemicals are called **metabolites**), the products usually pass into the urine or feces. Drugs and their metabolites can appear in other places, as well, such as the sweat, saliva, or expired air.

---

metabolites
the chemical products of metabolism

The liver uses various enzymes to metabolize naturally occurring and foreign substances. These enzymes are associated with the cellular membranes and are often referred to as *microsomal* enzymes. The rate at which liver cells metabolize some substances can be increased under certain conditions. This increased rate is referred to as liver **enzyme induction** and can occur if a particular drug is taken repeatedly over a period of time. Barbiturates, opiates, and other depressants can all cause liver enzyme activity to increase, which in turn increases the body's capacity to remove the drug and clear it from the body more rapidly. However, enzymes are seldom totally specific; this means that other drugs that are metabolized by the same enhanced enzymes will also be metabolized at an accelerated rate. Increased liver enzyme activity lowers the effective concentration of a drug, which creates drug tolerance. This means that the

---

enzyme induction
an increase in the metabolic capacity of an enzyme system

---

same dose of a drug becomes less effective with continued use due to increased metabolism. The drug user must escalate the dose to compensate for the metabolic adjustments.

The kidneys are probably the next most important organ for drug elimination because they remove metabolites and foreign substances from the body. The kidneys are made up of several million complex filtration units, called *nephrons*, that constantly filter substances in the blood. Nephrons conserve and return to the blood valuable substances that should be saved and concentrate and excrete metabolic wastes, toxic substances, as well as drugs and their metabolites in the urine. It is estimated that the kidneys filter nearly 200 liters of fluid from the blood each day, and over 99% of the fluid returns to the blood along with potassium, sodium, bicarbonate, glucose, and other substances. The kidneys not only remove water-soluble substances from the blood but also regulate blood pressure and control sodium, potassium, and chloride levels in the body. The rate of excretion of some drugs by the kidneys can be altered by making the urine more acidic or more alkaline. For example, nicotine and amphetamines can be cleared faster from the body by making the urine slightly more acidic and salicylates and barbiturates by making it more alkaline. Such techniques are used in emergency rooms and can be useful in the treatment of drug overdosing.

The body may eliminate small portions of drugs through perspiration and exhalation. About 1% of consumed alcohol is excreted in the breath and thus may be measured with a breathalyzer; this technique is used by police officers in evaluating suspected drunk drivers. Most people are aware that consumption of garlic will change body odor because garlic is excreted through perspiration. Some drugs are handled in the same way. The mammary glands are modified sweat glands, so it is not surprising that many drugs are concentrated and excreted in milk during lactation, including antibiotics, nicotine, barbiturates, caffeine, and alcohol. Excretion of drugs in a mother's milk can be of particular concern during nursing, as the excreted drugs can be consumed by and have an effect on the infant.

Narcotics

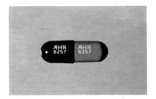

Controlled ingredient: codeine phosphate 30 mg
Other ingredient: acetaminophen 325 mg
Trade name: **Phenaphen with Codeine No. 3**

Controlled ingredients: oxycodone hydrochloride 4.5 mg,
oxycodone terephthalate 0.38 mg
Other ingredient: acetaminophen 500 mg
Trade name: **Tylox**

Controlled ingredient: hydrocodone 5 mg
Other ingredient: phenyltoloxamine 10 mg
Trade name: **Tussionex**

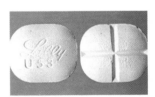

Controlled ingredient: methadone hydrochloride 40 mg
Trade name: **Methadone HCl Diskets**

Controlled ingredient: propoxyphene hydrochloride 65 mg
Other ingredient: aspirin 325 mg
Trade name: **Darvon with A.S.A.**

Controlled ingredient: Pentazocine hydrochloride 50 mg
Trade name: **Talwin**

CNS Depressants

BARBITURATE

■ Controlled ingredient: amobarbital sodium 200 mg
Trade name: **Amytal Sodium**

■ Controlled ingredient: pentobarbital sodium 100 mg
Trade name: **Nembutal Sodium**

■ Controlled ingredient: secobarbital sodium 100 mg
Trade name: **Seconal Sodium**

■ Controlled ingredient: phenobarbital 60 mg
Trade name: **Phenobarbital**

BARBITURATE-LIKE

■ Controlled ingredient: chloral hydrate 500 mg
Trade name: **Chloral Hydrate**

■ Controlled ingredient: glutethimide 500 mg
Trade name: **Doriden**

Controlled ingredient: methaqualone 300 mg
Trade name: **Quaalude - 300**
(no longer marketed in the U.S.)

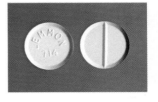

Controlled ingredient: meprobamate 600 mg
Trade name: **Miltown 600**

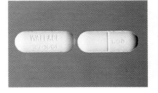

Controlled ingredient: methyprylon 300 mg
Trade name: **Noludar - 300**

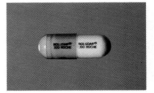

Controlled ingredient: ethchlorvynol 750 mg
Trade name: **Placidyl**

BENZODIAZEPINES

Controlled ingredient: alprazolam 1 mg
Trade name: **Xanax**

Controlled ingredient: chlordiazepoxide hydrochloride 25 mg
Trade name: **Librium**

Controlled ingredient: clorazepate dipotassium 22.5 mg
Trade name: **Tranxene - SD**

Controlled ingredient: diazepam 10 mg
Trade name: **Valium**

Controlled ingredient: flurazepam 30 mg
Trade name: **Dalmane**

Controlled ingredient: lorazepam 2.0 mg
Trade name: **Ativan**

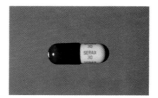

Controlled ingredient: oxazepam 30 mg
Trade name: **Serax**

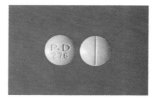

Controlled ingredient: prazepam 10 mg
Trade name: **Centrax**

Controlled ingredient: temazepam 30 mg
Trade name: **Restoril**

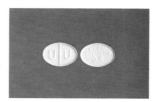

Controlled ingredient: triazolam 0.5 mg
Trade name: **Halcion**

CNS Stimulants

Controlled ingredient: amphetamine sulfate 10 mg
Trade name: **Benzedrine**

Controlled ingredients: amphetamine 10 mg,
dextroamphetamine 10 mg
Trade name: **Biphetamine '20'**

Controlled ingredient: dextroamphetamine sulfate 15 mg
Trade name: **Dexedrine**

Controlled ingredient: methamphetamine hydrochloride 15 mg
Trade name: **Desoxyn**

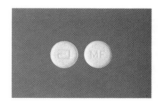

Controlled ingredient: phenmetrazine hydrochloride 75 mg
Trade name: **Preludin**

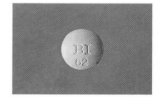

Controlled ingredient: methylphenidate hydrochloride 20 mg
Trade name: **Ritalin**

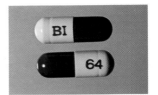

■ Controlled ingredient: phendimetrazine tartrate 105 mg
Trade name: **Prelu-2**

■ Controlled ingredient: mazindol 2 mg
Trade name: **Sanorex**

■ Controlled ingredient: phentermine hydrochloride 37.5 mg
Trade name: **Adipex-P**

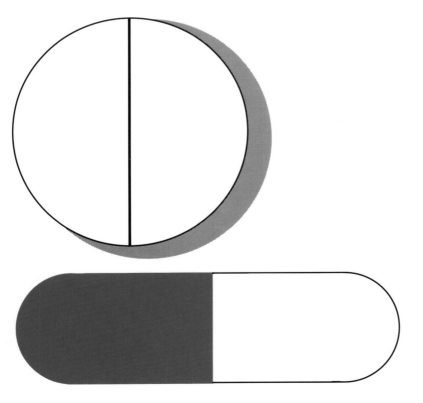

The poppy Papaver *somniferum* is the main source of nonsynthetic narcotics such as heroin, morphine, and codeine. It has been used by civilizations for thousands of years because of its medicinal and abuse potential.

The milky fluid containing the narcotic drug oozes from incisions in the unripe seedpod.

Since ancient times narcotic-rich fluid has been scraped from the seedpod by hand and air dried to produce opium.

■ Crude opium.

■ Crudely processed opium results in adulterated narcotics such as this Mexican heroin.

■ Large quantities of narcotics are harvested from poppy fields such as this.

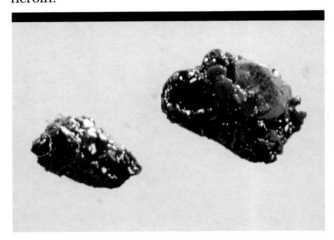

■ Black tar heroin.

■ Southwest Asian heroin.

■ Highly refined, pure heroin is a white powder such as this heroin from Asia.

BIOTRANSFORMATION The process of changing the chemical or pharmacological properties of drugs by metabolism (such as that which occurs in the liver) is called **biotransformation.** During biotransformation, a large variety of enzymes constantly transform drugs and other products to substances that can be eliminated more readily from the body. Any interference or modification in the enzymes involved in metabolism of the drugs (such as enzyme induction; see above) can influence the effects of the drug and the drug products on the body.

---

biotransformation

the process of changing the chemical properties of a drug, usually by metabolism

---

If a drug is transformed rapidly, before it can cause toxic effects, there usually is no problem. However, if there is a delay in transformation of potentially toxic substances, serious consequences may disrupt the homeostatic balance systems of the body. For example, phenylketonuria (PKU) is a genetic disease in which the normal rate of metabolism of the amino acid phenylalanine is greatly reduced. A person with this disease has a gene that fails to code for the enzyme that metabolizes phenylalanine. The resulting increased level of phenylalanine can damage the developing brain during the first two years of life, causing severe mental retardation.

Although biotransformation of drugs usually forms metabolites, which are less pharmacologically active and less toxic, in some cases, a drugs' break-down products are more active and/or more toxic. The drug acetaminophen is a common OTC analgesic (Tylenol) and in therapeutic doses is very safe. However, when extremely high doses are consumed, a metabolite is formed that can cause severe, even fatal damage to the liver. This is one example of a commonly used drug that can have toxic side effects because it has been metabolized. The toxic metabolites of other drugs have been shown to cause cancer, liver and kidney damage and allergic reactions. It is apparent that, while

drug metabolism is usually beneficial, it can sometimes be detrimental. Other compounds that show increasing toxicity as a result of metabolism are listed in Table 4-5.

In general, biotransformation reactions convert lipid-soluble drugs into less lipid-soluble and more water-soluble metabolites that are more easily eliminated by the kidneys. Most drugs are not sufficiently water soluble to be eliminated in their original form by the kidneys; consequently, these metabolic transformations are necessary if the drugs are to be excreted from the body.

PHYSIOLOGICAL VARIABLES THAT MODIFY DRUG EFFECTS

As previously mentioned, individuals' responses to drugs can vary greatly, even when the same doses are administered in the same manner. This variability can be especially troublesome when dealing with drugs that have a low therapeutic index. Many of these variables result from differences in body size, composition, or functions and include the following:

Age—Changes in body size and make-up occur throughout the aging process, from infancy to old age. Changes in the rates of drug absorption, biotransformation, and elimination also occur as a

---

TABLE 4-5 Compounds that increase their toxicity following biotransformation

Compound	Product
Ethylene glycol	Oxalic acid
Methanol	Formaldehyde
Parathion	Paraoxon
Pyridine	N-Methylpyridinium chloride
Chloral hydrate	Trichloroethanol chloride
Codeine	Morphine

Source: T. A. Loomis, *Essentials of Toxicology*, 3rd ed. (Philadelphia: Lea & Febiger, 1978), p. 60. Used with permission of the author and publisher.

consequence of getting older. As a general rule, children and elderly persons should be administered low drug doses (calculated as drug quantity/weight) due to immature or compromised body processes.

Gender—Variations in drug responses due to gender usually relate to differences in body size, composition, or hormones (male versus female types; e.g., androgens versus estrogens). However, most clinicians find many more similarities than differences between males and females relative to their responses to drugs.

Pregnancy—During the course of pregnancy, unique factors must be considered when administering drugs. For example, the physiology of the mother changes as the fetus develops and puts additional stress on organ systems, such as the heart, liver, and kidneys. This increased demand can make the woman more susceptible to the toxicity of some drugs. In addition, as the fetus develops, it can be very vulnerable to drugs with **teratogenic** (causing abnormal development) properties. Consequently, it is usually advisable to avoid taking any drugs during pregnancy, if possible.

---

teratogenic
something that causes physical defects in the fetus

PATHOLOGICAL VARIABLES THAT MODIFY DRUG EFFECTS

Individuals with diseases or compromised organ systems need to be particularly careful when taking drugs. Some diseases can damage or impair organs that are vital for appropriate and safe responses to drugs. For example, hepatitis (inflammation and damage to the liver) interferes with the metabolism and disposal of many drugs, resulting in a longer duration of drug action and increased likelihood of side effects. Similar concerns are associated with kidney disease, which has compromised renal activity and diminished excretion capacity. Because many drugs affect the cardiovascular system (especially drugs of abuse, such as stimulants), patients with a history of cardiovascular disease (i.e., heart attack, stroke, hypertension, or abnormal heart rhythm) need to be particularly careful when using drugs. They should be aware of those medicines that stimulate the cardiovascular system, especially those that are self-medicated, such as OTC decongestants. Such drugs should either be avoided or only used under the supervision of a physician.

T h i n k   A b o u t   I t . . .

1. Why is the most effective or direct method of taking a drug often also the most dangerous?
2. What are the main pharmacokinetic factors that can alter the speed of onset or the nature of drug effects among individuals?
3. Your friend complains of lower-back pain. You have a drug that was prescribed for you to treat neck pain. What are the potential problems of sharing this drug with your friend and administering it in a manner identical to that prescribed for you?

TOLERANCE TO DRUGS

Tolerance is said to develop when the response to the same dose of a drug decreases with repeated use. In other words, you must increase the dose in order to elicit the same response. The extent of tolerance and the rate at which it is acquired depends on the drug, the person using the drug, and the dosage and frequency of administration. Some drug effects may be reduced more rapidly than others when drugs are used frequently. Tolerance to effects that are rewarding or reinforcing often causes users to increase the dosage. Sometimes, abstinence from a drug can reduce tolerance.

The body does not necessarily develop tolerance to all effects of a drug equally. For example, with repeated use, a moderate degree of tolerance develops to most effects of alcohol and barbiturates. A heavy drinker may be able to consume two or three times the alcohol tolerated by an occasional drinker. Little tolerance develops, however, to the lethal toxicity of these drugs. A heavy user of sedatives is just as susceptible to death by overdose as a nontolerant person, even though the heavy user has been forced to increase doses to maintain the relaxing effects of the drug. In contrast, frequent use of opiate narcotics such as morphine can cause profound tolerance, even to the lethal effects of these drugs. Heavy users have been known to use with relatively few problems up to 10 times the amount that would kill a nonuser. Obviously, the mechanism that causes death by CNS depressants such as alcohol and sedatives is different from that that causes death by narcotics. This is demonstrated by the fact that tolerance develops to one but not the other mechanism.

The exact mechanisms by which the body adapts or becomes tolerant to different drug effects are not completely understood, but several processes have been suggested. Drugs like barbiturates stimulate the body's production of metabolic enzymes, primarily in the liver, that deactivate the drugs. This is called *drug disposition tolerance* and refers to the rate at which the body disposes of the drug. In addition, there is evidence that a considerable degree of central nervous system tolerance to some drugs may develop independently of changes in the rate of absorption, metabolism, or excretion. This is called *pharmacodynamic tolerance* and reflects the adaption of nervous tissue or other target tissue (which may include changes in receptors) to the drug, so that the effect of the same concentration of drug decreases. A person tolerant to alcohol, for example, can be relatively unaffected by several glasses of wine, resulting in a high level of alcohol in the blood. It is uncertain whether this situation represents some general molecular adaptation to the drug at the level of the individual nerve cell or is a specific brain response to counteract the sedating effects and maintain normal function (i.e., a counter-balancing excitatory system is enhanced to compensate for the depression caused by the alcohol).

Another type of drug response that can appear to be tolerance but is a learned adjustment is called *behavioral compensation.* Drug effects that are trou-

bling may be compensated for or hidden by the drug user. Thus, alcoholics learn to speak and walk slowly to compensate for the slurred speech and stumbling gait they usually experience. To an observer, it might appear as though the pharmacological effects of the drug are diminished, but they are actually unchanged. Consequently, this type of adaptation is not a true form of tolerance.

THE REBOUND EFFECT

Once tolerance to a drug develops, **physical dependence** may or may not result, depending on the type of drug used. Hallucinogens like LSD cause tolerance but do not appear to cause significant physical dependence. Many other drugs—like barbiturates, opiates, alcohol, and other depressants—may result in tolerance as well as physical dependence (see Table 4-6).

physical dependence
the result of physiological changes or adaptations that occur in response to the frequent presence of a drug

In general, the drugs that cause physical dependence also cause a condition called the **rebound effect,** which is a form of drug withdrawal. This is sometimes known as the *paradoxical effect* because the symptoms at this stage are nearly opposite of the direct effects of the drug. For example, a person taking barbiturates or benzodiazepines will be greatly depressed physically but upon withdrawal become extremely irritable, hyperexcited, nervous, and generally show symptoms of extreme stimulation of the nervous system, even life-threatening seizures. All of this constitutes the rebound effect.

rebound effect
a form of withdrawal; paradoxical effects that occur when a drug has been eliminated from the body

TABLE 4-6 Tolerance, dependence, and withdrawal properties of common drugs of abuse

Drug	Tolerance	Psychological Dependence	Physical Dependence	Withdrawal Symptoms (includes rebound effects)
Barbiturates	+ +	+ +	+ + +	Restlessness, anxiety, vomiting, tremors, seizures
Alcohol	+ +	+ +	+ + +	Cramps, delirium, vomiting, sweating, hallucinations, seizures
Benzodiazepines	+	+ +	+ +	Insomnia, restlessness, nausea, fatigue, twitching, seizures (rare)
Narcotics (heroin)	+ + +	+ +	+ + +	Vomiting, sweating, cramps, diarrhea, depression, irritability, gooseflesh
Cocaine, amphetamines	+*	+ + +	+ +	Depression, anxiety, drug craving, need for sleep ("crash"), anhedonia
Nicotine	+	+	+	Highly variable, craving, irritability, headache, increased appetite, abnormal sleep
Caffeine	+	+	+	Anxiety, lethargy, headache, fatigue
Marijuana	+	+	+	Irritability, restlessness, decreased appetite, weight loss, abnormal sleep
LSD	+ +	+	−	Minimal
PCP	+	+	+	Fear, tremors, some craving, problems with short memory

Key: + + + Intense   + Some
          + + Moderate   − Not significant
*Can sensitize

REVERSE TOLERANCE (SENSITIZATION)

Under some conditions, a response to a drug is elicited that is the opposite of tolerance. This is known as **reverse tolerance,** or sensitization. When sensitized, a drug user will have the same response to a lower dose of a drug that he or she did to the initial, higher dose. This seems to occur in users of marijuana, and some hallucinogens, as well as amphetamines and cocaine (Drew and Glick 1990).

reverse tolerance
an enhanced response to a given drug dose; opposite of tolerance

Although explanations of reverse tolerance are still unclear, some researchers believe that it depends on how often and how much of the drug is consumed. It has been speculated that this heightened response may reflect changes in the receptors (site of drug action) or brain neurotransmitters to subsequent administration of these drugs. The reverse tolerance that occurs with cocaine use may be responsible for the psychotic effects or the seizures caused by overdosing this drug (Jaffe 1990).

CROSS-TOLERANCE

A phenomenon known as cross-tolerance is seen with certain types of drugs. Namely, if a person develops a tolerance to one drug, he or she will also show tolerance to other related drugs. This effect may be due to altered metabolism resulting from chronic drug use. For example, a heavy drinker will usually exhibit tolerance to barbiturates, other depressants, and anesthetics because the alcohol has changed his or her liver and CNS metabolic enzymes. Cross-tolerance might also occur among drugs that cause similar pharmacological actions; for example, if adaptations have occurred in populations of receptors that cause tolerance to one drug, such receptor changes might also result in tolerance to other similar drugs that exert their effects by interacting with that same receptor. This type of cross-tolerance has been shown to develop among some of the hallucinogens, such as LSD, mescaline, and psilocybin.

PHYSICAL DEPENDENCE

Physical dependence is a physiological state of adaptation to a drug. It is often the result of developing a tolerance to a drug and contributes to withdrawal symptoms (or abstinence syndrome) when administration of the drug is stopped (usually abruptly). As with tolerance, the reasons for physical dependence and withdrawal are not fully understood, but dependence can make it very difficult for individuals to break their drug habits. A summary of types of physical dependence from some drugs of abuse is provided in Table 4-6.

Physical dependence may develop with high-intensity use of such common drugs as alcohol, barbiturates, and other CNS depressants. However, with moderate, intermittent use of these drugs, most people do not become physically dependent. Those who do become physically dependent experience damaged social and personal skills and relationships and impaired brain and motor functions. By contrast, potent opiate narcotics also tend to induce pronounced tolerance and physical dependence demonstrated by their intense withdrawal effects, but usually the dependence has little impact on daily activities and social interactions in chronic narcotic users. As long as users have undisturbed access to narcotics, they can often function normally in their personal and professional lives (Kreek 1983). The reason for the difference in the impact of physical dependence on CNS depressants and narcotics is not clear.

CROSS-DEPENDENCE

Withdrawal symptoms resulting from physical dependency can be prevented by administering a sufficient quantity of the original drug or one with similar pharmacological activity. The latter case, in which different drugs can be used interchangeably to prevent withdrawal symptoms, is called *cross-dependence*. For example, barbiturates and other CNS depressants can be used to treat the abstinence syndrome of the chronic alcoholic. Another example is the use of methadone, a long-acting narcotic, to treat withdrawal from heroin. Such therapeutic strategies allow the substitution of safer and more easily managed drugs for dangerous drugs of abuse.

PSYCHOLOGICAL FACTORS

The general effect of most drugs is greatly influenced by a variety of psychological and environmental factors. Unique qualities of an individual's personality, his or her past history of drug experience, attitudes toward the drug, expectations of its effects, and motivation for use are extremely influential. These factors are often referred to collectively as the person's **mental set.** The *setting*, or total environment, in which a drug is taken may also modify its effect.

---

mental set
the collection of psychological and environmental factors that influence an individual's response to drugs

---

The set and setting are particularly important in influencing the responses to psychoactive drugs (drugs that alter the functions of the brain). For example, ingestion of LSD, a commonly abused hallucinogen, can cause pleasant, even spiritual-like experiences in comfortable, congenial surroundings. In contrast, when the same amount of

LSD is consumed in hostile, threatening surroundings, the effect can be frightening, taking on a nightmarish quality.

THE PLACEBO EFFECT

The psychological factors that influence responses to drugs, independent of their pharmacological properties, are known as **placebo effects.** The word *placebo* is derived from Latin and means "I shall please." The placebo effect is most likely to occur when an individual's mind set is susceptible to suggestion. A placebo drug is a pharmacologically inactive compound that causes the user to think some therapeutic change has occurred from its use.

---

placebo effects
effects caused by suggestion and psychological factors, not the pharmacological activity of a drug

---

In certain persons and/or in particular settings, a placebo substance may have surprisingly powerful consequences. For example, a substantial component of most pain is perception. Consequently, placebos administered as pain relievers and promoted properly can provide dramatic relief. Therefore, in spite of what appears to be a drug effect, the placebo is not considered a pharmacological agent because it does not alter any body functions by its chemical nature.

The early Greek physician and anatomist Galen described the placebo principle in the second century A.D. when he stated, "He cures most in whom most are confident." In therapeutic situations, placebos have been reported to relieve many complaints: headaches, gastrointestinal discomfort, cold-related symptoms, depression, insomnia, and so on. The bulk of medical history may actually be a history of confidence in the cure—a history of placebo medicine—because many effective cures of the past have been shown to be without relevant pharmacological action, suggesting that their effects were psychologically mediated. In fact, even today, some individuals argue that placebo effects

are a significant component of most drug therapy, particularly when using OTC medications. Medical researchers currently are investigating so-called psychological cures, attempting to identify which factors contribute to this interesting phenomenon. It is important when testing new drugs for effectiveness that drug experiments be conducted in a manner that allows a distinction between pharmacological and placebo effects. This can usually be done by treating with the real drug or a placebo that appears like the drug and comparing the responses to both treatments.

In some situations, perhaps placebos, or the power of suggestion, activate endogenous systems that help to relieve medical problems or associated symptoms. This is likely the explanation for the effectiveness of placebos against pain. A family of *peptides* (called *endorphins*) produced by the body has action similar to morphine and other opiate narcotics (Hughes 1975). The endorphins, among other things, are potent endogenous analgesics (substances that block pain) that provide the means for the body to defend itself against the debilitating effects of extreme pain. Research has shown that placebos cause the release of the endorphins to control pain. Other placebo effects may have similar biochemical basis in that they cause the release of endogenous substances that influence the body's functions and alter the course of disease.

Which factors make placebos effective?

1. A positive attitude by the health provider
2. The idea that more is always better; thus, two capsules are better than one
3. The patient's perspective—for example, injections are more effective than just taking tablets
4. Color—a large brown, purple, or red pill is more effective than a white one
5. Taste—a bad-tasting substance is more active than a neutral-tasting one (Evans 1977)

Effectiveness is also related to the physician-patient relationship; for example, it has been shown that treatment involving appropriate physical contact (often perceived as an expression of concern and empathy) is more beneficial than treatment without physical contact, such as by phone. These and many other factors have a significant influence on the placebo impact. The clinician who is aware of such psychological issues can use them to therapeutic benefit. The clinician who chooses to ignore these placebo-related factors often meets with frustration and therapeutic failure in spite of rendering appropriate medical care.

PSYCHOLOGICAL DEPENDENCE

Some drugs cause a condition known as **psychological dependence,** or *habituation.* The World Health Organization (WHO) states that psychological dependence instills a feeling of satisfaction and psychic drive that requires periodic or continuous administration of the drug to produce a desired effect or to avoid psychological discomfort. This sense of dependence usually leads to repeated self-administration of the drug in a fashion described as abuse. This type of dependence may be found independent of or associated with physical dependence. Psychological dependence does not produce the physical discomfort, rebound effects, or life-threatening consequences that can be associated with physical dependence. Even so, psychological dependence does produce intense craving and strong urges that frequently lure former drug abusers back to their habits of drug self-administration. In many instances, psychological aspects may be more significant than physical dependence in maintaining chronic drug use. Thus, the major problem with opiate dependence is not the physical aspects because withdrawal can be successfully achieved in a few weeks; rather, strong urges often cause a return to chronic narcotic use because of psychological dependence.

psychological dependence
dependence that results because a drug produces
pleasant mental effects

Figure 4-8 shows a diagram of how dependence is thought to develop. If the first drug trial is rewarding, a few more rewarding trials will follow until drug use becomes a conditioned pattern of behavior. Continued positive psychological reinforcement with the drug leads, in time, to primary psychological dependence. Primary psychological dependence, in turn, may lead to uncontrollable compulsive abuse of any psychoactive drug in certain susceptible persons and cause physical dependence. The degree of drug dependence is contingent upon the nature of the psychoactive substance, the quantity used, and the characteristics of the person and his or her environment. It is often not possible to draw a sharp line between use and abuse. There are many shades of gray between the drug user and the drug addict.

Even strong psychological dependence on some psychoactive substances does not necessarily result in injury or social harm. For example, typical dosages of mild stimulants such as coffee usually do not induce harmful reactions. Even though the effects on the central nervous system are barely detectable by a casual observer, strong psychological dependence on mild stimulants like tobacco and caffeine-containing beverages may develop. If a five- to ten-cup-a-day coffee drinker tries to stop drinking or a two-pack-a-day cigarette smoker tries to stop smoking for three days, he or she may experience minor withdrawal symptoms. Although this type of dependence is partly psychological, it is nevertheless real. The heavy coffee drinker deprived of the stimulant probably will report feeling jittery and having headaches and even muscular fatigue. Many of us have known friends or relatives who are a real nuisance when they are in the early stages of their latest attempt to stop smoking or give up coffee. Thus, even mild stimulants may cause some dependence; however, the fact that their use does not typically induce antisocial behavior distinguishes them from most of the other forms of dependence-producing drugs.

ADDICTION AND ABUSE: WHO BECOMES DRUG DEPENDENT?

The term *addiction* has many meanings. It is often used interchangeably with *dependence,* either physiological or psychological; other times, it is used

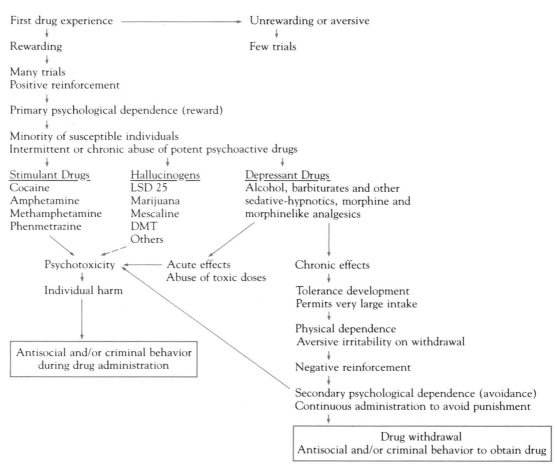

FIGURE 4-8 Steps in the process of drug abuse rejection *Source:* M. H. Seevers, "Psychopharmacological Elements of Drug Dependence," *Journal of the American Medical Association* 206, no. 6 (1968): 1263–1266. Reprinted by permission of the American Medical Association.

synonymously with the term *drug abuse* (i.e., *drug addiction*).

The traditional model of the addiction-producing drug is based on opiate narcotics and requires the individual to develop tolerance and both physical and psychological dependence (see Figure 4-8). This model often is not satisfactory because only a few commonly abused drugs seem to fit its parameters. It is clearly inadequate for many other drugs that can cause serious dependency problems.

Because it is difficult to assess the contribution of physical and psychological factors to drug dependency, it becomes difficult to determine if all psychoactive drugs truly cause drug addiction. To alleviate confusion, it has been suggested that the term *dependence* (either physical or psychological) be used in place of *addiction*. However, because of its acceptance by the public, the term *addiction* is not likely to disappear from general use.

There has been speculation that the only means by which drug dependence can be eliminated from society is to prevent exposure to those drugs that have potential abuse liability. Because some drugs are such powerful, immediate reinforcers, it is feared that rapid dependence (psychological) will occur when anyone uses them. While it may be true that most people, under certain conditions, could become dependent on some drug with abuse potential, in reality, most people who have used psychoactive drugs do not develop significant psychological or physical dependence. For example, approximately 87% of those who use alcohol experience minimal personal injury and social consequence. Of those who have used stimulants, depressants, or hallucinogens for illicit recreational purposes, only 10% to 20% become dependent (Jaffe 1990).

Why some people readily develop dependence on psychoactive drugs and others do not is not well understood. One factor may be heredity, which predisposes some people to drug abuse. For example, research has shown a fourfold increase in the likelihood of alcoholism among children whose parents are alcoholics. In addition, studies of identical and fraternal twins have revealed that there is greater similarity in the rate of alcoholism for identical than for fraternal twins. Because identical twins have 100% of their genes in common while fraternal twins share only 50%, these results suggest that genetic factors can be important in determining the likelihood of alcohol dependence (Schuckit 1987). It is possible that similar genetic factors contribute to other types of drug dependence, as well.

If a drug causes a positive effect in the user's view, it is much more likely to be abused than if it causes an aversive experience. Perhaps genetic factors influence the brain or personality so that some people find taking drugs an enjoyable experience (at least initially) while others find the effects very unpleasant and uncomfortable (**dysphoric**). Other factors that could also contribute significantly to drug use patterns include (1) peer pressure (especially in the initial drug experimentation); (2) home, school, and work environment

(Mello and Griffith 1987); and (3) mental state. It is estimated that 20% to 30% of those who abuse drugs, particularly stimulants, are attempting to self-medicate some form of mental disorder; for example, the stimulant cocaine is frequently used to self-treat depression (Weiss et al. 1989). One of the most effective treatments for cocaine abuse is the antidepressant desipramine (Kosten 1989).

---

dysphoric
characterized by unpleasant mental effects; the opposite of euphoric

---

It is difficult to identify specific factors that influence the risk of drug abuse. (Some of the possible influences are discussed in Chapter 2.) If such factors could be identified, those at greatest risk for drug abuse could be determined and informed of their vulnerability. It has been suggested by some that the CNS limbic system (that part of the brain that controls mood; see Chapter 5) is affected by many of the drugs of abuse in such a way that it rewards the user and reinforces the drug abuse pattern (Jaffe 1990). More specifically, evidence suggests that all of the readily abused drugs increase the activity of some CNS systems that use the messenger substance dopamine (Koob and Bloom 1988). (This will be discussed in greater detail in Chapter 5.)

Think About It . . .

1. Why would tolerance and a rebound effect lead to physical dependence and abuse of a drug?
2. Why do you think that people who abuse drugs are often very concerned about the environment in which they take them?
3. What is the relationship between psychological and physical dependence for a substance of abuse?

K E Y   T E R M S

withdrawal	parenteral	enzyme induction
haptene	blood-brain barrier	biotransformation
tolerance	threshold	teratogenic
potency	plateau effect	physical dependence
toxicity	acute	rebound effect
margin of safety	chronic	reverse tolerance
therapeutic index	cumulative effect	mental set
synergism	biological half-life	placebo effects
pharmacokinetics	metabolism	psychological dependence
enteral	metabolites	dysphoric

S U M M A R Y

1. All drugs have intended and unintended effects. The unintended effects of drugs can include effects such as nausea, altered mental states, dependence, and a variety of allergic responses.

2. Many factors can affect the way an individual responds to a drug: dose, inherent toxicity, potency and pharmacokinetic properties such as the rate of absorption into the body, the way it is distributed throughout the body, and the manner and rate it is metabolized and eliminated. The form the drug is in as well as the manner in which it is administered can also affect the response to a drug.

3. *Potency* is determined by the amount of a drug necessary to cause a given effect. *Toxicity* is the ability of the drug to adversely affect the body. A drug that is very toxic is very potent for causing a harmful effect.

4. A drug's *margin of safety* relates to the difference in the drug doses that cause a therapeutic or a toxic effect; the bigger the difference, the greater the margin of safety. The *therapeutic index* is a method to quantify the margin of safety;

a large therapeutic index is desirable.

5. *Additive* interactions occur when the effects of two drugs are combined; for example, the analgesic effects of aspirin plus acetaminophen are additive. *Antagonistic* effects occur when the effects of two drugs cancel; for example, the stimulant effects of caffeine tend to antagonize the drowsiness caused by antihistamines. *Synergism* (potentiation) occurs when one drug enhances the effect of another; for example, alcohol enhances the CNS depression caused by Valium.

6. Pharmacokinetic factors include absorption, distribution, biotransformation, and elimination of drugs.

7. Many physiological and pathological factors can alter the response to drugs. For example, age, gender, and pregnancy are all factors that should be considered when making drug decisions. In addition, some diseases can alter the way in which the body responds to drugs. Medical conditions associated with the

liver, kidneys, and cardiovascular system are of particular concern.

8. Drugs that are described as *fat soluble* can dissolve in oily or fatty solutions. These drugs can pass across membranes in the body because membranes have a high fat content. Fat-soluble drugs can enter almost any organ of the body. They can also enter into cells throughout the body.

9. In order for psychoactive drugs to influence the brain and its actions, they must pass through the blood-brain barrier. Many of these drugs are fat soluble and able to pass through capillary walls from the blood into the brain.

10. The *threshold dose* is the minimum amount of a drug necessary to have an effect. The *plateau effect* is the maximum effect a drug can have, regardless of dose. The *cumulative effect* is the build-up of drug concentration in the body due to multiple doses taken within short intervals.

11. The liver is the primary organ for metabolism of drugs and many naturally occurring substances in the body, such as hormones. By altering the molecular structure of

drugs, the metabolism usually inactivates drugs and makes them easier to eliminate through the kidneys. Liver function can sometimes be stimulated (called *induction*) or inhibited (called *tolerance*). These changes affect the rate at which some drugs are metabolized.

12. *Biotransformation* is the process that alters the molecular structure of a drug. Metabolism contributes to biotransformation.

13. Drug tolerance causes a decreased response to a given dose of a drug. It can be caused by increased metabolism and elimination of the drug by the body or by a change in the systems or receptors that are affected by the drug.

14. *Physical dependence* is characterized by the adaptive changes that occur in the body due to the continual presence of a drug. These changes are often chemical in nature and reduce the response to the drugs and cause *tolerance*. If drug use is stopped after physical dependence has occurred, the body finds itself overcompensated, causing a *rebound* response. Rebound effects are similar to the *withdrawal* that occurs because drug use is stopped for an extended period. *Psychological dependence* occurs because drug use is rewarding, bringing euphoria, increased energy, or relaxation.

15. Suggestion can have a profound influence on a person's drug response. Health problems with significant psychological aspects are particularly susceptible to the effects of placebos. An example is pain. Because much of pain is related to its perception, a placebo can substantially relieve pain discomfort. This placebo effect may relate to the release of a natural pain-relieving substance, such as endorphins. Other placebo responses may likewise be due to the release of endogenous factors in the body.

R E F E R E N C E S

Blackshear, P. J. "Implantable Drug-Delivery Systems." *Scientific American* 241, no. 6 (1979): 66–73.

Drew, K. L., and S. Glick. "Role of D-1 and D-2 Receptor Stimulation Sensitization to Amphetamine-Induced Circling Behavior and in Expression and Extinction of the Pavlovian Conditioned Response." *Psychopharmacology* 101 (1990): 465–471.

Drug Facts and Comparisons. St. Louis: Lippincott, 1991.

Evans, F. J. "The Power of a Sugar Pill." In *Ethical Issues in Modern Medicine*, edited by R. Hunt and J. Arras. Palo Alto, CA: Mayfield, 1977.

Graedon, J. *The People's Pharmacy.* New York: St. Martin's, 1976.

Henderson, G. "Designer Drugs: Past History and Future Prospects." *Journal of Forensic Sciences* 33 (1988): 569–575.

Hughes, J. "Isolation of an Endogenous Compound from the Brain with Pharmacological Properties Similar to Morphine." *Brain Research* 88 (1975): 295–308.

Jaffe, H. "Drug Addiction and Drug Abuse." In *The Pharmacological Basis of Therapeutics*, 8th ed., edited by A. Gilman, T. Rall, A. Nies, and P. Taylor. New York: Plenum, 1990.

Koob, G., and F. Bloom. "Cellular and Molecular Mechanisms of Drug Dependence." *Science* 242 (1988): 715–723.

Kosten, T. "Pharmacotherapeutic Interventions for Cocaine Abuse: Matching Patients to Treatments." *The Journal of Nervous and Mental Disease* 177 (July 1989): 379–389.

Kreek, M. *Health Consequences Associated with the Use of Methadone.* NIDA Treatment Research Monograph Series, no. 83. Washington, D.C.: Department of Health, Education, and Welfare, 1983.

Loomis, T. A. *Essentials of Toxicology*, 3rd ed. Philadelphia: Lea & Febiger, 1978.

Martin, E. W. *Hazards of Medication.* Philadelphia: Lippincott, 1971.

Mello, K., and R. Griffith. "Alcoholism and Drug Abuse: An Overview." In *Psychopharmacology: The Third Generation of Progress*, edited by H. Meltzer. New York: Raven, 1987.

Schuckit, M. "Biology of Risk for Alcoholism." In *Psychopharmacology: The Third Generation of Progress*, edited by H. Meltzer. New York: Raven, 1987.

Seevers, M. H. "Psychopharmacological Elements of Drug Dependence." *Journal of the American Medical Association* 206 (1968): 1263–1266.

Weiss, R., M. Griffin, and S. Mirin. "Diagnosing Major Depression in Cocaine Abuser: The Use of Depression Rating Scales." *Psychiatry Research* 28 (1989): 335–343.

Homeostatic Systems and Drugs

LEARNING OBJECTIVES

On completing this chapter, you will be able to:

1. Explain the similarities and differences between the nervous system and endocrine system.
2. Describe how a neuron functions.
3. Describe the role of receptors in mediating the effects of hormones, neurotransmitters, and drugs.
4. Distinguish between receptor agonists and antagonists.
5. Describe the different features of the principal neurotransmitters.
6. Outline the principal components of the central nervous system and explain their general functions.
7. Identify which brain areas are most likely to be affected by drugs of abuse.
8. Distinguish between the sympathetic and parasympathetic nervous systems.
9. Identify the principal components of the endocrine system.
10. Explain how and why anabolic steroids are abused and what social impact that abuse has.

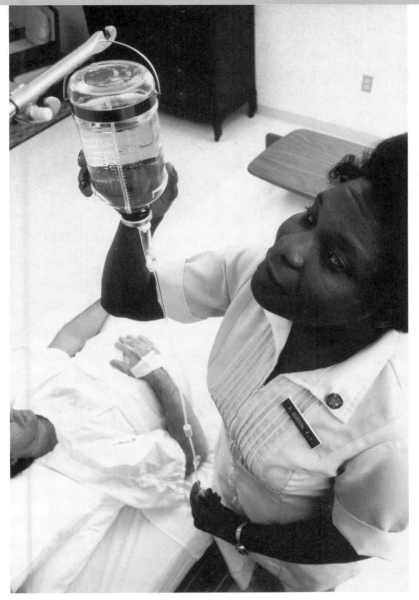

Photo: Jon Riley/Medichrome

DID YOU KNOW THAT . . .

- The brain is composed of 10 billion neurons that communicate with each other by releasing chemical messengers called *neurotransmitters.*
- Many drugs exert their effects by interacting with specialized protein regions in cell membranes called *receptors.*
- Some natural chemicals, produced by the body, have the same effect as narcotic drugs; these chemicals are called *endorphins.*
- The pleasant sensations that encourage continual use of most drugs of abuse are due to stimulation of dopamine activity in the limbic system.
- Drugs that affect the neurotransmitter dopamine usually alter both mental state and motor activity.
- The hypothalamus is the principal brain region for control of endocrine systems.
- The anabolic steroids often abused by athletes are chemically related to testosterone, the male hormone.
- Even though anabolic steroids can stimulate muscle growth in boys and females, it has not been proven that their use affects muscle development in mature men.
- The long-term effects of low-dose, intermittent use of anabolic steroids are not known.
- Anabolic steroids are considered controlled drugs by the Drug Enforcement Administration (DEA) and have been classified as Schedule III substances.

Why is the body susceptible to the influence of drugs and other substances? Part of the answer is that the body is constantly adjusting and responding to its environment in order to maintain internal stability or equilibrium. This delicate process of dynamic adjustments—homeostasis—is necessary to optimize body functions and essential for survival. These continual compensations help to maintain physiological and psychological balances and are mediated by the release of endogenous chemicals (e.g., hormones). Many drugs exert intended or unintended effects by altering the activity of these substances, which changes the function of nervous or endocrine systems. For example, all drugs of abuse profoundly influence mental states by altering chemical messages in the brain and alter endocrine function by affecting the release of hormones. By understanding the mechanisms of how drugs alter these body processes, we are able to recognize drug benefits and risks and devise therapeutic strategies to deal with ensuing problems.

This chapter is an introduction to the nervous system and endocrine structures. We will begin with the concept of homeostasis and how it is achieved. The basic elements of the nervous system will be discussed next, followed by an examination of its major divisions: the central, autonomic, and peripheral nervous systems. The components and operation of the endocrine system are discussed in specific relation to drugs. The use of contraceptives and steroids are given as examples.

HOMEOSTASIS AND CONTROL

The body continuously adjusts to both internal and external changes in the environment. To cope with these adjustments, the body systems have elaborate self-regulating mechanisms. The name given to this compensatory action is **homeostasis**, which refers to the maintenance of internal stability or equilibrium. Homeostasis is responsible for the regulation of body temperature, glucose (sugar) levels in the blood, and the amount of water inside and outside the cells. The two principal systems that help human beings maintain homeostasis are the nervous system and the endocrine system. They are often referred to, respectively, as the *coordinating* and *regulating* systems. They greatly influence each other and work together closely.

homeostasis
maintenance of internal stability; often biochemical in nature

The endocrine system consists of secreting glands (e.g., adrenal, thyroid, and pituitary) that produce biochemical agents. The biochemical agents, called **hormones** (e.g., adrenalin, steroids, insulin, and sex hormones), are information-transferring substances. Hormones are usually secreted into the bloodstream and carried by the blood to all the organs and tissues of the body. Hormones affect selected tissues that are designed to receive the information (see Figure 5-1). They may stimulate new tissue growth, assist in storage of nutrients, depress the activity of cells, or act in many other ways necessary to maintain homeostasis.

hormones
regulatory chemicals released by endocrine systems

Hormones are often called primary chemical messengers. Within the target cell are secondary chemical messengers that pick up the signal from

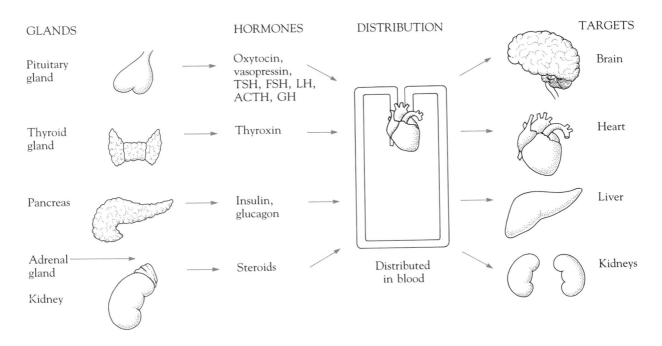

FIGURE 5-1   Endocrine gland function

the hormone and convert it into cellular changes, altering genes (chromosome expression), enzyme functions, or energy stores. Cyclic adenosine monophosphate (cAMP) is one of these secondary messengers. It is not known how many secondary messengers actually exist in the body, but they play an essential role in the chain of events that convert a hormonal signal into some cellular change.

Hormones and secondary chemical messengers may be highly selective with regard to the cells or organs they influence, or they may be very general and influence the whole body. The endocrine system, more or less, sets the limits for proper functioning of the nervous system. Because hormones are carried in the blood, the action of the endocrine system is much slower and usually more generalized than that of the nervous system. The interpretation of the chemical messages in the various parts of the body is quite complex and is only now being deciphered by scientists.

The nervous system also functions by means of biochemical substances that help regulate the transfer of electrical impulses between **neurons** (the principal cells of the nervous system). Neurons produce their effects more rapidly than the endocrine system. The nervous system receives and interprets stimuli, and it also transmits impulses to organs that either become more active or more depressed in response to these impulses.

neurons
the principal cells in nervous systems; conduct electrochemical impulses and release neurotransmitters

Because we are interested in the effects of psychoactive drugs and because the nervous system is the system most affected by such drugs, we will concentrate primarily on this system and its homeostatic function. However, some endocrine systems will also be discussed in order to understand their role in mediating drug effects.

THE BUILDING BLOCKS OF THE NERVOUS SYSTEM

The nervous system is composed of the brain, the spinal cord, and all the neurons (nerve cells) that connect to the other organs and tissues of the body (see Figure 5-2). It enables people to receive information about their internal and external environment and to make the appropriate responses essential to survival. Some scientists have said that we know more about the surface of the moon than we do about our nervous system. While this may be an exaggeration, it indicates our lack of understanding about neurological functions. Considerable money and effort are currently being dedicated to explore the mechanisms whereby the nervous system functions and processes information. New exciting discoveries are being reported routinely.

THE NEURON: THE BASIC STRUCTURAL UNIT OF THE NERVOUS SYSTEM*

The building block of the nervous system is the nerve cell, or neuron. Each neuron is in close contact with other neurons, forming a complex network. There are over 10 billion neurons in the human brain, each of which is composed of similar parts (see Figure 5-3), although they may differ in some structural aspects depending on their location and function. Neurons do not form a continuous network. They always remain separate, never actually touching, although they are very close. The point of communication between one neuron and another is a tiny gap called a **synapse**. It may be only 0.00002 millimeter, but it is essential for proper functioning of the nervous system (see Figure 5-4).

FIGURE 5-2   Structure of the nervous system

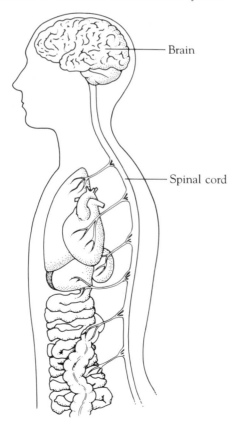

- Brain

- Spinal cord

---

synapse

a minute gap between the neuron and target cell across which neurotransmitters travel

---

The neuron has a cell body with a nucleus and **dendrites**, which are short, treelike branches that pick up information from the environment and surrounding neurons. A **receptor** is a special protein in the membrane of the receiving neuron; it is usually located near the synaptic junction (the point where two neurons make contact) and interacts with specific **neurotransmitters** (the chemical messengers released from synaptic vesicles in the sending neuron to influence the receiving neurons; see Figure 5-4). The interaction between the transmitter molecule and the protein receptor triggers a response in the receiving neuron. Some dendrites are able to change sensory information—

*This section (pp. 128–132) is based largely on Stevens 1979.

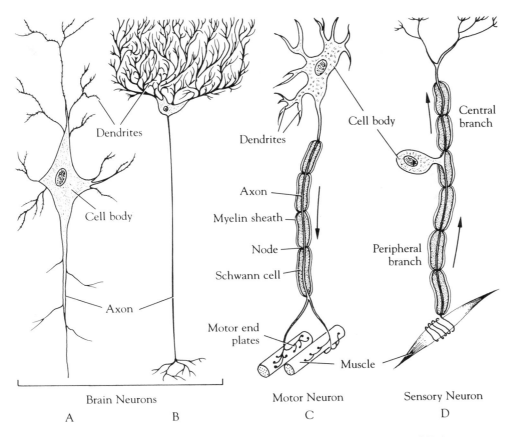

FIGURE 5-3 Neurons: A and B are brain neurons; C is a motor neuron; and D is a sensory neuron.

such as light, sound, or scent—into electrical activity that is then carried along the neurons to brain regions where it can be processed. *Transduction* is the term used for the conversion of one type of input into a different form of signal.

dendrites
short branches of neurons that receive transmitter signals

receptor
a special region in a membrane that is activated by natural substances or drugs to alter cell function

neurotransmitters
chemical messengers released by neurons

The other branch of the neuron is the **axon**, a threadlike extension that receives information from the dendrites in the form of an electrical impulse; then, like an electrical wire, it transmits the impulse to the termination point. Some axons may be quite long; for example, some extend from the spinal cord to the toes. Thus, an electrical impulse is transmitted from dendrite to axon to the terminals. The electrical information is usually a series of pulses, each with an amplitude of about .10 volt and lasting .001 to .002 seconds. The electrical impulses are normally not affected by drugs directly because they are generated by the neuron cell membrane. However, a few drugs (i.e., local anesthetics like lidocaine) can influence information processing by acting on and changing

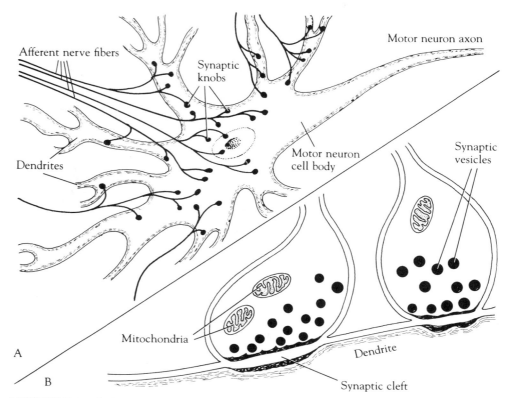

FIGURE 5-4 (A) Each neuron may have many synaptic knobs. They are designed to deliver short bursts of a chemical transmitter substance into the synaptic cleft, where it can act on the surface of the nerve cell membrane. Before release, molecules of the chemical transmitter are stored in numerous vesicles, or sacs. (B) A close-up of the synaptic knobs, showing the synaptic vesicles and mitochondria. Mitochondria are specialized structures that help supply the cell with energy. The gap between the synaptic knob and the membrane is the synaptic cleft.

the cell membrane and interfering with impulse transmission.

---

axon

an extension of the neuronal cell body along which electrochemical signals travel

---

At the synapse, information is transmitted chemically, not electrically, to the next neuron. The following list shows the series of steps involved in information transmission in the nervous system in response to excitatory transmitters (see also Figure 5-5):

1. Receptors on the dendrites or cell bodies receive an excitatory neurotransmitter and convert its effects to an electrical impulse, which is relayed to the axon.
2. The axon picks up the impulse and conducts it to terminals.
3. Neurotransmitters are released from terminals from minute storage structures called *vesicles.*
4. Neurotransmitters diffuse across the synapse to receptor sites on other neurons, where

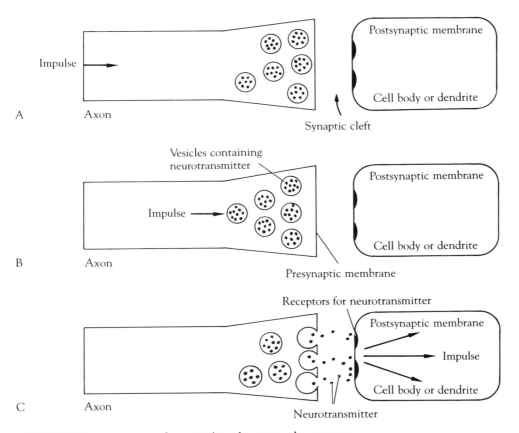

FIGURE 5-5 Movement of a nerve impulse across the synapse

these chemicals act on receptor sites to generate an electrical impulse.

5. Dendrites transmit electrical impulses to the axon, and the cycle begins again.

Some responses to external stimuli (such as pain) may occur solely in the spinal cord, without impulses being processed by the brain. These rapid responses are called **reflexes**. Thus, the immediate retraction of the hand after being burned on a stove is mediated by this reflex process. In contrast, with visual and auditory stimuli, the initial stimuli are detected by sensory organs in the head (the eyes and ears), converted to neuronal impulses, and transmitted directly to the brain, without passing through the spinal cord. For simplicity, only the major functions and mechanisms of the nervous system will be discussed.

reflexes
automatic responses to stimuli that do not require brain processing

There are two types of synapses: (1) the excitatory synapse, which initiates an impulse when stimulated and causes release of neurotransmitters, and (2) the inhibitory synapse, which, because of its inhibitory influence, diminishes the likelihood of either an impulse in the axon or release of neurotransmitters. A neuron may have over 10,000 synapses connecting it to other neurons and their potential information (see Figure 5-4). The final neuronal activity (i.e., whether a transmitter is released) is a summation of these many excitatory and inhibitory synaptic signals.

THE NATURE OF DRUG RECEPTORS

Receptors in membranes help regulate the activity of cells in the nervous system and throughout the body. These are selective protein sites on specific cells that react to endogenous messenger substances (chemicals produced and released within the body), such as neurotransmitters and hormones. These receptors serve to process the complex information each cell receives as it attempts to maintain metabolic constancy, or homeostasis, and fulfill its functional role. Many drugs used therapeutically and almost all drugs of abuse exert their effects on the body by directly or indirectly interacting (either to activate or antagonize) with these receptors.

The discovery of receptors that interact with specific drugs has led to some interesting results. For example, there are opiate receptors (sites of narcotic action) naturally present in the animal brain (Snyder 1977). Why would the brain have receptors for opiate narcotics, which are plant chemicals? This discovery suggested the existence of internal (endogenous) substances in the body that normally act at these receptor sites. This led to the discovery that the body produces its own opiates, the **endorphins**. Specific receptors have also been found for other drugs such as the central nervous system (CNS) depressant Valium. Because of this discovery, it is speculated that endogenous substances exist that mimic Valium's effects and help to provide natural sedation and relaxation for the body (Izquierdo 1989). Pres-

ently, several research laboratories are attempting to identify the natural chemical messenger that normally acts at the Valium receptor (referred to as the benzodiazepine receptor).

Much remains unknown about how receptors respond to or interact with drugs. However, using molecular biology techniques, many of these receptors have been found to initiate a cascade of linked chemical reactions, which can change intracellular environments, resulting in either activation or inactivation of cellular functions. Receptors that have been isolated and identified include protein molecules; it is believed that the shape of the protein is essential in regulating a drug's interaction with a cell. If the drug is the proper shape and size and has a compatible electrical charge, it may substitute for the endogenous messenger substance and activate the receptor protein by causing it to change its shape, or conformation. This process is like a "lock-and-key" arrangement, with only certain shapes of chemicals (the keys) being able to interact and activate a receptor (the "lock").

AGONISTIC AND ANTAGONISTIC EFFECTS ON DRUG RECEPTORS

A drug may have two different effects on a receptor when interaction occurs: **agonistic** or **antagonistic**. As shown in Figure 5-6, an agonistic drug interacts with the receptor and produces some type of cellular response, whereas an antagonistic drug interacts with the receptor but prevents that response. By analogy, using the lock-and-key model, a key can be used to open a lock (agonistic effect), whereas another key that fits in the lock but does not work can jam it (antagonistic effect).

agonistic
a type of substance that activates a receptor

antagonistic
a type of substance that blocks a receptor

endorphins
neurotransmitters that have narcoticlike effects

An agonistic drug mimics the effect of a substance (such as a neurotransmitter) that is naturally

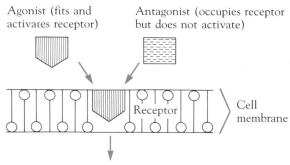

Agonist (fits and activates receptor)

Antagonist (occupies receptor but does not activate)

Receptor

Cell membrane

When this receptor is occupied and activated, it causes a cellular function to be either enhanced or antagonized

FIGURE 5-6 Interaction of agonist and antagonist with membrane receptors

produced by the body and interacts with the receptor to cause some cellular change. An antagonist has the opposite effect. It inhibits the sequence of metabolic events that a natural substance or an agonist drug can stimulate without initiating an effect itself.

Antagonistic drugs can act either reversibly or irreversibly. The *reversible* (also referred to as *competitive*) type of antagonist blocks a reaction from occurring by occupying a specific receptor. The antagonist prevents the activating substance from reaching the receptor, just as a key that is jamming a lock prevents use of the correct key. However, if the antagonist is a reversible type, high concentrations of an agonist can reverse the blockade by displacing the antagonist from the receptor site.

In contrast, an *irreversible* (also called *noncompetitive*) type of antagonist cannot be reversed because chemical changes occur that permanently attach the antagonist to the receptors and make the receptors nonresponsive to stimulation by agonists; even high concentrations of an agonist cannot reverse this permanent blockade. Usually, the cell eventually recovers from the effects of the noncompetitive antagonist by making new, unoccupied receptor molecules; this may be compared to replacing an entire jammed lock.

Many drugs affect the synthesis, storage, or deactivation of neurotransmitters. By acting at any synthesis, storage, or deactivation step, a drug may modify or block information transmitted by neurotransmitters. Many drugs mimic and some block the receptor sites where neurotransmitters work. Some receptors might be altered with continual drug use and become increasingly sensitive to even a small impulse or, conversely, insensitive after drug treatment.

NEUROTRANSMITTERS: THE MESSENGERS

As previously mentioned, the impulse from one neuron is transferred to the next by means of biochemical messengers called *neurotransmitters*. Many drugs affect the nervous system by influencing transmitter function, so it is important to develop some understanding of what these biochemical substances are, how they are produced by the body, how they transfer information, and how the body disposes of them.

Experimental evidence shows that many different neurotransmitters exist, although much remains to be learned about their specific functions. These biochemical messengers are released from specific neurons. Some of the best understood transmitters include acetylcholine, norepinephrine, epinephrine, dopamine, serotonin, gamma-aminobutyric acid (GABA), and substance P (a peptide). Each neurotransmitter affects only its specific receptors; all neurotransmitters differ in shape and do not fit into other receptor configurations (Kandel et al. 1991). Drugs can also affect these receptors if they are sufficiently similar in shape to the neurotransmitters. Figure 5-7 sum-

Acetylcholine

Chemical type: Choline product

Location: CNS—Basal ganglia, cortex, reticular activating system

PNS—Neuromuscular junction, parasympathetic system

Action: Excitatory and inhibitory

Norepinephrine

Chemical type: Catecholamine

Location: CNS—Limbic system, cortex, hypothalamus, reticular activating system, brain stem, spinal cord

PNS—Sympathetic nervous system

Action: Usually inhibitory; some excitation

Epinephrine

Chemical type: Catecholamine

Location: CNS—Minor

PNS—Adrenal glands

Action: Usually excitatory

Key: CNS—Central nervous system
PNS—Peripheral nervous system

Dopamine

Chemical type: Catecholamine

Location: CNS—Basal ganglia, limbic system, hypothalamus

Action: Usually inhibitory

Serotonin (5-HT)

Chemical type: Tryptophan-derivative

Location: CNS—Basal ganglia, limbic system, brain stem, spinal cord, cortex

Other—Gut, platelets, cardiovascular

Action: Inhibitory

GABA

Chemical type: Amino acid

Location: CNS—Basal ganglia, limbic system, cortex

Action: Inhibitory

Substance P

Chemical type: Peptide (small protein)

Location: CNS—Basal ganglia, hypothalamus, brain stem, spinal cord

Other—Gut, cardiovascular system

Action: Excitatory

FIGURE 5-7   Features of common neurotransmitters

marizes some of the important features about the common neurotransmitters.

ACETYLCHOLINE   Large quantities of acetylcholine (ACh) are found in the brain. ACh was first identified as a neurotransmitter in the peripheral nervous system. It is synthesized in the neuron by combining molecules of choline (provided by diet and also manufactured in the body) and acetyl CoA (from glucose metabolism). Acetylcholine is one of the major neurotransmitters in the autonomic portion of the peripheral nervous system (which will be discussed later in the chapter).

Neurons that respond to ACh are distributed throughout the brain. Depending on the region, ACh can have excitatory or inhibitory effects. However, in order for any neurotransmitter to work, it must interact with receptors on the neuron receiving the transmitter molecule at what is called a *postjunctional receptor site*. The *cholinoceptive sites*, which are receptors activated by acetylcholine, have been divided into two main subtypes based on the response to two drugs derived from plants: muscarine and nicotine. Muscarine (the substance in mushrooms that causes mushroom poisoning) and similarly acting drugs activate **muscarinic** receptors. Nicotine, whether experimentally administered or inhaled by smoking tobacco, stimulates **nicotinic** receptors.

muscarinic
a receptor type activated by ACh; usually inhibitory

nicotinic
a receptor type activated by ACh; usually excitatory

Neurotransmitters are inactivated after they have done their job by removal, metabolism (by enzymes), or reabsorption into the neuron. If a deactivating enzyme is blocked by a drug, the effect of the transmitter may be prolonged or intensified. For example, acetylcholine stimulates nicotinic receptors that cause strong contraction of muscles. The acetylcholine is metabolized by the deactivating enzyme, acetylcholinesterase, into the choline and acetate molecules, and the muscles relax. Some nerve gases developed by the military for chemical warfare purposes block the acetylcholinesterase enzyme. The target receptors in the presence of these drugs continue to be stimulated because the ACh has not been metabolized. This continual firing of electrical impulses causes muscle paralysis due to the persistent muscle contraction. Some of the phosphate pesticides act like these nerve gases and were developed as byproducts of nerve gas research. Thus, they can be dangerous if they are misused.

CATECHOLAMINES **Catecholamines** comprise the neurotransmitter compounds norepinephrine, epinephrine, and dopamine, which are grouped according to their chemical structure (see Appendix B). Neurons that synthesize catecholamines convert the amino acids phenylalanine or tyrosine to a compound called *L-DOPA*. Subsequently, the L-DOPA is converted to dopamine, followed by conversion to norepinephrine, and finally to epinephrine. Hence, phenylalanine, tyrosine, and L-DOPA are called precursors for the catecholamines.

---

catecholamines
a class of biochemical compounds, including the transmitters norepinephrine, epinephrine, and dopamine

---

Unlike acetylcholine, after acting at their receptors, most of the catecholamines are taken back up into the neurons that released them to be used over again; this is called *reuptake*. There is also an enzymatic breakdown system involving the two enzymes catechol-0-methyltransferase

(COMT) and monoamine oxidase (MAO), which metabolize the catecholamines to inactive compounds. The reuptake process and the activity of these enzymes, especially monoamine oxidase, can be greatly affected by some of the drugs that will be discussed. If these deactivating enzymes are blocked, the concentration of norepinephrine and dopamine may build up in the brain, causing a significantly increased stimulatory effect. Amphetamine and cocaine, for example, prevent the reuptake of norepinephrine and dopamine in the brain, resulting in continual stimulation of neuron receptors until the transmitters are depleted. Such depletion of catecholamines may result in depression, or the "crash" that occurs after high doses of amphetamines or cocaine are used.

Norepinephrine and Epinephrine. Although norepinephrine and epinephrine are structurally very similar, their receptors are selective and do not respond with the same intensity to either transmitter or to **sympathomimetic** drugs. Just as the receptors to acetylcholine can be separated into muscarinic and nicotinic types, the norepinephrine and epinephrine receptors are separated into the categories of alpha and beta. Receiving cells may have alpha- or beta-type receptors or both. When both types of receptors are activated, the response to one is usually stronger and dominates the response to the other. Epinephrine and norepinephrine differ mainly in the ratio of their effectiveness in stimulating alpha and beta receptors. Norepinephrine acts predominantly on alpha receptors and has little action on beta receptors.

---

sympathomimetic
agents that mimic the effects of norepinephrine or epinephrine

---

The antagonistic (blocking) action of many drugs that act on these catecholamine receptors can be selective for alpha, whereas others block only beta receptors. This distinction can be therapeutically useful. For example, beta receptors tend to stimulate the heart, while alpha receptors constrict blood vessels; thus, a drug that selectively affects beta receptors can be used to treat heart ailments without altering the state of the blood vessels, or **vasculature.**

---

vasculature
relating to the blood vessels

Dopamine. Dopamine is also a catecholamine transmitter that is particularly influenced by drugs of abuse. Most drugs that elevate mood, have abuse potential, or cause psychotic behavior in some way enhance the activity of dopamine, particularly in brain regions associated with limbic structures (areas that regulate mood and mental states). In addition, dopamine is an important transmitter in controlling movement and fine-muscle activity. Thus, drugs that affect dopamine neurons can alter all of these functions.

SEROTONIN   Serotonin (5-hydroxytryptamine, or 5HT) is synthesized in neurons and elsewhere (e.g., gastrointestinal tract and platelet-type blood cells) from the dietary source of tryptophan. Tryptophan is one of the essential amino acids, meaning that humans do not have the ability to synthesize it and must obtain it through diet. Normally, about 2% of the tryptophan in the diet is converted to serotonin. Serotonin is degraded by the enzyme monoamine oxidase; thus, drugs that alter this enzyme affect levels of not only the catecholamines but also serotonin.

Serotonin is also found in the upper brainstem, which connects the brain and the spinal cord (see Figure 5-8). Axons from serotonergic neurons are distributed throughout the entire central nervous system. Serotonin, for the most part, inhibits action on its target neurons. One important role of the serotonergic neurons is to prevent overreaction to various stimuli, which can cause aggressiveness, excessive motor activity, exaggerated mood swings, insomnia, and abnormal sexual behavior. Serotonergic neurons also help regulate the release of hormones from the hypothalamus.

Alterations in serotonergic neurons, serotonin synthesis, and degradation have been proposed to be factors in mental illness and contribute to the side effects of many drugs of abuse. In support of this hypothesis is the fact that drugs like psilocybin and LSD, which have serotoninlike chemical structures, are frequently abused because of their hallucinogenic properties and can cause psychotic effects.

T h i n k   A b o u t   I t . . .

1. Why are most organ systems controlled by both excitatory and inhibitory nervous and endocrine systems?
2. What would be the clinical value of using a drug that blocks a neurotransmitter or hormone that normally is released to stimulate the heart?
3. Why is it important for the body to have chemical messengers that can be quickly released and rapidly inactivated?

MAJOR DIVISIONS OF THE NERVOUS SYSTEM

The nervous system can be divided into three components: the central (CNS), the autonomic (ANS), and the peripheral (PNS) nervous systems. The CNS and ANS exercise most of the body's integrative or homeostatic control. The PNS consists of the nerves outside the skull and spinal cord that connect the brain and spinal cord to the extremities of the body and send sensory information to the brain to be analyzed and acted on. As such, the PNS plays an indirect role in integrative processes and contributes to the effects of psychoactive drugs. The ANS is partially controlled by the CNS and helps to mediate CNS regulation of muscles and glands, so these two functional components are not truly separate. However, because each has distinctive characteristics, they will be discussed separately, as will the PNS.

THE CENTRAL NERVOUS SYSTEM

The CNS consists of the brain and spinal cord (see Figure 5-8). The human brain is an integrating

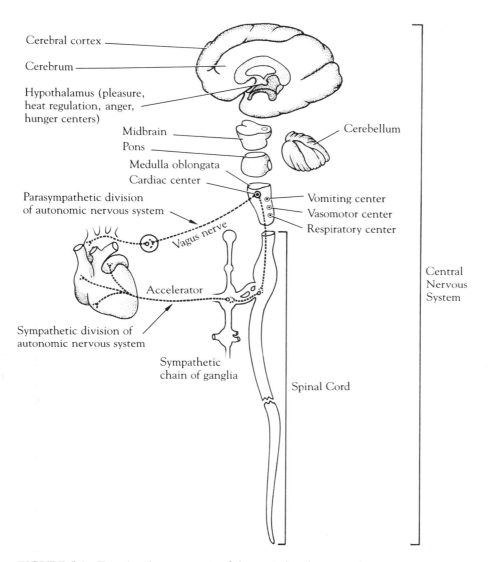

FIGURE 5-8 Functional components of the central and autonomic nervous systems

(information-processing) and storage device un-equaled by the most complex computers. Not only can it handle a great deal of information simultaneously from the senses, but it can evaluate and modify the response to the information rapidly. Although the brain weighs only three pounds, with its 10 billion neurons, it has the potential to perform a multitude of functions. For our purposes, we will discuss those parts of the brain most likely to be influenced by **psychoactive** drugs: the (1) reticular activating system, (2) basal ganglia, (3) limbic system, (4) cerebral cortex, and (5) hypothalamus.

psychoactive
drugs that affect mood or alter the state of consciousness

THE RETICULAR ACTIVATING SYSTEM   The reticular activating system (RAS) is an area of the brain that receives input from all the sensory systems as well as from the cerebral cortex. The RAS is at the junction of the spinal cord and the brain, and it has a vast network of multiple synaptic neurons extending throughout the brain (see Figure 5-9). Because of this complex, diffuse network, the RAS is very susceptible to the effects of drugs. The RAS is sensitive to the effects of LSD, potent stimulants such as cocaine and amphetamines, and CNS depressants such as alcohol and barbiturates.

One of the major functions of the RAS is to control the brain's state of arousal (sleep versus awake). Arousal is especially linked to activity in the cerebral cortex. If the cortex is not aroused, it cannot handle input from the sensory system. The RAS is stimulated by sensory input and will initiate its own impulses to the cerebral cortex, which becomes alert if the impulses are of sufficient intensity or cause alarm. After the cortex is activated, the person is awake, and the nervous system is active and ready to receive and process further stimuli from the environment. The RAS can also filter out distracting stimuli, allowing the person to concentrate intently, even to the point of being unaware of severe injury until the immediate, pressing situation is over.

Norepinephrine and acetylcholine are important neurotransmitters in the RAS. High levels of epinephrine, norepinephrine, or sympathomimetic drugs activate both the RAS and the cerebral cortex. Compounds like amphetamines increase the response of the RAS and diminish its ability to screen out nonessential stimuli, thus confusing the system with exaggerated sensations. On the other hand, drugs that block the actions of acetylcholine, called **anticholinergic** drugs, sup-

FIGURE 5-9   Sagittal section of the brain, showing the major parts

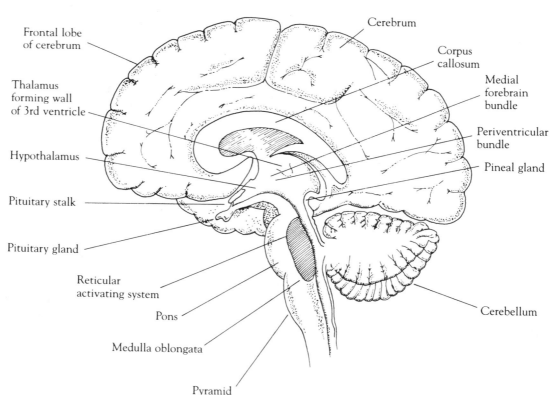

Frontal lobe of cerebrum

Thalamus forming wall of 3rd ventricle

Hypothalamus

Pituitary stalk

Pituitary gland

Reticular activating system

Pons

Medulla oblongata

Pyramid

Cerebrum

Corpus callosum

Medial forebrain bundle

Periventricular bundle

Pineal gland

Cerebellum

press RAS activity, causing sleepiness. Thus, use of antihistamines, which have anticholinergic activity, often causes annoying drowsiness; they are sometimes used as sleep aids in OTC medications.

---

anticholinergic
agents that antagonize the effects of acetylcholine

THE BASAL GANGLIA The basal ganglia are the primary centers for involuntary and fine tuning of motor function involving, for example, posture and muscle tone. Two important neurotransmitters in the basal ganglia are dopamine and acetylcholine. Damage to neurons in this area may cause Parkinson's disease, the progressive yet selective degeneration of the main dopaminergic neurons in the basal ganglia. This process results in an imbalance between dopamine and acetylcholine. The imbalance in these transmitters interferes with regulation of muscle activity by the brain and causes the person to be debilitated, with postural rigidity, tremors, and a decrease in facial expressiveness. Parkinson's disease may be treated with the drug L-DOPA, which is converted to dopamine in the brain and replenishes the depleted stores of this transmitter. Dopamine itself is not used in therapy, partly because it will not cross the blood-brain barrier and reach the area where it is needed.

There is a close association between control of motor abilities and control of mental states. Both functions rely heavily on the activity of dopamine-releasing neurons. Consequently, drugs that affect dopamine activity usually alter both systems, resulting in undesired side effects. For example, heavy use of the phenothiazine tranquilizers (like Thorazine, Stelazine, etc.) in the treatment of psychotic patients causes Parkinsonlike symptoms. If such drugs are given daily over several years, problems with motor functioning may become permanent. Drugs of abuse, such as stimulants, increase dopamine activity, causing enhanced motor activity as well as psychotic behavior.

THE LIMBIC SYSTEM The limbic system includes an assortment of linked brain regions located near and including the hypothalamus (see Figure 5-9). Besides the hypothalamus, the limbic structures include the thalamus, hippocampus, amygdala, median forebrain bundle, and front portion of the cerebral cortex. Functions of the limbic and basal ganglia structures are inseparably linked; often, drugs that affect one system also affect the other.

The primary roles of limbic brain regions include regulating emotional activities (e.g., fear, rage, and anxiety), memory, modulation of basic hypothalamic functions (such as endocrine activity), and activities such as mating, procreation, and caring for the young. In addition, reward centers are also believed to be associated with limbic structures. It is almost certain that the mood-elevating effects of even the narcotic opiates (e.g., heroin) are mediated by the limbic systems of the brain.

Recent studies in laboratory animals have shown that most stimulant drugs of abuse (e.g., amphetamines and cocaine) are self-administered through cannula surgically placed into limbic structures (such as the median forebrain bundle and frontal cerebral cortex). This is done by linking injection of the drug into the cannula with a lever press by the animal (Koob and Bloom 1988). It is thought that euphoria or intense "highs" associated with these drugs are due to their effects on these brain regions. Some of the limbic system's principal transmitters include dopamine, norepinephrine, and serotonin; dopamine activation appears to be the primary reinforcement that accounts for the abuse liability of most drugs (Koob and Bloom 1988).

THE CEREBRAL CORTEX The unique features of the human cerebral cortex gives humans a special place among animals. The cortex is a layer of gray matter made up of nerves and supporting cells that almost completely surrounds the rest of the brain and lies immediately under the skull (see Figure 5-10). It is responsible for the interpretation of incoming information and for the initiation of voluntary motor behavior. The center for speech and areas for perception of sensation from all parts of the body are located in the cortex.

The cerebral cortex can be divided into receiving areas, output areas, and association areas.

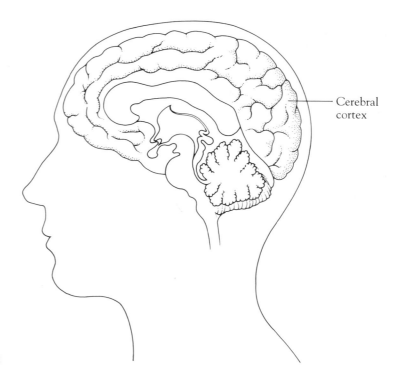

Cerebral cortex

FIGURE 5-10 Human cerebral cortex

The receiving areas obtain input from the various senses such as touch, pain, sight, smell, and sound. Drugs that affect the electrical activity, the receptors, the connecting neurons, or the synapses in the pathways from the site of sensory activation to the cortex will thus affect the response of the individual to that stimulus. Consequently, many psychoactive drugs, such as hallucinogens, dramatically alter the perception of sensory information by the cortex and cause strange behavior.

The part of the cortex that has developed most in the evolutionary process is called the *association cortex*. In large part, the ratio of association cortex to cerebral cortex is a good index of the extent to which an animal functions independently of the environment; that is, the larger the association cortex, the more independent the animal. The association areas do not directly receive input from the environment nor do they directly initiate output to the muscles or the glands. The association areas may store memories or control complex behaviors. Some psychoactive drugs disrupt the normal func-

tioning of these areas and thereby interfere with an individual's ability to deal with complex issues.

THE HYPOTHALAMUS The hypothalamus (see Figures 5-8 and 5-9) is located near the base of the brain. It integrates information from many sources and serves as the CNS control center for the autonomic nervous system and many vital support functions. It is also the primary point of contact between the nervous and the endocrine systems. Because the hypothalamus controls the ANS, it is also responsible for maintaining homeostasis in the body and participates in functions mediated by the limbic system (see above).

The hypothalamus contains groups of neurons called *nuclei*. Some of these nuclei monitor blood levels of various biochemical substances essential to the homeostasis of the body. If the level of a particular substance in the blood deviates from the normal range, the hypothalamic neurons send impulses to appropriate control centers to restore normal levels. It is now known that most of the body's hormones are regulated, in part, by the hypothalamus. If a hormone level drops below a certain point, a signal is sent from the hypothalamus to the appropriate gland (such as adrenal, thyroid, sex glands, etc.), which will release the needed hormone.

Because the hypothalamus is very vascular, many drugs are quickly carried in the blood to this region. The rate at which drugs affect the hypothalamus depends on how these compounds pass across the blood-brain barrier. Because of the vital regulatory role of the hypothalamus, drugs that alter its function can have a major impact on systems that control homeostasis. The catecholamine transmitters are particularly important in regulating the function of the hypothalamus; thus, drugs that alter the activity of norepinephrine and dopamine are likely to alter the activity of this brain structure.

THE AUTONOMIC NERVOUS SYSTEM

The ANS is an integrative, or regulatory, system that does not require conscious control (i.e., you do not have to think about it). It is usually considered primarily a motor or output system, and most of its synapses are outside the CNS. A number of drugs cannot enter the CNS because of the blood-brain barrier and thus affect the ANS only. The ANS is divided into two functional components, the sympathetic and the parasympathetic nervous systems. Both systems send neurons to most visceral organs and to smooth muscles, glands, and blood vessels (see Figure 5-11).

The two components of the ANS generally have opposite effects on an organ or its function. The working of the heart is a good example of sympathetic and parasympathetic control (see Figure 5-8). Stimulation of the parasympathetic nervous system slows the heartrate, whereas stimulation of the sympathetic nerves accelerates it. These actions constitute a constant biological check-and-balance, or regulatory system. Because the two parts of the ANS work in opposite ways much of the time, they are considered physiological antagonists. These two systems control most of the internal organs, the circulatory system, and the glandular system. The sympathetic system is normally active at all times; the degree of activity varies from moment to moment and from organ to organ. The parasympathetic nervous system is organized mainly for limited, focused activity and usually conserves and restores energy rather than expends it. For example, it slows the heartrate, lowers blood pressure, aids in absorption of nutrients, and is involved in emptying the urinary bladder. Table 5-1 lists the structures and/or functions of the sympathetic and parasympathetic nervous systems and their effects on each other.

The two branches of the autonomic nervous system use two different neurotransmitters. The parasympathetic branch releases acetylcholine at its synapses, whereas the sympathetic neurons release norepinephrine. An increase in epinephrine

TABLE 5-1 Sympathetic and parasympathetic control

Structure or Function	Sympathetic	Parasympathetic
Heartrate	Speeds up	Slows
Breathing rate	Speeds up	Slows
Stomach wall	Slows motility	Increases
Skin blood vessels (vasomotor function)	Constricts	Dilates
Iris of eye	Constricts (pupil enlarges)	Dilates
Vomiting center	Stimulates	

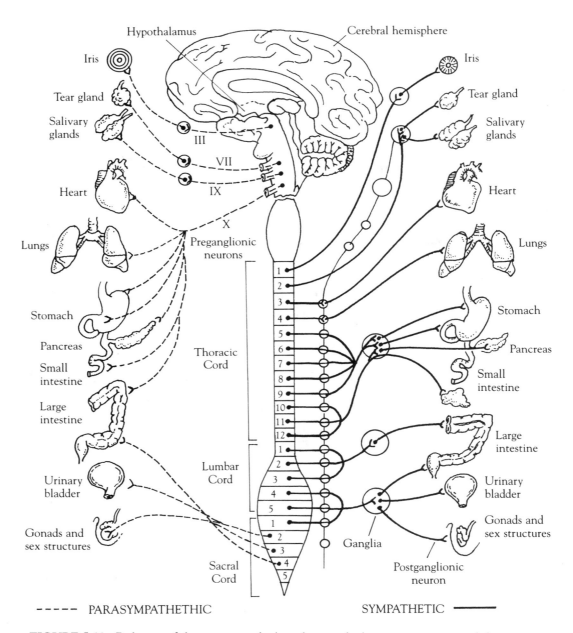

FIGURE 5-11 Pathways of the parasympathetic and sympathetic nervous systems and the organs affected

in the blood or the administration of drugs that mimic norepinephrine cause the body to respond as if the sympathetic nervous system had been activated. As previously mentioned, such drugs are referred to as *sympathomimetics*. Thus, taking amphetamines (which, among other things, cause the release of norepinephrine and epinephrine) raises blood pressure, speeds up heartrate, slows down motility of the stomach walls, and may cause the pupils of the eyes to enlarge; other so-called "uppers," like cocaine, may have similar effects.

Drugs that affect acetylcholine release, metabolism, or its interaction with its respective receptor are referred to as *cholinergic* drugs and can either mimic or antagonize the parasympathetic nervous system according to pharmacological action.

Think About It...

1. Why do drugs of abuse usually also affect motor activity?

2. You work for a drug company that has found a drug that stimulates the release of dopamine, norepinephrine, epinephrine, serotonin, and acetylcholine from neurons in the central nervous system and peripheral nervous system. Is this drug likely to be very useful for therapy? Defend your answer.

3. You are a physician treating a patient whose heart is beating rapidly and unpredictably. What type of a drug would you want to prescribe for this patient? Describe how it might work to achieve the therapeutic objective.

THE ENDOCRINE SYSTEM AND DRUGS

As explained earlier in this chapter, the endocrine system consists of glands, which are ductless (meaning that they secrete directly into the bloodstream) and release chemical substances called *hormones*. These hormones are essential in the regulation of many vital functions, including metabolism, growth, tissue repair, and sexual behavior, to mention just a few. In contrast to neurotransmitters, hormones tend to have a slower onset and

a longer duration of action with a more generalized target. Although a number of tissues present throughout the body are capable of producing and releasing hormones, three of the principal sources of these chemical messengers are the pituitary gland, the adrenal glands, and the sex glands.

ENDOCRINE GLANDS AND REGULATION

The pituitary gland is often referred to as the *master gland*. It controls many of the other glands comprising the endocrine system by releasing regulating factors and growth hormone. The hypothalamus, besides controlling the brain functions already mentioned, helps control the activity of the pituitary gland and thereby has a very prominent effect on the endocrine system.

The adrenal glands are located near the kidneys and are divided into two parts: the outer surface, called the *cortex*, and the inner part, called the *medulla*. The adrenal medulla is actually a component of the sympathetic nervous system and releases adrenaline (another name for *epinephrine*) during sympathetic stimulation. The hormones released by the adrenal cortex are called *corticosteroids*, or frequently just *steroids*. Steroids help the body to respond appropriately to crises and stress. In addition, small amounts of male sex hormones, called *androgens*, are also released by the adrenal cortex. The androgens produce **anabolic** effects that increase the retention and synthesis of proteins, causing increases in the mass of tissues such as muscles and bones.

---

anabolic
chemicals able to convert nutrients into tissue mass

Sex glands are responsible for the secretion of male and female sex hormones that help regulate the development and activity of the respective reproductive systems. The organs known as *gonads* include the female ovaries and the male testis. The activity of the gonads is regulated by hormones released from the pituitary gland and, for the most part, is suppressed until puberty. After activation, estrogens and progesterones are released from the ovaries and the androgens (principally testosterone) are released from the testis. These hormones are responsible for the development and maintenance of the secondary sex characteristics. They influence not only sex-related body features but also emotional states, suggesting that these sex hormones enter the brain and significantly impact the functioning of the limbic systems.

For the most part, drugs prescribed to treat endocrine problems are intended as replacement therapy. For example, diabetic patients suffer from a lack of insulin from the pancreas, so therapy consists of insulin injections. Patients who suffer from dwarfism have insufficient growth hormone from the pituitary gland; thus, growth hormone is administered to stimulate normal growth.

CONTRACEPTION

For women, female sex hormones are often given as replacement therapy. Estrogen supplements are given to women who experience depression or headaches associated with menopause to compensate for the cessation of estrogen secretion. Another very common use of female hormones is as a contraceptive strategy. These medications consist of synthetic derivatives of estrogens and/or progesterone (called **progestins**) and are usually intended to prevent pregnancy (although under some conditions they can be used to enhance the chances of pregnancy).

progestins
compounds similar to the female hormone progesterone

The female reproductive cycle is regulated by a complex pattern of hormonal signals between the hypothalamus and the reproductive system. Estrogen and progesterone play an important role in this activity and substantially influence maturation of the female egg (ovum) in the ovaries, its release (called *ovulation*), and preparation of the uterus for implantation of the fertilized egg, or embryo. The appropriate hormonal signals for this reproductive process require a particular sequence of these two hormones—estrogen and progesterone—in specific proportions. During pregnancy, large quantities of both are released by the body in order to block subsequent ovulation and prevent the formation of additional embryos. Oral contraceptives take advantage of this effect and include relatively high doses of the female hormones either in combination ("the pill") or separately (progestin in the "minipill") and fool the body into thinking that it is pregnant.

THE ABUSE OF HORMONES: ANABOLIC STEROIDS

Androgens are the hormones most likely to be abused. Testosterone is the primary natural androgen and is produced by the testis. Naturally produced androgens are essential for normal growth and development of male sex organs as well as secondary sex characteristics such as male hair patterns, voice changes, muscular development, and fat distribution. The androgens are also necessary for appropriate growth spurts during adolescence (*Drug Facts and Comparisons* 1991). Accepted therapeutic use of the androgens is usually for replacement in males with abnormally functioning testis. In such cases, the androgens are administered prior to puberty and for prolonged periods during puberty in order to stimulate proper male development.

THE EFFECTS OF ANABOLIC STEROIDS ON ATHLETES   There is no question that androgens have an impressive effect on development of tissue; in particular, they cause pronounced growth of muscle mass and a substantial increase in body weight in young men with deficient testis function. Because of these effects, androgens are classified as **anabolic** (able to stimulate the conversion of nutrients into tissue mass) **steroids** (because chemically, they are similar to the steroids).

anabolic steroids
compounds chemically like the steroids that stimulate production of tissue mass

Many athletes and trainers have assumed (although convincing evidence is still lacking) that, in very high doses, androgens can also enhance muscle growth above that achieved by normal testicular function. Based on this assumption, male and female athletes as well as nonathletes who are into body building have been attracted to these drugs in hopes of enlarging muscle size and improving their athletic performances as well as their physiques. While the androgens might cause some of the desired anabolic effects, they also cause unwanted sex changes. Consequently, attempts have been made to identify steroids that retain the anabolic effects but have minimal androgen (masculinization) impact. As yet, it has not been possible to separate the two; thus, the secondary sex changes have been a persistent problem associated with the use of these drugs.

Weight lifters started using androgens in the 1950s to build muscle mass and increase strength as well as improve their physiques. Today, steroid use is widespread throughout all sports, at all levels of competition, and among all ages. Concern about the use of steroids has grown as publicity about the problem has increased. A well-publicized example involved Canadian sprinter Ben Johnson, whose gold medal was taken away in the 1988 Olympics after it was discovered that he had been using steroids. It is estimated that approximately 50% of the athletes who abuse androgens obtain these steroids illegally, while the other 50% obtain them with prescriptions written by physicians (Wilson 1990).

Neither the short- nor long-term effects of androgen abuse are yet understood. While it is clear that, in both women of all ages and boys, use of

At 5'1", 114 lbs., 18 year-old Caroline McCarthy held the 1986 National Power Lifting Champion title for squat lifting 319 lbs. *Photo:* © Gary Walts/The Image Works

the androgens increases muscle mass, their effects on mature men are not so apparent. Nonetheless, many anecdotal stories are told in locker rooms of athletes who experienced dramatic increases in muscle size and strength because of steroid use. Certainly, such testimonials have enhanced the demand for these hormones, whether through legitimate or illegitimate means (Wilson 1990).

Although several studies have verified that large doses of androgens increase muscle mass (Griggs et al. 1989), the influence of these hormones on athletic performance is not so easily determined. Yet many athletes, coaches, and trainers are convinced of their virtues and have included them as an integral part (either blatantly or coercively) of their training programs.

The risks caused by androgens are not well understood. Most certainly, the higher the doses and the longer the use, the greater the potential damage these drugs can do to the body. Many of

Let's Get the Facts

How Steroids Can Affect the Body

Anabolic steroids are compounds derived from testosterone, the male hormone, or prepared synthetically to promote general body growth. Large doses over extended periods can cause health problems.

In Men
Large doses decrease the production of testosterone, leading to breast growth, shrinking of the testes, and impotence.

In Women
Steroids bring out male characteristics: decreased breast size, deeper voice, growth of facial hair, acne, and enlarged clitoris.

In Teen-Agers
Steroids can stunt growth by closing the epiphyseal growth plates, the spongy parts of bones that expand during growth.

Breast soreness and, in some cases, breast cancer can develop in either sex.

In Pregnancy
Steroids may cause the development of male features in female fetuses and premature growth and development of male features in male fetuses.

Steroids can cause aggressive behavior, mood swings, and depression. Brain tumors also can form.

Acne and accelerated balding in men are also side effects.

Steroids promote atherosclerosis, or hardened arteries, by increasing blood levels of cholesterol and decreasing levels of "good cholesterol," which the body uses to fight heart disease.

Tumors of the liver, liver cancer, and hepatitis can develop in both sexes.

Chills, diarrhea, feeling of abdominal or stomach fullness

Reduced fertility can occur in women, and in men, decreased sexual ability.

Source: Arizona Republic, U.S. Pharmacopeial Convention Inc. Permission pending.

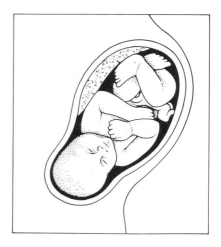

the identified side effects of these hormones are listed in the Let's Get the Facts box. However, not everyone is convinced that steroid use is dangerous and should be outlawed. Some professional trainers even claim that low-dose, intermittent use can enhance athletic performance while causing no health risk. For additional views of this controversy, see the For You to Consider box.

Several studies have demonstrated that anabolic hormones particularly affect the limbic structures of the brain. Consequently, these drugs can cause excitation and a sense of superior strength and performance in some users. These effects, coupled with increased aggressiveness, could encourage continual use of these drugs. Other CNS effects, however, may be disturbing to the user. Symptoms that may occur include uncontrolled rage (referred to as "roid rage"), headaches, anxiety, insomnia, and perhaps paranoia (*Drug Facts and Comparisons* 1991; Pope and Katz 1991).

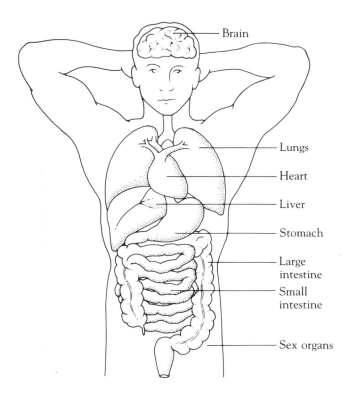

For You to Consider...

The Anabolic Steroid Debate

Advocates

1. Angelo Isyianko was a Canadian sprinter, ranked fourth in the world in 1982 and a two-time winner of the Canadian Female Athlete of the Year Award. According to Isyianko, use of steroids by athletes wasn't cheating because everyone was doing it. To be the best, you have to be willing to take the risks, even if it means using steroids. She claims that, when using small amounts intermittently, steroids have no serious effects. Even though she was stripped of her 50-meter world record when her use of steroids was discovered, Isyianko says she would continue to use steroids if she were still competing.

2. Dan Deschesne was a one-time body builder turned trainer for professional athletes. He used to sell steroids on the "black market." Deschesne has authored a handbook on so-called proper use of steroids for athletes. He claims that use of low doses of anabolic steroids under his supervision can effectively and safely increase strength and physical performance.

3. Charles Francis was the coach who put Ben Johnson on steroids. He claims that steroids are not unethical by themselves but only because they have been banned and made illegal. According to Francis, if steroid use is monitored by a physician and the drug is prescribed in low doses for limited duration, it is safe and effective.

Opponents

1. Cindy Olivaray was a member of the U.S. National Cycling Team in 1981 and won three national cycling titles as well as a silver medal in the 1983 World Cycling Championships. She tested positive for steroids in 1984 and was kicked off the team. Olivaray claims she is not proud that she used steroids and claims that none of her accomplishments mean anything to her because she feels she cheated; it was the drugs that made her win. Olivaray developed hepatitis, and a cancerous growth rapidly spread on her back before it was surgically removed. She believes that her steroid use contributed to both problems.

2. Steve Corsen was a pro football player for nine years. Corsen claims that team physicians recklessly treated his injuries with steroids and other drugs so he could quickly get back on the football field to play. He claims that he was encouraged to use steroids to improve his performance. The use of these drugs reflects the attitude to win at all costs. Corsen was one of the first pro football players to admit he used steroids. He now writes and lectures against steroid use in sports.

3. Senator Joseph Biden from Delaware supports the illegalization of steroids. Biden feels that the use of steroids is unfair and gives an artificial advantage that has nothing to do with what sports are all about.

4. The American Medical Association (AMA) has officially opposed the use of anabolic steroids to promote athletic performance. The AMA believes that, even though everything is not known about the long-term effects of these hormones, the unnecessary use of steroids presents a significant health risk.

Source: From *Sports and Drugs Series* on "Morning Edition," National Public Radio, January 14, 1991, 10:00 A.M.

CURRENT ABUSE PATTERNS AND RESPONSES In attempts to enhance performance, athletes may take dosages of steroids up to 100 times the therapeutic range. In addition, some users take several different androgens together (called "stacking") for extended periods; little is known about the consequences of this form of androgen abuse. Although the precise extent of androgen misuse is not clear, some estimates claim that 7% of male high school seniors have used these hormones. While many androgen users were involved in school-sponsored sports (especially football and wrestling), 35% have no involvement in organized athletics. In college, androgen use approximates 20% among athletes (*AHFS Drug Information* 1991).

The medical community has become very concerned about the inappropriate use of androgens. Attempts have been made to prevent abuse by implementing education programs, drug screening, and associated penalties when rules are violated. To help prevent abuse, anabolic steroids were recently classified as a controlled drug by the Drug Enforcement Administration (DEA). The Anabolic Steroids Control Act of 1990 placed these drugs into Schedule III of the Controlled Substances Act, effective February 27, 1991. The term *anabolic steroid* is defined in this act as "any drug or hormonal substance chemically and pharmacologically related to testosterone (other than estrogens, progestins, and corticosteroids) that promotes muscle growth" (Federal Register 1991). This requires anyone who distributes or dispenses anabolic steroids to be registered with the DEA. Persons distributing androgens who are not properly authorized can be imprisoned for not more than five years and be·required to pay fines as deemed appropriate. If the offense involves providing drugs to an individual under 18 years of age, the violation is punishable by not more than 10 years in prison.

How effective will these strategies be in preventing the disturbing practice of steroid use? Enforcement of the act began soon after its implementation. For example, in July 1991, federal drug agents in Phoenix, Arizona, made 21 arrests and seized 3 gymnasiums after it was reported that athletes were using anabolic steroids (Associated Press, 1991). It remains to be seen if such prosecution will significantly alter the use pattern of these hormones.

Think About It . . .

1. Should the FDA regulate hormones differently than other drugs?
2. What special risks are associated with the abuse of anabolic steroids?
3. You are the principal gymnast on your university team. Your coach offers to provide you with intermittent, low doses of anabolic steroids to improve your strength and performance. This will help you qualify for the conference championships. How would you respond to this offer?

KEY TERMS

homeostasis	reflexes	vasculature
hormones	endorphins	psychoactive
neurons	agonistic	anticholinergic
synapse	antagonistic	anabolic
dendrites	muscarinic	progestins
receptor	nicotinic	anabolic steroids
neurotransmitters	catecholamines	
axon	sympathomimetic	

SUMMARY

1. The nervous and endocrine systems help to mediate internal and external responses to the body's surroundings. Both systems release chemical messengers in order to achieve their homeostatic functions. These messenger substances are called *neurotransmitters* and *hormones*

and exert their functions through receptors. Many drugs exert their effects by influencing these chemical messengers.

2. The neuron is the principal cell type in the nervous system. This specialized cell consists of dendrites, a cell body, and an axon. It communicates with other neurons and organs by releasing neurotransmitters, which can cause either excitation or inhibition at their target sites.

3. The chemical messengers from glands and neurons exert their effects by interacting with special protein regions in membranes called *receptors*. Because of their unique structures, receptors only interact with molecules that have specific configurations. Activation of receptors can initiate a chain of events within cells, resulting in changes in gene expression, enzyme activity, or metabolic function.

4. *Agonists* are substances or drugs that stimulate receptors. *Antagonists* are substances or drugs that attach to receptors and prevent them from being activated.

5. A variety of different substances are used as neurotransmitters by neurons in the body. The classes of transmitters include the catecholamines, serotonin, acetylcholine, GABA, and peptides. These transmitters are excitatory, inhibitory, or sometimes both, depending on which receptor is being activated. Many drugs selectively act to either enhance or antagonize these neurotransmitters and their activities.

6. The central nervous system consists of the brain and spinal cord. Regions within the brain help to regulate specific functions. The hypothalamus controls endocrine and basic body functions. The basal ganglia is primarily responsible for controlling motor activity. The limbic system regulates mood and mental states. The cerebral cortex helps interpret, process, and respond to input information.

7. The limbic system and its associated transmitters, especially dopamine, is a major site of action for the drugs of abuse. Substances that increase the activity of dopamine cause a sense of well-being and euphoria, which encourages psychological dependence.

8. The autonomic nervous system is composed of the sympathetic and parasympathetic systems; neurons associated with these systems release noradrenalin and acetylcholine as their transmitters, respectively. These systems work in an antagonistic fashion to control unconscious, visceral functions such as breathing and cardiovascular activity. The parasympathetic nervous system usually helps to conserve and restore energy in the body, while the sympathetic nervous system is continually active.

9. The endocrine system consists of glands that synthesize and release hormones into the blood. Distribution via blood circulation carries these chemical messengers throughout the body, where they act on specific receptors. Some of the principal structures include the pituitary, adrenals, and thyroid glands, as well as the pancreas.

10. Anabolic steroids are structurally related to the male hormone testosterone. They are often abused by both male and female athletes trying to build muscle mass and enhance performance. The continual use of high doses of anabolic steroids can cause annoying and dangerous side effects. The long-term effects of low, intermittent doses of these drugs has not been determined. Because of concern by most medical authorities, anabolic steroids are controlled substances and have been classified as Schedule III substances.

R E F E R E N C E S

AHFS Drug Information. Bethesda MD: Amer ican Society of Hospital Pharmacists, 1991.

Associated Press release, 11 July, 1991.

Drug Facts and Comparisons. St. Louis, MO: Lippincott, 1991.

Federal Register 56 (13 February 1991): 3754.

Griggs, R., W. Kingston, R. Jozetowicz, B. Herr, G. Forbes, and D. Hallibday. "Effect of Testosterone on Muscle Mass and Muscle Protein Synthesis." *Journal of Applied Physiology* 66 (1989): 498–503.

Izquierdo, I. "A Game with Shifting Mirrors." *Trends in Pharmacological Sciences* 10 (1989): 473–475.

Kandel, E., J. Schwartz, and T. Jessell, eds. *Principles of Neural Science,* 3rd ed. New York: Elsevier, 1991.

Koob, G., and R. Bloom. "Cellular and Molecular Mechanisms of Drug Dependence." *Science* 242 (1988): 715–723.

Pope, H., and D. Katz. "What Are the Psychiatric Risks of Anabolic Steroids?" *Harvard Mental Health Letter* 7 (April 1991): 8.

Snyder, S. H. "Opiate Receptors in the Brain." *New England Journal of Medicine* 296 (1977): 266–271.

Stevens, C. F. "The Neuron." *Scientific American* 241, no. 3 (1979): 55–65.

Wilson, J. "Androgens." In *The Pharmacological Basis of Therapeutics,* 8th ed., edited by A. Gilman, T. Rall, A. Nies, and P. Taylor. New York: Plenum, 1990.

CNS Depressants: Sedative-Hypnotics

CHAPTER OUTLINE

The History of CNS Depressants / **The Effects of CNS Depressants: Benefits and Risks** / **Types of CNS Depressants** ▪ Benzodiazepines: Valium-Type Drugs ▪ Barbiturates ▪ Other CNS Depressants / **Patterns of Abuse with CNS Depressants** ▪ Treatment for Withdrawal

LEARNING OBJECTIVES

On completing this chapter, you will be able to:

1. Identify the primary drug groups used for CNS depressant effects.
2. Explain the principal therapeutic uses of the CNS depressants and how the effects relate to drug dose.
3. Explain why CNS depressant drugs are commonly abused.
4. Identify the differences and similarities between benzodiazepines and barbiturates.
5. Relate how benzodiazepine dependence usually develops.
6. Describe the differences in effects between short- and long-acting CNS depressants.
7. Explain the current status of methaqualone.
8. Describe the CNS depressant properties of antihistamines and compare their therapeutic usefulness to that of benzodiazepines.
9. List the four principal types of persons who abuse CNS depressants.
10. Identify the basic principles in treating dependence on CNS depressants.

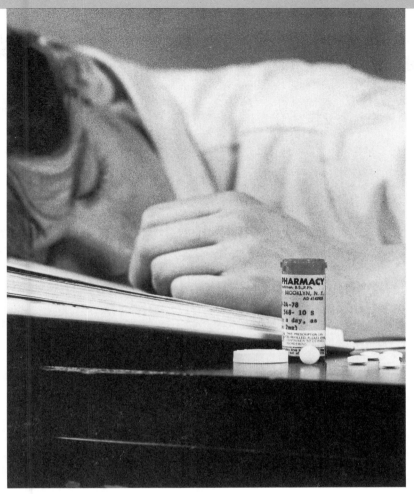

Source: Laimute E. Druskis/Stock, Boston

Central nervous system (CNS) depressants are some of the most widely used and abused drugs in existence. Why? They are able to relieve stress and anxiety and even induce sleep—effects that appeal to many people, particularly those who are struggling with problems and looking for a break, physically and emotionally. However, CNS depressants produce a host of serious side effects, including problems with tolerance and dependence. Ironically, many of the individuals who have become dependent on depressants have obtained them through legitimate means: a prescription given by a physician. Although depressants are available on the "streets," this is not the bulk of the problem. In fact, homemakers are often prone to this type of drug abuse.

In this chapter, we will begin with a review of the history of CNS depressants, in terms of both development and use, followed by a discussion of the effects these drugs produce, positive and negative. Each of the major types of depressant drugs will then be reviewed in detail: benzodiazepines, barbiturates, and other smaller categories. We will conclude with an examination of abuse patterns of depressant drugs, including discussion of treatment of drug dependence and withdrawal.

THE HISTORY OF CNS DEPRESSANTS

Before the era of modern drugs, the most common depressant used to ease tension, cause relaxation, and help people forget their problems was alcohol. These effects no doubt accounted for the immense popularity of alcohol and help explain why this traditional depressant is the most commonly abused drug of all time. (Alcohol will be discussed in detail in Chapter 7.)

Attempts to find CNS depressants other than alcohol that could be used to treat nervousness and anxiety began in the 1800s with the introduction of bromides. These drugs were very popular until their toxicities became known. In the early 1900s, bromides were replaced by barbiturates. Like bromides, barbiturates were initially heralded as safe and effective depressants; however, problems with tolerance, dependence, and lethal overdoses became evident. It was learned that the doses of barbiturates required to treat anxiety also could cause CNS depression, affecting respiration and impairing mental functions. The margin of safety for barbiturates was too narrow, so research for a safer CNS depressant began again.

It was not until the 1950s that the first benzodiazepines were marketed as substitutes for the dangerous barbiturates. Benzodiazepines were originally viewed as extremely safe and free from the problems of tolerance, dependence, and withdrawal that occurred with the other drugs in this category (Mondanaro 1988, 95). Unfortunately, benzodiazepines have been found to be less than ideal antianxiety drugs. Although relatively safe when used for short periods, long-term use can cause dependence and withdrawal problems much like those associated with their depressant predecessors. These problems have become a major concern of the medical community, which will be discussed in greater detail later in the chapter.

Many of the people who have become dependent on CNS depressants such as benzodiazepines began use of the drugs under the supervision of a physician. Some clinicians routinely prescribe CNS depressants for cases of stress, anxiety, or apprehension, without trying nonpharmacological approaches, such as psychotherapy. It is quicker and less troublesome for a clinician to write a prescription to cure emotional problems (hoping that it will resolve itself in time) than to spend time counseling a patient, helping him or her to work out

For You to Consider...

Valium: From Therapeutics to Abuse

A woman who had been abandoned as a child was then left by her husband for another woman. To deal with the emotional trauma and her sense of being unwanted, the patient was prescribed Valium. Over the next few years, the stress in her life continued unabated, due to frequent periods of unemployment and associated financial difficulties as well as serious problems with her children. The patient became dependent on Valium and continued to use it daily for 15 years. This drug had been the only therapy for this woman's emotional problems during the entire period. Because of concern about drug dependence, psychotherapy was attempted to help the patient deal with her continuing problems. With counseling, she was weaned from the Valium and eliminated her benzodiazepine dependence (Mondanaro 1988).

difficulties. This practice sends an undesirable and often detrimental message to patients: that is, that CNS depressants are a simple solution to their complex, stressful problems.

Consequently, during the 1970s and 1980s, there was an epidemic of prescriptions for CNS depressants. For example, in 1973, 100 million prescriptions were written for benzodiazepines alone. Approximately twice as many women as men were taking the drugs at this time, which continues to be the case. Many homemakers made CNS depressants a part of their household routine, as described in the lyrics of the rock song "Mother's Little Helper" on the Rolling Stones' album *Flowers:*

> Things are different today
> I hear every mother say
> "Mother needs something today to calm her
>   down"
> And though she's not really ill,
> there's a little yellow pill.
> She goes running for the shelter
> Of her "mother's little helper"

> And it helps her on her way,
> Gets her through her busy day.★

As the medical community became more aware of the problem, the use of depressants declined. In 1984, 70 million prescriptions of benzodiazepines were written (Mondanaro 1988), and even fewer were written in 1990 (*Pharmacy Times* 1991). Today, efforts are again being made by pharmaceutical companies and scientists to find new classes of CNS depressants that can be used to relieve stress and anxiety without causing serious side effects such as dependence and withdrawal.

THE EFFECTS OF CNS DEPRESSANTS: BENEFITS AND RISKS

The CNS depressants are a diverse group of drugs that share an ability to reduce CNS activity and diminish the brain's level of awareness. Besides the benzodiazepines, barbituratelike drugs, and alcohol, depressant drugs also include antihistamines and opioid narcotics like heroin (see Chapter 8).

Depressants are often classified according to the degree of their medical effects on the body. For instance, **sedatives** cause mild depression of the CNS and relaxation. This drug effect is used to treat extreme anxiety. Many sedatives also have muscle-relaxing properties that enhance their relaxing effects.

sedatives
CNS depressants used to relieve anxiety, fear, and apprehension

Depressants are also used to promote sleep. **Hypnotics** (from the Greek god of sleep, Hypnos) are CNS depressants that encourage sleep by inducing drowsiness. Often when depressants are used as hypnotics, they have **amnesiac** effects, as

CNS depressants can be used
as hypnotics to initiate sleep.
Source: Jeff Dunn/Stock, Boston

well. As already mentioned, the effects produced
by depressants can be very enticing and encourage
inappropriate use.

hypnotics
CNS depressants used to induce drowsiness and
encourage sleep

amnesiac
causing the loss of memory

For You to Consider...

Depressant Abuse: The First Experience

The following account tells of the depression experienced
by a high school student when he used heroin for the
first time:

> I got really scared when I began to feel that feeling of
> relaxation spreading through me. I felt sort of like my
> whole body was falling apart, like I was turning into a
> big blob of jelly or something. I wanted it to go away,
> but it came on more and more. After a few minutes
> it got so that I wanted to fall asleep, but just as I be-
> gan to doze off, I got this fear that I might never
> wake up again, like I was going to die. And also I got
> really sick to my stomach. I didn't actually blow lunch,
> but I felt like I was about to for about three hours.
>
> I don't know [why I took heroin again]. I guess I fig-
> ured that it would be better the next time. Like
> other people could get a good high out of it, so I fig-
> ured I ought to be able to, too. And I did. Like now I
> never get scared and it's real nice (Pope 1971, 118).

The effects of the CNS depressants tend to be
dose dependent (see Figure 6-1). Thus, a larger
dose of a sedative may have a hypnotic effect.
Often the only difference between a sedative and
a hypnotic effect is the dosage. By increasing the
dose still further, an anesthetic state can be reached.
Anesthesia is deep depression of the CNS and is
used to achieve a controlled state of unconsciousness so a patient can be treated, usually by surgery,
in relative comfort and without memory of an unpleasant experience. With the exception of ben-

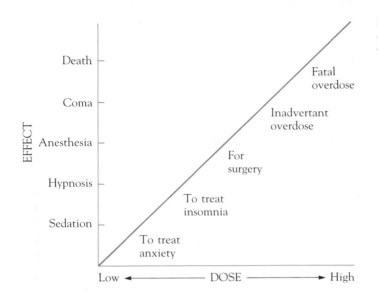

FIGURE 6-1 Dose-dependent effects of CNS depressants

zodiazepines, if the dose of most of the depressants is increased much more, coma or death will ensue because the CNS becomes so depressed that vital centers controlling breathing and heart activity cease to function properly.

---

anesthesia
a state characterized by loss of sensation or consciousness

It is important to realize that all CNS depressants are not "created equal." Some have wider margins of safety; others have a greater potential for nonmedicinal abuse. These differences are important when considering the therapeutic advantages of each type of CNS depressant. In addition, unique features of the different types of depressants make them useful for treatment of other medical problems. For example, some barbiturates and benzodiazepines are used to treat forms of epilepsy or acute seizure activity, while opioid narcotics are important in the treatment of many types of pain. Some of these unique features will be dealt with in greater detail when the individual drug groups are discussed. The benzodiazepines, barbiturate-

like drugs, and antihistamines are dealt with in this chapter. Other CNS depressants, such as alcohol and opiates, are covered in Chapters 7 and 8, respectively.

TYPES OF CNS DEPRESSANTS
BENZODIAZEPINES: VALIUM-TYPE DRUGS

Benzodiazepines are by far the most frequently prescribed CNS depressants for anxiety and sleep. In fact, two of the top-selling prescription drugs in the United States during 1990 were the benzodiazepines Xanax and Halcion (*American Druggist*, February 1991). Because of their wide margin of safety (death from an overdose is almost unheard of), benzodiazepines have replaced barbituratelike drugs in use as sedatives and hypnotics. Benzodiazepines were originally referred to as the *minor tranquilizers*, but this terminology erroneously implied that they had pharmacological properties similar to those of antipsychotic drugs (the major tranquilizers), when in fact they are very different. Consequently, the term *minor tranquilizer* is rarely used today.

The forerunners of benzodiazepines included

a muscle relaxant called *mephenesin*. Because mephenesin was short acting, research was done to find an agent of longer duration. In 1952, a new compound, *meprobamate*, was developed that seemed to satisfy the need. It was marketed as Miltown in 1955 and met with immediate and phenomenal acceptance. Sales went from $7,500 to $500,000 between May and December 1955.

The first true benzodiazepine, *Librium*, was developed for medical use and marketed about 1960; the very popular drug Valium came on the market about the same time. In fact, Valium was so well received that, from 1972 to 1978, it was the top-selling prescription drug in the United States. Its popularity continues to this day, as it still ranks in the top 20 of prescribed drugs (*Pharmacy Times* 1991).

Because of dependence problems in 1970, the U.S. Bureau of Narcotics and Dangerous Drugs restricted the number of times a prescription for meprobamate could be refilled. It and the other benzodiazepines are now classified as Schedule IV drugs due to their abuse liability. In recent years, there has been considerable concern that benzodiazepines are overprescribed because of their con-

siderable safety; it has been said, somewhat facetiously, that the only way a person could die from using the benzodiazepines would be to choke on them. The American Medical Association (AMA) has become very concerned about this overconfident attitude toward benzodiazepines and has warned doctors against prolonged and unsupervised administration of these drugs.

MEDICAL USES Benzodiazepines are used for an array of therapeutic objectives, including the relief of anxiety (referred to as **anxiolytics**), treatment of neurosis, muscle relaxation, alleviation of lower-back pain, treatment of some convulsive disorders, induction of sleep (hypnotic), relief from withdrawal symptoms associated with narcotic and alcohol dependence, and induction of amnesia usually for preoperative administration (administered just prior to or during surgery or very uncomfortable procedures).

anxiolytics
drugs that relieve anxiety

Let's Get the Facts

Common Clinical Uses of Benzodiazepines

One of the most frequent uses of Librium (chlordiazepoxide) and Valium (diazepam) is in detoxification for withdrawal from alcohol. One of these is often the first drug that an alcoholic receives in "detox" because, as a CNS depressant, it calms the detoxifying alcoholic and allows him or her to go through withdrawal without the terrible effects of delirium tremens (violent shaking).

Valium is a frequent preanesthetic

drug given to patients just prior to major surgery. It helps to relax the patient for the procedure and in many cases keeps him or her from remembering the emotional and physical stress of the surgical experience. Valium is also used on an outpatient basis for minor procedures such as hand, arm, and dental surgery to make the patient more comfortable.

Xanax has been widely used in the treatment of intense fears, or *phobias*. Recently, the Food and Drug Administration (FDA) also approved the use of Xanax for treatment of anx-

iety attacks, which are sudden, inexplicable feelings of extreme terror or impending doom (*Medical Letter* 17 May 1991).

Clonazepam is used in the treatment of some types of seizures in children, but tolerance develops quickly to this action so use is limited. Valium is often the drug of choice to treat the very dangerous condition of status epilepticus: abrupt, severe, generalized seizures brought on by incidents such as trauma to the head and high fevers. If not quickly treated, status epilepticus can be fatal (Rall and Schleifer 1990).

MECHANISMS OF ACTION   In contrast to barbiturate-type drugs, which cause general depression of most neuronal activity, benzodiazepines selectively affect those neurons that have receptors for the neurotransmitter gamma-aminobutyric acid (GABA). GABA is a very important inhibitory transmitter in several brain regions: the limbic system, the reticular activating system, and the motor cortex (see Chapter 5). In the presence of benzodiazepines, the inhibitory effects of GABA are increased. Depression of activity in these brain regions likely accounts for the ability of benzodiazepines to alter mood (a limbic function), cause drowsiness (a reticular activating system function), and relax muscles (a cortical function). The specific GABA-enhancing effect of these drugs explains the selective CNS depression caused by benzodiazepines.

Of considerable interest is the observation that these Valium-like drugs act on specific receptor sites that are linked to the GABA receptors in the CNS. As yet, no endogenous substance has been identified that naturally interacts with this so-called benzodiazepine site. However, it is very likely that a natural benzodiazepine does exist that activates this same receptor population and serves to reduce stress and anxiety by natural means. Several laboratories are attempting to locate an endogenous benzodiazepinelike substance.

TYPES   Because benzodiazepines are so popular and thus profitable, new related drugs are routinely being released into the pharmaceutical market. Currently, approximately 12 benzodiazepine compounds are available in the United States.

Benzodiazepines are distinguished primarily by their duration of action (see Table 6-1). As a general rule, the short-acting drugs are used as hypnotics to treat insomnia, thus allowing the user to awake in the morning with few after effects (such as a hangover). The long-acting benzodiazepines tend to be prescribed as sedatives, giving prolonged relaxation and relief from persistent anxiety. Some of the long-acting drugs can exert a relaxing effect for up to 2 to 3 days. One of the reasons for the long action in some benzodiazepines is that they are converted by the liver into metabolites that are as active as the original drug.

TABLE 6-1   Half-lives of various benzodiazepines

Drug	Half-life (hours)
Alprazolam (Xanax)	12–15
Chlordiazepoxide (Librium)	5–30
Clonazepam (Klonopin)	18–50
Clorazepate (Tranxene)	30–100
Diazepam (Valium)	20–80
Halazepam (Paxipam)	14
Lorazepam (Ativan)	10–20
Oxazepam (Serax)	5–20
Prazepam (Centrax)	30–100
Quazepam (Doral)	39
Temazepam (Restoril)	10–17
Triazolam (Halcion)	1.5–5.5

Source: Adapted from *Facts & Comparisons, Drug Newsletter* 10 (February 1991): 10.

For example, Valium (diazepam) has a half-life of 20 to 80 hours and is converted by the liver into several active metabolites, including oxazepam (which itself is marketed as a therapeutic benzodiazepine—see Table 6-1).

SIDE EFFECTS   Reported side effects of benzodiazepines are drowsiness, lightheadedness, lethargy, impairment of mental and physical activities, skin rashes, nausea, diminished libido, irregularities in the menstrual cycle, blood cell abnormalities, and increased sensitivity to alcohol and other CNS depressants. In contrast to barbiturate-type drugs, only very high doses of benzodiazepines have a significant impact on respiration. There are actually few verified instances of death resulting from overdose of benzodiazepines alone. Almost always, serious suppression of vital functions occurs when these drugs are combined with other depressants, most often alcohol.

There is no clear evidence of permanent, irreversible damage to neurological or other physiological processes, even with long-term benzodiazepine use. Benzodiazepines have less effect on **REM sleep** (rapid eye movement, the restive phase) than do barbiturates. Consequently, sleep under the influence of benzodiazepines is more likely to be restful and satisfying. However, prolonged use of hypnotic doses of benzodiazepines may cause rebound increases in REM sleep and insomnia when the drug is stopped.

REM sleep
the restive phase of sleep associated with dreaming

On rare occasions, benzodiazepines can have **paradoxical** effects, producing unusual responses such as nightmares, anxiety, irritability, sweating, and restlessness. Bizarre, uninhibited behavior—such as extreme agitation with hostility, paranoia, and rage—may occur, as well. One such case was reported in 1988 in Utah. A 63-year-old patient who was taking Halcion (a relatively short-acting benzodiazepine) murdered her 87-year-old mother. The suspect claimed that the murder was committed as a consequence of the action of the drug and that she was innocent of committing a crime. Her defense was successful, and she was acquitted of murder. After her acquittal, the woman initiated a $21 million lawsuit against Upjohn Pharmaceuticals for marketing Halcion, which she claimed is a dangerous drug. The lawsuit was settled out of court for an undisclosed amount ("British spark" 3 October 1991). Only time will tell the impact of this case on the future use of Halcion and the other benzodiazepines.

paradoxical
an unexpected effect

There is no obvious explanation for these strange benzodiazepine-induced behaviors, although it is possible that, in some people, the drugs mask inhibitory centers of the brain and allow expression of antisocial behavior that is normally suppressed and controlled.

TOLERANCE, DEPENDENCE, WITHDRAWAL, AND ABUSE   As with most CNS depressants, frequent, chronic use of benzodiazepines can cause tolerance, dependence (both physical and psychological), and withdrawal. However, such side effects are usually not as severe as those of most other depressants and occur only after using the drugs for prolonged periods.

Withdrawal can mimic the condition for which the benzodiazepine is given; for example, withdrawal symptoms can include anxiety or insomnia. In such cases, the clinician may be fooled into thinking that the underlying emotional disorder is still present and resume drug therapy without realizing that the patient has become drug dependent. In situations where users have consumed high doses of benzodiazepine over the long term, more severe, even life-threatening withdrawal symptoms may occur; depression, panic, paranoia, and convulsions have been reported. Severe withdrawal can often be avoided by gradually weaning the patient from the benzodiazepine. It is very unusual to find nontherapeutic drug-seeking behavior in a patient who has been properly removed from benzodiazepines, unless that individual already has a history of drug abuse. In other words, it is not likely that use of benzodiazepines alone will cause patients to become drug addicts for the rest of their lives.

Long-term use of benzodiazepines (periods longer than three to four months) to treat anxiety or sleep disorders has not been shown to be therapeutically useful. Even so, this is a common indiscriminate practice and has been suggested by some clinicians to be responsible for the largest group of prescription drug-dependent people in the United States. Possibly as many as one million individuals in the United States continue to take benzodiazepines because they have become physically dependent through such inappropriate use (Mondanaro 1988, 100).

Benzodiazepines are also commonly combined with illicit drugs. For example, narcotic users frequently combine benzodiazepines with weak heroin to enhance the narcotic effect. It is very common to find heroin users who are dependent on narcotics as well as depressants (Jaffe 1990).

Let's Get the Facts

**Abstinence Syndrome Associated
with Benzodiazepines**

Withdrawal symptoms that frequently occur when the use of a long-acting benzodiazepine is stopped abruptly usually follow this pattern:

Days 1–3: May feel fine

Days 3–4: Restlessness, agitation, headaches, problem eating, and inability to sleep

Days 4–6: The above symptoms plus twitching of facial and arm muscles and feeling of intense burning in the skin

Days 6–7: The above symptoms plus seizures

Source: American Hospital Formulary Service 1991, 1333–1339.

Another frequent combination is the use of benzodiazepines with stimulants such as cocaine. Some addicts claim that this combination enhances the pleasant effects of the stimulant and reduces the "crashing" that occurs after using high doses. (More is said about benzodiazepine abuse later in this chapter.)

Think About It . . .

1. You are a physician treating a stressed patient whose mother has just died. You have the option of prescribing either a benzodiazepine or a barbiturate to help her deal with her sorrow. Which type of drug would you select? What steps would you take to prevent dependence from occurring?

2. Twice as many prescriptions of CNS depressants are written for females as for males. Why do you think this is so?

3. Your life has become very stressful due to problems at work and home. You go to see your physician for help. He gives you a prescription for Halcion. You are aware of the controversy concerning this drug. How would you respond to the doctor's suggested treatment?

BARBITURATES

Barbiturates are defined as "barbituric acid derivatives used in medicine as sedatives and hypnotics." Barbituric acid was synthesized by A. Bayer (of aspirin fame) in Germany in 1864. The reason for choosing the name *barbituric acid* is not known. Some have speculated that the compound was named after a girl Barbara whom Bayer knew. Others think that Bayer celebrated his discovery on the Day of St. Barbara in a tavern that artillery officers frequented. (St. Barbara is the patron saint of artillery men.)

The first compound, *barbituric acid*, has little effect on CNS activity, but with slight modification, it becomes a barbiturate, which is a CNS depressant. The first barbiturate, barbital (Veronal), was used medically in 1903. The names of the barbiturates all end in *-al*, indicating a chemical relationship to barbital, the first one synthesized.

Historically, barbiturates have played an important role in therapeutics because of their effectiveness as sedative-hypnotic agents, routinely used in the treatment of anxiety, agitation, and insomnia. However, because of their narrow margin of safety and their abuse liability, barbiturates have been largely replaced by safer drugs.

Uncontrolled use of barbiturates can cause a state of acute or chronic intoxication. Initially, there may be some loss of inhibition, euphoria, and behavioral stimulation, a pattern often seen with moderate consumption of alcohol. When taken to relieve extreme pain or mental stress, barbiturates may cause delirium and other side effects that can include nausea, nervousness, rash, and diarrhea. The person intoxicated with barbiturates may have difficulty thinking and making judgments, may be emotionally unstable, may be uncoordinated and unsteady when walking, and may slur speech (not unlike the drunken state caused by alcohol).

When used for their hypnotic properties, barbiturates cause an unnatural sleep. The user awakens feeling tired, edgy, and quite unsatisfied, most likely because barbiturates markedly suppress the REM phase of sleep. (As discussed above, REM sleep is necessary for the refreshing renewal that usually accompanies a good sleep experience.) Because benzodiazepines suppress REM sleep (as do all CNS depressants) less severely than barbiturates, use of benzodiazepines as sleep aids is generally better tolerated.

Continued misuse of barbiturate drugs has a cumulative toxic effect on the CNS that is more life threatening than misuse of opiates. In large doses or in combination with other CNS depressants, barbiturates may cause death from respiratory or cardiovascular depression. Because of this toxicity, barbiturates are involved in many drug-related deaths, accidental and suicidal. Repeated misuse induces severe tolerance to and physical dependence on these drugs. Discontinuation of a short-acting barbiturate (see Table 6-3) in persons who are using large doses can cause dangerous withdrawal effects such as life-threatening seizures. Table 6-2 summarizes the range of effects of barbiturates and other depressants on the mind and body.

Concern about the abuse potential of barbiturates has caused the federal government to include some of these depressants in the Controlled Substance Act. Consequently, the short-acting

barbiturates, such as pentobarbital and secobarbital, are Schedule II drugs, while the long-acting barbiturates, such as phenobarbital, are classified as Schedule IV.

EFFECTS AND CLINICAL USES   Barbiturates have many pharmacological actions. They depress the activity of nerves and skeletal, smooth, and cardiac muscles and impact the CNS in several ways, ranging from mild sedation to coma, depending on the dose. At sedative or hypnotic dosage levels, only the CNS is significantly affected. Higher anesthetic doses cause slight decreases in blood pressure, heartrate, and flow of urine. The enzyme systems in the liver are also affected by barbiturates; liver damage may result in hypersensitive users or if high doses are consumed over a long period of time. Barbiturates combine with one of the main enzymes in the liver, cytochrome P-450, and interfere with the metabolism normally mediated by this enzyme; the result is to prolong the effects of those drugs that are targets of its metabolic activity. In addition, barbiturates can also induce increased microsomal enzyme activity, which accelerates the metabolism and shortens the action of other drugs (Harvey 1980). Because of the complex effect on drug-metabolizing enzymes, caution must be taken whenever using barbiturates with other medication.

TABLE 6-2   Effects of barbiturates and other depressants on the body and mind

	Body	Mind
Low dose	Drowsiness	Decreased anxiety, relaxation
	Trouble with coordination	Decreased ability to reason and solve problems
	Slurred speech	
	Dizziness	Difficulty in judging distance and time
	Staggering	
	Double vision	Amnesia
	Sleep	
	Depressed breathing	Brain damage
	Coma (unconscious and cannot be awakened)	
	Depressed blood pressure	
High dose	Death	

Low doses of barbiturates relieve tension and anxiety, effects that give several barbiturates substantial abuse potential. It is not surprising that the clinical use of the barbiturates has diminished dramatically in recent years. The side effects of barbiturates are extensive and severe. They lack selectivity and safety; they have a greater tendency for tolerance, dependence, withdrawal, and abuse; and they cause problems with drug interaction. Thus, barbiturates have been replaced by benzodiazepines in most treatments; however, they are still included in a number of combination products for the treatment of an array of medical problems, such as gastrointestinal disorders, hypertension, asthma, and pain (Rall 1990). Their use in such preparations is very controversial. The long-acting phenobarbital is still frequently used for its CNS depressant activity to alleviate or prevent convulsions in some epileptic patients and seizures caused by strychnine, cocaine, and other stimulant drugs. Thiopental (Pentothal) and other ultrashort- and short-acting barbiturates are used as anesthesia for minor surgery and as preoperative anesthetics in preparation for major surgery.

MECHANISM OF ACTION AND ELIMINATION The precise mechanism of action for barbiturates is unclear. Like benzodiazepines, barbiturates likely interfere with activity in the reticular activating system, the limbic system, and the motor cortex. However, in contrast to benzodiazepines, barbiturates do not seem to act at a specific receptor site; they likely have a general effect on the activity of certain neurons due to effects on calcium and chloride (elements necessary for normal activity in many neurons). These changes in calcium and chloride appear to enhance the activity of the inhibitory transmitter GABA. Because benzodiazepines also increase GABA activity (but in a more selective manner), these two types of drugs have overlapping effects. But because the mechanisms whereby they exert their effects are different, it is not surprising that these two types of depressants also have different pharmacological features, as well.

Barbiturates can be classified in terms of duration of action (see Table 6-3). In general, the more lipid soluble the barbiturate is, the more easily it enters the brain, the faster it will act, and the more potent it will be as a depressant. Barbiturates are eliminated through the kidneys at varying rates. The rate of removal depends primarily on how quickly the barbiturate is metabolized in the liver to a lipid-insoluble metabolite. Excretion of barbiturates is faster when the urine is alkaline, which can be manipulated to treat barbiturate poisoning.

Because barbiturates are not completely removed from the body overnight, even the short-acting ones used for insomnia can cause subtle distortions of mood and impaired judgment and motor skills the following day. The user may have mild withdrawal symptoms such as hyperexcitability, nausea, and vomiting even after short-term

TABLE 6-3 Classifications of common barbiturates

Classification	Duration of Pharmacological Effect	Drug
Ultrashort acting	¼ to 3 hours	Thiopental (Pentothal)
Short acting	3 to 6 hours	Amobarbital (Amytal)
		Pentobarbital (Nembutal)
		Secobarbital (Seconal)
Intermediate acting	6 to 12 hours	Butabarbital (Butisol)
Long acting	12 to 24 hours	Phenobarbital (Luminal)

use (Harvey 1980). The long-acting barbiturates like phenobarbital are metabolized more slowly and cause an extended drug hangover.

The fat solubility of barbiturates is also an important factor in the duration of their effects. Barbiturates that are the most fat soluble move in and out of body tissues (such as the brain) rapidly and are likely to be shorter acting. Fat-soluble barbiturates also are more likely to be stored in fatty tissue; consequently, the fat content of the body can influence the effects the user experiences. Because women have a higher body-fat ratio than men, their reaction to barbiturates may be slightly different.

TOLERANCE AND DEPENDENCE The development of tolerance is usually necessary for true physical dependence to occur. Two types of tolerance result when barbiturates are taken repeatedly at short intervals:

1. *Drug-disposition tolerance* results from enzyme induction in the liver. Enzyme stimulation increases metabolism of the barbiturate, which means an increase in the average dose is required to achieve the same pharmacological effect.
2. *Pharmacodynamic tolerance* is caused by adaptation of nervous tissue to the barbiturate; this response can also result in cross-tolerance to other CNS depressants and causes barbiturate addicts to become resistant to other general depressants, including alcohol.

Drug-disposition tolerance reaches its peak in a few days, whereas pharmacodynamic tolerance develops over a period of weeks to months with chronic administration of gradually increasing barbiturate dosages (Harvey 1980).

Development of physical dependence on barbiturates is a relatively slow process, requiring weeks or months before withdrawal symptoms would occur if use of the drug were abruptly stopped. Doses of 200 milligrams (mg) to 400 mg of pentobarbital or secobarbital can be taken daily for a year with little or no physical dependence. Daily doses of between 400 mg and 600 mg for more than one month are required to induce withdrawal symptoms when the drug is discontinued (Smith, Wesson, and Seymour 1979).

Withdrawal from depressants after dependence has developed causes hyperexcitability because of the rebound of depressed neural systems. Qualitatively (but not quantitatively), the withdrawal symptoms are similar for all sedative-hypnotics.

Table 6-4 gives details on the barbiturates abused most frequently.

Think About It . . .

1. Why is the long-acting barbiturate phenobarbital so effective in the treatment of some types of convulsions?
2. Why might women respond differently to the fat-soluble barbiturates than men?
3. Why do barbiturates used as sleep aids tend to cause unrestful sleep?
4. Barbiturates appear to be less desirable as therapeutic depressants than benzodiazepines. Should the Food and Drug Administration (FDA) require that barbiturates be removed from the market? Why?

OTHER CNS DEPRESSANTS

While benzodiazepines and barbiturates are by far used most frequently to produce CNS depressant effects, many other agents, representing an array of distinct chemical groups, can similarly reduce brain activity. Although the mechanisms of action might be different for some of these drugs, if any CNS depressants (alcohol included) are combined, they will interact in a synergistic manner and can suppress respiration in a life-threatening manner. Thus, it is important to avoid such mixtures if possible. Even some over-the-counter (OTC) products such as cold and allergy medications contain drugs with CNS depressant actions.

NONBARBITURATE DRUGS WITH BARBITURATE-LIKE PROPERTIES This category of depressants that are not barbiturates but act like them includes several drugs that are chemically unrelated but produce CNS depression effects. They all cause substantial tolerance, physical and psychological

TABLE 6-4 Details on the most frequently abused barbiturates

Drug	Nicknames	Dose and Description	Effects
amobarbital (Amytal)	blues, blue heavens, blue devils	65- or 200-mg blue capsule	Moderately rapid action; duration of 3 to 6 hours; takes 15 to 30 minutes for effect.
pentobarbital (Nembutal)	nembies, yellow jackets, yellows	30- or 100-mg yellow, 50-mg orange-and-white capsule	Short acting; dose of 30 to 50 mg is usually sufficient to induce sleep; for true hypnosis, as little as 100 mg is sufficient for a 6- to 8-hour period of fretful sleep without much hangover; will cause euphoria and excitation at first, so it is abused.
phenobarbital (Luminal)	purple hearts	Purple tablet	A long-acting barbiturate particularly well suited for treatment of epilepsy. Daily doses of 60–250 mg are routinely used in adults. Because of its long action it is not often abused.
secobarbital (Seconal)	reds, red devils, red birds, Seccy	50-, 100-mg red capsule	Short acting with a prompt onset of action; usually lasts under 3 hours and is commonly abused to produce intoxication and euphoria by blocking inhibitions.
tuinal (50% amobarbital and 50% secobarbital)	tooeys, double-trouble, rainbows	50-, 100-, 200-mg capsule, blue body with red-orange cap	Results in a rapidly effective, moderately long-acting sedative; sedative dose is around 50 mg; hypnotic dose is 100 to 200 mg.

Note: A fatal overdose from each commonly used barbiturate is usually about 10 times the hypnotic dose. Death is from respiratory failure.

dependence, and withdrawal symptoms. The therapeutic safety of these CNS depressants is more like that of barbiturates than benzodiazepines; consequently, like barbiturates, these agents have been replaced by the safer and easier to manage benzodiazepines.

Because these drugs have significant abuse potential, they are restricted much like other CNS depressants. In this group of depressants, methaqualone is a Schedule II drug; glutethimide and methyprylon are Schedule III drugs; chloral hydrate and ethchlorvynol are Schedule IV drugs. The basis for the classification is the relative potential for physical and psychological dependence.

Abuse of Schedule II drugs may lead to severe or moderate physical dependence or high psychological dependence, and abuse of Schedule III drugs may cause moderate physical and psychological dependence. Schedule IV drugs are considered much less likely to cause either type of dependence.

CHLORAL HYDRATE   Chloral hydrate, or "knock-out drops," has the unsavory reputation of being a drug that is slipped into a person's drink to make him or her unconscious. The combination of chloral hydrate and alcohol was given the name "Mickey Finn" on the waterfront of the Barbary Coast of San Francisco when sailors were in short supply. As legend has it, the name of one of the bars dispensing unwanted knock-out drops was Mickey Finn's. An unsuspecting man would have a friendly drink and wake up as a crew member on an outbound freighter to China.

It takes about 30 minutes for chloral hydrate (Noctec) to take effect. It is metabolized to trichloroethanol, which is the active hypnotic agent. Alcohol accelerates the rate of conversion and potentiates the CNS depressant effect. Chloral hydrate does not depress the CNS as much as a comparable dose of barbiturates. It is a good hypnotic, but it has a narrow margin of safety. Chloral hydrate is a stomach irritant, especially if given repeatedly and in fairly large doses. Addicts may take enormous doses of the drug; as with most CNS depressants, chronic, long-term use of high doses will cause tolerance and physical dependence (Rall and Schleifer 1990).

ETHCHLORVYNOL   Ethchlorvynol (Placidyl) is a short-acting sedative-hypnotic drug. It causes side effects in some people, such as facial numbness, blurred vision, nausea, dizziness, gastric upset, and skin rash. Abusers may take up to 4 grams (g) a day. A dose of 10 g to 25 g can cause death. Chronic high-dose use causes the development of tolerance and physical as well as psychological dependence. Because of synergistic interaction, use of ethchlorvynol and ethanol together can be potentially lethal. Placidyl is sometimes found as a "street" drug.

GLUTETHIMIDE   Glutethimide (Doriden) is another example of a barbituratelike drug that has been abused and causes severe withdrawal symptoms. Doriden causes side effects similar to those of Placidyl. In addition, it induces blood abnormalities in sensitive individuals, such as a type of anemia and abnormally low white cell counts. In children, the drug may cause paradoxical excitement (unusual agitation and stimulation). Nausea, fever, **tachycardia,** and convulsions occasionally occur in patients who have been taking this sedative regularly in moderate doses. The sedative dose for adults is 125 mg to 250 mg one to three times a day. As a hypnotic, the dose is usually 250 mg to 500 mg at bedtime.

---

tachycardia
rapid beating of the heart

Doriden seems to have a smaller margin of safety than barbiturates. Continual use causes tolerance and physical dependence. Doriden was used more commonly as a "street" drug before it was definitely proven to be addictive and tighter controls were instituted.

METHYPRYLON   Methyprylon (Noludar) is a short-acting nonbarbiturate that is used as a sedative and hypnotic. Its effects are similar to those of Doriden, and it is capable of causing tolerance, physical dependence, and addiction much like barbiturates. Death has occurred during untreated withdrawal. Dosage for sedation is 50 mg to 100 mg three or four times a day. For inducing sleep, the dosage is usually 200 mg to 300 mg.

METHAQUALONE   Few drugs have become so popular so quickly as methaqualone. It is a barbituratelike sedative-hypnotic that was introduced in India in the 1950s as an antimalarial agent. Its sedative properties, however, were soon discovered. It was available in the United States as Quaalude, Mequin, and Parest.

After several years of "street" abuse, methaqualone was classified as a Schedule II drug. Since 1985, methaqualone has not been manufactured in the United States because of adverse publicity. It is interesting to note, however, that large amounts of illegal methaqualone are still imported into the United States from Colombia, Mexico, and Canada. It is referred to by "street" names such as *Ludes, Sopors,* or *714s.*

In humans, methaqualone accumulates in fatty tissue and readily enters the brain, like barbiturates. Also like barbiturates, methaqualone stimulates the activity of some metabolizing enzymes in the liver and may therefore induce tolerance. Common side effects are fatigue, dizziness, anorexia, nausea, vomiting, diarrhea, sweating, dryness of the mouth, depersonalization, headache, and paresthesia of the extremities (a pins-and-needles feeling in the fingers and toes). Hangover is frequently reported.

The standard hypnotic dose of methaqualone is 150 mg to 300 mg, whereas the average dose for daytime sedation is 75 mg three to four times daily. Coma may occur if a dose of 2 g is taken. During coma, methaqualone does not cause as marked a depression of heartbeat and respiration as do barbiturates. Doses between 8 g and 20 g can be fatal; lower doses can be fatal if methaqualone is taken with alcohol or other sedative-hypnotics because of potentiation of the CNS depression. Mild overdosage causes an excessive CNS depression much like that from barbiturates. Severe overdoses can cause delirium, restlessness, muscle spasms, and even convulsions (Harvey 1980).

High doses of methaqualone can cause psychological and physical dependence and dangerous withdrawal symptoms when drug use is stopped. People who have taken 600 mg to 3,000 mg of methaqualone daily experience insomnia, abdominal cramps, headaches, anorexia, and nightmares when drug use is discontinued. Severe grand mal (major motor) convulsions may occur after withdrawal from high doses; the symptoms are similar to the delirium tremens that occur during withdrawal from alcohol.

ANTIHISTAMINES Antihistamines are drugs used in both nonprescription and prescription medicinal products. The most common uses for antihistamines are to relieve the symptoms associated with the common cold, allergies, and motion sickness (see Chapter 13). Although frequently overlooked, many antihistamines cause significant CNS depression and are used both as sedatives and hypnotics. For example, the agents hydroxyzine (Visteril) and promethazine (Phenergan) are prescribed for their sedative effects, while diphenhydramine is commonly used as an OTC sleep aid.

The exact mechanism of CNS depression caused by these agents is not totally known but appears to relate to their blockade of acetylcholine receptors in the brain (i.e., they antagonize the muscarinic receptor types). This **anticholinergic** activity (see Chapter 5) helps to cause relaxation and sedation and can be viewed as a very annoying side effect when these drugs are being used to treat allergies or other problems.

anticholinergic
antagonizing the activity of acetylcholine receptors

Therapeutic Usefulness and Side Effects. Antihistamines are viewed as relatively safe agents with some annoying but rarely dangerous side effects. In comparison with other more powerful CNS depressants, antihistamines do not appear to cause significant physical or psychological dependence or abuse problems. However, tolerance to antihistamine-induced sedation occurs quite rapidly. Reports of significant cases of withdrawal problems when use of the antihistamines is stopped are rare. This may be due to the fact that these agents are used as antianxiety drugs for only minor problems and for short periods of time (often only for a single dose).

One significant problem with antihistamines is the variability of responses they produce. Different antihistamines work differently on different people. Usually, therapeutic doses will cause decreased alertness, relaxation, slowed reaction time, and drowsiness. But it is not uncommon for some individuals to be affected in the opposite manner;

that is, an antihistamine can cause restlessness, agitation, and insomnia. There are even cases of seizures caused by toxic doses of antihistamine, particularly in children (Farrison and Rall 1990). Other annoying side effects of antihistamines relate to their anticholinergic effects, including dry mouth, constipation, and urinary retention. These factors probably help to discourage the abuse of these drugs.

Even though antihistamines are relatively safe in therapeutic doses, they can contribute to serious problems if combined with other CNS depressants. Because of this potentially dangerous interaction, patients who have been prescribed other sedative-hypnotics should be aware of consuming drugs that contain antihistamines. For example, many OTC cold, allergy, antimotion, and sleep-aid products contain antihistamines and should be avoided by patients using the potent CNS depressants.

PATTERNS OF ABUSE WITH CNS DEPRESSANTS

The American Medical Association (AMA 1965) has characterized those types of persons who are most inclined to abuse CNS depressants. Namely, individuals prone to abuse include:

1. Those who seek sedative effects to deal with emotional stress, trying to escape from problems they are unable to deal with. Sometimes, these individuals are able to persuade clinicians to administer depressants for their problems; other times, they self-medicate with depressants that are obtained illegally.
2. Those who seek the excitation that occurs, especially after some tolerance has developed; instead of depression, they feel exhilaration and euphoria.
3. Those who try to counteract the unpleasant effect or withdrawal associated with other drugs of abuse, such as some stimulants, LSD, and other hallucinogens.
4. Those who use sedatives in combination with other depressant drugs such as alcohol

and heroin. Alcohol plus a sedative gives a faster "high" but can be dangerous because of the multiple depressant effects and synergistic interaction. Heroin users often resort to barbiturates if their heroin supply is compromised.

As mentioned above, depressants are commonly abused in combination with other drugs. In particular, opioid narcotic users take barbiturates, benzodiazepines, and other depressants to augment the effects of a weak batch of heroin or a rapidly shrinking supply. Chronic narcotic users also claim that depressants help to offset tolerance to opioids, thereby requiring less narcotic to achieve a satisfactory response by the user. It is not uncommon to see joint dependence on both narcotics and depressants.

Another common use of depressants is by alcoholics to soften the withdrawal from ethanol or to help create a state of intoxication without the telltale odor of alcohol. It is interesting that similar strategies are also used therapeutically to help detoxify the alcoholic. For example, long-acting barbiturates or benzodiazepines are often used to wean an alcohol-dependent person. Treatment with these depressants helps to reduce the severity of withdrawal symptoms, making it easier and safer for alcoholics to eliminate their drug dependence.

In general, those who chronically abuse the CNS depressants prefer (1) the short-action barbiturates, such as pentobarbital and secobarbital, (2) the barbituratelike depressants, such as meprobamate, glutethimide, methyprylon, and methaqualone; or (3) the faster-acting benzodiazepines, such as diazepam (Valium), alprazalam (Xanax), or lorazepam (Ativan). (However, most nonabusing people do not find the benzodiazepines particularly reinforcing [Woods et al. 1987].)

Dependence on sedative-hypnotic agents can develop insidiously. Often a long-term patient has been treated for persistent insomnia or anxiety with daily exposures to a CNS depressant. When an attempt to withdraw the drug is made, the patient becomes agitated, unable to sleep, and severely anxious; a state of panic may be experienced when deprived of the drug. These signs are frequently mistaken for a resurgence of the medical condition being treated and not recognized as part of a withdrawal syndrome to the CNS depressant. Consequently, the patient is restored to his or her supply of CNS depressant, and the symptoms of withdrawal subside. Such conditions generally lead to a gradual increase in dosage as tolerance to the sedative-hypnotic develops. The patient becomes severely dependent on the depressant, both physically and psychologically, and the drug habit becomes an essential feature in the user's daily routines. Only after severe dependence has developed does the clinician often realize what has taken place. The next stage is the unpleasant task of trying to wean the patient from the drug (**detoxification**) with as little discomfort as possible.

---

detoxification
elimination of a toxic substance, such as a drug, and its effects

---

Because of the similarities between alcohol and barbituratelike drugs, it is common to see individuals who abuse both types of depressants. One of the dangers is that these people use both drugs together. Due to the synergism that exists between CNS depressants in general, such a mixture can severely suppress respiration and cardiovascular function, often with deadly consequences. Knowledge of this dangerous interaction is quite common among the drug-using population; consequently, many suicide attempts are made by self-administering high doses of barbituratelike drugs with a chaser of ethanol.

As with other drugs of abuse, the prevalence of illicit CNS depressant use is on the decline. In 1990, 5% of high school seniors reported non-medicinal use of these agents during their lifetime, as compared to 12% in 1985 and 18% in 1975 (*NIDA Notes* 1991).

At this point, an explanation is in order regarding statistics of drug use: You will note that, throughout this book, figures that report trends in drug use are usually based on samples of high school and college students—namely, teen-agers and young adults. The primary reason for this is

that studies based on older populations are non-existent, for the most part. It is difficult to survey large groups of adults in a controlled manner; student groups are much more accessible. This is true for a lot of social science research.

You could argue whether student groups are in fact representative of society as a whole. Can findings about drug use among teens and young adults be extrapolated in this manner? It is a legitimate question. We argue that such findings are representative in the sense that they likely predict future drug use. Research has shown that patterns of drug use established in youth will likely be maintained later in life. Thus, current trends in drug use by society's youngest members have significant long-term implications.

TREATMENT FOR WITHDRAWAL

All sedative-hypnotics, including alcohol and benzodiazepines, can produce physical dependence and a barbituratelike withdrawal syndrome if taken in sufficient dosage over a long enough period. Withdrawal symptoms include anxiety, tremors, nightmares, insomnia, anorexia, nausea, vomiting, seizures, delirium, and maniacal activity.

The duration and severity of withdrawal depends on the particular drug taken. With short-acting depressants—such as pentobarbital, secobarbital, meprobamate, and methaqualone—withdrawal symptoms tend to be more severe. They begin 12 to 24 hours after the last dose and peak in intensity between 24 and 72 hours later. Withdrawal from long-acting depressants—such as phenobarbital, diazepam, and chlordiazepoxide—develops more slowly and is less intense; symptoms peak on the fifth to eighth day (Smith et al. 1979).

Not surprisingly, the approach to detoxifying a person dependent on a sedative-hypnotic depends on the nature of the drug itself (i.e., to which category of depressants does it belong), the severity of the dependence, and the duration of action of the drug. The general objectives of detoxification are to eliminate drug dependence (both physical and psychological) in a safe manner while minimizing discomfort. Having achieved these objectives, it is hoped that the patient will be able to remain free of dependence on all CNS depressants.

Often the basic approach for treating severe dependence on sedative-hypnotics is substitution of either pentobarbital or the longer-acting phenobarbital for the offending CNS depressant. Once substitution has occurred, the long-acting barbiturate dose is gradually reduced. Use of a substitute is necessary because abrupt withdrawal for a person who is physically dependent can be dangerous and cause life-threatening seizures. This substitution treatment uses the same rationale as the treatment of heroin withdrawal by methadone replacement. Detoxification also includes supportive measures such as vitamins, restoration of electrolyte balance, and prevention of dehydration. The patient must be watched closely during this time because he or she will be apprehensive, mentally confused, and unable to make logical decisions (Smith et al. 1979).

It is important to remember that elimination of physical dependence does not necessarily result in a cure. The problem of psychological dependence can be much more difficult to deal with. If an individual is abusing a CNS depressant because of emotional instability, personal problems, or a very stressful environment, eliminating physical dependence alone will not solve the problem. Drug dependence is likely to recur because the cause of the problem has not been addressed. These types of patients require intense psychological counseling and must be trained to deal with their problems in a more constructive and positive fashion. Without such psychological support, benefits from detoxification will only be temporary, and therapy will ultimately fail.

If the person is addicted to both alcohol and barbiturates, the phenobarbital dosage must be increased to compensate for the double withdrawal. Many barbiturate addicts who go to a hospital for withdrawal are also dependent on heroin. In such cases, the barbiturate dependence should be dealt with first because the associated withdrawal can be life threatening. Detoxification from any sedative-hypnotic should be done under close medical supervision, most often in a hospital (Smith et al. 1979).

Think About It...

1. Several OTC antihistamines are also CNS depressants. Why are these drugs rarely abused?
2. What personality types are most likely to abuse CNS depressants?
3. Why are long-acting barbiturates and benzodiazepines most often used to treat withdrawal from alcohol?

KEY TERMS

sedatives

hypnotics

amnesiac

anesthesia

anxiolytics

REM sleep

paradoxical

tachycardia

anticholinergic

detoxification

SUMMARY

1. Several unrelated drug groups cause CNS depression, but only a few are actually used clinically for their depressant properties. The most frequently prescribed CNS depressants are benzodiazepines including drugs such as Valium, Xanax, and Halcion. Barbiturates once were popular but, because of their severe side effects, they are not used by most clinicians. Much like barbiturates, drugs such as chloral hydrate, glutethimide, and methaqualone are little used today. Finally, some antihistamines, such as diphenhydramine, hydroxyzine, and promethazine, are still occasionally used for their CNS depressant effects.

2. The clinical value of CNS depressants is dose dependent. At low doses, these drugs relieve anxiety and promote relaxation (sedatives). At higher doses, they can cause drowsiness and promote sleep (hypnotics). At even higher doses, some of the depressants cause anesthesia and are used for patient management during surgery.

3. Because CNS depressants help to relieve anxiety and reduce stress, they are viewed as desirable by many people. But if used frequently over long periods, they can cause tolerance that leads to dependence.

4. The principal reason benzodiazepines have replaced barbiturates in the treatment of stress and insomnia is that benzodiazepines have a greater margin of safety and are less likely to alter sleep patterns. Benzodiazepines enhance the GABA transmitter system in the brain, while the effects of barbiturates are less selective. Even though benzodiazepines are safer than barbiturates, dependence and significant withdrawal problems will result if the drugs are used indiscriminately.

5. Often benzodiazepine dependence occurs with patients who are suffering some stress or anxiety disorder and are under a physician's care. If the physician is not careful and the cause of the stress is not resolved, drug treatment can drag on for weeks or months. After prolonged therapy, tolerance develops to the drug, so that when benzodiazepine use is stopped, withdrawal occurs, which itself causes agitation. What is really a rebound response to the drug might appear as the effects of emotional stress, so use of benzodiazepine is continued until the patient becomes severely dependent.

6. The short-acting CNS depressants are preferred for treatment of insomnia. These drugs help the patient get to sleep and then are inactivated by the body; when the user awakes the next day, he or she is less likely to experience residual effects than with long-acting drugs. The short-acting depressants are also preferred for abuse because of their relatively fast and intense effects. In contrast, the long-acting depressants are better suited to treating persistent problems such as anxiety and stress. The long-acting depressants are also used to help wean dependent persons from their use of the short-acting compounds such as alcohol. The long-acting drug is substituted for the short-acting drug to block the severe withdrawal effects; drug doses are then gradually reduced until the dependent person is free of the depressant.

7. Although at one time very popular, methaqualone is no longer legally available in the United States due to abuse problems. Even so, methaqualone continues to be found in the "streets" because it is smuggled across the Mexican and Canadian borders into the United States.

8. Many antihistamines cause sedation and drowsiness due to their anticholinergic effects. Several of these agents are useful for short-term relief of anxiety and are available in OTC sleep aids. The effectiveness of these CNS depressants is usually less than

that of benzodiazepines. Because of their anticholinergic actions, antihistamines can cause some annoying side effects and are not likely to be used for long periods; thus, dependence or abuse rarely develops.

9. The people most likely to abuse CNS depressants include individuals who (a) use drugs to relieve continual stress; (b) paradoxically feel euphoria and stimulation from depressants; (c) use depressants to counteract the unpleasant effects of other drugs of abuse, such as stimulants; and (d) combine depressants with alcohol and heroin to potentiate the effects.

10. The basic approach for treating dependence on CNS depressants is to detoxify in a safe manner while minimizing discomfort. This is achieved by substituting a long-acting barbiturate or benzodiazepine, such as phenobarbital or Valium, for the offending CNS depressant. The long-acting drug causes less severe withdrawal symptoms over a longer period of time. The dependent person is gradually weaned from the substitute drug until depressant free.

R E F E R E N C E S

American Druggist, February 1991, 62.

American Hospital Formulary Service. "Benzodiazepines." In AHFS Drug Information. Bethesda, MD: American Society of Hospital Pharmacists, 1991.

American Medical Association Committee on Alcoholism and Addiction, 1965. Dependence on barbiturates and other sedative drugs. Journal of the American Medical Association 193:673–677.

"British Spark U.S. Debate by Banning Halcion Sales." Salt Lake City Tribune, 3 October 1991, A-2.

Facts & Comparisons, Drug Newsletter 10 (February 1991): 10.

Farrison, J., and T. Rall. "Histamine, Bradykinin, 5-Hydroxytryptamine, and the Antagonists." In The Pharmacological Basis of Therapeutics, 8th ed., edited by A. Gilman, T. Rall, A. Nies and P. Taylor. New York, Pergamon, 1990.

Harvey, S. C. "Hypnotics and Sedatives." In The Pharmacological Basis of Therapeutics, 6th ed., edited by A. Gilman, L. Goodman, and A. Gilman. New York: Macmillan, 1980.

Jaffe, J. "Drug Addiction and Drug Abuse." In The Pharmacological Basis of Therapeutics, 8th ed., edited by A. Gilman, T. Rall, A. Nies, and P. Taylor. New York: Pergamon, 1990.

Medical Letter 33 (17 May 1991): 43–44.

Mondanaro, J. Chemically Dependent Women. Lexington, MA: Lexington Books/D.C. Heath, 1988.

NIDA Notes 6 (Spring 1991): 35.

Pharmacy Times, April 1991, 58.

Pope, G. Voices from the Drug Culture. Cambridge, MA: The Sanctuary, 1971.

Rall, T. "Hypnotics and Sedatives: Ethanol." In The Pharmacological Basis for Therapeutics, 8th ed., edited by A. Gilman, T. Rall, A. Nies, and P. Taylor. New York: Pergamon, 1990.

Rall, T., and S. Schleifer. "Drugs Effective in the Therapy of the Epilepsies." In The Pharmacological Basis of Therapeutics, 8th ed., edited by A. Gilman, T. Rall, A. Nies, and P. Taylor. New York: Pergamon, 1990.

Smith, D. E., D. R. Wesson, and R. B. Seymour. "The Abuse of Barbiturates and Other Sedative-Hypnotics." In Handbook on Drug Abuse, edited by R. I. DuPont, A. Goldstein, and J. H. O'Donnell. Washington, D.C.: NIDA/Department of Health, Education, and Welfare, 1979.

Woods., J., J. Katz, and B. Winger. "Abuse Liability of Benzodiazepines." Pharmacological Review 39 (1987):254–390.

Alcohol

CHAPTER OUTLINE

LEARNING OBJECTIVES

On completing this chapter, you will be able to:

1. Identify the psychoactive ingredient in alcoholic beverages, and tell why it is a dangerous substance.

2. Describe how alcoholic beverages are made.

3. Relate the role of alcoholic beverages to trends in American history.

4. Identify three types of poisonous alcohols, and name the fourth type used in alcoholic beverages.

5. Trace what factors affect the concentration of alcohol in the blood.

6. Name the short-term physical effects of drinking alcohol.

7. Name some possible physical effects of prolonged heavy alcohol consumption.

8. Describe recent trends in U.S. alcohol consumption, and identify use and abuse patterns in various age, sex, and ethnic groups, as well as risks during pregnancy.

9. Describe use and abuse patterns among elderly and homeless populations.

10. Characterize the effects of drinking and driving, and assess attitudes toward this problem.

11. Define *alcoholism,* and relate three stages of the disease.

12. Describe the potential causes of alcoholism.

13. Identify three social or psychological explanations for alcoholism.

14. Characterize the range of strategies for preventing the ill effects of alcoholism on society.

15. Identify two stages of treatment for alcoholism, and name three helping agencies for treatment.

Source: Cary Wolinsky/Stock, Boston

DID YOU KNOW THAT ...

- Even though alcohol is one of the most used and abused drugs, most people do not view it as a drug.
- There are many types of alcohol; only one, ethyl alcohol, is fit for human consumption and is found in so-called alcoholic beverages. Other alcohols are poisonous to humans, including methyl alcohol (wood alcohol), ethylene glycol (used as an antifreeze), and iso-propyl alcohol (antiseptic or rubbing alcohol).
- Problem drinking and alcoholism cost the United States over $48 billion dollars in 1986.
- Drinking problems are most common in individuals who are male, young, and single.
- African-Americans have high rates of abstention from alcohol and low rates of heavy drinking.
- Of all U.S. minority groups, Asian-Americans have the highest rates of abstention, the lowest rates of heavy drinking, and the lowest levels of drinking-related problems.
- The Egyptians made wine some 6,000 years ago. So-called liquors were developed in the Middle Ages.
- As a rule of thumb, it will take as many hours as the number of drinks consumed to sober up completely.
- Alcohol is involved in one-third to one-half of all highway fatalities.
- Most problem drinkers are employed, family-centered people.
- The alcohol industry generates more than $65 billion a year in revenue and spends more than $1 billion a year on advertising.

Among the many myths that surround drinking alcohol is the assumption that it is society's most acceptable and best-controlled psychoactive substance. A survey of the preceding facts shows that this is not true. In reality, alcohol may produce the most disastrous and widespread social damage of any mind-altering substance, costing a huge loss of life through accidents, the loss of mental and physical health through addiction, and a host of economic costs to people, communities, and nations. Alcohol is, in fact, one of the most used and abused drugs, as it is consumed by people at all social levels. Surveys of both high school seniors and college students on drug use indicate that approximately 90% of students use alcohol.

In this chapter, we will consider the widespread use and abuse of alcohol. Background will be provided on the history of alcohol in society and also on the nature of alcoholic substances. The bulk of the chapter will address problems with alcohol use and abuse, including a thorough discussion of alcoholism and treatment and prevention recommendations.

THE PERVASIVE COSTS OF ALCOHOL USE

The term *alcohol* refers to a class of chemical agents that possess very diverse properties. In everyday usage, however, the word *alcohol* refers to the specific agent **ethanol** (ethyl alcohol, or grain alcohol) that belongs to this family of chemicals. Ethanol is the psychoactive ingredient found in so-called alcoholic beverages. Oddly enough, because of its availability and high degree of acceptance in U.S. society, ethanol is unique in that most individuals do not consider it a true drug but rather a **social substance.** As a result of this casual attitude toward ethanol, people are not as cautious about its consumption as they are about administering other equally potent or controlled drugs. The tragic consequences, which will be discussed at length throughout this chapter, are almost beyond comprehension. The misuse of ethanol and its impact on society far exceeds that of any other psychoactive substance, either legal or illegal.

ethanol
the consumable type of alcohol that is the psychoactive ingredient in alcoholic beverages; often called grain alcohol

social substance
refers to when alcohol is not perceived as a drug

How serious is the consumption of ethanol? There are approximately 100 million Americans who drink alcohol (Liska 1990, 218) and between 9 and 10 million are alcoholics. Alcohol-related consequences affect not only drinkers themselves but also their spouses, children, friends, and employers, as well as strangers with whom they may come in contact.

There are 18 million problem drinkers in the United States and approximately 23,000 alcohol-related traffic deaths per year (*In These Times* 1989). In addition to traffic accidents, alcohol-involved injuries and deaths, serious medical consequences, and birth defects, alcohol abuse has been implicated in violence, crime, marital discord, and job loss.

There are also serious economic consequences. Problem drinking and alcoholism cost the United States over $48 billion in 1986: about 46% in lost production, 29% in health and medical costs, 13% in motor vehicle accidents, 7% in violent crimes, 4% in social responses (public education on highway safety, role of alcohol abuse in decreased production, and so on), and 1% in fire losses. The personal and societal costs are summarized in Table 7-1.

ALCOHOL IN SOCIETY

Alcohol has been part of human culture since the beginning of recorded history. The technology for alcohol production is ancient. Several basic ingredients and conditions are needed: sugar, water, yeast, and warm temperatures.

The process of making alcohol, called **fermentation,** is a natural one. It occurs in ripe fruit and berries and even in honey that wild bees leave in trees. These substances have sugar and water and are found in warm climates, where yeast spores are transported through the air. Animals such as elephants, baboons, birds, wild pigs, and bees will seek and eat fermented fruit. Elephants under the influence of alcohol have been observed bumping into one another and stumbling around. Intoxicated bees fly an unsteady beeline toward their

TABLE 7-1   Costs of problem drinking and alcoholism in the United States

Life expectancy	Reduced 10–12 years compared to nonalcoholic
Mortality rate	Increased at least 2.3 times over expected rate
Family members affected (spouses, children)	At least 36 million people
Alcohol-related traffic deaths	70 per day; 26,000 per year
Industrial deaths and injuries	Estimated 12,600 deaths; 2,200,000 injuries in 1975 were alcohol related
Civilian aviation accidents	44% of all accidents in which pilot died were alcohol related
Drownings: boating accidents, swimmers	Up to 69% were alcohol related
Fire fatalities	Up to 83% were alcohol related; 53% of victims were alcoholics
Fire burns	Up to 62% were alcohol related; 23% of victims were alcoholics
Injuries from falling	Up to 70% of all deaths and 63% of all injuries were alcohol related
Homicides	50% were alcohol related
Suicides	More than one-third were alcohol related
Rapes	50% of rapists and 31% of victims had been drinking immediately before the assault
Assaults	72% of attackers and 79% of victims had been drinking immediately before the assault
Child abuse	Up to 77% of child abusers had been drinking immediately before the offense; 40% of child-abusing parents have history of drinking problem
Robberies	Up to 72% of robbers were drinking immediately before committing the robbery
Arrests	One-third of the 10.2 million arrests in 1977 were for drunkenness, driving under the influence, and so on; costs for arrests, trials, and jail: $100 million per year
Absenteeism from work	Three times the rate for employees without a drinking problem
Cost of lost production and services	About $20 billion in 1975 (total for industry, government, and military)

Source: Based on data from *Facts about Alcohol and Alcoholism* (Washington, D.C.: National Institute on Alcohol Abuse and Alcoholism, 1980).

hives. Birds eating fermented fruit become so uncoordinated that they cannot fly, or if they do, they crash into windows or branches.

---

fermentation
the biochemical process in which yeast converts sugar into alcohol

---

Fermented honey, called *mead*, may have been the first alcoholic beverage. The Egyptians had breweries 6,000 years ago; they credited the god Osiris with introducing wine to humans. The ancient Greeks used a large amount of wine and credited the god Bacchus (or Dionysus) with introducing the drink. Today, we use the words *bacchanalia* and *Dionysian* to refer to revelry and drunken events. The Hebrews were also heavy users of wine. The Bible mentions that Noah, just nine generations after Adam, made wine and became drunk.

Alcohol is produced by a single-celled microscopic organism, one of the yeasts, which by a metabolic form of combustion breaks down sugar, releasing carbon dioxide and forming water and ethyl alcohol as a waste product. Carbon dioxide creates the foam on a glass of beer and the fizz in champagne. Fermentation continues until the sugar supply is exhausted or the concentration of alcohol reaches the point at which it kills the yeast (12% to 14%). Thus, 12% to 14% is the natural limit of alcohol found in fermented wines or beers.

The **distillation** device, or *still*, was developed by the Arabs around 800 A.D. and was introduced into medieval Europe around 1250 A.D. (see Figure 7-1). By boiling the fermented drink and gathering the condensed vapor in a pipe, a still increases the concentration of alcohol, potentially up to 50%

FIGURE 7-1 A medieval still

or more. Because distillation made it easier for people to get drunk, it greatly intensified the problem of alcohol abuse. However, even before the arrival of the still, alcoholic beverages had been known to cause problems in heavy users. It had been noticed that some individuals were sensitive to alcoholic beverages and became dependent on them.

distillation
the process used when fermented mixtures of cereal grains or fruits are heated in a still

ALCOHOL IN THE WESTERN WORLD

The word *alcohol* is derived from the Arabic *alkuhl*, which means "something subtle" or "the essential spirit of wine." Arnauld de Villeneuve, a professor of medicine at the University of Montpellier toward the end of the thirteenth century, thought it was the universal panacea and called the distillate *aqua vitae*, or "water of life." Later, the Irish used the distillation technique on fermented grain and called the drink *usquebaugh*, the Irish-Gaelic equivalent of *aqua vitae*. The word gradually became *whiskey*. The Scots used fermented ("malted") barley; they dried it in kilns fired with burning peat, which gives Scotch whiskey its distinctive flavor. The Dutch distilled a strong drink from fermented fruit juice, which they called *brandewijn*, or "burnt (distilled) wine" (Roueché 1960).

From the Middle Ages on, wines in which a higher concentration of alcohol was added were called **fortified wines;** they had a concentration of about 20% alcohol. The wines were given names according to the types of grape used or the regions where they were made. The most famous and perhaps most enduring of these wines are sherry, port, madeira, muscatel, and champagne.

The Greek god of wine, Bacchus (or Dionysus)

fortified wines
wines with a higher than usual concentration of alcohol

Medieval physicians used alcohol in medicinal preparations, and it was a natural step from this to make a *liqueur*—a fortified spirit containing various herbs. Many liqueurs, or cordials, also contained sugar and even minerals. Drambuie, Chartreuse, and Benedictine are examples of old liqueurs that are still made today. Benedictine is made by the Benedictine monks, who keep the recipe a secret.

In the 1600s, the Dutch distilled alcohol from grain with juniper berries added for flavor and called the concoction *junever,* the origin of the word *gin.* Gin had a bad reputation in Europe during the eighteenth century and later, when it was used as a drug to pacify crying babies and also as an agent for infanticide, sometimes mixed with laudanum (an opium preparation). About the same time gin was made, the Russians were fermenting a strong drink from potatoes or grain that had to be diluted with water. It was named *vodka,* for "little water," and still is used heavily in Russia.

ALCOHOL IN AMERICA

Alcoholic beverages have played an important role in the history of the United States. The Pilgrims stopped at Plymouth Rock instead of going farther south because "[their] victuals were much spent, especially [their] beer." A decade later, the Puritans stocked their ship, the *Arabella,* with 10,000 gallons of wine, 42 tons of beer, and 14 tons of water (Lee 1963).

Although the early settlers were straightlaced, they did not frown on drinking in moderation. Homemade beers and wines were an important source of fluid and nutrition for early American farmers. Sanitation was unknown, and the family well was often contaminated by human and animal wastes. Cows' milk was known to transmit "milk sickness" (tuberculosis).

Although the alcoholic content of "home brew" must have helped to make the rugged nature of pioneer life more endurable, the alcohol was primarily a preservative for the beverage. Homemade beers and wines were not purified as commercial products are today (Royce 1989). The nutritional and medicinal value of the yeast left over from the brewing process had been recognized by people around the world for centuries. Because American colonial beers and wines were not clarified but were consumed with the spent yeast, they supplied many of the vitamins and minerals needed for good nutrition (Brown 1978).

Rum, the alcoholic essence of fermented molasses, was probably invented by the first European settlers in the West Indies. The manufacturing of rum became New England's largest and most profitable industry in the so-called triangular trade. Yankee traders would sail with a cargo of rum to the west coast of Africa, where they bartered the "demon" for slaves. From there, they sailed to the West Indies, where they bartered the slaves for molasses. They took the molasses back to New England, where it was made into rum, thus completing the triangle. For many years, the New England distilleries flourished and the slave trade proved highly lucrative. This continued until 1807, when an act of Congress prohibited the importation of slaves. About this time, too, agricultural production of corn and rye made domestic whiskey cheaper (Roueché 1960).

Whiskey production in America was introduced by a post–Revolutionary War wave of Scottish and Irish settlers to whom the making of pot-still whiskey was a natural phase of farming. Almost every home had a still or fermentation crock to make beers, wines, or whiskeys. Whiskey first came into prominence as a backwoods substitute for rum in western Maryland and Virginia, southwestern Pennsylvania, and eastern Kentucky. Because it cost more to transport a barrel of flour made from the grain than the flour would have sold for in eastern markets, farmers converted grain into whiskey.

In 1794, many of these farmers became incensed when the new U.S. government levied a tax on liquor. Because they considered whiskey an economic necessity and used it as a medium of exchange, the farmers refused to pay the tax and tarred and feathered the revenue officers. President Washington, alarmed, summoned the militia of several states under the command of Alexander Hamilton and put down the rebellion. The consequences of this insurrection were significant: The federal government was in essence strengthened, and its authority regarding the right to make and enforce federal laws was established at the expense of the local farmers.

The period of heaviest drinking in America began during Jefferson's term of office (1800–1808). The nation was going through uneasy times, trying to stay out of the war between Napoleon and the British allies. There was an increase in the transient population, especially in the seaport cities, and the migration westward had begun. Heavy drinking had become a major form of recreation and a "social lubricant" at elections and public gatherings. Thus, the temperance movement began with the goal of *temperance* in the literal sense: "moderation." In the 1830s, at the peak of this early campaign, temperance leaders (many of whom drank beer and wine) recommended abstinence only from distilled spirits. Over the next decades, partly in connection with religious revivals, the meaning of *temperance* was gradually altered from "moderation" to "total abstinence." All alcoholic beverages were attacked as being unnecessary, harmful to health, and inherently poisonous. Over the course of the nineteenth century, the demand gradually arose for total prohibition (Austin 1978).

Almost every civilized country has passed prohibition laws, but few have worked for long. Attempts to control, restrict, or abolish alcohol have been made in the United States, but they have all met with abysmal failure. From 1907 to 1919, 34 states passed prohibition laws. Finally, in 1919, the Eighteenth Amendment to the Constitution was ratified in an attempt to stop the rapid spread of alcoholic addiction. As soon as such a widely used substance became illegal, criminal activity to satisfy the huge demand for alcohol flourished. Illegal routes were developed for purchasing liquor. Numerous not-so-secret "speakeasies" developed as illegal places where people could buy alcoholic beverages, and "bootlegging" was a widely accepted activity. In effect, then, such developments filled the vacuum for many drinkers during Prohibition.

During this time, doctors and druggists prescribed whiskey and other alcoholic patent medicines. By 1928, doctors made an estimated $40 million per year writing prescriptions for whiskey (Austin 1978). Patent medicines flourished, with alcoholic contents as high as 50%. Whisko, a "nonintoxicating stimulant," was 55 proof (or 27.5% alcohol). Another, Kaufman's Sulfur Bitters, was labeled "contains no alcohol" but was 40 proof (20% alcohol) and did not contain sulfur. There were dozens of others, many of which contained other types of drugs, such as opium.

Both Prohibitionists and its critics were shocked by the violent gang wars that broke out between rivals seeking to control the lucrative "black market" in liquor. More important, a general disregard for the law developed. Corruption among law enforcement agents was widespread. Organized crime was born and grew to be the nation's most gigantic "business." In reaction to these developments, political support rallied against Prohibition, resulting in its repeal in 1933 by the Twenty-first Amendment.

Since then, alcoholic beverages have had a relatively secure place in the American political and social scene, with varying degrees of regulation within states and local jurisdictions. Current projections for alcohol use and abuse show little change, even across selected age groups (see Figure 7-2). In short, alcohol use starts at an early age and remains heavily ingrained in American culture.

Think About It . . .

1. What social conditions might have contributed to the common attitude that alcohol use is under control in U.S. society or that it is not an especially frightening substance?

2. In an attempt to define what is *moderation* in drinking, consider the drinking patterns of three people you know (do not name them). What differences do you observe in how each reacts to a certain amount of alcohol? Are their reactions common enough to create a working definition for *moderation*?

3. In an effort to define what makes laws restricting alcohol consumption effective or ineffective, describe a law that you think is ineffective (explain why) and one that you think is effective.

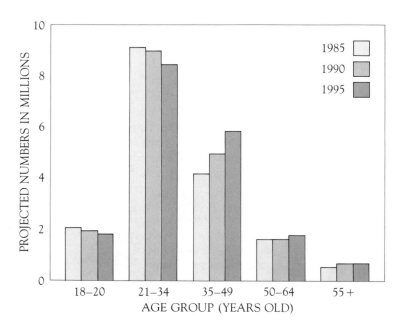

FIGURE 7-2 Projections of combined alcoholics and alcohol abusers, United States: Resident, noninstitutionalized population, 1985–1995 *Source:* G. D. Williams et al., "Demographic Trends, Alcohol Abuse and Alcoholism, 1985–1995," *Alcohol Health and Research World* 11, no. 3 (1987): 80–83.

THE PROPERTIES OF ALCOHOL

An alcohol is a chemical structure that has a hydroxyl group (OH, for one oxygen and one hydrogen atom) attached to a carbon atom. Of the many types of alcohol, several are important in this context. The first is **methyl alcohol** (methanol, or wood alcohol), so called because it is made from wood products. Its metabolites are poisonous. Small amounts (4 ml) cause blindness, affecting the retina, and larger amounts (80 ml to 150 ml) are usually fatal (Ritchie 1980). Methyl alcohol is added to ethyl alcohol (ethanol or grain alcohol, the drinking type) intended for industrial use so that people will not drink it. The mixture known as *denatured alcohol methyl alcohol* is sometimes found added to "bootleg" liquor.

---

methyl alcohol
wood alcohol, or methanol

Another type of poisonous alcohol, **ethylene glycol,** is used in antifreeze, and a third type, **isopropyl alcohol,** is commonly used as rubbing

alcohol and as an antiseptic (a solution for preventing the growth of microorganisms). They are also poisonous if consumed. Pure ethyl alcohol (ethanol) is recognized as an official drug in the U.S. pharmacopoeia, although the various alcoholic beverages as such are no longer listed for medical use.

---

ethylene glycol
alcohol used as antifreeze

isopropyl alcohol
rubbing alcohol, sometimes used as an anesthetic

Alcohol can be used as a solvent for other drugs or as a preservative in tinctures and elixirs. It is used to cleanse, disinfect, and harden the skin and to reduce sweating. Seventy-percent alcohol is an effective bactericide. However, it should not be used on open wounds because it will dehydrate the injured tissue and make damage worse. Since it cools the skin by evaporation, alcohol-saturated sponges are commonly used to reduce fever. Alcohol may be used as a solvent for the irritating oil in poison ivy and may prevent the formation of rash if used quickly enough after contact. Alcohol may be deliberately injected in or near nerves to treat severe pain; it causes local anesthesia and deterioration of the nerve. For the elderly or convalescent who enjoys it, a drink of ethanol before meals will improve appetite and digestion (Ritchie 1980). In small amounts, ethanol alcohol is used by many physicians as a CNS depressant or sedative for convalescent and geriatric patients.

In all alcoholic beverages—beer, wine, liqueurs or cordials, and distilled spirits—the psychoactive agent is the same: ethanol. The concentration of alcohol is usually about 4% by volume in American beers; 10% to 12% in table wines; 17% to 20% in cocktail and dessert wines, such as sherries; 22% to 50% in liqueurs; and 40% to 50% (80 to 100 proof) in distilled spirits. The amount of alcohol is expressed either as a percentage by volume or in the older proof system, based on the military assay method. To make certain that they were getting a high alcohol content in the liquor, the British military would place a sample on gunpowder and touch a spark to it. If the alcohol content was over 50%, it would burn and ignite the gunpowder. This was "proof" that there was at least 50% alcohol. If the distilled spirits were "under proof," the water content would prevent the gunpowder from igniting. The percentage of alcohol volume is one-half the proof number. For example, 100-proof whiskey has a 50% alcohol content.

In addition, alcoholic beverages contain a variety of other chemical constituents, some of which come from the original grains, grapes, and other fruits and some of which come from added flavorings or colorings. Other constituents are produced during fermentation, distillation, or storage. These nonalcoholic constituents, called **congeners,** contribute to the effects of certain beverages, either directly affecting the body or affecting the rate at which the alcohol content is absorbed into the blood. Beers and wines contain organic compounds, minerals, and salts, none that are toxic. The higher molecular-weight alcohols, or fusel oils, are toxic, but usually found in such low concentrations that there is no appreciable hazard. Vodka

and gin tend to have lower concentrations of congeners than whiskeys and rum.

---

congeners

nonalcoholic substances found in alcoholic beverages

THE PHYSICAL EFFECTS OF ALCOHOL

How does alcohol work in the body? Figure 7-3 graphically illustrates how alcohol is absorbed into the body. The body is affected by alcohol in two ways. First, alcohol has direct contact with the mouth, esophagus, stomach, and intestine, acting as an irritant and an **anesthetic** (blocking sensitivity to pain). Second, alcohol enters the bloodstream quickly and directly from the stomach and even more rapidly through the walls of the small intestine. Once the alcohol is in the small intestine, its absorption is largely independent of the presence of food, unlike its action in the stomach, where food retards absorption.

---

anesthetic

a drug that blocks sensitivity to pain

The rate at which alcohol enters the blood is a key factor in the blood-alcohol concentrations to which the brain is exposed. This rate largely determines the behavioral and physical responses to alcoholic beverages. On the behavioral side, the drinking situation, the drinker's mood, and his or her attitude and previous experience with alcohol will all contribute to the reaction to drinking. People have individual patterns of psychological functioning that may affect their reactions to alcohol, as well. For instance, the time it takes to empty the stomach may be either slowed down or speeded up by anger, fear, stress, nausea, and the condition of the stomach tissues.

The blood-alcohol level produced depends on

6. BRAIN.—Alcohol goes to the brain almost as soon as it is drunk. The bloodstream carries it there. Alcohol keeps passing through the brain until the liver has had time to change (oxidize) all the alcohol into carbon dioxide, water, and energy.

5. LIVER.—As the bloodstream carries the alcohol around the body, it carries it through the liver too. The liver changes the alcohol to water, carbon dioxide, and energy. This process is called oxidation. The liver can oxidize (change into water, carbon dioxide, and energy) only about one-half ounce of alcohol an hour. This means that until the liver has time to oxidize all of the alcohol, the alcohol keeps on passing through all parts of the body, including the brain.

4. BLOODSTREAM.—The bloodstream then carries the alcohol to all parts of the body, such as the brain, heart, and liver.

1. MOUTH.—Alcohol is drunk.

2. STOMACH.—Alcohol goes right into the stomach. A little of the alcohol goes through the wall of the stomach and into the bloodstream. But most of the alcohol goes down into the small intestine.

3. SMALL INTESTINE.—Alcohol goes from the stomach into the small intestine. Most of the alcohol then goes through the walls of the intestine and into the bloodstream.

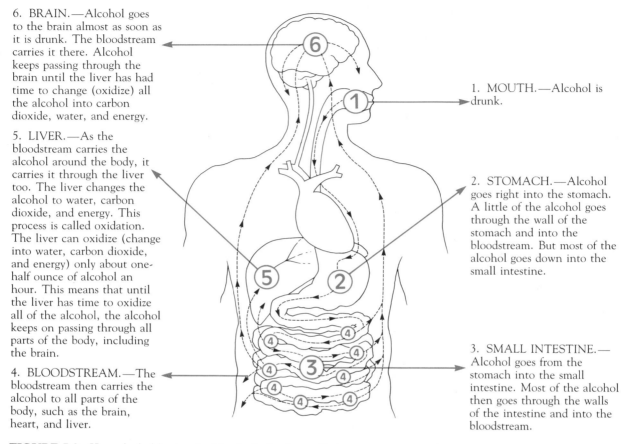

FIGURE 7-3 How alcohol is absorbed in the body *Source:* National Institute on Alcohol Abuse and Alcoholism, *Alcohol Health and Research World* (Washington, D.C.: U.S. Department of Health and Human Services, 1988).

the presence of food in the stomach, the rate of consumption of the alcohol, the concentration of the alcohol, and the drinker's body composition. Fatty foods, meat, and milk slow the absorption of alcohol, allowing more time for its metabolism and reducing the peak concentration in the blood. When alcoholic beverages are taken with a substantial meal, peak blood-alcohol concentrations may be as much as 50% lower than they would have been had the alcohol been consumed by itself. When large amounts of alcohol are consumed in a short period, the brain is exposed to higher peak concentrations. Generally, the more alcohol in the stomach, the greater the absorption rate. There is,

however, a modifying effect of very strong drinks on the absorption rate. The absorption of drinks stronger than 100 proof is inhibited. This may be due to blocked passage into the small intestine or irritation of the lining of the stomach, causing mucus secretion, or both.

The presence of congeners in alcoholic beverages also modifies the rate of absorption. High concentrations of congeners slow alcohol absorption. The net result is that the effects of beer and wine are felt more slowly than those of distilled spirits, even when the same amounts of alcohol are consumed. Diluting an alcoholic beverage with water also helps to slow down absorption, but mixing with carbonated beverages increases the absorption rate. The carbonation causes the stomach to empty its contents into the small intestine more rapidly, causing a more rapid "high." The carbonation in champagne has the same effect.

Once in the blood, alcohol is uniformly distributed throughout all tissues and fluids, including fetal circulation in pregnant women. Because the brain has a large blood supply, its activity is quickly affected by a high alcohol concentration in the blood. Body composition—the amount of water available for the alcohol to be dissolved in—is a key factor in blood-alcohol concentration. The greater the muscle mass, the lower the blood-alcohol concentration that will result from a given amount of alcohol. This is because muscle has more fluid volume than fat. For example, the blood-alcohol level produced in a 180-pound man drinking 4 ounces of whiskey will be substantially lower than that of an equally muscular 130-pound man drinking the same amount over the same period. The larger man will show fewer effects. A woman of equivalent weight to a given man will have a higher blood-alcohol level because women on average have a higher percentage of fat. Thus, they will be affected more by identical drinks.

Alcoholic beverages have almost no vitamins, minerals, protein, or fat—just large amounts of a carbohydrate that is unlike any other. It cannot be used by most cells; it must be metabolized by an enzyme (alcohol dehydrogenase) that is found almost exclusively in the liver. Alcohol provides more calories per gram than carbohydrate or protein and only slightly less than pure fat. Because alcohol does provide calories, the drinker's appetite may be satisfied, and he or she may not eat properly, causing malnutrition.

The tolerance developed to alcohol is comparable to that of barbiturates (see Chapter 6). Pharmacodynamic tolerance causes the nervous system to adapt to the continual presence of alcohol; thus, more of the drug is needed to produce the same effects. Behavioral tolerance allows the person to adjust to the effects of alcohol on speech, vision, and motor control (Jaffe 1980). Some people have a higher tolerance for alcohol and can more easily disguise intoxication.

SHORT-TERM EFFECTS

The impact of alcohol on the central nervous system (CNS) is similar to that of sedative/hypnotic agents such as barbiturates. Alcohol apparently depresses CNS activity at all doses, producing definable results.

At low to moderate doses, **disinhibition** often occurs, resulting from depression of inhibitory centers in the brain. The effects on behavior are variable and somewhat unpredictable. To a large extent, the social setting and mental state determine the individual's response to alcohol consumption. For example, alcohol can cause one person to become euphoric, friendly, and talkative but another to become aggressive and hostile. Low to moderate doses also interfere with motor activity, reflexes, and coordination. Often, this impairment isn't apparent to the affected person.

---

disinhibition

the loss of conditioned reflexes due to depression of inhibitory centers of the brain

---

In moderate quantities, alcohol slightly increases the heartrate; slightly dilates blood vessels in the arms, legs, and skin; and moderately lowers blood pressure. It stimulates appetite, increases production of gastric secretions, and markedly stimulates urine output.

At higher doses, the social setting has little influence on the expression of depressive actions of the alcohol. The CNS depression incapacitates the individual, causing difficulty in walking, talking, and thinking. These doses tend to induce drowsiness and cause sleep. If large amounts of alcohol are consumed rapidly, severe depression of the motor control area of the brain occurs, producing uncoordination, confusion, disorientation, stupor, anesthesia, coma, and even death.

The lethal level of alcohol is between 0.4% and 0.6% by volume in the blood. Death is caused by severe depression of the respiration center in the brainstem, although the person usually passes out before drinking this much. Though an alcoholic person may metabolize the drug more rapidly, the alcoholic toxicity level stays the same. In other words, it takes the same amount of alcohol to kill a nondrinker as a drunk. The amount of alcohol required for anesthesia is very close to the toxic level, which is why it is not used as an anesthetic. See Table 7-2 for a summary of the psychological and physical effects of various blood-alcohol concentration levels.

As a rule, it will take as many hours as the number of drinks consumed to sober up completely. Drinking black coffee, taking a cold shower, breathing pure oxygen, and so forth will not hasten the process. Stimulants like coffee may help keep the drunk person awake but will not improve judgment or reflexes to any significant extent. Drinking coffee only produces a wide-awake drunk.

Because of the disinhibition, relaxation, and

sense of well-being mediated by alcohol, some degree of psychological dependence often develops, and the use of alcoholic beverages at social gatherings becomes routine. Unfortunately, many people become so dependent on the psychological influences of alcohol that they become compulsive in its continual consumption. These individuals can be severely handicapped, often unable to function normally in society. They are distinguished by the term **alcoholic**.

alcoholic
a person who is addicted to alcohol

Besides the psychological effects, physical dependence also can result from the regular con-

TABLE 7-2 Psychological and physical effects of various blood-alcohol concentration levels

Number of Drinks*	Blood-Alcohol Concentration	Psychological and Physical Effects
1	0.02%–0.03%	No overt effects, slight mood elevation
2	0.05%–0.06%	Feeling of relaxation, warmth; slight decrease in reaction time and in fine-muscle coordination
3	0.08%–0.09%	Balance, speech, vision, hearing slightly impaired; feelings of euphoria, increased confidence; loss of motor coordination
	0.10%	Legal intoxication in most states; some have lower limits
4	0.11%–0.12%	Coordination and balance becoming difficult; distinct impairment of mental faculties, judgment
5	0.14%–0.15%	Major impairment of mental and physical control; slurred speech, blurred vision, lack of motor skills
7	0.20%	Loss of motor control—must have assistance in moving about; mental confusion
10	0.30%	Severe intoxication; minimum conscious control of mind and body
14	0.40%	Unconsciousness, threshold of coma
17	0.50%	Deep coma
20	0.60%	Death from respiratory failure

Source: Modified from data given in Ohio State Police Driver Information Seminars and the National Clearinghouse for Alcohol and Alcoholism Information, 5600 Fishers Lane, Rockville MD 85206.

Note: For each hour elapsed since the last drink, subtract 0.015% blood-alcohol concentration, or approximately one drink.

*One drink = one beer (4% alcohol, 12 oz.) or one highball (1 oz. whiskey).

sumption of large quantities of alcohol. The consequence becomes apparent when ethanol use is abruptly interrupted and withdrawal symptoms result. For example, alcohol-dependent individuals have periods of rebound hyperexcitability marked by anxiety, agitation, confusion, insomnia, and delirium. The excitation might progress to convulsions and death. Short-term, intermittent episodes of mild to moderate alcohol consumption appear to exert only reversible and transient effects on the CNS. However, the extended use of large quantities of alcohol have been associated with permanent brain damage and dementia (destruction of thinking capabilities).

THE HANGOVER A familiar after effect of overindulgence is fatigue combined with nausea, upset stomach, headache, sensitivity to sounds, and ill temper—the hangover. The symptoms are usually most severe many hours after drinking, when little or no alcohol remains in the body. There is no simple explanation for what causes the hangover (other than having had too much to drink). Theories include accumulation of acetaldehyde (a metabolite of ethanol), dehydration of the tissues, poisoning due to tissue deterioration, depletion of important enzyme systems needed to maintain routine functioning, an acute withdrawal response and metabolism of the congeners in alcoholic beverages.

The body loses fluid in two ways through alcohol's **diuretic** action: (1) the water content, such as in beer, will increase the volume of urine, and (2) the alcohol depresses the center in the hypothalamus of the brain that controls release of a water-conservation hormone (antidiuretic hormone). With less of this hormone, urine volume is further increased. Thus, after drinking heavily, especially the highly concentrated forms of alcohol, the person is thirsty. However, this by itself does not explain the symptoms of hangover.

---

diuretic
a drug or substance that increases the production of urine

The type of alcoholic beverage you drink may influence the hangover that results. Some people are more sensitive to particular congeners than others. For example, some drinkers have no problem with white wine but an equal amount of some red wine will give them a hangover. Whiskeys, scotch, and rum may cause worse hangovers than vodka or gin, given equal amounts of alcohol, because vodka and gin have fewer congeners. There is little evidence that mixing different types of drinks per se causes a worse hangover. What is more likely is that more than the usual amount of alcohol is consumed because of trying a variety of drinks.

How should you treat a hangover? A common technique is to take a drink of the same alcoholic beverage that caused the hangover. This is called "taking the hair of the dog that bit you" (from the old notion that the burnt hair of a dog is an antidote to its bite). This might help the person who is physically dependent, the same way giving heroin to a heroin addict will ease the withdrawal symptoms. The "hair of the dog" method might work by depressing the centers of the brain that interpret pain or by relieving a withdrawal response. Also consider the psychological factors involved in having a hangover; distraction or focusing attention on something else may ease the effects.

Another folk remedy is to take an analgesic compound like an aspirin-caffeine combination before drinking. Aspirin would help control headache; the caffeine may help counteract the depressant effect of the alcohol. These ingredients would have no effect on the actual sobering-up process. Products like aspirin, caffeine, and Alka-Seltzer can irritate the stomach lining to the point where the person feels worse.

LONG-TERM EFFECTS

Light or moderate drinking apparently do little permanent harm. (The exception is moderate drinking during pregnancy, in which case alcohol has little effect on the mother but can cause irreversible mental retardation in her child.) But when taken in large doses over long periods of time, alcohol can cause structural damage to several major organs: the heart, the kidneys, the liver, the brain, and the gastrointestinal system.

Prolonged heavy drinking causes various types of muscle disease and tremor. One essential muscle affected by alcohol is the heart, the myocardium. Laboratory investigations have shown that alcohol is directly toxic to the heart and to other muscles, as well. It causes irregular heartbeat, which can be fatal. A common example of this is "holiday heart," so called because people drinking heavily over a weekend turn up in the emergency room with a dangerously irregular heartbeat. Chronic excessive use causes congestive heart failure. Malnutrition and vitamin deficiencies associated with prolonged heavy drinking contribute to cardiac abnormalities (Ritchie 1980).

Heavy alcohol consumption also affects the kidneys. Alcohol's diuretic action is due to its ability to decrease the secretion of the compound called *antidiuretic hormone* (ADH) from the brain. ADH normally decreases the formation and excretion of urine from the kidney; consequently, interference with the activity of ADH by ethanol results in diuresis (increased urine formation).

Liver damage commonly results from heavy drinking. Liver disease occurs because metabolizing alcohol has priority over the liver's normal functions. Its final stage, **cirrhosis** (scarring) of the liver, occurs about six times more frequently in alcoholics than in nondrinkers (Blake et al. 1988). Approximately 15% of those individuals who chronically consume large amounts of ethanol suffer from cirrhosis.

---

cirrhosis

scarring of the liver and destruction of fibrous tissues; results from alcohol abuse

---

Cirrhosis is the general name for many types of liver damage that are similar in appearance. The heavy drinker develops a fatty liver first, which is reversible if drinking stops. When alcohol is present, the liver uses it, and the liver's regular fuel (fatty acids) and proteins, accumulate. The engorged liver cells die, triggering the next stage, an inflammatory process called *alcoholic hepatitis*. Cellular death and inflammation cause the last stage, in which scar tissue forms barriers that interfere with bloodflow to liver cells that are still alive, further decreasing liver function. The fibrous scar tissue cannot carry out any of the normal functions of the liver for detoxification or metabolism. At this point, the liver is irreversibly damaged with nonfunctional fibrous tissue. Vitamin deficiency and malnutrition (especially protein deficiency, common in alcoholics) are important factors in the development of cirrhosis. Nevertheless, alcohol in the proportion of daily calories routinely consumed by alcoholics (35% to 50% of daily calories) will cause development of cirrhosis even with an adequate diet (Lieber 1976).

Heavy drinking over many years may result in serious mental disorders and permanent, irreversible damage to the brain and peripheral nervous system. Memory, judgment, and learning ability can deteriorate severely. Korsakoff's syndrome is a characteristic psychotic condition caused by alcohol use and the associated nutritional and vitamin deficiencies. Patients cannot remember recent events and compensate for their memory loss with confabulation (making up fictitious events that the patient accepts as fact). Polyneuritis—an inflammation of the nerves that causes burning and prickly sensations in the hands and feet—has the same origin. B-complex vitamins are often used to treat polyneuritis and memory deficit, but the damage is not always reversible (Seixas 1980).

Heavy drinkers have lowered resistance to pneumonia and other infectious diseases. While malnutrition is a factor, lowered resistance also may occur in well-nourished heavy drinkers. Heavy drinking appears to affect the bone marrow, where various blood cells are formed. The suppression of the bone marrow contributes to alcoholic anemia, in which red blood cell production cannot keep pace with the need (Aldo-Benson 1988). Heavy drinkers are also likely to develop alcoholic bleeding disorders because they have too few platelets to form clots (Seixas 1980).

Alcohol, especially when undiluted, irritates the gastrointestinal tract. Nausea, vomiting, and diarrhea are mild indications of trouble. The more frequently consumption takes place, the greater the irritation; one out of three heavy drinkers suffers from chronic gastritis. Alcohol in high concentrations is a very irritating substance and continual exposure of the gastrointestinal lining to this compound can cause inflammation and acute gastric distress. Further, the heavy drinker has double the probability of developing cancer of the mouth and other tissues on the way to the stomach. If a person also smokes, the risk for oral cancers goes up 15 times.

Think About It . . .

1. Given the high percentage of the U.S. population that abuses alcohol and the high mortality rate associated with it, why do you think alcohol is still a legal drug?
2. Name three different types of alcohol and how each is used.
3. What would you do if your best friend developed a drinking problem? List the criteria you would use to characterize problem drinking.

HOW WIDESPREAD IS ALCOHOL USE AND ABUSE?

While estimates of consumption levels for the world's developed countries are somewhat variable, apparent per capita consumption of alcoholic beverages began to level off in most industrialized countries except the United States during the mid-1970s. And by the mid-1980s, many countries, including the United States, were experiencing declines over previous levels of consumption. Of the 25 countries surveyed between 1979 and 1984, nearly two-thirds experienced declines or stability in levels of per capita consumption, as shown in Figure 7-4. Only four of the nine countries where consumption increased had rates of increase greater than 1%. In contrast, consumption in some developing countries has continued to increase.

In the United States, alcohol consumption has dropped sharply since 1981, as is evident from data for the decade 1977 to 1987 shown in Figure 7-5. The decline in consumption of spirits led the dropoff, as shown in Figure 7-6. Beer consumption remained at the 1986 level of 1.34 gallons per capita, the lowest level of consumption since 1978 and 4% lower than the 1981 peak level of 1.39 gallons (see Figure 7-6). By 1987, for the first time in more than 10 years, wine consumption had also leveled off.

What explains the steady decline in alcohol consumption since 1981? Changing demographics may be a reason. For instance, the proportion of the population over age 60 continues to increase, and alcohol consumption in this age group is low. The 1980s were a rather conservative decade, and the social acceptability of heavy drinking decreased steadily. There has been an increase in public awareness of the risks associated with alcohol use. Drinking people have turned away from distilled spirits toward beverages with lower alcohol content. People have also become increasingly more health conscious. The general population is now preoccupied with maintaining a healthy diet and adequate physical fitness. Such attitudes militate against constant alcohol use and abuse.

ALCOHOL USE IN AMERICAN POPULATION GROUPS

The drop in American consumption of alcohol has been strong in the general population over 30. The 1988 National Household Survey (NIDA 1988) indicates that the number of current drinkers declined from 113 million in 1985 to 106 million in 1988.

There continue to be significant variations in drinking patterns among specific population groups. Polls from Gallup (Gallup Report 1987) and Harris (1988) show sharp differences in alcohol use among various groups.

SOCIAL-CLASS DIFFERENCES Those in higher social classes—as measured by a combination of income, occupation, and education—showed a greater likelihood of drinking. In a poll, 79% of the upper class, 66% of the middle class, and 48% of the lower class reported drinking alcoholic beverages.

RELIGIOUS DIFFERENCES A Lou Harris poll (reported in Armor et al. 1976) found that, with re-

FIGURE 7-4   Average annual rate of change in per capita alcohol consumption: 25 countries, 1979–1984 *Source:* From Brazeau, Ron and Margo Sparrow. *International Survey: Alcoholic Beverage Taxation and Control Policies*, 6th ed. Ottowa: Brewers Association of Canada, 1986.

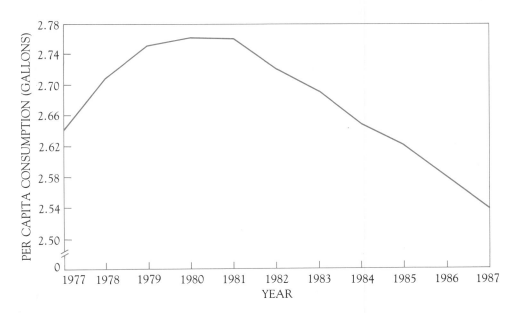

FIGURE 7-5 Apparent U.S. per capita consumption of pure alcohol: 1977–1987 *Source:* National Institute of Alcohol Abuse and Alcoholism, *Apparent Per Capita Alcohol Consumption: National, State and Regional Trends, 1977–1987,* Surveillance report no. 13 (Washington, D.C. United States Department of Health and Human Services, 1989).

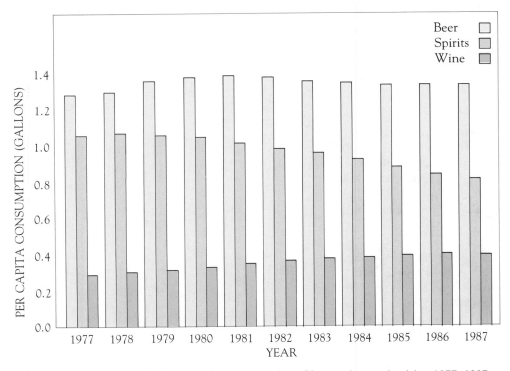

FIGURE 7-6 Apparent U.S. per capita consumption of beer, wine, and spirits: 1977–1987 *Source:* National Institute of Alcohol Abuse and Alcoholism, *Apparent Per Capita Alcohol Consumption: National, State and Regional Trends, 1977–1987,* Surveillance report no. 13 (Washington, D.C. United States Department of Health and Human Services, 1989).

gard to religion, 60% of Protestants and 78% of Catholics reported drinking. In the South, Southern Baptists, known for advocating abstinence, reported that 45% drank. While this religious group has the lowest percentage of drinkers, its members are more likely to experience conflict in social relationships when alcohol use is a factor.

REGIONAL DIFFERENCES Both the Harris (1988) and Gallup (1990) polls indicate that, overall, northerners drink significantly more than southerners.

GENDER DIFFERENCES Women (56%) are less likely to drink than men (77%) (Gallup Report 1990).

AGE DIFFERENCES Age correlates with the amount of alcohol consumed. In the Harris poll (1988), 77% of the respondents under age 30 drank, and the likelihood of abstaining from alcohol increased significantly with age. Approximately 49% of respondents over 50 years old indicated they had not consumed alcoholic beverages during the year prior to the poll taken by the Harris poll.

ALCOHOL ABUSE IN SPECIFIC POPULATIONS

While many different types of people use and abuse alcohol, concern over patterns of abuse has led social researchers to focus on the common characteristics of various groups that seem most at risk. In this section, we will identify and survey the distinctive problems of alcohol abuse experienced by several categories of people in America.

ADOLESCENTS AND YOUNG ADULTS Results from the 1988 National High School Senior Survey showed that, "for the first time in several years, the proportion of seniors who can be categorized as 'current drinkers' (had one or more drinks in the past 30 days) declined significantly (from 66 percent to 64 percent)" (NIAAA 1990, 26). To a large extent, this decline is believed to be the result of a growing awareness of the potential hazards of both drug and alcohol use (Johnston et al. 1988).

While these findings are favorable, the level of alcohol use by young people remains alarming. The data in Table 7-3 show that, from 1975 to 1989, approximately 91% of high school seniors had tried alcohol. Other data from 1987 show that:

Two-thirds of high school seniors were current drinkers.

More than one-third indulged in occasional heavy drinking.

Nearly one-third did not perceive a great risk in having four to five drinks nearly every day.

TABLE 7-3 High school senior survey trends in lifetime prevalence: 1975–1989

Class of	Percentage Who Ever Used Alcohol*
1975	90.4
1976	91.9
1977	92.5
1978	93.1
1979	93.0
1980	93.2
1981	92.6
1982	92.8
1983	92.6
1984	92.6
1985	92.2
1986	91.3
1987	92.2
1988	92.0
1989	90.7

Source: National Institute on Drug Abuse, *Monitoring the Future Study* (Ann Arbor, MI: Institute for Social Research, 1990).

Note: This information was gathered in annual nationwide surveys conducted for the National Institute on Drug Abuse by the University of Michigan Institute for Social Research. The 1989 survey involved more than 17,000 high school seniors from public and private schools.

*"Ever used" means "used at least one time."

Nearly one-third reported that most or all of their friends got drunk at least once a week.

Nearly 10% had first used alcohol by the sixth grade (Johnston et al. 1988).

On the bright side, however, there is little continuity in drinking behavior during the transition years between adolescence and young adulthood. Drinking levels tend to decline substantially by age 30. Older adults display decreases in alcohol consumption patterns; there are more abstainers and fewer heavy drinkers in this age group than in the younger age groups. Generally, if we exclude cases of more serious stressful life experiences and older patients who have been hospitalized for non–alcohol-related causes, the prevalence of drinking-related problems is lower among older people.

WOMEN   In the national survey conducted by the National Institute on Alcohol Abuse and Alcoholism (NIAAA) it is estimated that, in 1985, there were 3.3 million women alcoholics and another 2.4 million women who abused alcohol in the U.S. population (Williams et al. 1987). Alcoholism is usually viewed as a male problem, yet the relative incidence of alcohol abuse by women is increasing. Reliable statistics suggest that approximately one-third of alcohol abusers and alcoholics are women (Chatham 1990, 5).

To avoid severe criticism, most alcohol-abusing women drink alone or at home. High incidence of alcohol abuse is found in women who are unemployed and looking for work, while less alcohol abuse is likely to occur with women employed part time outside the home. Divorced or separated women, women who never marry, and those who are unmarried and living with a partner are more likely to use and abuse alcohol. Other high-risk groups are women in their twenties and early thirties and women with heavy-drinking husbands or partners. Wilsnack et al. (1986) found that women who experience depression or reproductive problems also demonstrate heavier drinking behavior.

Looking at specific age groups, the following conclusions can be drawn:

1. Women in the 21- to 34-year-old age group were least likely to report alcohol-related problems if they had stable marriages and were working full time. Thus, young mothers with full-time occupation reported less reliance on alcohol in comparison to childless women without full-time work.
2. In the 35- to 49-year-old age group, the heaviest drinkers were divorced or separated women without children in the home.
3. In the 50- to 64-year-old age group, the heaviest drinkers were women whose husbands or partners drank heavily.
4. Women 65 years and older comprised less than 10% of drinkers with drinking problems (NIAAA 1990).

Interestingly, more alcohol consumption is also found in women who closely perform so-called masculine gender roles, such as female executives and women in traditional blue-collar occupations.

Fetal Alcohol Syndrome. Women who are alcoholics or who drink heavily during pregnancy have a higher rate of spontaneous abortion, suggesting that alcohol is toxic to the developing embryo. Infants born to drinking mothers have a high probability of being afflicted with **fetal alcohol syndrome (FAS)**. These children have a characteristic pattern of facial deformities (see Figure 7-7), growth deficiency, and mental retardation. The growth deficiency occurs in embryonic development, and the child usually does not catch up after birth. Mild to moderate mental retardation does not appear to improve with time, apparently because the growth impairment affects growth of the brain, as well.

---

fetal alcohol syndrome (FAS)
a condition affecting children born to alcohol-consuming mothers that is characterized by facial deformities, growth deficiency, and mental retardation

---

The severity of FAS appears to be dose-response related: The more the mother drinks, the

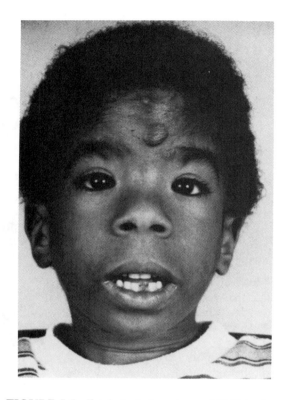

FIGURE 7-7   Fetal alcohol syndrome (FAS) is characterized by facial deformities, as well as growth deficiency and mental retardation. *Source:* Courtesy of Dr. Marilyn T. Miller. From "Fetal Alcohol Syndrome," by M. Miller, J. Israel, and J. Cuttone, *Journal of Pediatric Ophthalmology and Strabismus,* 1980, 18 (4), 6–15. Reprinted by permission of the author and publisher.

worse off the infant is. A safe, lower level of alcohol consumption has not been established for pregnant women. Birthweight decrements have been found at levels corresponding to about two drinks per day, on average. Clinical studies have established that alcohol clearly causes the syndrome; it is not related to the effects of smoking, maternal age, parity (number of children a woman has borne), social class, or poor nutrition (Streissguth et al. 1980). Studies in experimental animals show that ethanol by itself can cause all of the damage associated with FAS (Brown et al. 1979; Clarren et al. 1988; Miller 1988, 1987).

THE ELDERLY   Most old people who are diagnosed as alcoholics or alcohol abusers fall into two categories: (1) those who were previously addicted to alcohol and (2) those who have come to abuse alcohol through the pressures of loneliness, neglect, ill health, severe depression, or side effects of medication. The latter group includes by far the largest number of elderly abusers.

However, when comparisons are made between younger age groups and persons in their sixties and older, overall alcohol use is lower in older-aged groups. The lower use of alcohol in the elderly population has been attributed to:

1. chronic health problems, combined with fear of alcohol interference with strong medication
2. decreased income
3. increased sensitivity and less tolerance for alcohol (resulting partly from the loss of body mass leading to less body water content)
4. changes in lifestyle resulting from retirement
5. the diminished capacity of drinking found in aging peer members

ETHNIC AND RACIAL GROUPS   Four major racial and ethnic minority groups in the United States have been surveyed in terms of their percentages of nondrinkers (abstinence rates), heavy drinkers, and people subject to alcohol-related health problems. African-Americans comprise 12% of the population in the United States, and they are the largest minority group in the total population. African-Americans display high rates of abstention and low rates of heavy drinking, but they are extremely high risk for health problems in which alcohol is a factor, such as liver cirrhosis, heart disease, and cancers of the esophagus, mouth, larynx, and tongue.

The next largest minority group is Hispanics, comprising 7% of the total population. Members of this group, particularly Mexican-Americans, have high rates of both abstinence and heavy drinking and a higher prevalence of drinking-related problems than other racial and ethnic groups.

Asian-Americans represent 2% of the total population. They have the highest rates of abstention, the lowest rates of heavy drinking, and the lowest levels of drinking-related problems.

Native American groups—including American Indians and Alaskan Natives—are the smallest racial minority, comprising 1% of the total population. Native Americans vary widely in alcohol use but, as a whole, have very high mortality rates from causes that are most likely to be alcohol related: cirrhosis, unintentional injuries, homicide, and suicide. Native Americans are likely to feel stress from displacement and rejection from their homeland, as well as from high unemployment—all contributing factors to alcohol abuse. Many new alcohol rehabilitation programs for Native Americans have been started, and it is not unusual to find traditional tribal shamans assisting in these health and rehabilitation programs.

Among white Europeans, the heaviest drinking groups were the Irish, Italians, Jews, northern WASPs (white Anglo-Saxon Protestants), Slavs, Germans, and Scandinavians. More abstinence was found among Latins and southern WASPs (Cahalan and Room 1974; Greeley et al. 1980; Health and Human Services 1987).

THE HOMELESS It is estimated that 250,000 Americans are homeless on most nights, and as many as 3 million may experience some type of homelessness each year (Ropers and Bayer 1987). Alcohol abuse and alcohol dependence are serious problems among the homeless. Prevalence estimates for current alcohol abuse and alcoholism range from 20% to 48% (Wright et al. 1987). Alcohol abuse among the homeless intensifies other major problems, such as health and psychiatric disorders.

Think About It...

1. Elaborate on world alcohol consumption rates. Have they been increasing or decreasing? Cite percentages.
2. Consider the data presented in the section on "Alcohol Use in American Groups." Explain why there are social-class, religious, regional, gender, and age differences in alcohol consumption.
3. A close friend says that his or her ethnic grandparents always offer and drink wine with their adolescent grandchildren. Your friend says that, if alcohol use is presented to be normal to children while they are growing up, they will display moderate drinking behavior as adults. Do you agree or disagree with this argument? Back up your views with some evidence.

ATTITUDES TOWARD DRINKING AND DRIVING

Alcohol is involved in one-third to one-half of all highway fatalities in the United States. Serious problem drinking has been implicated in almost half of these alcohol-related deaths; the other half involved young drinkers and social drinkers with high blood-alcohol levels at the time of the accident. One-third of all traffic injuries are also related to alcohol (NHTSA 1988).

Such widespread destruction has prompted relatives and friends of victims of drunk drivers to form volunteer groups, which lobby for mandatory jail sentences and revocation of driving licenses for drivers convicted of driving while intoxicated. Such measures have proven to be successful deterrents to drunken driving in several European countries.

The leading cause of injury deaths in the United States is motor vehicle crashes (Baker et al. 1984). In the United States, 46,386 people die in traffic accidents in a given year; approximately half of the deaths are alcohol related (NHTSA 1988). The National Highway Traffic Safety Administration (NHTSA) defines a *fatality* or *traffic crash* as alcohol involved or alcohol related when a participant (driver, pedestrian, or bicyclist) has a measured or estimated blood-alcohol concentration (BAC) of 0.01% or above (NHTSA 1988; NIAAA 1990). In most states, the legal limit for intoxication is a BAC of 0.10% or greater.

Alcohol-related car accidents are particularly common among youth. Each year, 40% of all teenage deaths result from traffic accidents (NIAAA 1990), and another 40,000 youth are disfigured in accidents involving alcohol. In an effort to address this high-risk group, the NHTSA has devised a test that gauges the attitudes of teen-agers toward drinking and driving. The NHTSA wants to encourage young people to consider social-psychological factors associated with their urge to drink and drive or to ride with drinking friends. The two-part test lets respondents evaluate themselves and then compare their own knowledge, values, and beliefs about alcohol with an average profile compiled from responses of the students. See Figure 7-8 for a copy of the test. Anyone can benefit from taking this test and plotting results against the profile for Pennsylvania teens in Figure 7-9.

FIGURE 7-8   Attitudinal test for drinking and driving

Part 1: Alcohol Knowledge Test

In response to each statement, circle either T (true) or F (false).

T F   1. Mixing different kinds of drinks can increase the effect of alcohol.

T F   2. The average 4-oz. drink of wine is less intoxicating than the average 1-oz. drink of hard liquor.

T F   3. A can of beer is less intoxicating than an average drink of hard liquor.

T F   4. A cold shower can help sober up a person.

T F   5. A person can be drunk and not stagger or slur his or her speech.

T F   6. It is easy to tell if people are drunk even if you don't know them well.

T F   7. A person drinking on an empty stomach will get drunk faster.

T F   8. People's moods help determine how they are affected by alcohol.

T F   9. A person who is used to drinking can drink more.

T F   10. A person who weighs less can get drunk faster than a heavier person.

T F   11. Of every ten traffic deaths, up to five are caused by drinking drivers.

T F   12. The surest way to tell if the person is legally drunk is by the percent of alcohol in the blood.

T F   13. People who are drunk cannot compensate for it when they drive.

T F   14. In a fatal drunk-driving accident, the drunk is usually not the one killed.

T F   15. Drinking black coffee can help sober up a person.

T F   16. Alcoholic beverages are a stimulant.

Answers: (1) F, (2) F, (3) F, (4) F, (5) T, (6) F, (7) T, (8) T, (9) F, (10) T, (11) T, (12) T, (13) T, (14) F, (15) F, (16) F

Part 2: Alcohol Attitude Test

Directions: If you strongly agree with the following statements, write in 1. If you agree, but not strongly write in 2. If you neither agree nor disagree, write in 3. If you disagree, but not strongly, write in 4. If you strongly disagree, write in 5.

Set 1

____   1. If a person concentrates hard enough, he or she can overcome any effect that drinking may have on driving.

____   2. If you drive home from a party late at night when most roads are deserted, there is not much danger in driving after drinking.

____   3. It's all right for a person who has been drinking to drive, as long as he or she shows no signs of being drunk.

____   4. If you're going to have an accident, you'll have one anyhow, regardless of drinking.

____   5. A drink or two helps people drive better because it relaxes them.

____   Total score for questions 1 through 5

Set 2

____   6. If I tried to stop someone from driving after drinking, the person would probably think I was butting in where I shouldn't.

____   7. Even if I wanted to, I would probably not be able to stop someone from driving after drinking.

____   8. If people want to kill themselves, that's their business.

____   9. I wouldn't like someone to try to stop me from driving after drinking.

____   10. Usually, if you try to help someone else out of a dangerous situation, you risk getting yourself into one.

____   Total score for questions 6 through 10

WHAT IS ALCOHOLISM?

To many people, the stereotype of an alcoholic is the skid-row or homeless derelict. In fact, this stereotype makes up less than 5% of America's problem drinkers. Most are employed, family-centered people, leading what may appear to be normal lives. Estimates vary, but it is believed that about three-fourths of problem drinkers are men and one-fourth are women. The proportion of women has risen in recent years, perhaps because they are increasingly willing to acknowledge the

FIGURE 7-8 *Continued*

Set 3

____ 11. My friends would not disapprove of me for driving after drinking.

____ 12. Getting into trouble with my parents would not keep me from driving after drinking.

____ 13. The thought that I might get into trouble with the police would not keep me from driving after drinking.

____ 14. I am not scared by the thought that I might seriously injure myself or someone else by driving after drinking.

____ 15. The fear of damaging the car would not keep me from driving after drinking.

____ Total score for questions 11 through 15

Set 4

____ 16. The 55 mph speed limit on the open roads spoils the pleasure of driving for most teen-agers.

____ 17. Many teenagers use driving to let off steam.

____ 18. Being able to drive a car makes teenagers feel more confident in their relations with others their age.

____ 19. An evening with friends is not much fun unless one of them has a car.

____ 20. There is something about being behind the wheel of a car that makes one feel more adult.

____ Total score for questions 16 through 20

Set 5

____ 21. I usually do things that everybody else is doing.

____ 22. What my friends think of me is the most important thing in my life.

____ 23. I would ride in a friend's car even if that person had been drinking a lot.

____ 24. Often I do things just so I won't feel left out of the group I'm with.

____ 25. I often worry about what other people think about things I do.

____ Total score for questions 21 through 25

Set 6

____ 26. Adults try to stop teenagers from driving just to show their power.

____ 27. I don't think it would help me to go to my parents for advice.

____ 28. I feel I should have the right to drink if my parents do.

____ 29. My parents have no real understanding of what I want out of life.

____ 30. I wouldn't dare call my parents to come and take me home if either I or a friend I was with got drunk.

____ Total score for questions 26 through 30

Scoring the Self-Test

Set 1   13–25 points: realistic in avoiding drinking-driving situations; 5–6 points: tends to make up excuses to combine drinking and driving.

Set 2   15–25 points: takes responsibility to keep others from driving when drunk; 5–9 points: wouldn't take steps to stop a drunk friend from driving.

Set 3   12–25 points: hesitates to drive after drinking; 5–7 points: is not deterred by the consequences of drinking and driving.

Set 4   19–25 points: perceives auto as means of trans-portation; 5–14 points: uses car to satisfy psy-chological needs, not just transportation.

Set 5   16–25 points: cares about what others think, but acts according to own beliefs and values; 5–10 points: goes along with the crowd.

Set 6   18–25 points: accepts adult and parental respon-sibility and concern for one's safety; 5–10 points: rejects parental concern or control.

Source: Courtesy of National Highway Traffic Safety Administration, National Center for Statistics and Analysis, from *Drug Driving Facts* (Washington, D.C.: NHTSA, 1988).

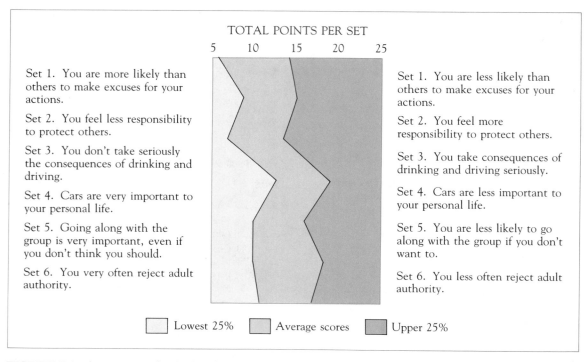

TOTAL POINTS PER SET

5   10   15   20   25

Set 1. You are more likely than others to make excuses for your actions.

Set 2. You feel less responsibility to protect others.

Set 3. You don't take seriously the consequences of drinking and driving.

Set 4. Cars are very important to your personal life.

Set 5. Going along with the group is very important, even if you don't think you should.

Set 6. You very often reject adult authority.

Set 1. You are less likely than others to make excuses for your actions.

Set 2. You feel more responsibility to protect others.

Set 3. You take consequences of drinking and driving seriously.

Set 4. Cars are less important to your personal life.

Set 5. You are less likely to go along with the group if you don't want to.

Set 6. You less often reject adult authority.

Lowest 25%   Average scores   Upper 25%

FIGURE 7-9   Assessment of attitudes about drinking and driving   *Source:* Courtesy of National Highway Traffic Safety Administration, National Center for Statistics and Analysis, from *Drug Driving Facts* (Washington, D.C.: NHTSA, 1988).

problem and seek treatment. Female problem drinkers may therefore now be more visible rather than numerous (see "Women," earlier in this chapter).

Alcoholism is a state of physical and psychological addiction to the psychoactive substance ethanol. It was once viewed as a vice and dismissed as "sinful," but over the years, there has been a shift from this perspective to one that views alcoholism as a disease. The "sinfulness" perspective failed to focus on the fact that alcoholism is an addiction, an illness, and not the result of a lack of personal discipline and morality.

Attempts to expand the basic definition of *alcoholism* to include symptoms of the condition and psychological and sociological factors have been difficult; no one definition satisfies everyone. The

World Health Organization defines the *alcohol dependence syndrome* as a state, psychic and usually also physical, resulting from taking alcohol and characterized by behavioral and other responses that always include a compulsion to take alcohol on a continuous or periodic basis to experience its psychic effects and sometimes to avoid the discomfort of its absence; tolerance may or may not be present (NIAAA 1980).

The following is another widely accepted definition of *alcoholism:*

Alcoholism is a chronic behavioral disorder manifested by repeated drinking of alcoholic beverages in excess of the dietary and social uses of the community, and to an extent that interferes with the drinker's health or his social or economic functioning (Keller 1958).

For You to Consider...

Diagnosing Alcoholism

Many professionals who are in the position to diagnose alcohol problems are often slow to recognize them. Thus, the diagnosis of alcoholism is often made only when the illness is at advanced stages—when the victim is unable to control drinking, when he or she may no longer be able to maintain a family life or hold a job, or when malnutrition or organic damage is already present. Because alcoholics rarely volunteer information about their drinking, family physicians must make special efforts to discover the illness in its early stages. Unfortunately, there is no simple diagnostic procedure for detecting alcoholism.

Block (1980) has found the following questions useful in recognizing the early stages of alcoholism:

1. Does the patient desire to drink frequently?
2. Does the patient need to drink at a certain time of day? For example, does he or she anticipate drinking in the evening? Does he or she use alcohol to get to sleep?
3. Does the frequency of the patient's drinking go beyond ritual socializing? Is he or she more interested in getting "high" and maintaining that state? Is he or she disappointed if drinks are not served at a restaurant or party?
4. Is the patient's drinking criticized by his or her spouse or friends? Does he or she resent these remarks?
5. Does the patient drink to relieve discomfort or tension of any kind?
6. Does the patient take care to keep a good stock of liquor, "just in case"?
7. Does the patient prefer the company of those who drink as he or she does and avoid people who do not drink?

prodromal stage
Jellinek's (1952) term for early addiction to alcohol, the first stage

crucial stage
Jellinek's (1952) second stage of alcohol addiction

chronic stage
Jellinek's (1952) third stage of alcohol addiction

In the first stage, the individual develops a reputation for excess drinking and is frequently referred to as "a great party person." It is not unusual for this person to drink to excess and not be able to recall what happened the night before. Such *blackouts* are characterized by not remembering specific events while under the influence. The advanced prodromal stage includes defensiveness about drinking, gulping drinks, and excessive consumption of alcohol, more than that of peers.

During the middle, or crucial, stage the individual is aware that perhaps he or she is drinking excessively; attempts may be made to modify the amount of drinking that appears to be excessive. During this phase, the drinker may switch brands of alcohol, but the amount of alcohol consumed continues to be excessive. He or she may also attempt to implement discipline by surreptitiously abstaining for days or weeks. The individual at this stage begins to drink alone for the first time. After repeated excessive drinking, he or she may set limits as to when drinking is permissible, for instance, no drinking until after a certain hour of the day, like after 1:00 P.M. or 5:00 P.M. When the hour arrives, drinking to excess occurs. Sexual appetite is diminished at this stage of alcohol abuse, and it is not unusual for the individual to cancel appointments or call in sick at work. In sum, this stage is characterized by a loss of control over drinking, hiding the problem, and a number of health problems.

The chronic stage occurs after several years, generally during the middle years of life. Drinking has become uncontrollable, often going on for days at a time. Hospitalization for alcohol-caused symptoms may occur several times a year at this stage.

STAGES OF ALCOHOL ABUSE

Early research by Jellinek (1952) focused on three stages of alcohol addiction: (1) the early, or **prodromal stage**; (2) the middle, or **crucial stage**; and (3) the final, or **chronic stage.**

Relationships are severely strained and even curtailed; close friends and/or spouses are fully aware of the drinking problem. Withdrawal symptoms—such as sweating excessively, shaking uncontrollably, and hallucinating—are not uncommon. At this point, several forms of intervention are required: alcohol treatment and individual and group counseling programs.

CAUSES OF ALCOHOLISM

For many years, people with drinking problems were lumped together under the label *alcoholic*, and all were assumed to be suffering from the same illness. It has become evident that there are many kinds of drinking problems, many diverse types of people who have them, and many reasons why

For You to Consider...

Profile of a Runaway Addiction

The following describes the drift into deeper stages of alcoholism.

Her skin is smooth and her face is pretty. Her blue eyes are clear and radiant. They weren't always that way. Randi is sixteen. She has been through hell with alcohol.

"Most teenagers think you can't become an alcoholic so young," said Randi. "They think you have to be drinking for thirty years and be forty years old, and that because you may not drink every day, you can't have a problem." Randi offers herself as proof of yet another misconception.

Randi's first drinking experience was at a family Christmas party when she was nine. Her alcoholic uncle kept feeding her rum and Cokes. He thought it was funny to see his little niece stumble around, lose control of herself, not be able to speak clearly.

Randi got drunk, passed out, blacked out, and got sick her very first time. She drank very infrequently after that, until age thirteen. Life at home had become unbearable. She had endured years of sexual and physical

abuse by her stepfather. A cauldron of anger and guilt and helplessness had been building inside her, and it finally burst. "I just flew off the handle," she said. She was filled with hurt and despair. She discovered that alcohol was very good at numbing these feelings.

"I didn't think there was anything wrong with using alcohol this way," she said. "It made me forget anything going on, any problem, it just made me forget. It helped me escape my feelings. I was always very lonely and depressed, and I always thought drinking would make it better." The feelings would get soothed, temporarily. "But things never got better, only worse," she said.

Randi started hanging out with juniors and seniors—the "alcohol crowd," as she calls it. "To go out on a Friday night, there needed to be alcohol in the car or it just wasn't worth going out," she said.

She had always been a fine student, but by freshman year, Randi was absent 113 out of the 181 school days. "My grades went completely down the tubes. But, of course, I didn't have a problem. Not me." Randi laughed at her sarcasm.

More and more, drinking just seemed to be the thing to do. She

drank not only to forget, but to have fun, to be cool. "I think I always saw the glamor involved with alcohol. The adults sitting around drinking a glass of wine or whatever. I put it together with the social scene." She could not imagine life without it.

Randi's progression was rapid. She advanced from Friday night parties to weekend-long alcohol binges. "I needed it so much toward the end, it was such a desperation for it, that I would drink before I went to school . . . if I went to school."

She was committed to a psychiatric hospital for a year because of several drunken suicide attempts. She lied about her drinking. She carved a hole in the floor of her room to hide bottles. Still, she had denial.

"I didn't want to blame my problems on my drinking," she said. "I was addicted to alcohol, but I just thought I was tired, or getting sick. I never really put my problems together with my drinking until later."

Source: W. Coffey, *Straight Talk About Drinking: Teenagers Speak Out About Alcohol.* (Markham, Ontario, Canada: Penguin Books Canada Limited, 1988), pp. 110–112. Permission pending.

people begin and continue to drink to a harmful extent. The search for a single cause of alcoholism has shifted to interdisciplinary exploration of factors that might, singly or in combination, account for the development of problem drinking in various types of individuals.

There is no generally agreed upon model of how alcoholism starts; multiple circumstances are probably required to make a person become a problem drinker. A report by the Cooperative Commission on the Study of Alcoholism suggests that an individual who displays the following characteristics is more likely to develop trouble than most other persons:

1. Responds to beverage alcohol in a certain way, perhaps physiologically determined, experiencing intense relief and relaxation
2. Has certain personality characteristics, such as difficulty in dealing with others and difficulty in overcoming depression, frustration, and anxiety
3. Is a member of a culture in which there is both pressure to drink and culturally induced guilt and confusion regarding what kinds of drinking behavior are appropriate.

The importance of the different casual factors of alcoholism no doubt varies from one individual to another. Research into physiological, psychological, and sociological dimensions of this problem and integration of the findings in these and other areas have resulted in greater understanding of the conditions that precede, underlie, and maintain problem drinking (NIAAA 1980).

PHYSIOLOGICAL FACTORS Much research on causation has been devoted to finding physiological factors—either in the alcoholic beverage itself or in the biological make-up of the alcoholic—that could account for alcoholic addiction. Vitamin deficiencies and hormone imbalances have been suggested as causes of alcoholism. However, investigations show that the nutritional and hormonal problems found in individuals with advanced alcoholism are results, not causes, of excessive drinking (Sherlock 1984; Mezey 1985). Allergy has been blamed for some cases of alcoholism, but there is no proof that alcoholic individuals are generally allergic to alcohol itself or to other components of alcoholic beverages. Another theory suggests that alcoholism is caused by some nonalcoholic component of beer, wine, whiskey, rum, or brandy. There is also no proof of this.

A major difficulty with research into causes of alcoholism is that, although laboratory animals can be made dependent on alcohol and this process can be studied, there is no good model to study the spontaneous development of alcoholism as it occurs in humans. For example, if minute quantities of an alcohol solution are injected directly into rats' brains every two or three hours for several days, they will drink alcohol whenever it is offered to them. However, the drug must initially be forced on them in this or some other manner to make them dependent. Strains of mice have been bred that demonstrate a selective preference for alcohol, which they drink in large amounts. This preference is genetically determined; it is not affected even when the young mice are raised by females of a different strain or are exposed to various conditions of stress or isolation. However, the mice of these heavy-drinking strains also happen to be able to metabolize alcohol much more rapidly than mice of other strains. Thus, it is difficult to determine whether their increased alcohol intake is related to a particular taste for alcohol or to their ability to consume more alcohol without becoming intoxicated. As described earlier, under controlled conditions, both alcoholic and normal subjects have an increased rate of alcohol metabolism while consuming relatively large amounts (Lumeng and Li 1986). Therefore, the mouse data are probably irrelevant to the study of alcoholism (Goodwin 1979).

Alcoholism occurs more frequently in children of alcoholics and probably has a hereditary basis. Cotton (1979) studied 39 familial alcoholism studies over a 10-year period. She discovered that, in most studies, an alcoholic is much more likely than a nonalcoholic to have a parent or other relative who is also an alcoholic; at least 25% of the alcoholics had alcoholic fathers. This research suggests that approximately one-fourth of any sample of alcoholics will have at least one parent who is also alcoholic.

Many studies found high rates of alcoholism

among the parents of alcoholics (McCord 1988). Fathers and brothers of alcoholics were more likely to have alcohol problems than mothers and sisters of alcoholics. This probably reflects the finding that there is a greater amount of alcoholism among males (Rydelius 1981). Overall, many studies find that having a close relative who is an alcoholic is a major risk factor for developing alcoholism.

Another interesting finding is that there is a 55% or higher concordance rate for alcoholism in identical twins, compared to a 28% rate for same-sex fraternal twins. In addition, studies using either the half-sibling method or adoption samples demonstrate a four times or higher increase in alcoholism for the children of alcoholics over those of nonalcoholics, even when the children had been separated from their natural parents shortly after birth and raised without knowledge of their parents' drinking problem. Children adopted through the same adoption agencies but without alcoholic biological parents showed low rates of alcoholism even if they were raised by an alcoholic parent figure or experienced a subsequent severe psychological trauma, such as parental death or divorce (Schuckit and Rayes 1979).

Several genetic diseases are transmitted in a sex-linked manner, such as through the female parent on the X sex chromosome. Other genetic diseases are caused by defects in the somatic, or nonsex, chromosomes and can be transmitted through either parent. The genetic mode of transmission of alcoholism, if there is one, is not certain. One study looked at the rate of alcoholism in the grandsons of known alcoholic men to see if there was a difference in genetic transmission through the mother or the father; it found no substantial difference between the two groups of grandsons. The rate of alcoholism by the time the grandsons were 50 years or older was 43%, approximately three times that of the general male population and even higher than that of the brothers of alcoholic persons. The results do not support either a sex-linked or a recessive gene but are compatible with the assumption of a dominant gene (Kaij and Dock 1975). (To be sure, however, alcoholism also occurs in children of teetolers.)

The extent to which genetic factors might contribute to alcoholism in the population is un-

known. It is not as clear cut as the genetic contribution to the development of diabetes, for example, although there are parallels. Perhaps future studies will clarify the role of genetics in the development of alcoholism.

PSYCHOLOGICAL FACTORS Although the terms *prealcoholic personality* and *alcoholic personality* have been used, there is little agreement on the identity of alcoholic personality traits or whether they may be the cause or the result of excessive drinking. Clinical psychologists and psychiatrists with a psychoanalytic perspective have described alcoholic drinkers who are in treatment as neurotic, maladjusted, unable to relate effectively to others, sexually and emotionally immature, isolated, dependent, unable to withstand frustration or tension, poorly integrated, and marked by deep feelings of sinfulness and unworthiness. Some therapists have suggested that alcoholism is a disastrous attempt at the self-cure of some inner conflict and that it might well be called "suicide by ounces." These observations are based on clinical impressions of alcoholics who are already in treatment because they were arrested, sick enough to be committed, rich enough to enter one clinic, or poor enough to enter another. No long-term studies have answered the question: What was the person like before he or she drank (Aronow 1980)?

Other perspectives involve *social learning* (Becker 1966; Sutherland 1947) and *reinforcement* (Akers 1985) theoretical explanations. **Social learning theory** emphasizes that alcohol use and later abuse result from early socialization experiences. Alcohol-drinking parents and/or significant others serve as role models who in effect teach children that drinking is okay.

---

social learning theory
a theory that asserts that alcohol use and later abuse result from early socialization experiences

---

Reinforcement theory explains alcohol use as resulting from some kind of positive "stroking," or benefit received from drinking. Peers and the mass media, including cinema and advertising in magazines and billboards, help reinforce the idea that consuming alcohol is expected and required during times of crisis, boredom, and celebration. By drinking, the individual may feel more accepted than if he or she abstained. Drinking may also bring attention from others that the drinker felt was lacking.

reinforcement theory
a theory that asserts that alcohol use results from positive "stroking," leading to satisfying feelings

SOCIOLOGICAL FACTORS Sociological explanations point to factors responsible for excessive drinking outside the individual: family drinking practices; peer influence; role of the mass media, particularly advertising; and the degree to which people are bonded to major social institutions (e.g., family, religion, economic and political systems).

Because people are shaped by their social links, the influence exerted by the factors listed above—and by how people interpret this influence—may strongly determine whether they consume alcohol and, if so, how much. Sociologists believe that, while addiction is both physiological and social, the consumption of alcohol *before* the addiction stage is determined by the quality of social interaction with family, peers, and the like. Other broader sociological approaches look at which societies consume the least and the most amounts of alcohol, and how, and then explain these differences in consumption.

Families that have children who do not experience significant alcohol problems are families that have the lowest incidence of alcoholism. The social psychological profile of these families emphasizes the following habits and attitudes:

1. The children are exposed to alcohol early in life, within a strong family or religious group.
2. The beverage is served in very diluted and small quantities. It is considered mainly as a food and usually consumed with meals. Ab-

stinence is socially acceptable. It is no more rude or ungracious to decline a drink than to decline a piece of bread.
3. Parents present a constant example of moderate drinking. Excessive drinking or intoxication is not socially acceptable. It is not considered stylish, comic, or tolerable.
4. No moral importance is attached to drinking; it is not viewed as proof of adulthood or virility.
5. Finally and perhaps most important, there is wide and usually complete agreement among members of the family on what might be called the "ground rules" of drinking (Aronow 1980; NIAAA 1980; Ullman 1958).

Think About It...

1. Cite three findings regarding women and alcohol use and abuse.
2. With regard to alcohol use and abuse, how do African-Americans, Hispanics, Asian-Americans, and Native Americans differ in the consumption of alcohol?
3. Assume that the person you are dating has started to drink more than you feel is healthy. Is he or she becoming an alcoholic? What factors characterize alcoholism?

PREVENTION OF ALCOHOL ABUSE

Prevention programs are aimed at reducing the individual use of alcohol and eliminating health problems that arise from alcohol consumption. Prevention efforts focused on the social conditions that foster alcohol abuse are usually undertaken by law enforcement officials, health professionals, educators, legislators, business leaders, and other concerned citizens. Such programs are based on prevention strategies closely tied to research.

Prevention programs and research concentrate on the following kinds of activities and areas of concern (NIAAA 1990, 210–233):

Basic Prevention Methods

1. Increase the price of alcoholic beverages. This has been found to curtail the amount

of alcohol consumed, especially among the youngest age groups. The larger benefit is fewer driving-under-the-influence auto accidents.

2. Monitor advertising and portrayals of alcohol consumption on television, in movies, and in newspapers and magazines.

Specific Social Environments

3. Research how the family influences attitudes toward drinking.
4. Prevent or discourage drinking during working hours. Focus on how the working environment promotes or can reduce alcohol consumption.
5. Analyze drinking establishments. Research shows that most cases of continued drinking while under the influence occur in licensed drinking establishments. Are there particular types of bars where heavy drinking occurs? Does the size of the drinking group influence how much is consumed?

Individual Characteristics

6. Analyze how age, gender, and ethnic differences affect consumption rates and the risk of becoming an alcoholic. Analyze personality traits in children and adults that are associated with the amount of alcohol consumed in later life.
7. Analyze accidents and trauma. How does the excessive use of alcohol lead to more accidents (such as fires, burns, and falls)?
8. Analyze how alcohol consumption contributes to violence, namely, family violence and marital stability.
9. Focus on adolescent risk factors and peer-group formation. How does peer support of drinking lead to excessive individual use of alcohol? Analyze the relationship between smoking and drinking.

Applied Prevention

10. Increase the minimum drinking age. States that have increased the minimum drinking age from 18 to 21 also experience a reduction in fatal auto accidents.

11. Use planning and zoning ordinances to prevent the consumption and sale of alcoholic beverages in residential areas.
12. Toughen drinking-and-driving laws. Use a deterrent model, consisting of fines, license revocation, and imprisonment so as to prevent driving while intoxicated (DWI).
13. Develop more alcohol education programs, workshops, and videos, especially mandatory education for persons convicted of DWI offenses.
14. Initiate server-training programs to educate people who are responsible for serving alcohol in private and public places.
15. Improve transportation services/alternatives, including designated-driver programs and safe-ride programs. In a designated-driver program, one person in a group is selected to abstain from drinking and becomes responsible for driving the other members. Safe-ride programs offer drinkers alternatives to driving themselves, providing free cab service or other means of transportation.

Programs to Change Individual Behaviors

16. Make prevention information readily available in grade schools, boys and girls clubs, recreational centers, and public housing developments.

TREATMENT OF ALCOHOLISM

Alcoholism is a treatable illness from which about two-thirds of those affected can recover; that is, they can stop the compulsion to consume alcohol by their own efforts. Many of the misunderstandings about alcoholism make it difficult for alcoholics to seek and get the help they need. For instance, some people think of alcoholism as a form of moral weakness rather than an illness. This stigma causes problem drinkers and their families to hide the problem rather than face it and seek treatment. There is a widespread belief, even among physicians, that alcoholism is not treatable and that the alcoholic is unmanageable and unwilling to be helped. None of these assumptions is true.

About 70% of alcoholics are men and women who are married and living with their families, who hold jobs, and who are accepted and reasonably respected members of their communities. For those of this group who seek treatment, the outlook is optimistic.

One obstacle to treatment is that many individuals deny their alcoholism, even to themselves. They will not be inclined to seek treatment until the pain, severity, and duration of their drinking problem become overwhelming or until a personal crisis forces assessment. As the circumstances in such a person's life fluctuate and become less painful, the motivation for recovery lessens; such an alcoholic may then discontinue treatment and relapse into a serious alcoholic condition.

In fact, it is quite possible for a person with a drinking problem to recover completely. This does not mean that he or she is cured; rather, it means that he or she can stop or control compulsive or uncontrolled drinking.

REHABILITATION METHODS* Rehabilitation for alcohol abuse means a return to successful living without the need to have alcohol. The patient is rehabilitated when he or she has reestablished and can maintain a good family life, work record, and respectable position in the community. Relapses may occur, but they do not mean that the problem drinker or the treatment effort has failed.

Satisfactory rehabilitation of alcoholics can be expected in at least 60% of cases, according to the National Institute on Alcohol Abuse and Alcoholism (NIAAA). Some therapists report success in 70% to 80% of cases. The recovery rate depends on the personal characteristics of the patient, the competence of the therapist, the availability of treatment facilities, and the support of the family, employer, and community. Unfortunately, the prognosis is less optimistic for chronic alcoholics and patients with alcoholic psychoses, who are usually placed in psychiatric hospitals. Less than

10% to 12% of this segment of the alcoholic population achieves full recovery.

The type of therapy provided is less important than the patient's personal characteristics and environmental experiences. Motivation is the most important characteristic, followed by high socioeconomic status and social stability. Similar results are obtained regardless of whether treatment is provided in expensive inpatient settings or in less expensive outpatient and intermediate care settings. In outpatient therapy, the length of time the patient stays in treatment seems to have a positive effect on the outcome; this is a function of the patient's motivation. As with any other illness, the earlier treatment is begun, the better the prospects for improvement. Nonetheless, many alcoholics have been treated successfully after many years of excessive drinking.

ASPECTS OF TREATMENT METHODS The treatment of alcoholism consists of getting the alcoholic safely through the withdrawal period, correcting the chronic health problems associated with alcoholism, and helping him or her to change long-term behavior so that destructive drinking patterns are not continued. The individual may begin treatment during a spell of temporary sobriety, during a severe hangover, or during acute intoxication. For many, it will be during the drying out, or withdrawal, stage.

Getting through Withdrawal. An alcoholic who is well nourished and in good physical condition can go through withdrawal with reasonable safety as an outpatient. However, an acutely ill alcoholic needs medically supervised care. A general hospital ward is best for preliminary treatment.

The alcohol withdrawal syndrome is quite similar to that described in Chapter 6 for barbiturates and other sedative hypnotics. Symptoms typically appear within 12 to 72 hours after total cessation of drinking but can appear whenever the blood-alcohol level drops below a certain point. The alcoholic has severe muscle tremors, nausea, weakness, and anxiety. This condition is called the **delirium tremens (DTs),** or the "shakes." Grand mal seizures can occur but are less common

*This section on rehabilitation is based largely on information from the National Institute on Alcohol Abuse and Alcoholism (1980).

than in barbiturate withdrawal, and there may be terrifying hallucinations.

---

delirium tremens (DTs)
a condition that affects chronic abusers of alcohol during alcohol withdrawal; characterized by agitation, hallucinations, and involuntary body tremors

---

The syndrome reaches peak intensity within 24 to 48 hours. About 5% of the alcoholics in hospitals and perhaps 20% to 25% who suffer the DTs without treatment die as a result. Phenobarbital, chlordiazepoxide (Librium), and diazepam (Valium) are commonly used to prevent withdrawal symptoms. Controlled withdrawal may take from 10 to 21 days and cannot safely be hurried. Simultaneously, the alcoholic may need treatment for malnutrition and vitamin deficiencies (especially the B vitamins). Pneumonia is also a frequent complication (Jaffe 1980).

Once the alcoholic patient is over the acute stages of intoxication and withdrawal, CNS depressants may be continued for a few weeks, with care taken not to transfer dependence on alcohol to dependence on the depressants. Long-term treatment with sedatives (Librium, Valium) does not prevent a relapse of drinking or assist with behavioral adaptation. A prescription of disulfiram (Antabuse) may be offered to encourage patients to abstain from alcohol; it blocks metabolism of acetaldehyde, and drinking any alcohol will result in a pounding headache, flushing, nausea, and other unpleasant symptoms. The patient must decide about two days in advance to stop taking Antabuse before he or she can drink. Antabuse is an aid to other supportive treatments, not the sole method of therapy.

Psychological and Behavioral Therapies.
After withdrawal symptoms are over, the person usually goes right back to drinking unless he or she can be persuaded to start other therapy to address the factors underlying the drinking problem. Most successful therapists say that pleading, exhortation, telling the patient how to live his or her life, and urging him or her to use more willpower are useless strategies and may even be destructive. They emphasize the need to create a warm, concerned relationship with the patient.

Psychotherapy is quite effective for some patients. For alcoholics, it is directed more to action, focusing on the patient's immediate life situation and drinking problem. Many therapists bring members of the patient's family into the therapy program; family support and understanding are often crucial to success. Sometimes a member of the family, perhaps more emotionally disturbed than the patient, may unconsciously support the alcoholic's drinking behavior.

A psychotherapeutic approach begins by getting the patient (and perhaps his or her family) to accept alcoholism as an illness, not as a moral problem or weakness. The patient must genuinely accept the idea that he or she needs help. Once these attitudes have been established, the therapist and patient try (1) to solve those problems that can be readily handled and (2) to find an approach that will enable the patient to live with those problems that cannot be solved.

Behavioral psychologists believe that drinking is learned behavior. Behavioral therapies try to reverse the reinforcement pattern so that abstinence or moderate drinking brings reward or avoids punishment. Techniques used include aversion therapies, assertiveness, relaxation, biofeedback (see Chapter 15), blood-alcohol discrimination training, and controlled drinking. The current trend is to observe drinking patterns and develop techniques that will change them. Analysis of drinking behavior focuses on cues and stimuli, attitudes and thoughts, specific behaviors, and consequences of drinking. These factors are complex and highly individualized; careful assessment is required in order to change the attitudes and behaviors that lead a given patient to excessive drinking. No one treatment plan is suitable for everyone.

Sobering up means that the alcoholic must face a backlog of personal, family, financial, and social problems. Without help to work out these alcohol-related problems, the alcoholic will probably return to the same escape method as before: drinking. Moreover, effective treatment must be conducted on a consistent basis in order to deal with the root of the problem. Treatment should not constitute random sessions after occasional drinking episodes. Rather, treatment should be tailored to the individual's needs and rate of progress.

HELPING AGENCIES FOR ALCOHOL REHABILITATION It is important to remember that the alcoholic commonly has several social problems that must be successfully handled if the drinking is to stop. Many organizations and agencies, staffed largely by nonmedical personnel, aid countless thousands of alcoholics and help them reestablish better relations at home, at work, and in the community.

Alcoholics Anonymous (AA) is a loosely knit, voluntary fellowship of alcoholics whose sole purpose is to help themselves and one another get sober and stay sober. AA has been characterized first as a way back to life and then as a way of living.

In the AA approach, the alcoholic must admit that he or she lacks control over drinking behavior and that his or her life is unmanageable and intolerable. For some alcoholics, this realization may not come until they have lost everything and everyone. For a few, it may occur sooner, for instance, when they are arrested by police or are warned by their employers. At this point, "the individual must decide to turn over his life and his will to a power greater than his own." Much of the program has a nonsectarian, spiritual basis. Over 356,000 members belong to about 19,000 groups in the United States, and more than 200,000 members participate in 11,500 groups in Canada and other countries. Despite its scope, AA reaches only a small percentage of the approximately 10 million alcoholics and problem drinkers in the United States.

During the early years of AA, some members insisted that "only an alcoholic can understand an alcoholic." As a result, there was little cooperation between AA workers and physicians, clergy, and social workers. Through understanding of one another's roles, most AA members no longer hold this view and cooperate increasingly with professional therapists. Conversely, professionals strongly encourage membership in AA as part of the treatment programs in detoxification centers, general and psychiatric hospitals, clinics, and prisons.

However, many professionals emphasize that, as valuable and widely accessible as AA is, it should not be considered as a complete form of treatment for all alcoholics; instead, it should be viewed as a support to other forms of therapy. Some alcoholics simply do not fit the AA approach but can be helped by other treatment modalities. The AA model has been used for treatment of other drug addictions, such as heroin.

Al-Anon and Alateen were formed to help families cope with alcoholic members. Al-Anon is for spouses and other relatives of alcoholics; it does not matter whether the alcoholic is in AA or another rehabilitation program. Members learn that they are not alone in this predicament and benefit from the experiences of others. Alateen is a parallel organization for teen-age children of alcoholic parents. (These organizations are listed in most phone directories.)

The National Council on Alcoholism (NCA) provides leadership in public education, advocacy of enlarged government involvement in prevention and treatment, and consultation services, particularly to industry. There are more than 200 member councils across the United States. At the community level, information and referral service and short-term pretreatment counseling are offered to problem drinkers and their families.

The Salvation Army and the Volunteers of America provide food, shelter, and rehabilitation services, often through halfway houses. Many religious groups have also developed programs and therapy groups to aid alcoholics and their families. Most clergy have training in counseling and some in psychotherapy; they provide a valuable service.

The Department of Transportation (DOT) has become involved in alcohol rehabilitation in an attempt to reduce the thousands of deaths and hundreds of thousands of serious accidents that occur on the highways each year because of drinking. The DOT has developed an information program to persuade people to prevent their friends from driving while drunk and a technical assistance program to help state and local governments develop systems for apprehending drunk drivers and bringing them for treatment.

The National Institute on Alcohol Abuse and Alcoholism (NIAAA) provides federal policy guidance on alcohol-related problems. It also channels funds for research, training, prevention, and development of community-based services for treatment of alcoholics, a national information and education program, and other special projects.

The Veterans Administration (VA) hospitals conduct the largest alcoholism treatment and research program in the United States; over 100,000 alcoholic patients are treated yearly. Eligible alcoholic veterans are treated at no charge. Treatment for acute intoxication is available at any VA hospital in the country, and many offer comprehensive follow-up treatment and rehabilitation services.

Alcohol use and abuse is of concern to U.S. industry, as well. It is estimated that business, industry, and government employ about 5.8 million problem drinkers—up to 6% of the nation's labor force and perhaps 10% of its executives. Because the problem is substantial, the federal government and many industries have initiated programs to help employees whose job performance suffers due to their use of alcohol. Organized labor has also become involved. The unions have developed their own training programs and provide services for members in trouble with alcohol; some of these programs have been included in contract agreements. A good evaluation of job-based alcohol abuse treatment programs is presented in the *Handbook on Drug Abuse* (Trice 1979) (see also Roman 1988; Nathan and Skinstad 1987; Berg and Skutle 1986).

Job-based treatment programs have an average 70% success rate. Because the drinking problem is identified much earlier in alcoholic employees than in unemployed persons, treatment is begun before physical health has entirely deteriorated, before financial resources are totally gone, and while emotional support still exists in the family and community. Also, the threat of job loss motivates employees to accept treatment. (See the chapter Appendix for a self-quiz regarding alcohol use and abuse.)

Think About It . . .

1. Of the 16 prevention methods presented, which do you think are the top 5? Give reasons for your choices.
2. What do you think is the most effective type of treatment of alcoholics? Find research studies to support your opinion.
3. Visit a local AA meeting, and report your observations.

K E Y   T E R M S

ethanol
social substance
fermentation
distillation
fortified wines
methyl alcohol
ethylene glycol

isopropyl alcohol
congeners
anesthetic
disinhibition
alcoholic
diuretic
cirrhosis

fetal alcohol syndrome (FAS)
prodromal stage
crucial stage
chronic stage
social learning theory
reinforcement theory
delirium tremens (DTs)

S U M M A R Y

1. Ethanol is the psychoactive ingredient found in alcoholic beverages. The ill effects of its misuse exceed those of any other legal or illicit drug. Alcohol abuse is responsible for a large proportion of traffic deaths, birth defects, health problems, and economic losses.

2. Alcoholic beverages are made by fermentation, which consists of changing fruit or grain into ethanol, using sugar, water, yeast, and warm temperatures to aid the process. When distilled, fermented liquids can reach a high alcohol content.

3. Alcoholic beverages were a staple of nutrition and agricultural production in early America. After the Revolution, the federal government regulated spirits by placing an excise tax on liquor. Since then, many attempts to control, restrict, or abolish alcohol have been made in the United States. All such laws have failed because of public nonsupport and even outcry and rebellion.

4. Of the four main types of alcohol, three are poisonous: (a) methyl alcohol, or wood alcohol; (b) ethylene glycol, used in antifreeze; and (c) isopropyl alcohol, used as a rubbing alcohol and an antiseptic. The fourth type, ethyl alcohol, or ethanol, is the psychoactive ingredient in all alcoholic beverages—beers, wines, liquors and cordials, and distilled spirits.

5. The concentration of alcohol in the blood depends on the presence of food in the stomach, the rate of alcohol consumption, the concentration of alcohol, and the drinker's bodyweight. Alcoholic beverages contain no vitamins, minerals, proteins, or fat.

6. The short-term effects of alcohol consumption include depression of inhibitory centers at low to moderate doses. Consumed in moderate quantities, alcohol produces an increase in heart rate and slight lowering of blood pressure; in higher doses, the CNS depression incapacitates the drinker and may be lethal. The after effect of overindulgence is known as a *hangover*.

7. The long-term effects of alcohol taken in large doses include structural damage to several major organs and various forms of chronic inflammation.

8. From 1977 to 1987, alcohol consumption in the United States and elsewhere steadily declined, for a variety of reasons. Alcohol use and abuse is unevenly distributed. Adolescents and young adults are most at risk for abuse. Millions of women also abused alcohol in the United States in the 1980s; they were most likely never to have been married or to be living with a partner who also abused alcohol. Women who consume any amount of alcohol while pregnant run the risk of poisoning the infant and causing mild to severe forms of mental and physical retardation. There are also sharp differences in alcohol consumption among American ethnic groups.

9. In comparison to all other age groups, the least amount of alcohol is consumed by the elderly. Alcohol abuse among the homeless ranges from 20% to 40%.

10. Alcohol is involved in one-third to one-half of all highway fatalities; young drinkers are involved in the most fatal accidents. It is important for young people to become aware of their social and

psychological attitudes in connection with drinking and driving.

11. *Alcoholism* is a disease characterized by both psychological and physical addiction to alcohol. Jellinek's classical research (1952) found three stages of alcohol addiction: the early, or prodromal, stage; the middle, or crucial, stage; and the final, chronic stage.

12. Potential causes of alcoholism include unique personality characteristics, cultural values that promote consumption, and a number of possible hereditary explanations.

13. Potential psychological explanations of the tendency toward alcoholism include clinical, psychoanalytic, and socialization and learning theories. Sociological explanations stress the importance of societal influences.

14. Prevention strategies for alcoholism range from increasing the prices of alcoholic beverages to research on how the family influences attitudes toward drinking to how raising the minimum drinking age affects the number of fatal auto accidents.

15. Alcohol treatment views alcoholism as a treatable illness from which two-thirds of those affected can recover. Treatment focuses on rehabilitative methods, getting past the DTs, and psychological and behavioral therapies. Helping agencies include AA, Al-Anon, Alateen, the VA, and industrial programs.

A P P E N D I X

A SELF-QUIZ ON FACT AND FANCY ABOUT ALCOHOL

Indicate whether the following statements are True (T) or False (F) by circling the appropriate letter.

T F   1. Alcohol is a drug; it can cause tolerance and physical dependence.

T F   2. Alcohol may be a stimulant in small doses because after a few drinks, the user is often animated and active.

T F   3. Alcohol can cause death by overstimulating the nervous system.

T F   4. Alcohol has no nutritional value.

T F   5. Alcohol is absorbed into the bloodstream and digested the same way foods are.

T F   6. It is possible to prevent symptoms of a hangover by eating fats or carbohydrates or by taking massive doses of vitamins before heavy drinking.

T F   7. Drinking large quantities of black coffee or taking spiced juices will help sober you up.

T F   8. You can become intoxicated more rapidly on vodka or gin than on scotch or whiskey.

T F   9. Champagne often affects a person more rapidly than whiskey.

T F   10. A blood-alcohol level above 0.15% is considered legal intoxication in all states.

T F   11. A tall, obese person would be able to drink more without getting drunk than a short, obese person or a tall, muscular person.

T F   12. If a person is chilled in cold weather, taking a few drinks will increase the body temperature and warm him or her up.

T F   13. If a pregnant woman drinks, it will not harm the fetus.

T F   14. Alcohol is an aphrodisiac.

T F   15. Cirrhosis of the liver is not the most common effect of alcohol consumption in heavy drinkers.

T F   16. Alcohol can be used to treat snakebite.

T F   17. Alcohol can cure a cold.

T F   18. Social drinking is the first step toward alcoholism.

T F   19. Alcoholics tend to follow a predictable pattern of behavior in developing their problem.

T F   20. Most alcoholics are found on skid row or in squalid surroundings.

T F   21. All alcoholics have psy-
            chological problems that
            explain their becoming
            alcoholic.

T F   22. There is no cure for
            alcoholism.

T F   23. The son of an alcoholic
            has a higher probability

of becoming alcoholic re-
gardless of whether he is
raised with his natural
family or by nondrinking
foster parents.

ANSWERS

1. True. Ethyl alcohol is a central nervous system depressant drug. Prolonged, heavy use causes tolerance to its effects. In addition, the user may become physically dependent. Once the person becomes physically dependent, he or she will undergo withdrawal if drinking is reduced or stopped.

2. False. Alcohol first affects the higher cortical centers of the brain. When this region is depressed, persons lose their inhibitions and exhibit behaviors that are normally kept suppressed. This has been described as "removing the veneer of civilization." Thus, any stimulation that may occur is due to lowered inhibitions. Alcohol is correctly classified as a depressant.

3. False. The neural centers frequently become depressed as the dose of alcohol is increased. Death from an overdose of alcohol is rare but can occur from depression of respiration (see Table 7-2). Very rapid drinking, such as consuming a bottle of liquor without stopping to breathe, can block the gag reflex, and the person may choke to death. Also, the drinker may become unconscious and suffocate in his or her own vomit. In contrast, the brain is stimulated when an alcoholic is undergoing withdrawal. The brain may become so stimulated (rebound stimulation) that the person may go into convulsions and even die.

4. True. Alcohol has no nutritional value in the sense that it provides nothing that is needed by the body to grow or to maintain tissues. Alcohol provides more calories per gram than carbohydrates or protein and is only slightly less caloric than pure fat. Alcoholics commonly suffer from malnutrition caused by poor eating habits. But even a perfect diet will not prevent damage to the liver and brain caused by the excess consumption of alcohol over a long time.

5. False. Alcohol follows the same pathways for absorption into the bloodstream as food but does not need to be broken down by digestive enzymes first, as most foods do. Unlike food, alcohol is broken down into a toxic substance (acetaldehyde). Another difference is that alcohol can be absorbed directly through the walls of the stomach, although most of it is absorbed from the first part of the small intestine. Alcohol has a low molecular weight and is completely soluble in water, so it moves rapidly through the entire system.

6. False. There is no evidence that special diets have any effect on the rate of metabolism of alcohol. The presence of almost any kind of food (especially milk, fatty foods, and meat) in the stomach before the person starts drinking will slow the absorption of alcohol. Food will reduce the peak concentration of blood alcohol the person would have had after drinking on an empty stomach. The alcohol will still be metabolized at its constant rate, about one-half ounce per hour. Massive doses of vitamins have not been shown to have any effect on the severity of hangovers. Little harm would be done by taking quantities of the water-soluble B complex vitamins, but the lipid-soluble vitamins (A, D, and E) could be toxic.

7. False. Coffee has been given to more drunks to help sober them up than any other remedy. Coffee does contain the mild stimulant caffeine, but caffeine does not increase the rate at which alcohol is metabolized. Black coffee will simply produce a more alert drunk; it will not significantly improve his or her judgment or driving skills. Coffee has some diuretic effect, but the amount of alcohol excreted unchanged in the urine is very small. Drinking spiced tomato juice or other juice will reduce the rate of absorption of alcohol from the gastrointestinal tract, as will most foods. Drinking coffee and spiced juice would help if they replaced a final drink of alcohol.

8. False. The *amount* of alcohol taken, not the *type*, is the problem. It does not matter what the drink is, unless it is over 100 proof or is carbonated (see question 9). If a drink is 80-proof alcohol instead of 60-proof, it has more alcohol per unit volume and thus is more potent. An alcoholic drink containing around 40% alcohol enters the blood faster than drinks with a higher concentration (over 100 proof).

9. **True.** The carbonation in champagne, mixers, and carbonated wines make the stomach contents pass through more quickly into the small intestine, from which the alcohol is efficiently absorbed. Thus, a person feels an effect from a carbonated alcoholic beverage first, then from a drink around 40% (80-proof) alcohol content, and then from a highly concentrated drink (over 100-proof).

10. **True.** Because alcohol plays a significant role in traffic accidents, most states have set legal intoxication at a blood-alcohol level of 0.10% or lower. The average person with a blood-alcohol level of 0.10% or 0.15% is 7 to 25 times (respectively) more likely to have a fatal accident than the driver with no alcohol in his or her blood (Ritchie 1980). About 4 to 5 ounces of whiskey, gin, or vodka drunk by an average man (160–170 pounds) over a period of 1 hour would give a blood-alcohol concentration of about 0.10%.

11. **False.** The drinker's size and body composition are factors in blood-alcohol concentration. Fatty tissue has a lower percentage of water than muscle, so there is less water for the alcohol to dissolve in. An obese person therefore is affected to a greater extent than a lean, muscular person of the same height because more alcohol is dissolved in the obese person's blood and reaches the central nervous system. A short, fat person is affected more than a tall, fat person.

12. **False.** In cold weather, the peripheral blood vessels automatically constrict to prevent loss of heat. However, alcohol dilates these vessels and overrides the body's attempt to regulate heat loss, thus making the person susceptible to frostbite and hypothermia (a life-threatening loss of body heat). Frequently, alcohol has a tendency to cause a drop in blood pressure, which causes further susceptibility to chilling and frostbite. Drinking in cold weather is a dangerous way to warm up.

13. **False.** Alcohol readily crosses the placenta from the woman's blood to the fetus. It is probably the most common agent causing mental retardation known to the Western world (Ritchie 1980). The amount of alcohol necessary to produce fetal alcohol syndrome is unknown, and a safe limit has not been established. Women are cautioned to eliminate daily consumption for the duration of pregnancy and to avoid drinking heavily on any single occasion, such as a party.

14. **False.** Alcohol has been linked with sexuality throughout history; however, its function is not to stimulate desire but to suppress inhibitions, including sexual inhibitions. As Ogden Nash put it, "Candy is dandy, but liquor is quicker." Sexuality is greatly influenced by psychological factors, and alcohol can make a person more susceptible to suggestion. As a person continues to drink, his or her sexual ability diminishes because of loss of neural control and coordination. Shakespeare refers to this in Macbeth: "Lechery, sir, it provokes, and unprovokes; it provokes the desire, but it takes away the performance."

15. **True.** About 8-15% of alcoholics develop cirrhosis, and nearly 75% have abnormal liver function but not cirrhosis. More alcoholics have significant nutritional and vitamin deficiencies, damage to the heart and skeletal muscle, an inflamed stomach lining, and brain damage than have actual cirrhosis.

16. **False.** The idea that taking alcohol is useful in treating snakebite goes back over 2,000 years to the Greeks. Alcohol was thought to be a specific antidote that neutralized the venom (Roueché 1960). This claim has no basis.

17. **False.** Alcohol cannot cure a cold or alleviate its symptoms. Its only benefit would be to make the person relaxed and sleepy enough to go to bed and keep him or her from spreading the virus. It could potentiate with antihistamine drugs in producing sedation.

18. **True.** Social drinking is usually the first step toward alcoholism, but most social drinkers do not become alcoholics. Alcoholism today is considered a disease. The term *alcoholism* refers to a complex set of conditions that involve physiological, psychological, and sociological factors.

19. **False.** Until the early 1950s, it was believed that alcoholics progressed along a sequence of controlled social drinking, occasional escape from tension ("escape drinking"), blackouts, loss of ability to stop at one drink, and finally, physical dependence (Jellinek 1952). This is no longer generally accepted to be true (Aronow 1980; Cahn 1970).

20. **False.** Most alcoholics are found in the middle class of society. They are found in every type of occupation and across all ethnic and age groups. It is surprising how many housewives are found to be in the later stages of alcoholism yet have been able to keep this fact hidden for years.

21. **False.** There are three major hypotheses about the cause of alcoholism.

(a) *Personality:* Alcoholics are thought to be insecure, anxious, oversensitive, and in general, dissatisfied with themselves. Alcohol gives such people a temporary escape and a way to cope.

(b) *Biochemical defects:* The alcoholic might have an abnormal physiological constitution, a hypothesis related to genetic causes for alcoholism. A purely biochemical or genetic hypothesis has not been proven, however.

(c) *Social causes:* This hypothesis suggests that social conditions associated with religion and culture, escape mechanisms in society, attitudes toward drinking, and age are responsible for alcohol abuse. Some societies have such ambivalent or complex goals that an individual may be pressured to find an escape; alcohol often provides that escape. Drinking might tend to run in families because family members never learn how to cope; moreover, they may all select the same escape route.

22. **True.** After the alcoholic is safely through the detoxification phase, many treatment programs are available that have high rates of success in helping the person live a normal life. However, alcoholics are not cured in the sense that few can ever resume social drinking in a controlled manner. Abstention is usually necessary.

23. **True.** Male offspring of alcoholics have a higher than average chance of becoming alcoholic. The probability is estimated at four times higher than that for the offspring of nonalcoholics.

Source: Reprinted with permission, National Highway Traffic Safety Administration.

R E F E R E N C E S

Akers, R. L. *Deviant Behavior: A Social Learning Approach.* 3rd ed. Belmont, CA: Wadsworth, 1985.

Alcoholics Anonymous World Services, Inc. *Alcoholics Anonymous: The Story of How Many Thousands of Men and Women Have Recovered from Alcoholism.* 3rd ed. New York: AA, 1976.

Aldo-Benson, M. A. "Alcohol Directly Suppresses b Cell Response to Antigen." *Federation Proceedings* 2, no. 6 (1988): 9–12.

Armor, D. J., J. M. Polich, and H. B. Stambul. *Alcoholism and Treatment.* Santa Monica, CA: Rand Corporation, 1976.

Aronow, L. *Alcoholism, Alcohol Abuse, and Related Problems: Opportunities for Research.* Washington, D.C.: National Academy, 1980.

Austin, G. A. *Perspectives on the History of Psychoactive Substance Use.* National Institute on Drug Abuse Research Issues no. 23. Washington, D.C.: Department of Health, Education, and Welfare, 1978.

Baker, S. P., B. O'Neil, and R. Karpf. *Injury Fact Book.* Lexington, MA: Heath, 1984.

Becker, H. S. *Outsiders: Studies in the Sociology of Deviance.* New York: Free Press, 1966.

Berg, G., and A. Skutle. "Early Intervention with Problem Drinkers." In *Treating Addictive Behaviors: Processes of Change,* edited by W. R. Miller and N. Heather. New York: Plenum, 1986.

Blake, J. E., K. V. Compton, W. Schmidt, and H. and Orrego. "Accuracy of death certificates in the diagnosis of alcoholic liver cirrhosis." *Alcoholism* No. 12 (1988): 168–172.

Block, M. A. Motivating the alcoholic patient. In *Alcoholism: A Practical Treatment Guide,* edited by S. E. Glitlow and H. S. Peyser. New York: Grune and Stratton, 1980.

Brazeau, Ron and Margo Sparrow. *International Survey: Alcoholic Beverage Taxation and Control Policies,* 6th ed. Ottowa: Brewers Association of Canada, 1986.

Brown, N. H., E. H. Goulding, and S. Fabro. "Ethanol Embryotoxicity: Direct Effects on Mammalian Embryos in Vitro." *Science* 206 (1979): 573–575.

Brown, S. C. "Beer and Wines of Old New England." *American Scientist* 66 (1978): 460–467.

Cahalan, D., and R. Room. *Problem Drinking among American Men.* New Brunswick, NJ: Rutgers Center for Alcohol Studies, 1974.

Cahn, S. *The Treatment of Alcoholics: An Evaluative Study.* New York: Oxford University, 1970.

Chatham, L. R. "Understanding the Issues: An Overview." In *Women: Alcohol and Other Drugs,* edited by R. C. Engs, Alcohol Drugs Problems Association. Dubuque, IA: Kendall/Hunt, 1990.

Clarren, S. K., S. J. Astley, and D. M. Bowden. "Physical Anomalies and Developmental Delays in Nonhuman Primate Infants Exposed to Weekly Doses of Ethanol During Gestation." *Teratology* 37 (1988): 561–569.

Coffey, W. *Straight Talk about Drinking: Teenagers Speak Out about Alcohol.* Markham, Ontario, Canada: Penguin Books Canada Limited, 1988.

Cotton, N. S. "The Familial Incidence of Alcoholism: A Review." *Journal of Studies on Alcohol* 40 (1979): 89–116.

Gallup, G., Jr. *The Gallup Poll: Public Opinion, 1985.* Wilmington, DE: Scholarly Resources, 1985.

Gallup Report. *Alcohol Use and Abuse in America.* Report no. 299. Princeton, NJ: The Gallup Poll, September 1990.

Gallup Report. *Alcohol Use and Abuse in America.* Report no. 265. Princeton, NJ: The Gallup Poll, October 1990.

Goodwin, D. W. "Alcoholism and Heredity." *Archives of General Psychiatry* 36 (1979): 57–61.

Greeley, A. M., W. C. McCreedy, and G. Theison. *Ethnic Drinking Subcultures.* New York: Praeger, 1980.

Harris, L. S., ed. *Problems of Drug Dependence.* Washington, D.C.: U.S. Government Printing Office, 1988.

Health and Human Services, Department of. *Sixth Special Report to the U.S. Congress on Alcohol and Health.* Rockville, MD: NIAAA, 1987.

"In These Times." Chicago, IL, October 18–24, 1989.

Jaffe, J. H. "Drug Addiction and Drug Abuse." In *The Pharmacological Basis of Therapeutics,* 6th ed., edited by A. G.

Gilman, L. S. Goodman, and A. Gilman. New York: Macmillan, 1980.

Jellinek, E. M. "Phases of Alcohol Addiction." *Quarterly Journal of Studies on Alcohol* 13 (1952): 673–684.

Johnston, L. D., P. M. O'Malley, and J. G. Bachman. *Illicit Drug Use, Smoking, and Drinking by America's High School Students, College Students, and Young Adults, 1975–1987.* Department of Health and Human Services Publication no. (ADM) 89-1602. Rockville, MD: ADAMHA, 1988.

Johnston, L. D., P. M. O'Malley, and J. G. Bachman. *National Trends in Drug Use and Related Factors among American High School Students and Young Adults, 1975–1986.* Department of Health and Human Services Publication no. (ADM) 87-1535. Washington, D.C.: NIDA, 1987.

Johnston, L. D., P. M. O'Malley, and J. G. Bachman. *Drug Use Among American High School Students, College Students, and Other Young Adults: National Trends through 1985.* Rockville, MD: NIDA, 1986.

Johnston, L. D., P. M. O'Malley, and J. G. Bachman. *Use of Licit and Illicit Drugs by America's High School Students: 1975–1984.* Washington, D.C.: NIDA, 1985.

Kaij, L., and J. Dock. "Grandsons of Alcoholics: A Test of Sex-Linked Transmission of Alcohol Abuse." *Archives of General Psychiatry* 32 (1975): 1379–1381.

Keller, M. "Alcoholism: Nature and Extent of the Problem." *Understanding Alcoholism, Annals American Academy Political and Social Science* 315 (1958): 1–11.

Lee, H. *How Dry We Were: Prohibition Revisited.* Englewood Cliffs, NJ: Prentice-Hall, 1963.

Lieber, C. S. "The Metabolism of Alcohol." *Scientific American* 234, no. 3 (1976): 25–33.

Liska, Ken. *Drugs and the Human Body,* 3rd ed. New York: Macmillan, 1990.

Lumeng, L., and T.-K. Li. "The Development of Metabolic Tolerance in the Alcohol-Preferring P Rats: Comparison of Forced and Free-Choice Drinking of Ethanol." *Pharmacological Biochemical Behavior* 25, no. 5 (1986): 1013–1020.

McCord, J. "Identifying Developmental Paradigms Leading to Alcoholism." *Journal of Studies on Alcohol* 49 (1988): 357–362.

Mezey, E. "Effect of Ethanol on Intestinal Morphology, Metabolism, and Functions." In *Alcohol Related Diseases in Gastroenterology*, edited by H. K. Kommerell and B. Seitz. Berlin: Springer-Verlag, 1985.

Miller, J. D., and I. H. Cisin. *Highlights from the National Survey on Drug Abuse: 1982*. Washington, D.C.: NIDA, 1983.

Miller, M. "Effect of Prenatal Exposure to Ethanol on the Development of Cerebral Cortex: I." *Alcoholism (NY)* 12 (1988): 440–449.

Miller, M. "Effect of Prenatal Exposure to Alcohol on the Distribution and Time of Origin of Corticospinal Neurons in the Rat." *Journal of Comparative Neurology* 257 (1987): 372–382.

Miller, M., J. Israel, and J. Cuttone. "Fetal Alcohol Syndrome." *Journal of Pediatric Ophthalmology and Strabismus* 18, no. 4 (1980): 6–15.

Nathan, P. E., and A. H. Skinstad. "Outcomes of Treatment for Alcohol Problems: Current Methods, Problems, and Results." *Journal of Consulting Clinical Psychology* 55 (1987): 332–340.

National Highway Traffic Safety Administration, National Center for Statistics and Analysis. *Drug Driving Facts*. Washington, D.C.: NHTSA, 1988.

National Institute on Alcohol Abuse and Alcoholism. *Seventh Special Report to the U.S. Congress on Alcohol and Health*. Rockville, MD: NIAAA, 1990.

National Institute on Alcohol Abuse and Alcoholism. *Apparent Per Capita Alcohol Consumption: National, State, and Regional Trends, 1977–1987*. Surveillance Report no. 13. Rockville, MD: NIAAA, 1989.

National Institute on Alcohol Abuse and Alcoholism. *Alcohol Health and Research World*. Washington, D.C.: United States Department of Health and Human Services, 1988.

National Institute on Alcohol Abuse and Alcoholism. *Facts about Alcohol and Alcoholism*. Washington, D.C.: U.S. Government Printing Office, 1980.

National Institute on Alcohol Abuse and Alcoholism. *Drinking Etiquette for Those Who Drink and Those Who Don't!*, Washington, D.C.: U.S. Government Printing Office, 1978.

National Institute on Drug Abuse. *Monitoring the Future Study*. Ann Arbor, MI: Institute for Social Research, 1990.

National Institute on Drug Abuse. *National Household Survey on Drug Abuse: Main Findings, 1985*. Department of Health and Human Services Publication No. (ADM) 88-1586. Rockville, MD: NIDA, 1988.

National Institute on Drug Abuse. *Facts about Alcohol and Alcoholism*. Washington, D.C.: U.S. Government Printing Office, 1980.

Ohio State Police Driver Information Seminars and the National Clearinghouse for Alcohol and Alcoholism Information. Rockville, MD.

Ritchie, J. M. "The Aliphatic Alcohols." In *The Pharmacological Basis of Therapeutics*, 6th ed., edited by G. Gilman, L. S. Goodman, and A. Gilman. New York: Macmillan, 1980.

Roman, P. M. "Growth and Transformation in Workplace Alcoholism Programming." In *Recent Developments in Alcoholism*, edited by M. Galanter. Vol. 6. New York: Plenum, 1988.

Ropers, R. H., and R. Bayer. "Homelessness as a Health Risk." *Alcohol Health Research World* 11, no. 3 (1987): 38–41.

Roueché, B. *The Neutral Spirit: A Portrait of Alcohol*. Boston: Little, Brown, 1960.

Royce, J. E. *Alcohol Problems and Alcoholism*. Rev. ed. New York: Free Press, 1989.

Rydelius, P. -A. "Children of Alcoholic Fathers: Their Social Adjustment and Their Health Status over 20 Years." *Acta Paediatrica Scandinavica: Supplement* (Stockholm) 286 (1981): 1–89.

Schuckit, M. A., and V. Rayes. "Ethanol Ingestion: Differences in Blood Acetaldehyde Concentrations in Relatives of Alcoholics and Controls." *Science* 203 (1979): 54–55.

Seixas, F. A. "The Medical Complications of Alcoholism." In *Alcoholism: A Practical Treatment Guide*, edited by S. E. Peyser and H. S. Gitlow. New York: Grune & Stratton, 1980.

Sherlock, S. "Nutrition and the Alcoholic." *Lancet* 1 (1984): 436–438.

Streissguth, A. P., S. Landesman-Dwyer, J. C. Martin, and D. W. Smith. "Teratogenic Effects of Alcohol in Humans and Laboratory Animals." *Science* 209 (1980): 353–361.

Sutherland, E. H. *Principles of Criminology*. Philadelphia: J. B. Lippencott, 1947.

Trice, H. M. "Job-based Alcohol and Drug Abuse Programs: Recent Program Developments and Research." In R. L. DuPont, A. Goldstein, and J. O. O'Donnell, ed.: NIDA 1979.

Ullman, A. D. "Sociocultural Backgrounds of Alcoholism." In *Understanding Alcoholism, Annals of the American Academy Political and Social Science*, edited by S. D. Bacon. 315 (1958): 48–54.

Williams, G. D., F. S. Stinson, D. A. Parker, T. C. Harford, and V. Noble. "Demographic Trends, Alcohol Abuse and Alcoholism, 1985–1995." Epidemiologic Bulletin no. 15. *Alcohol Health and Research World* 11, no. 3 (1987): 80–83.

Wilsnack, S. C., R. W. Wilsnack, and A. D. Klassen. "Epidemiological Research on Women's Drinking, 1978–1984." In *Women and Alcohol: Health-Related Issues*. Research Monograph no. 16. Washington, D.C.: U.S. Government Printing Office, 1986.

Wright, J. D., J. W. Knight, E. Weber-Burdin, and J. Lam. "Ailments and Alcohol: Health Status among the Drinking Homeless." *Alcohol Health and Research World* 11, no. 3 (1987): 22–27.

Analgesics: NSAIDS and Narcotics

CHAPTER OUTLINE

Analgesic Drugs: An Overview / **The Nature of Pain** ▪ Physiological Aspects ▪ Pain Classifications ▪ Pain Assessment / **Nonmedicinal Pain Therapy** ▪ Behavioral Modification / **Medicinal Pain Therapy** ▪ Nonsteroidal Antiinflammatory Drugs (NSAIDS) ▪ Opioid Narcotic Analgesics ▪ Miscellaneous Analgesic Drugs

LEARNING OBJECTIVES

On completing this chapter, you will be able to:

1. Identify the factors that contribute to the pain experience.
2. Identify the components of the pain pathway.
3. Distinguish between the pain *threshold* and pain *tolerance*.
4. List nonmedicinal strategies that have been used to control pain.
5. Explain the similarities and the differences between the therapeutic uses of nonsteroidal antiinflammatory drugs (NSAIDS) and narcotic analgesics.

6. Explain the difference between the analgesic mechanisms of action for NSAIDS and narcotic analgesics.
7. Identify and compare the therapeutic uses and side effects of NSAIDS.
8. Identify the abuse patterns for heroin.
9. Outline the stages of heroin dependence.
10. List the withdrawal symptoms that result from narcotic dependence, and discuss the significance of tolerance.

11. Describe the use of methadone in treating narcotic addiction.
12. Identify the unique features of fentanyl that make it appealing to illicit drug dealers but dangerous to narcotic addicts.
13. Distinguish among the narcotic agents fentanyl, morphine, codeine, pentazocine, and propoxyphene.
14. List the drugs besides NSAIDS and narcotic analgesics that are used to treat pain.

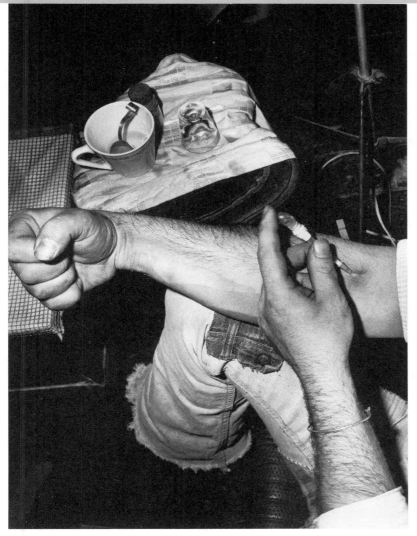

Source: Charles Gatewood/Stock, Boston

DID YOU KNOW THAT . . .

- A major component of pain perception is psychological and learned behavior.
- The release of natural substances called *endorphins* can block even intense pain and likely contributes to the analgesic effects of some nonmedicinal techniques used to relieve pain, such as acupuncture.
- NSAIDS, like aspirin, increase pain thresholds, while narcotic analgesics, like codeine, increase pain tolerance.
- Long-term, chronic pain is often a learned behavior and persists even after the original cause of the pain no longer exists.
- Salicylates, such as aspirin, were originally derived from the chemical salian, which comes from willow bark.
- Aspirin was originally used in the late nineteenth century to treat rheumatic fever and gout.
- By the end of the nineteenth century, almost 1 million Americans were addicted to opiates, primarily due to the use of patent medicines that contained opium products.
- Narcotics are the most potent analgesics available today.
- Some people, called "chippers," can continue to use opioid narcotics daily without significantly altering their lifestyle and ability to function.
- Because heroin addicts often "mainline" the drug and share needles, almost one-half of these persons have been exposed to the AIDS virus.

Pain is an aversive sensory device that serves both as a warning and a motivation to either avoid or resolve conditions threatening the integrity and function of the body. Because pain is so unpleasant, we go to great lengths to eliminate its sources.

The most common type of pain is short term, localized, and associated with trauma or injury to the body. This type of pain, if intense, can result in isolation or immobilization of the damaged body part. Once healing occurs, the pain subsides while functionality and mobility return. Chronic, long-term pain is very different and poorly understood. It is frequently persistent and associated with degenerative processes; for example, chronic lower-back pain is often related to deterioration of the vertebra resulting in pinched nerves and inflammation. Chronic pain afflicts nearly 75 million Americans, with about 60% experiencing enough pain to be partially incapacitated. Most major hospitals and health care institutions in the United States have pain clinics to help these patients achieve some degree of relief.

In this chapter, we will discuss the nature of pain from both psychological and physiological perspectives. The analgesic features of NSAIDS agents will be addressed in some detail. The narcotic opioids will be discussed relative to their colorful history, dependence properties, and clinical usefulness. The discussion of analgesics will conclude with brief descriptions of other medicinal pain-relieving techniques.

ANALGESIC DRUGS: AN OVERVIEW

Because pain can be caused by many different factors, expressed in a variety of ways, and altered by so many influences, therapeutic strategies also differ, depending on the type of pain being treated. The use of **analgesic** drugs has become an integral part of most pain therapy. These agents block pain while allowing consciousness. The two distinct pharmacological classes of agents routinely recommended to treat pain include (1) aspirinlike nonsteroidal antiinflammatory drugs (NSAIDS) and (2) narcotic (**opioid;** opium-drived) analgesics.

analgesic
related to drugs that block pain without causing unconsciousness

opioid
relating to the drugs that are derived from opium

While pain relief is positive reinforcement for taking analgesics, the ability of analgesics to block pain does not make these drugs addicting. Consequently, drugs such as aspirin and other NSAIDS do not have abuse liability; in the absence of pain, there is no perceived pharmacological action by these drugs. In contrast, the narcotic analgesics do have substantial abuse potential; in fact, this addicting property is independent of their pain-relieving action. Thus, people not suffering pain can develop narcotic dependence as readily as those with intense pain.

We will discuss NSAIDS and narcotic analgesics in detail later in this chapter. The purpose of this overview is to provide a foundation for understanding the nature of pain, which is the next topic.

THE NATURE OF PAIN

Each person perceives and reacts to pain differently. Both the perception of and reaction to pain are, to a large extent, learned. Culture often dictates what is an acceptable response to pain. Appropriate reactions to pain might differ according to age and gender. For example, in American culture, expressions of pain are more likely to be accepted in girls but discouraged in boys. Also, part of growing up and becoming an adult is to endure pain and discomfort without complaining.

The effect of a placebo illustrates well the important role of psychological factors in the perception of pain. As discussed in Chapter 5, placebos can substantially diminish the response to pain, independent of other treatment. By the power of suggestion, pain perception is altered and the associated discomfort is relieved.

PHYSIOLOGICAL ASPECTS

Of course, pain is not all psychological; thus, treatments of the physiological factors that control pain are therapeutically useful in its management. To understand why these treatments work, it is necessary to understand the nature of the systems that initiate and regulate pain.

ENDORPHINS: ENDOGENOUS PAIN REGULATORS
An important system that helps to control pain intensity is regulated by endogenous substances called *endorphins*. These chemicals are peptides (small proteins) that are released in the brain and spinal cord and from the adrenal glands in response to stress or under certain psychological conditions. The endorphins serve as transmitter chemicals in the central nervous system (CNS) (see Chapter 5) and have been shown to potently modulate pain transmission at the level of the spinal cord, brainstem, and pain centers in the brain. Specifically, when released, endorphin transmit-

ters selectively activate receptors designated as opioid type and block pain transmission.

The endorphin system has particular relevance to narcotic analgesics. Just like endorphin peptides, narcotics block pain by activating opioid receptors. The effects of these drugs on the opioid receptors also account for other narcotic pharmacological actions, including their abuse liability. (Again, this will be discussed at greater length later in this chapter.)

It has also been proposed that endorphin systems can be influenced by psychological factors. It is possible that pain relief caused by administration of placebos or nonmedicinal manipulations is due to endorphin release. This suggests that physiological and psychological factors are intertwined in the regulation of pain, which makes it impossible to deal with one without considering the other.

PAIN MECHANISMS   The pain systems consist of:

1. Detector devices that are activated by chemicals released by painful stimuli, called **nociceptors**
2. Initiator substances that are released from the surrounding tissues and activate the nociceptors
3. Special neurons that conduct the pain impulse to the spinal cord and ultimately to the pain centers in the thalamus of the brain
4. Neurotransmitter substances that control the activity of the pain neurons

nociceptors
receptors that are activated by painful sensations

For a summary of the elements of the pain systems, see Figure 8-1. Each of these elements and their significance in the management of pain will be discussed in detail.

Pain Sites. The entire surface of the body, except the eyes and the nails, is covered with skin.

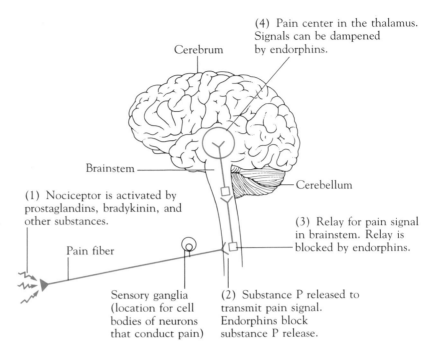

FIGURE 8-1 Pain pathway and mediating substances. (1) A pain sensation starts at the nociceptor. An impulse is initiated in the pain fiber of the sensory ganglia and travels to the spinal cord. (2) In the cord, substance P, a pain transmitter, is released [or (3) can be blocked by endorphins] and activates another neuron so that the message can ascend the spinal cord and eventually activate the pain center in the thalamus. (4) At this point, the individual senses that pain is occurring. Endorphins can block the impulse at several places in the pathway and reduce the magnitude of the pain message that reaches the thalamus.

Cerebrum

(4) Pain center in the thalamus. Signals can be dampened by endorphins.

Brainstem

Cerebellum

(1) Nociceptor is activated by prostaglandins, bradykinin, and other substances.

(3) Relay for pain signal in brainstem. Relay is blocked by endorphins.

Pain fiber

Sensory ganglia (location for cell bodies of neurons that conduct pain)

(2) Substance P released to transmit pain signal. Endorphins block substance P release.

Skin contains receptors for pain, temperature, and pressure. Some parts of the skin have more nociceptors (pain receptors) than others. Fingertips have a large number of pain receptors, for instance, whereas the skin on the back has only scattered receptors. Thus, a sharp needleprick on the fingertip will cause pain, but one on the back may cause no pain. This insensitivity to pain on the back was known to "witch hunters" in the Middle Ages and in the 1600s in Salem, Massachusetts. These insensitive areas were called "witches' spots" and were thought of as areas where demons hid.

Organs such as the liver, kidneys, spleen, and pancreas are insensitive to mechanical or chemical stimulation. Pain that arises in these organs is usually caused by interference with their blood supply. The uterus is another pain-insensitive organ because it has few pain receptors; it can be surgically cut or electrocauterized (burned to stop bleeding) with very little sensation of pain. Pain can occur during childbirth as the cervix of the uterus is dilated, or enlarged, to permit delivery. One of the organs most sensitive to pain is the testicle; squeezing or striking the testicle causes intense pain that may cause vomiting and even shock.

The brain itself can feel no pain because it lacks pain receptors, but the meninges (membranes that cover the brain and spinal cord) and the blood vessels in the brain send pain impulses in response to stimuli. Infection of the meninges causes one of the most severe forms of pain known, which characterizes the disease meningitis. Less severe but more common is the headache. Because almost everyone experiences headaches, this pain is treated more often than any other type. Headaches can be caused by several different factors and are classified as well as treated according to the cause (see Table 8-1).

Nociceptors and Pain Neurons. The nociceptors are very much like other receptors in the body that perceive warmth, cold, and touch. All of these sensations apparently can produce pain if they are intense enough. The nociceptors are located on neurons leading to the spinal cord and brain. The chain of neurons carrying pain messages is often called a **pain tract** or pathway. The

TABLE 8-1 Classification of major types of headaches

Type	Description	Mechanism
Vascular	Throbbing pain	Dilation of branches of the carotid artery
Migraine	Accompanied by other neurological signs, such as nausea, blurred vision, sensitivity to light, and clammy skin	Cause unknown; perhaps caused by changes in serotonin systems
Cluster	Short-lived attacks of severe, intense, one-sided head pain that occurs in clusters	Migrainelike; perhaps mechanisms are related
Others		
Hypertension		Associated with high blood pressure
Hangover		Associated with intense alcohol consumption
Toxins and drugs		Vasodilation caused by chemicals
Muscle contraction (tension)	Steady, nonthrobbing pain	Tight and tender muscles in head and neck region
Structural	Steady, dull, aching pain	Pressure on or inflammation in cranial structures
Sinus	Begins in morning and persists throughout day; worsens by moving head	Inflammation due to infection and pressure build-up from sinus fluids
Dental	Constant dull ache	Diseased tooth or dental surgery causes inflammation and irritated tissues
Eye	"Eye strain"	Most likely tension headache due to constant muscle adjustments to unfocused vision

neuronal fibers that relay pain messages to the spinal cord and brain can cause the perception of different types of pain. The A-delta fibers carry pain quickly and give the feeling of pricking or sharp pain. The C-fibers are slow and give a sensation of dull, diffuse, or burning pain.

pain tract
the system of neurons that transmit the pain message to the thalamus in the brain

Pain is interpreted in specific areas of the cerebral cortex after the pain message travels through the pain tracts to and through the thalamus. The thalamus (see Figure 8-1) is believed to be a pain-signal terminal, or switchboard (Bond 1979) and is linked to the emotional centers of the brain through the limbic system and hypothalamus. It is likely that their close connections account for the interaction between emotional states and pain.

Pain-Initiating Substances. Naturally occurring chemical substances are involved with the initiation of pain at the nociceptor and contribute to transmission along the pain pathway until the message reaches the brain. These substances, histamine and the peptide **bradykinin,** are present in

bradykinin
an endogenous peptide that initiates pain

the tissue fluid surrounding a severe wound. Both endogenous chemicals cause intense pain if injected subcutaneously. Thus, these substances appear to be critical initiators of some types of pain responses.

There is evidence that, when tissue is damaged, other substances can initiate pain. **Prostaglandins** are released from injured tissues as are bradykinin, histamine, and substances called *leukokines* (so named because they come from the white cells called *leukocytes*). These substances contribute to the symptoms of inflammation: Tissue becomes swollen with fluid and blood, causing mechanical pressure on pain receptors, and the pain neurons become more sensitive to pain stimuli, thus lowering the pain threshold (see following section). NSAIDS block the initiation of pain impulses by preventing the synthesis of prostaglandins. Because these endogenous chemicals initiate inflammatory symptoms, NSAIDS also are good antiinflammatory agents and are commonly used to treat inflammatory diseases, such as arthritis.

---

prostaglandins
endogenous chemicals that, when released, contribute to pain and inflammatory responses

---

Another peptide, substance P, functions as a neurotransmitter and likely assists in passing the pain message from neuron to neuron in the pain tract. This endogenous compound is found in nerves known to transmit pain impulses and is released from nerve endings in the spinal cord to relay the pain message on to neurons that connect with the brainstem. It is likely that the endorphins and narcotic drugs exert some of their analgesic effects by blocking substance P release, so the pain transmission does not get further than the spinal cord (see Figure 8-1).

PAIN CLASSIFICATIONS

Pain is often classified according to its location. **Visceral pain,** such as intestinal or stomach cramps, arises from the internal organs of the body

and is perceived as a diffuse, burning experience. Narcotics are effective in reducing pain of this type. **Somatic pain** arises in the skeletal muscles, bones, skin, teeth, and associated structures. This type of pain is easily localized and relieved by NSAIDS drugs, although narcotic analgesics can also be effective.

---

visceral pain
that associated with internal organs, involuntary muscles, and blood vessels

somatic pain
that associated with musculoskeletal structures, including bones, voluntary muscles, skin, and teeth

---

Another way of classifying pain relates to the type of neuron or fiber that carries the pain signal and the pain type. *Bright pain* is associated with the large, fast neurons (A-delta); it has a low threshold (i.e., the stimulus does not need to be powerful; see below) and lasts a relatively short period of time. Dull, aching pain and diffuse or burning pain are associated with small, slow-acting neurons, or C-fibers. Such pain requires a more intense stimulus and lasts for a longer period of time. Take, for example, the bright pain you would experience from hitting your finger with a hammer; the dull pain is the long-term ache afterward.

PAIN ASSESSMENT

In order to evaluate the effectiveness of analgesics, it is important to have means by which to measure pain intensity. **Pain threshold** is the level at which a stimulus is first recognized as unpleasant (the "ouch!" point), whereas **pain tolerance** is that greater level of stimulation at which the subject says he or she can't stand any more. Pain threshold is more dependent on physiological factors, and pain tolerance depends on psychological factors. NSAIDS-type drugs tend to raise the pain threshold because more stimulation is required to initiate a pain sensation. Narcotic analgesics raise pain tolerance because more pain is required before becoming unbearable.

pain threshold
the minimum amount of pain necessary to cause pain

pain tolerance
the maximum amount of pain that can be tolerated

The increase in stimulus intensity that will cause a barely detectable difference in the degree of pain is called a *just noticeable difference* (JND). By applying a variety of stimulus intensities between the level of no pain at all and the most intense pain that the subject can tolerate, it has been found that the average person can discern approximately 22 JNDs. By contrast, vision brightness detection has about 100 JNDs and hearing about 120 JNDs. For measuring pain, two JNDs are equal to one measure of pain intensity. This unit, often called a *DoL*, can be useful when comparing the effectiveness of analgesics. However, remember that all pains are not the same. For example, pain due to heat, pain from a blow to the elbow, or pain from the teeth each have different properties and may respond to therapy differently. When assessing analgesic effectiveness, it is not sufficient to know that an analgesic increases the pain tolerance; it is also important to know the type of pain the drug is most likely to relieve.

NONMEDICINAL PAIN THERAPY

Although analgesic drugs are clearly an essential component to most approaches of pain treatment, several nonmedicinal techniques have proven useful, with or without drugs, including physiotherapy, manipulation, counterirritation, acupuncture, and electrical stimulation (see Table 8-2). Because the mechanisms involved in these pain-relieving techniques are not well understood, their effectiveness is sometimes questioned; however, some of these strategies, such as counterirritation and acupuncture, have been practiced for thousands of years by enlightened societies.

There is likely some physiological explanation for the pain relief caused by some of these techniques; for example, acupuncture and electrical stimulation have been shown to release the endogenous analgesics, the endorphins. However, due to ignorance about these strategies, they have often been misused, and many pain sufferers have been victimized by quacks claiming to be able to relieve pain discomfort with these techniques.

BEHAVIORAL MODIFICATION

Behavioral modification is often used to help people suffering from chronic pain manage their discomfort by altering behavior patterns and attitudes.

TABLE 8-2   Nonmedicinal pain therapy

Strategy	Technique	Possible Explanation
Physiotherapy	Massage and application of heat and cold	Relax spasms of vascular wall
Manipulation	Movement of spine as done by chiropractors and osteopaths	Relieve pressure on pinched nerves from the spinal cord
Counterirritation	Application and massaging with liniments and irritating chemicals	Sensory distraction by a second stimulation decreases awareness of pain
Acupuncture	Small needles placed and rotated in specific locations for certain pains	Causes release of endorphins; also causes counterirritation
Electrical stimulation	Electrodes, powered by battery pack, implanted into major nerves near spinal cord; pain is relieved with electrical stimulation	Blocks pain impulse from traveling up the spinal cord to the brain
Hypnosis	Relaxation	Diverts attention away from pain

(Remember, perception is a major factor in pain intensity.) Doing so can often decrease or eliminate the need for medication. Approximately 80% of chronic pain sufferers have no identifiable physical basis for their symptoms.

Treatment of a chronic pain patient first requires an evaluation so it can be determined whether there is still a physical cause for the pain behavior (**respondent pain**) or whether the person is expressing learned pain behavior (**operant pain**). Both types of pain are genuine and require help. A behavioral analysis of a chronic pain patient begins with the attitude that it is irrelevant whether the pain has a real or an imaginary basis. The relevant question is: What factors influence or control the pain?

---

respondent pain
that caused by physical factors

operant pain
that due to learned behavior

Behavioral modification is often used to help manage pain discomfort by replacing drugs and excessive rest with "well behavior," such as specially designed exercise programs. These techniques are intended to distract patients from their pain and have them dwell on restoring strength and mobility. The physician asks such things as "How far did you walk yesterday?" instead of "How do you feel?" The physiotherapist will not encourage patients to exercise more than they say they can tolerate but will only praise them when they complete their current exercise quotas.

Behavioral modification has proven successful in many cases. A high percentage of patients have avoided further surgery, hospitalization, and medication. Many have been able to return to work. One pain specialist has commented, "People who have something better to do don't hurt as much" (Fordyce 1976; Greenberg 1979).

Clearly, drugs are not the only solution to pain, especially in chronic sufferers. Other techniques can assist or even sometimes totally replace drugs to relieve the discomforts of such pain. While the effectiveness of some nonmedicinal strategies are questionable, there are techniques that, when done properly, can be very useful in pain management. It is recommended that a physician be consulted when deciding which approach is most likely to be successful.

Think About It...

1. Placebos are often effective in relieving pain. Is it ethical for doctors to use placebos instead of legitimate analgesics without informing the patient?
2. What kinds of personality types do you think would have low pain tolerance?
3. Why do you think behavioral modification may be effective in controlling chronic pain when analgesic drugs are not?

MEDICINAL PAIN THERAPY

Because pain intensity is dependent on many physiological and psychological influences, several types of drugs with distinct pharmacological actions can alter the pain experience. The two principal types of analgesics to be discussed are NSAIDS and narcotic drugs. Both are popular with clinicians and patients because, when used properly, they provide pain relief without interfering with the patient's daily routine. Other drugs that are used for pain relief are also discussed briefly.

NONSTEROIDAL ANTIINFLAMMATORY DRUGS (NSAIDS)

For the treatment of most short-term, mild to moderate pain, NSAIDS are the analgesics of choice. While this group includes drugs that are not chemically related, nevertheless, they relieve (1) similar kinds of pain, (2) fevers (**antipyretic** action), and (3) inflammation. Drug groups classified as NSAIDS include the *salicylates*, such as aspirin, which are available over the counter (OTC); *acetaminophen* (active ingredient in Tylenol), also available OTC; and the newer (developed after 1970) *nonsalicylate* NSAIDS, of which only ibuprofen can be obtained OTC (active ingredient in Motrin, Advil, and Nuprin).

antipyretic
drugs that relieve fevers

NSAIDS block the activity of *cyclooxygenase*, the enzyme responsible for the synthesis of prostaglandins and related endogenous chemicals. The significance of this action is that prostaglandins are principal mediators of many types of pains, fevers, and inflammatory symptoms; consequently, drugs such as NSAIDS, which block the formation of prostaglandins, have analgesic, antipyretic, and antiinflammatory actions (see Figure 8-2). In addition, the common effect on prostaglandins by NSAIDS accounts for the fact that these drugs, with the exception of acetaminophen, also have similar side effects. The oldest and most thoroughly studied of NSAIDS agents is aspirin; it is considered to be the prototype drug and the basis of comparison for the other NSAIDS.

THE HISTORY OF ASPIRIN AND OTHER NSAIDS
The bark of the willow tree has long been known for its medicinal value. As far back as the mid-1700s, Reverend Edmund Stone described in a letter "an account of the success of the bark of willow in the cure of agues [fever]" (Insel 1990). The active antipyretic ingredient in willow bark,

called *salian*, was first isolated in 1829 by Leroux; in 1875, it was converted to *salicylic acid*. In the late nineteenth century, salicylic acid became very popular after its usefulness in the treatment of rheumatic fever and gout was discovered. The resulting popularity motivated a chemist by the name of Hoffman to synthesize acetylsalicylic acid, which was introduced by Bayer Pharmaceuticals under the trade name *aspirin* (see Figure 8-3). Thus, aspirin and other salicylates are chemically related and have similar pharmacological properties.

Because of the cost and inconvenience of extracting salian from willow bark and converting it into a salicylate, synthetic salicylates replaced the natural compounds. By the early 1900s, the antipyretic, antiinflammatory, and analgesic properties of salicylates were well known. Because of the therapeutic interest in these drugs, other salicylatelike compounds were discovered. Of these early nonsalicylate agents, only acetaminophen is still used today.

Over the past 20 years, a host of new NSAIDS have been developed and marketed (see Table 8-3). Due to the side effects of salicylates such as aspirin, the newer NSAIDS were developed as alternatives. While there are some differences in side effects between salicylates and other NSAIDS, for most people, salicylates are still the drugs of choice for treatment of minor to moderate aches and pains, fevers, and inflammation.

FIGURE 8-2 Mechanism of NSAIDS. NSAIDS inhibit prostaglandin synthesis by blocking the enzyme cyclooxygenase. The steroids block the enzyme phospholipase A. *Source:* Based on Insel 1990.

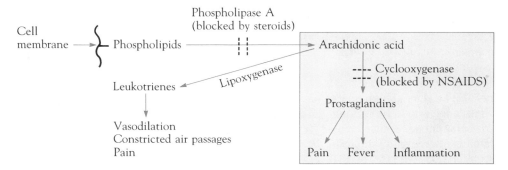

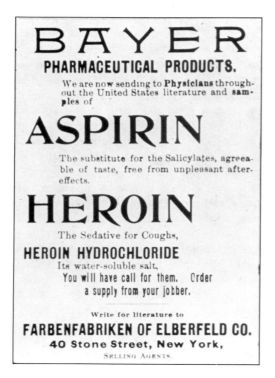

FIGURE 8-3 Bayer Pharmaceutical introduced two new products in the late 1800s: aspirin and heroin.

TABLE 8-3 More recently developed nonsalicylate NSAIDS

Drug Name	Trade Name
Ibuprofen	Motrin, Advil, Nuprin
Naproxen	Naprosyn
Diclofenac	Voltaren
Fenoprofen	Nalfon
Ketoprofen	Orudis
Meclofenamate	Meclomen

PHARMACOLOGICAL PROPERTIES   The principal pharmacological effects of NSAIDS are analgesia, blockage of symptoms associated with inflammation (i.e., relief of redness, swelling, and pain), and a decrease of body temperature during a fever.

Analgesic Action. NSAIDS relieve mild to moderate somatic pain associated with musculoskeletal structures such as bones, skin, teeth, joints, and ligaments. In contrast, these drugs are not effective in the treatment of severe pain or pain associated with visceral structures, such as the heart, stomach, intestines, and other internal organs.

Antiinflammatory Effects. Use of high doses (two to three times the analgesic dose) of all NSAIDS, except acetaminophen, relieves the symptoms of inflammation. Because of this antiinflammatory effect, NSAIDS are frequently

compared to a group of very potent antiinflammatory agents: the corticosteroids. In order to distinguish NSAIDS from corticosteroids, these drugs have been named *nonsteroidal* antiinflammatory drugs (NSAIDS). While steroids (which are adrenal hormones) and their synthetic derivatives potently block inflammation (see Figure 8-2), they do not possess analgesic or antipyretic activity like NSAIDS drugs.

Antipyretic Effects. All NSAIDS reduce fevers but do not alter normal body temperature. Doses required to achieve this therapeutic effect are comparable to those used for analgesic effects.

The frequent use of NSAIDS to eliminate fevers is very controversial. Some clinicians believe that fever may be a defense mechanism that assists in the destruction of infecting organisms, such as bacteria and viruses; thus, to interfere with fever may hamper the body's ability to rid itself of disease-causing microorganisms. Because no serious problems are apparently associated with fevers of 102° F or less, they are probably better left untreated (Lackner 1990).

THERAPEUTIC   CONSIDERATIONS   AND   SIDE EFFECTS   While NSAIDS are analgesic, antipyretic, and antiinflammatory drugs, there are significant distinctions among the agents in this group. First of all, acetaminophen is different from the other drugs because it has little significant antiinflammatory activity. Consequently, an acetaminophen-containing product like Tylenol would not be recommended for treating discomfort related to inflammation, such as arthritis. Second, for most pain, salicylates and acetaminophen have comparable relief action; the newer NSAIDS, such as ibuprofen (Motrin, Advil, and Nuprin) and naproxen (Naprosyn), have somewhat greater analgesic action.

When selecting NSAIDS drugs for pain relief, the side effects must be considered. Although salicylates, such as aspirin, are frequently used, they may cause problems for many people (see Table 8-4). Because of these side effects, salicylates are not recommended for: (1) children (because of the potential for Reyes Syndrome); (2) people with gastrointestinal problems, such as ulcers; or (3) individuals who have bleeding concerns (such as hemophilia), who are already taking anticlot drugs, who are scheduled for surgery, or who are near the term of pregnancy. For minor aches and pains, acetaminophen substitutes adequately for salicylates, and it has no effect on blood clotting and is not irritating to the stomach. In addition, acetaminophen does not influence the occurrence of Reyes Syndrome, a potentially deadly complication of colds, flu, and chicken pox in children (up to the age of 16 to 18 years) who are using salicylates (*Drug Facts and Comparisons* 1991).

Most of the newer NSAIDS (see Table 8-3) have side effects like salicylates. Of these, only ibuprofen is available OTC. These drugs also cause stomach irritation and prolong bleeding (because of their anticlotting action) but to a lesser degree than salicylates. It has not been determined if they promote Reyes Syndrome like salicylates. Acetaminophen is distinct from the other NSAIDS due to its lack of significant side effects when therapeutic doses are used.

T h i n k   A b o u t   I t . . .

1. Recently, the Food and Drug Administration (FDA) requested that the manufacturers of Tylenol stop promoting their product for the treatment of arthritis. Do you think the FDA was justified in making this request? Why?
2. Why are aspirin, acetaminophen, and ibuprofen referred to as nonsteroidal antiinflammatory drugs (NSAIDS)?
3. Why are most NSAIDS effective in the treatment of pain, inflammation, and fever?

OPIOID NARCOTIC ANALGESICS

Narcotic analgesics are one of the most frequently prescribed pain relievers today. It is possible to relieve most pain with narcotic analgesics, even that not adequately controlled by NSAIDS agents. The tremendous therapeutic benefit of the opioid narcotics comes with some risk: These agents have substantial abuse potential and can significantly interfere with respiration.

TABLE 8-4   Common side effects of OTC NSAIDS agents

Drugs	System Affected	Side Effects
Salicylates (aspirinlike)	Gastrointestinal	Irritation, bleeding, aggravation of ulcers
	Blood	Interference with clotting; prolongs bleeding
	Ears	Chronic high doses cause ringing (tinnitis) and hearing loss
	Pediatric	Reyes Syndrome
Acetaminophen	Liver	High acute doses or chronic exposure can cause severe damage
Ibuprofen (includes other newer NSAIDS)	Gastrointestinal	Similar to salicylates but less severe
	Blood	Similar to salicylates but less severe
	Kidneys	Damage in elderly or those with existing kidney disease

THE HISTORY OF NARCOTICS   The word *narcotic* has been used to label many substances, from opium to marijuana to cocaine. The translation of the Greek word *narkoticos* is "benumbing or deadening." The term *narcotic* is sometimes used to refer to a central nervous system (CNS) depressant, producing insensibility or stupor, and at other times to refer to an addicting drug. Most people would not consider marijuana among the narcotics today, although for many years, it was included in this category. Although pharmacologically, cocaine is not a narcotic either, it is still legally so classified. Perhaps part of this confusion is due to the fact that cocaine, as a local anesthetic, can cause a numbing effect.

The opium poppy, *Papaver somniferum*, from which opium and its narcotic derivatives are obtained, has been cultivated for millennia (see Figure 8-4). A 6,000-year-old Sumerian tablet has an ideograph for the poppy shown as "joy" plus "plant," suggesting that the addicting properties of this substance have been appreciated for many centuries. The Egyptians listed opium along with approximately 700 other medicinal compounds in the famous "Ebers Papyrus" (about 1500 B.C.). The ancient Greeks knew that opium was produced after the petals dropped, but before the seed pods matured. In the third century B.C. the Greek writer Theophrastus referred to a method for extracting poppy juice, *opion*, by grinding up the entire plant.

Homer's *Odyssey*, about 1000 B.C., mentions the use of a potion that sounds like an opiate. The spirits of the people, who had gathered in sad commemoration of Ulysses and his trying ordeals, were given a lift when:

FIGURE 8-4   The opium poppy

Helen, daughter of Zeus, poured into the wine they were drinking a drug, nepenthes, which gave forgetfulness of evil. Those who had drunk of this mixture did not shed a tear the whole day long, even though their mother or father were dead, even though a brother or beloved son had been killed before their eyes (as quoted in Scott 1969).

FIGURE 8-5 The Minoan goddess of sleep, wearing a headband of opium poppies

The Greek god of sleep, Hypnos, and the Roman god of sleep, Somnus, were portrayed as carrying containers of opium pods, and the Minoan goddess of sleep wore a crown of opium pods (see Figure 8-5). The opium pod can also be seen on Greek gold coins (see Figure 8-6). According to Greek mythology, the poppy was sacred to Demeter, the goddess of sowing and reaping, and to her daughter, Persephone.

During the so-called Dark Ages that followed the collapse of the Roman Empire, Arab traders actively engaged in traveling the overland caravan routes to China and to India, where they introduced opium. Eventually, both China and India grew their own poppies.

Opium in China. The opium poppy had a dramatic impact in China, causing widespread addiction. Initially, the seeds were used medically, as was opium later. However, by the late 1690s, opium was being smoked and used for diversion (see Figure 8-7). The Chinese government, fearful of the weakening of national vitality by the potent opiate, outlawed the sale of opium in 1729. The penalty for disobedience was death by strangulation. At one point, decapitation was decreed, a much more serious penalty than strangulation be-

FIGURE 8-6 A Greek gold coin dated 700 to 500 B.C. Note the opium poppy pod shown.

FIGURE 8-7 The Chinese government outlawed the sale of opium in 1729 in an attempt to stop its widespread use.

cause the Chinese believe the body must be intact in order to reach paradise.

Despite these laws and threats, the habit of opium smoking became so widespread that the Chinese government went a step further and forbade its importation from India, where most of the opium poppy was grown. The British East India Company (and later the British government in India) encouraged cultivation of opium. British companies were the principal shippers to the Chinese port of Canton, which was the only port open to Western merchants. During the next 120 years, a complex network of opium smuggling developed in China with the help of local merchants, who received substantial profits, and local officials, who pocketed bribes to ignore the smugglers. The amount of opium entering China rose from 200 chests in 1729 to 30,000 to 40,000 chests (weighing about 130 lbs. each) in 1838 (Austin 1978; Scott 1969).

Everyone involved in the opium trade, particularly the British, was profiting until the Chinese government ordered the strict enforcement of the edict against importation. Such actions by the Chinese caused conflict with the British government and helped trigger the Opium War of 1839 to 1842. Great Britain sent in an army, and by 1842, 10,000 British soldiers had won a victory over 350 million Chinese (see Figure 8-8).

Britain protested that the war was not over opium but rather high import tariffs and corrupt Chinese courts. In reality, the British wanted to force China to open its ports to trade. Because of the war, the Treaty of Nanking was signed in 1842; five ports were opened to the British, the island of Hong Kong was ceded to them, and an indemnity of $6 million was imposed on China to cover the value of the destroyed opium and the cost of the war. In 1856, a second Opium War broke out. Peking was occupied by British and

FIGURE 8-8 A famous cartoon, showing a British sailor shoving opium down the throat of a Chinese man, which dates back to the Opium War of 1839–1842.

French troops, and China was compelled to make further concessions to Britain. The importation of opium continued to increase until 1908, when Britain and China made an agreement to limit the importation of opium from India (Austin 1978).

Worldwide Opium Use. Meanwhile, in 1803, a young German named Frederick Serturner extracted and purified the active ingredient in opium. It was 10 times more potent than opium itself and was named *morphine* after Morpheus, the Greek god of dreams. This discovery increased worldwide interest in opium, and by 1832, a number of different alkaloids had been isolated from the raw material. In 1832, the second compound was purified, *codeine*, named after the Greek word for "poppy capsule" (Maurer and Vogel 1967).

The opium problem was further aggravated in 1853, when Alexander Wood perfected the hypodermic syringe and introduced it in Europe and then America. Christopher Wren and others had worked with the idea of injecting drugs directly into the body by means of hollow quills and straws, but the approach was never successful or well received. Wood perfected the syringe technique with the intent of preventing an addiction to morphine by injecting the drug directly into the veins rather than by oral administration. Unfortunately, just

the opposite happened: Injection of morphine increased the potency and the chance of dependence (Maurer and Vogel 1967).

The hypodermic syringe was used extensively during the Civil War to administer morphine for treating pain, dysentery, and fatigue. A large percentage of the men who returned from the war were addicted to morphine. Opiate addiction became known as the "soldier's disease" or "army disease." Nevertheless, historical analysis shows that these returning soldiers did not necessarily contribute significantly to opiate addiction in the United States.

By 1900, an estimated 1 million Americans were addicted to opiates (Abel 1980). The effects of long-term opiate use on many of those who became addicted during this era are related by an addict in the adjacent box. This drug problem was made worse due to (1) Chinese laborers, who brought with them to the United States opium to smoke (it was legal to smoke opium in the United States at that time); (2) the availability of purified morphine and the hypodermic syringe; and (3) the lack of controls on the large number of patent medicines that contained opium derivatives. Although opium smoking was not popular in the United States at the turn of the century, the use of morphine was. The widespread popularity of

For You to Consider...

The Life of an Opium Addict in Turn-of-the-Century America

The following account, published in 1907, tells of the typical life of an opium addict:

> Some settle down to a certain dose and adhere to it for years; others devote their lives to the effort of absorbing all the opiate they can crowd into their systems. The life of the former runs on uneventfully. They live, perform a certain limited series of mental and physical evolutions, but their progress ceases, their career culminates. They gradually retire from the activities of the community and grow yearly more contracted in their operations and their sympathies. Ambition is dead, incentive has perished—they just live and no more. The man collects his little rents, sees to his little kitchen garden, eats a trifle, wears his old clothes and sits alone at home, reading a bit, meditating long, ruminating most of the time, producing nothing; a quiet, inoffensive, retiring hermit; of no use to himself or to anybody else, neither hated nor loved by any mortal man. Only the druggist knows the truth (Sterne 1907).

opiate-containing patent medicines and morphine was probably the main reason for the spread of and increase in opium addiction.

Until 1914, when the Harrison Narcotic Act was passed (regulating opium, coca leaves, and their products), the average opiate addict was a middle-aged, southern, white woman who functioned well and was adjusted to her role as a wife and mother. She bought opium or morphine legally by mail order from Sears, Roebuck or at the local store, used it orally, and caused very few problems. A number of physicians were addicted, as well. One of the best-known morphine addicts was William Holsted, a founder of Johns Hopkins Medical School. Holsted was a very productive surgeon and innovator, although secretly an addict for most of his career. He became dependent on morphine as a substitute for his cocaine dependence (Brecher 1972).

Always looking for answers to medicinal mysteries, chemists found that modification of the morphine molecule resulted in a more potent compound. In 1898, diacetylmorphine was placed on the market as a cough suppressant by Bayer. It was to be a "heroic" drug, without the addictive potential of morphine, thus the name *heroin* (see Figure 8-3).

PHARMACOLOGICAL EFFECTS   Even though opioid narcotics have a history of being abused, they continue to be important therapeutic agents. The most common clinical use of these drug is as analgesics. Narcotics are effective in the relief of most types of pain. In contrast to NSAIDS, discussed earlier in this chapter, narcotic analgesics are effective in the treatment of pain originating from the internal organs (visceral pain) and can relieve even moderate to severe pain, if a potent agent is used. However, narcotics have no antipyretic or antiinflammatory action; thus, they are not useful in the treatment of fevers or inflammation. The differences in effects are due to the differences in the mechanisms of action between narcotics and NSAIDS. As already mentioned, NSAIDS block the synthesis of prostaglandins, while narcotics exert their effects by stimulating the opioid receptors (see below).

Opioid narcotics are also used to treat conditions not related to pain. For example, these drugs suppress the coughing center of the brain so they are effective **antitussives.** Codeine, a natural opioid narcotic, is commonly included in cough medicine. In addition, opioid narcotics slow the movement of materials through the intestines, which can be used to relieve diarrhea. Paregoric contains an opioid narcotic substance and is commonly used to treat severe diarrhea.

antitussive
drugs that block coughing

When used carefully by the clinician, opioid narcotics are very effective therapeutic tools. Drug abuse problems usually occur due to carelessness and poor drug management by either the health professional or the patient.

Mechanisms of Action. The opioid receptors are the site of action of the endorphin peptide transmitters. The opioid receptors are found throughout the brain, spinal cord, autonomic nervous system, and intestines and are associated with several important functions. One of the principal functions of the natural opioid transmitter systems is to diminish pain transmission throughout the pain pathway. Because narcotic drugs like morphine and heroin enhance the opioid system by stimulating opioid receptors, these drugs suppress pain perception.

The opioid receptors are also present in high concentration within the limbic structures of the brain. Due to the limbic system's role in drug dependence, this is likely the site of action related to the abuse potential of narcotic drugs.

Often, when using narcotics for analgesia, some of the pain remains, but the drugs change the user's attitude about the discomfort. When asked if the pain has been relieved by the analgesics, a patient frequently responds, "I can still feel the pain, but it no longer bothers me." This type of response suggests that the narcotic alters the brain's interpretation of the pain signal from being an unpleasant to a neutral experience. Narcotic analgesics in high doses can effectively relieve most types of pain (Jaffe and Martin 1990).

Side effects of narcotic analgesics include drowsiness, mental clouding, respiratory depression (suppressed breathing is usually the cause of death from overdose), nausea and vomiting, itching, constipation, inability to urinate, a drop in blood pressure, and constricted pupils. This array of seemingly unrelated side effects are due to widespread distribution of the opioid receptors throughout the body and their involvement in many physiological functions (Jaffe and Martin 1990).

Drugs that selectively antagonize the opioid receptors are able to block the effects of natural opioid systems in the body as well as reverse the effects of narcotic opiate drugs. When an opioid antagonist like the drug naloxone is administered alone, it has little noticeable effect. The antiopioid actions of naloxone are most apparent when the antagonist is injected into someone who has taken a narcotic opioid drug. For example, naloxone will cause (1) a recurrence of pain in the patient using a narcotic for pain relief, (2) the restoration of consciousness and normal breathing in the addict who has overdosed on heroin, and (3) severe withdrawal effects in the opioid abuser who has become dependent on the narcotics.

ABUSE AND DEPENDENCE   All of the opioid narcotic agents that activate opioid receptors have abuse potential and are classified as Scheduled drugs (see Table 8-5). There are differences, however, in their potencies, severity of side effects, likelihood of being abused, and clinical usefulness.

Heroin Abuse. Heroin is currently classified as a Schedule I drug by the Drug Enforcement Administration (DEA). It is not approved for any clinical use in the United States and is the most likely of the opioid narcotic drugs to be seriously abused.

Heroin was first used in the United States as a cough remedy and to combat addiction to other drugs. However, its inherent addictive properties were quickly discovered. When injected, heroin

TABLE 8-5 Common narcotics and their CSA schedules

Narcotic	Schedule*
Heroin	I
Morphine	II, III
Methadone	II
Fentanyl	II
Hydromorphone	II
Meperidine	II
Codeine	II, III, V
Pentazocine	IV
Propoxyphene	IV
Narcotics combined with NSAIDS	III

*According to Drug Enforcement Administration (DEA) classification, Controlled Substances Act (CSA).

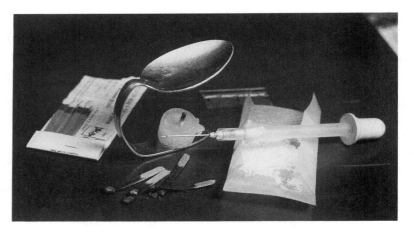

Heroin and its paraphernalia *Source:* Charles Gatewood/
Stock, Boston

is more addictive than other narcotics because of the rapid intense feeling of euphoria it induces. Heroin was banned from American medicine in 1924 although it is still used legally as an analgesic in other countries.

From 1970 through 1976, most of the heroin reaching the United States originated from the Golden Triangle region of Southeast Asia, which includes parts of Burma, Thailand, and Laos. During that period, the United States and other nations purchased much of the legal opium crop from Turkey in order to stop opium from being converted into heroin. From 1975 until 1980, the major heroin supply was from opium poppies grown in Mexico. The U.S. government furnished the Mexican government with helicopters, herbicide sprays, and financial assistance to destroy the poppy crop. Changes in political climates may well shift the source of supply back to the Golden Triangle, Turkey, or elsewhere in the future. The opium poppy can be cultivated commercially almost anywhere cheap labor is available during the brief harvesting season.

Heroin Combinations. Pure heroin is a white powder. Other colors, such as brown Mexican heroin, result from unsatisfactory processing of morphine or from adulterants. Heroin is usually "cut" (diluted) with lactose (milk sugar) to give it bulk and thus increase profits. When heroin first enters the United States, it may be up to 95% pure, but by the time it is sold to users, its purity may be anywhere from 3% to 5%.

Heroin has a bitter taste, so quite often it is "cut" with quinine, a bitter substance, to disguise the fact that the heroin content has been reduced. Quinine can be a deadly adulterant. Part of the "flash" from direct injection of heroin may be caused by quinine. It is an irritant, and it causes vascular damage, acute and potentially lethal disturbances in heartbeat, depressed respiration, coma, and death from respiratory arrest. Opiate poisoning causes acute pulmonary edema as well as respiratory depression. Heroin plus quinine has an unpredictable additive effect (Bourne 1976). To counteract the constipation caused by heroin, mannitol is often added for its laxative effect.

Profile of Heroin Addicts. Heroin addicts are always searching for the "dynamite bag" (the really potent one); however, if they do find an unusually potent batch of heroin, there is a good chance they will get more than they bargained for. Addicts are sometimes found dead with the needle still in the vein after injecting heroin. In such cases, the unsuspecting addict may have died in reaction to an unusually concentrated dose of this potent narcotic.

When addicts "shoot up" in groups, it is rare for more than one person to have an overdose reaction. Death associated with heroin injection is usually due to concurrent use of alcohol or barbiturates and not the heroin alone. It is typical for

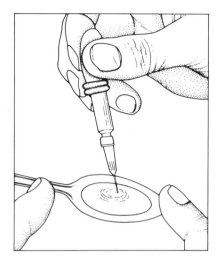

FIGURE 8-9 Heroin paraphernalia is usually simple and crude but effective: a spoon on which to dissolve the narcotic and a makeshift syringe with which to inject it.

addicts to have a common place where they can stash supplies and equipment for their heroin encounters. These locations, called "shooting galleries," serve as gathering places for addicts.

Some addicts become fixated on the drug's paraphernalia (see Figure 8-9), especially the needle. They can get a psychological "high" from playing with the needle and syringe. The injection process and syringe plunger action appear to have sexual overtones for them.

Heroin and Crime. In 1971, the Select Committee on Crime in the United States released a report on methods used to combat the heroin crisis

that arose in the 1950s and 1960s. This report was a turning point in setting up treatment programs for narcotic addicts. The report stated that drug arrests for heroin use had increased 700% since 1961, that there were as many as 4,000 deaths per year from heroin, and that the cost of heroin-related crimes was estimated to be over $3 billion a year. Other studies since that time have linked heroin addiction with crime (Hammersley et al. 1989).

It is important to realize that heroin per se does not cause criminal behavior but rather the setting in which the drug use occurs leads to crime. For example, the more a drug such as heroin is perceived as being illegal, desirable, and addictive, the more likely it will be used by deviant criminal populations. Another factor is that, as heroin availability declines, its cost rises, increasing the likelihood that people dependent on this drug will resort to crime to support their habits (Hammersley et al. 1989).

Patterns of Heroin Abuse. In the 1980s, U.S. attitudes toward narcotics changed when it became obvious that the problem was no longer confined to the inner city; narcotic use had infiltrated suburban areas and small towns. These new drug populations had more financial resources than people in the inner city and were usually able to obtain confidential medical surveillance. For these reasons, it has been and remains very difficult to determine the level of heroin use.

However, a study released in 1990 by the National Institute on Drug Abuse found that, from 1987 to 1988, the lifetime use of heroin and other opioid narcotics had declined in high school seniors and college students (see Table 8-6). A 1991

TABLE 8-6 Prevalence of heroin and other opioid (in parentheses) abuse in high school seniors and college students

Students	Annual Use		Lifetime Use	
	1987	1988	1987	1988
High school seniors	0.5% (5.3%)	0.5% (4.6%)	1.2% (9.2%)	1.1% (8.6%)
College (1–4 yrs post–high school)	0.2% (3.1%)	0.2% (3.1%)	0.6% (7.6%)	0.3% (6.3%)

Source: Johnston et al. 1989.

For You to Consider...

"Heroin Use Rises as Crack Wanes"

This headline in the New York Times (June 18, 1991) reflects the trendy and whimsical nature of heroin abuse. This article reveals how heroin dealers made inroads into New York City's illicit drug market in 1990 and 1991. Because of the waning popularity of "crack," middle-level cocaine dealers have been switching to heroin and on many street corners have replaced "crack" dealers. The resulting increase in heroin use has been subtle and seen mostly in poor people living in inner-city sections. A director at the New York City Association for Drug Abuse and Prevention claimed that "people are pulling away from 'crack' because of what it does to you in terms of destruction, how it tears the body down. A lot of people are afraid of that. . . . If people know you're a crackhead they think you're stupid, you can't be trusted." Because the effects of heroin are viewed as gentler and less destructive, a shift in drug use patterns has been taking place and may be heralding the beginning of a new narcotic epidemic (Treaster 1991).

report confirmed this decline in heroin use when it disclosed that total sales of heroin dropped from $15.5 billion in 1989 to $12.3 billion in 1990 (Meddis 1991).

This trend parallels similar reductions seen with other drugs of abuse and likely reflects a change in public attitudes about the recreational use of drugs. Even so, we should not be fooled into thinking that heroin abuse problems are disappearing. In fact, with the decline in the popularity of cocaine "crack," there has been evidence that "crack" dealers and users are switching to heroin, which may eventually lead to increased use of this narcotic.

Stages of Dependence. Initially, the effects of heroin are often unpleasant, especially after the first injection. It is not uncommon to experience nausea and vomiting or to feel sick after administration, but gradually, the euphoria overwhelms the aversive effects. There are two major stages in the development of a psychological dependence on heroin or other opioid narcotics.

1. There is a rewarding stage, in which euphoria and positive effects occur to at least 50% of users. These positive feelings and sensations increase with continued administration and encourage use.
2. Eventually, the heroin or narcotic user must take the drug to avoid withdrawal symptoms that start about 12 hours after the last dose. At this stage, it is said that "the monkey is on his back." This is psychological dependence. If one grain of heroin (about 65 mg) is taken over a two-week period on a daily basis, the user becomes physically dependent on the drug.

Methods of Administration. Many heroin users start by sniffing the powder or injecting it into a muscle (intramuscular) or under the skin ("skin popping"). Sometimes it is smoked, but most addicts consider this wasteful. In Vietnam, many of those who became addicted to heroin started out by smoking it with tobacco or marijuana or by sniffing it. The heroin available in Vietnam was nearly 95% pure.

Established heroin addicts usually **"mainline"** the drug (intravenous injection). The injection device can be made from an eyedropper bulb, part of a syringe, and a hypodermic needle (see Figure 8-9). "Mainlining" drugs causes the thin-walled veins to become scarred, and if done frequently, the veins will collapse. Once a vein is collapsed, it can no longer be used to introduce the drug into the blood. Addicts become expert in locating new veins to use: in the feet, the legs, even the temples. When addicts do not want "needle tracks" (scars) to show, they inject under the tongue or in the groin.

"mainlining"
intravenous injection of a drug of abuse

Heroin Addicts and AIDS. Needle sharing is a common occurrence in populations of heavy heroin users. Of significant concern is the transmission of deadly communicable diseases such as acquired immune deficiency syndrome (AIDS) when using dirty needles. A recently reported study of intravenous heroin users in Brooklyn and New York City revealed that, in 1988, approximately 54% of these individuals had been exposed to AIDS (as demonstrated by the presence of viral antibodies in their blood) compared to 46% in 1989 (Brown et al. 1990). These findings suggest that, while heroin use may be declining, the risk of contracting AIDS remains very high for the intravenous heroin user. Of course, if the decline in heroin abuse reverses, the number of heroin addicts contracting AIDS will almost certainly increase, as well.

Withdrawal Symptoms. After the effects of the heroin wear off, the addict usually has 4 to 6 hours in which to find the next dose before severe withdrawal symptoms begin. Symptoms start with a runny nose, tears, and minor stomach cramps. The addict may feel as if he or she is coming down with a bad cold. Between 12 and 48 hours after the last dose, the addict loses all of his or her appetite, vomits, has diarrhea and abdominal cramps, feels alternating chills and fever, and develops goose pimples all over (going "cold turkey"). Between 2 and 4 days later, the addict continues to experience some of the symptoms just described, as well as aching bones and muscles and powerful muscle spasms that cause violent kicking motions ("kicking the habit"). After 4 to 5 days, symptoms start to subside, and the person may get his or her appetite back. Attempts to move on in life will be challenging because compulsion to keep using the drug remains strong.

The severity of the withdrawal varies according to the purity and strength of the drug used and the personality of the user. The symptoms of withdrawal from heroin, morphine, and methadone are summarized in Table 8-7. Withdrawal symptoms from opioids such as morphine, codeine, meperidine, and others are similar, although the timeframe and intensity vary (Jaffe 1990).

T h i n k   A b o u t   I t . . .

1. With such a long history of abuse problems, why are narcotics still frequently used today by health professionals?
2. Why do you think heroin use is illegal in the United States but legal in other countries? What kinds of problems can this cause for drug regulatory agencies in the United States?
3. When would a narcotic analgesic be preferred over an NSAIDS analgesic for treating pain? Why?

OTHER NARCOTICS A large number of narcotics are used for medical purposes. However, many

TABLE 8-7 Symptoms of withdrawal from heroin, morphine, and methadone

Symptoms	Time in Hours		
	Heroin	Morphine	Methadone
Craving for drugs, anxiety	4	6	24–48
Yawning, perspiration, runny nose, tears	8	14	34–48
Pupil dilatation, goose bumps, muscle twitches, aching bones and muscles, hot and cold flashes, loss of appetite	12	16	48–72
Increased intensity of above, insomnia, raised blood pressure, fever, faster pulse, nausea	18–24	24–36	72 plus
Increased intensity of above, curled-up position, vomiting, diarrhea, increased blood sugar, foot kicking ("kicking the habit")	26–36	36–48	

are also distributed in the "streets": morphine, methadone, codeine, hydromorphone (Dilaudid), meperidine (Demerol), and other synthetics. A few of the most commonly abused opioids will be discussed briefly in the following sections. Except where noted, they are all Schedule II drugs.

Morphine. Morphine is the standard by which other narcotic agents are measured. It has been used to relieve pain from the time it was first isolated in 1803. Morphine has about one-half the analgesic potency of heroin but 12 times the potency of codeine.

Morphine is commonly used to relieve moderate to intense pain that cannot be controlled by less potent and less dangerous narcotics. Because of the potential for serious side effects, morphine is generally used in a hospital setting where emergency care can be rendered, if necessary. Most pain can be relieved by morphine if high enough doses are used; however, morphine works best against continuous dull pain.

The side effects that occur when using therapeutic doses of morphine include drowsiness, changes in mood, and inability to think straight. In addition, therapeutic doses depress respiratory activity; thus, morphine decreases the rate and depth of breathing as well as produces irregular breathing patterns. As with the other narcotics, morphine can cause an array of seemingly unrelated effects throughout the body, including nausea and vomiting, constipation, blurred vision, constricted pupils, and flushed skin.

The initial response to morphine is varied. In normal persons who are not suffering pain, the first exposure can be unpleasant, with nausea and vomiting being the prominent reactions. However, continual use often leads to a euphoric response and encourages dependence. When injected subcutaneously, the effects of heroin and morphine are almost identical; this is because heroin is rapidly metabolized in the body into morphine. However, after intravenous administration, the onset of heroin's effects is more rapid and more intense than those of morphine because heroin is more lipid soluble and enters the brain faster. Because heroin is easier to manufacture and is more

potent, it is more popular in illicit trade than morphine. Even so, morphine also has substantial abuse potential and is classified as a Schedule II substance.

Tolerance to the effects of morphine can develop very quickly if the drug is used continuously. For example, an addict who is repeatedly administering the morphine to get a "kick" or maintain a "high" must constantly increase the dose. Such users can build up to incredible doses. One addict reported using 5 grams of morphine daily; the normal analgesic dose of morphine is 50 to 80 *milligrams* (mg) a day (Jaffe 1990). Such high doses are extremely lethal in a person without tolerance to narcotics.

Methadone. Methadone was first synthesized in Germany in 1943, when natural opiate analgesics were not available because opium could not be obtained from the Far East during World War II. Methadone was first called *Dolophine*, after Adolph Hitler; one company still uses that trade name. (On the "street," methadone pills are often called "dollies.") Today, methadone is often substituted for heroin in the treatment of narcotic-dependent persons. It is an effective analgesic, equal to morphine if injected and more active if taken orally.

The physiological effects of methadone are the same as those of morphine and heroin. As a narcotic, methadone produces psychological dependence, tolerance, and then physical dependence if repeated doses are taken. Methadone is effective for about 24 to 36 hours; therefore, the addict must take methadone daily to avoid narcotic withdrawal. It is often considered as addictive as heroin if injected; consequently, because methadone is soluble in water, it is formulated with insoluble, inert ingredients to prevent it from being injected by narcotic addicts.

One of methadone's most useful properties is that of cross-tolerance with other narcotic drugs and a less intense withdrawal response. If it reaches a sufficiently high level in the blood, methadone blocks heroin euphoria. In addition, withdrawal symptoms of patients physically dependent on heroin or morphine and the post-addiction craving can be suppressed by oral administration of methadone. The usual dose of methadone is up to 40 mg per day; as much as 100 mg of methadone may be needed to treat severe withdrawal symptoms.

The value of substituting methadone for heroin is its longer action. Because addicts no longer need the heroin to prevent withdrawal, they often can be persuaded to leave their undesirable associates, drug sources, and dangerous lifestyles. The potential side effects from methadone are the same as those from morphine and heroin, including constipation and sedation; yet if properly used, methadone is a safe drug. The only documented death directly related to methadone treatment occurred when a patient was using the drug as prescribed but untreated, severe constipation resulted.

When injecting methadone, some people feel the same kind of euphoria that can be obtained from heroin. Methadone addicts receiving maintenance treatment sometimes become euphoric if the dose is increased too rapidly. There are cases of people who injected crushed methadone pills and developed serious lung conditions from particles that lodged in the tissue, creating a condition somewhat like emphysema. The number of deaths from methadone overdose has been higher than those from heroin in some major cities like New York. Many of these deaths are in young children who get into methadone brought home by parents in maintenance programs or teen-agers who try to shoot up with "street" methadone or methadone in combination with other drugs. Methadone overdoses can be reversed by the antagonist naloxone if the person is found in time.

Controlled Use of Methadone and Heroin. Some regular opiate users can keep jobs and are able to function quite normally. There are known cases of surgeons, lawyers, and other professionals who manage to perform while on opiates. Such narcotic users apparently are able to limit their use and do not become severely dependent.

Between one-third and one-half of those applying to methadone maintenance programs are turned away because they use heroin infrequently and are not considered to be truly dependent; they would likely become addicted to methadone during the course of treatment and be worse off. The estimated heroin-using population in the United States is between 3 and 4 million, of whom only 10% are addicted. An estimated 200,000 narcotic-dependent persons in the United States had received methadone maintenance as of 1988 (Arif and Westermeyer 1988).

Very little is known about controlled users, or "chippers." They are extremely secretive, in contrast to the usual addicts found in treatment programs. No common personality type was found in one study of "chippers"; however, one similarity was that they are more afraid of being forced into abstinence than of losing control and becoming dependent on narcotics. This type of user regulates the circumstances and frequency of heroin use to prevent detection, addiction, and side effects. Typical examples of self-imposed rules are using the drug only on Friday and Saturday evenings, budgeting the amount of money spent on heroin, and being careful to sterilize injection equipment (Zinsberg 1979).

Fentanyl. Fentanyl (Sublimaze) is a very potent narcotic analgesic (200 times more potent than morphine) that is often administered intravenously for general anesthesia. It is also used in transdermal systems (patches on the skin) in the treatment of chronic pain (Duragesic). Fentanyl is not a natural opiate compound but is readily synthesized and can be modified into drugs that retain potent narcotic properties.

It is estimated that some 100 different active forms of fentanyl could be synthesized; up to now, about 10 derivatives have appeared on the "streets." They are considered to be "designer" drugs (see Chapter 4); because of their great potency and ease of production, they have sometimes been used to replace heroin on the "streets." Fentanyl-type drugs can appear in the same forms and colors as heroin, so there is nothing to alert users that they have been sold a heroin substitute (Henderson 1988). Due to their powerful effects, these drugs are especially dangerous, and incredibly small doses can cause fatal respiratory depression in an unsuspecting heroin user. (One "designer" fentanyl, 3-methyl fentanyl, is 6,000 times more potent than heroin.) More than 100 deaths in California have been caused by overdoses of fentanyl-related drugs.

In spring 1991, four fentanyl-related deaths were identified in New York. Deaths from fentanyl overdoses have also occurred in other major U.S. metropolitan areas.

As yet, there is no reliable information regarding the extent of fentanyl abuse. (These drugs are sometimes very difficult to detect in the blood due to the small quantities used.) However, some authorities have speculated that fentanyl abuse has the potential to become a major drug problem in the United States (Henderson 1988).

Hydromorphone. Hydromorphone (Dilaudid) is prepared from morphine and used as an analgesic and cough suppressant. It is a stronger analgesic than heroin and is used to treat moderate to severe pain. Nausea, vomiting, constipation, and euphoria may be less marked with hydromorphone than with morphine (McEvoy 1991). On the "street," it is taken in tablet form or injected.

Meperidine. Meperidine (Demerol) is a synthetic drug that frequently is used as an analgesic for treatment of moderate pain; it can be taken in tablet form or injected. Meperidine is about one-tenth as powerful as morphine, and its use can lead to dependence. This drug has been given too freely by some physicians because tolerance develops, requiring larger doses to maintain its therapeutic action. With continual use, it causes physical dependence. Meperidine addicts may use large daily doses (3 to 4 g per day).

Codeine. Codeine is a naturally occurring constituent of opium and the most frequently prescribed of the narcotic analgesics. It is used principally to treat minor to moderate pain and as a cough suppressant. Maximum pain relief from codeine occurs with 30 to 50 mg. Usually, when prescribed for pain, codeine is combined with either a salicylate such as aspirin or with acetaminophen. NSAIDS and opioid narcotics interact in a synergistic fashion to give an analgesic equivalence greater than what can be achieved by NSAIDS or codeine alone.

Although not especially powerful, codeine may still be abused. Codeine-containing cough syrup is currently classified as a Schedule V drug. Because the abuse potential is considered minor, the FDA has ruled that codeine products can be sold without a prescription; however, the pharmacist is required to keep them behind the counter and must be asked in order to obtain codeine-containing cough medications. In spite of the FDA ruling, about 50% of the states have more restrictive regulations and require that codeine-containing cough products be available only by prescription.

Although codeine dependence is possible, it is not very common; most people that abuse codeine develop narcotic dependence previously with one of the more potent opioids. In general, large quantities of codeine are needed to satisfy a narcotic addiction; therefore, it is not commonly marketed on the "streets."

Pentazocine. Pentazocine (Talwin) was first developed in the 1960s in an effort to market an effective analgesic with low abuse potential. When taken orally, its analgesic effect is slightly greater than that of codeine. Its effects on respiration and sedation are similar to those of the other opioids, but it does not prevent withdrawal symptoms in a narcotic addict. In fact, pentazocine will precipitate withdrawal symptoms if given to a person on methadone maintenance who needs an analgesic (Lowinson and Millman 1979). Pentazocine is not commonly abused because its effects can be unpleasant, resulting in dysphoria. It is classified as a Schedule IV drug.

Propoxyphene. Propoxyphene (Darvon, Dolene) is structurally related to methadone, but it is a much weaker analgesic, about one-half as potent as codeine. Like codeine, propoxyphene is frequently given in combination with aspirin or acetaminophen. Although at one time an extremely popular analgesic, the use of propoxyphene has declined in the past few years as questions about its potency have been raised. Some research suggests this narcotic is no more effective in relieving pain than aspirin (McEvoy 1991). To a large extent, the new, more effective NSAIDS have replaced propoxyphene. In very high doses, it can cause delusions, hallucinations, and convulsions. Alone, propoxyphene causes little respiratory depression; however, when combined with alcohol or other CNS depressants, this drug can depress respiration.

Dextromethorphan. Dextromethorphan is a synthetic used in cough remedies and can be purchased without prescription. This drug does not have analgesic action nor does it cause typical narcotic dependence. However, there have been recent, scattered reports across the country of high school students abusing cough medicines with dextromethorphan. It is claimed that high doses of this drug can cause mild hallucinations and stimulation like PCP. Some abusers refer to the use of the antitussive product Robitussin as "roboing." As of 1991, the DEA had taken no steps to restrict the use of dextromethorphan.

Clonidine. Clonidine (Catapres) was discovered in the late 1970s. It is not a narcotic analgesic and has no direct effect on the opioid receptors; it stimulates receptors for noradrenalin, and its principal use is as an oral antihypertensive. Clonidine is mentioned here because it is the first nonaddictive, noneuphoriagenic prescription medication with demonstrated efficacy in relieving the effects of opiate withdrawal (such as vomiting and diarrhea). The dosing regimen is typically a 7- to 14-day inpatient treatment for opiate withdrawal. Length of treatment can be reduced to 7 days for withdrawal from heroin and short-acting opiates; the 14-day treatment is needed for the longer-acting methadone-type opiates. Because tolerance to clonidine may develop, opiates are discontinued abruptly at the start of treatment. In this way, the peak intensity of withdrawal will occur while clonidine is still maximally effective (Washington et al. 1985; Jaffe 1990).

One of the most important advantages of clonidine over other treatments for opiate withdrawal detoxification is that it shortens the time for withdrawal to 14 days compared to several weeks or months using standard procedures, such as methadone treatment. The potential disadvantage of taking clonidine is that it can cause serious side effects of its own, the most serious being significantly lowered blood pressure, which can cause fainting and blacking out (Washington et al. 1985). Overall, the lack of abuse potential makes clonidine particularly useful in the treatment of narcotic dependence.

MISCELLANEOUS ANALGESIC DRUGS

Other drugs besides NSAIDS and narcotics can also relieve pain. They are not used as analgesics in the same manner as the NSAIDS or narcotic agents because their mechanisms of action are different. The following are brief descriptions of some of these drugs and their therapeutic uses.

ANESTHETICS Anesthetics are used to block consciousness, which in turn reduces awareness and pain. These agents include barbiturates and volatile (gas) anesthetics such as ether and nitrous oxide; they are used almost exclusively to block pain and discomfort associated with surgery.

The first reference to the possibility of surgical anesthesia by inhalation was made in 1799 by the renowned scientist Humphrey Davy, who experimented with nitrous oxide (laughing gas). Nitrous oxide was used first used in dentistry with unpredictable results. During one demonstration in 1844, a patient awoke during a tooth extraction screaming in pain, causing skepticism in the medical community. Two years later, at Massachusetts General Hospital, William Morton, a dentist and a medical student, administered ether during removal of a neck tumor by John C. Warren, a respected surgeon. This surgery was completed with the patient being unconscious, and the skeptical physicians were greatly impressed. Since that time, many other anesthetics have been developed and continue to be used routinely today for in- and outpatient surgical procedures (Kennedy and Longnecker 1990).

SEDATIVES Antianxiety drugs are frequently used to relieve stress associated with pain. This effect is not to be confused with analgesia; sedatives do not alter the pain message itself, only the way in which the message is perceived. Namely, the alteration of pain perception by these drugs makes the pain more tolerable.

Sedatives include principally the CNS depressants that can relieve anxiety, such as the benzodiazepines (diazepam, or Valium; chlordiazepoxide, or Librium) and antihistamines (Phenergan; Vistiril). Sedatives are sometimes combined with narcotic analgesics, such as codeine. Most commonly, sedatives are given to patients prior to surgical procedures to help relieve their apprehension. If patients are relaxed, they are less likely to have severe responses to pain.

OTHER DRUGS   Other drugs that can relieve pain include tricyclic antidepressants (see Chapter 14) and even amphetamines (see Chapter 9). The mechanisms of action that make these drugs effective in pain relief are not well understood.

T h i n k   A b o u t   I t . . .

1. What is the advantage of substituting methadone for heroin in an addict who is not interested in breaking his or her narcotic dependence?
2. Why is fentanyl abuse so dangerous?
3. You are a physician treating a patient who has been in an automobile accident and is experiencing severe neck pain. This patient has a history of alcoholism. What drugs would you use to relieve the pain? Explain your selection.

K E Y   T E R M S

analgesic
opioid
nociceptors
pain tract
bradykinin

prostaglandins
visceral pain
somatic pain
pain threshold
pain tolerance

respondent pain
operant pain
antipyretic
antitussive
"mainlining"

S U M M A R Y

1. Pain is an aversive signal to the brain that warns of potential damage to the body. The pain experience is determined by chemical messengers and neurons that initiate and conduct the pain signal and interacting brain regions that process the message once it is received and determine how the pain will be tolerated. The perception of pain is controlled by previous experience, learned behavior, and expectations.

2. The pain pathway consists of detection devices (receptors) called *nociceptors* and transmitting neurons that are linked together by synapses and run from the site of the pain-initiating event to the spinal cord and terminate in the thalamus of the brain. Initiating substances, such as prostaglandins and bradykinin, stimulate the nociceptor and begin the pain signal. Conducting substances, or transmitters (such as substance P), pass the signal up the line from neuron to neuron. Modulating transmitters, such as endorphins, can diminish the signal by inhibiting

the release of the conducting transmitters.

3. The pain *threshold* is the level of stimulus necessary to cause an unpleasant sensation. NSAIDS-type drugs cause an increase in pain threshold. Pain *tolerance* is the amount of pain necessary to make the sensation unbearable. Narcotic analgesics work by increasing pain tolerance.

4. Nonmedicinal techniques used to control pain include behavior modification, physiotherapy, manipulation, counterirritation, acupuncture, electrical stimulation, and hypnosis. For some sufferers of pain—particularly chronic, long-term pain—such techniques can be useful and help to reduce or eliminate the need for medication. The mechanisms whereby these techniques work are unclear. However, it is likely that the release of endorphins contribute to some of their effectiveness. The response to these strategies is variable, and because of ignorance concerning such techniques, they are often used by untrained persons or even quacks to victimize suffering patients.

5. Both NSAIDS and narcotic analgesics are used principally to relieve pain. NSAIDS are most commonly used to treat mild to moderate forms of somatic (musculoskeletal) pain. The more potent narcotics can alleviate almost any type of pain if high enough doses are used; because of their side effects, they are usually reserved to treat moderate to severe visceral pain. Both categories of drugs can be used for other clinical purposes, as well. NSAIDS relieve the symptoms of inflammation and reduce fevers. In contrast, narcotic analgesics are also used to treat coughing and severe diarrhea.

6. NSAIDS exert their analgesic, antiinflammatory, and antipyretic effects by blocking the synthesis of prostaglandins that mediate these effects. Opioid narcotics exert their effects by stimulating opioid receptors that are associated with the pain pathway but are found in other brain regions (including the limbic system, likely the site responsible for their abuse potential) and throughout the body.

7. Salicylate NSAIDS, such as aspirin, cause significant irritation to the gut, interfere with blood clotting, and are linked with Reyes Syndrome in children with colds, flus, and chicken pox. In therapeutic doses, acetaminophen causes none of these side effects. The newer, nonsalicylate NSAIDS, such as ibuprofen, cause side effects like the salicylates except less severe. Therapeutically, NSAIDS have good analgesic and antipyretic effects. The newer NSAIDS tend to be more effective in their pain relief actions than either the salicylates or acetaminophen. All of the NSAIDS except acetaminophen also have good antiinflammatory effects.

8. Heroin is the most likely of the opioid narcotics to be severely abused; it is easily prepared from opium and has a rapid, intense effect. Heroin use is not limited to the inner-city ghettos but is found throughout the United States. From 1987 to 1991, the rate of narcotic use in the United States declined, although there was some evidence in 1991 that heroin was being substituted for "crack" as the popularity of cocaine diminished. The heroin addict usually "mainlines" the drug and often shoots up with other addicts in "shooting galleries." Persons dependent on narcotics such as

heroin commonly engage in criminal activities to support their habits.

9. When narcotics such as heroin are first used by persons not experiencing pain, the drugs can cause unpleasant, dysphoric sensations. However, euphoria gradually overcomes the aversive effects. The positive feelings increase with narcotic use, leading to psychological dependence. After psychological dependence, physical dependence occurs with frequent daily use, which reinforces the narcotic abuse. If the user stops taking the drug after physical dependence has occurred, severe withdrawal symptoms result.

10. Tolerance to narcotics can occur rapidly with intense use of these drugs. This tolerance can result in the use of incredibly large doses of narcotics that would be fatal to a nontolerant person. The withdrawal symptoms for narcotic dependency begin 4 to 6 hours after the last narcotic dose and become severe by 12 to 48 hours. The experience has been described as being like a bad case of the flu or a cold and includes a runny nose, stomach cramps, vomiting, diarrhea, chills and fever, and goose pimples. After 4 to 5 days, the symptoms begin to subside, but the urge to use the drug persists.

11. Methadone is frequently used to help narcotic addicts stop using heroin or one of the other more addicting drugs. Oral methadone relieves the withdrawal symptoms that would result from discontinuing narcotics. Methadone can also cause psychological and physical dependence, but it is less addicting than heroin and easier to control; namely, when

administered orally, methadone is a slower- and longer-acting drug. Because the effects of methadone last for 24 to 36 hours, it only needs to be administered once daily. Ultimately, the narcotic addict will be encouraged to stop using methadone; however, many addicts refuse and are maintained on methadone indefinitely.

12. Fentanyl is a very potent synthetic opioid narcotic. It is easily synthesized and can be converted into other fentanyllike drugs that are as much as 3,000 to 6,000 times more potent than heroin itself. Detection and regulation of these fentanyl derivatives by law enforcement agencies are very difficult. The fentanyl-type drugs are being used as heroin substitutes and have already killed many narcotic addicts due to their unexpected potency.

13. Fentanyl and related drugs are the most potent of the opioid narcotics, making them useful clinical agents but also very dangerous. Morphine is still used for treatment of moderate to severe pain, usually in hospital settings. Codeine is the most commonly prescribed of the narcotic analgesics and is used to treat moderate pain and excessive coughing. Because of its low potency, codeine is not as likely to be abused as morphine or heroin; codeine is often combined with NSAIDS to give better pain relief. Pentazocine is a unique narcotic because it has both agonist and antagonist properties; it is less likely to be abused than most of the other narcotics and often causes dysphoria. Propoxyphene is the least potent of the commonly used narcotic analgesics. Its usefulness has been questioned, causing a decline in its popularity; because of its low potency, large doses are required by narcotic addicts to satisfy their dependency.

14. Drugs other than NSAIDS or narcotic analgesics used to treat pain include general anesthetics (e.g., ether and nitrous oxide), sedatives (e.g., benzodiazepines and antihistamines), tricyclic antidepressants, and clonidine. The mechanisms of action of these drugs are unknown; they have limited usefulness in treating most pain.

R E F E R E N C E S

Abel, E. L. *Marijuana: The First Twelve Thousand Years.* New York: Plenum, 1980.

Arif, A., and J. Westermeyer, eds. "Pharmacotherapy." In *Manual of Drug and Alcohol Abuse.* New York: Plenum Medical, 1988.

Austin, G. A. *Perspective on the History of Psychoactive Substance Use.* NIDA Research Issues no. 24. Washington, D.C.: Department of Health, Education, and Welfare, 1978.

Bond, M. R. *Pain: Its Nature, Analysis, and Treatment.* New York: Churchill Livingstone, 1979.

Bourne, P. G., ed. *Acute Drug Emergencies: A Treatment Manual.* New York: Academic, 1976.

Brecher, E. M. *Licit and Illicit Drugs.* Boston: Little, Brown, 1972.

Brown, L., R. Phillips, D. Nurco, B. Primm, R. Battjes, and T. Nemoto. *HIV Infection in Intravenous Drug Abusers in NYC Drug Treatment Clinics: 1985–1989.* NIDA Research Monograph Series no. 105. Washington, D.C.: Department of Health, Education, and Welfare, 1990.

Drug Facts and Comparisons. St. Louis: Lippincott, 1991.

Fordyce, W. E. *Behavioral Methods for Chronic Pain and Illness.* St. Louis: Mosby, 1976.

Greenberg, J. "Psyching Out Pain." *Science News* 115 (1979): 332–333.

Hammersley, R., A. Forsyth, V. Morrison, and J. Davies. "The Relationship between Crime and Opioid Use." *British Journal of Addiction* 84 (1989): 1029–1043.

Henderson, G. "Designer Drugs: Past History and Future Prospects." *Journal of Forensic Sciences* 33 (1988): 569–575.

Insel, P. "Analgesic-Antipyretic and Antiinflammatory Agents: Drugs Employed in the Treatment of Rheumatoid Arthritis and Gout." In *The Pharmacological Basis of Therapeutics,* 8th ed., edited by A. Gilman, T. Rall, A. Nies, and P. Taylor. New York: Pergamon, 1990.

Jaffe, J., and M. Martin. "Opioid Analgesics and Antagonists." In *The Pharmacological Basis of Therapeutics,* 8th ed., edited by A. Gilman, T. Rall, A. Nies, and P. Taylor. New York: Pergamon, 1990.

Johnston, L., P. O'Malley, and J. Bachman. *Drug Use, Drinking, and Smoking: National Survey Results from High School, College, and Young Adult Populations, 1975–1988.* Washington, D.C.: NIDA/U.S. Department of Health and Human Services, 1989.

Kennedy, S., and D. Longnecker. "History and Principles of Anesthesiology." In *The Pharmacological Basis of Therapeutics,* 8th ed., edited by A. Gilman, T. Rall, A. Nies, and P. Taylor. New York: Pergamon, 1990.

Lackner, T. "Antipyretic Drug Products." In *Handbook of Nonprescription Drugs,* edited by E. Feldman et al. Washington, D.C.: American Pharmaceutical Association, 1990.

Lowinson, J. H., and R. B. Millman. "Clinical Aspects of Methadone Maintenance Treatment." In *Handbook on Drug Abuse,* edited by R. L. DuPont, A. Goldstein, and J. O'Donnell. Washington, D.C.: NIDA/Department of Health, Education, and Welfare, 1979.

Maurer, D., and V. Vogel. *Narcotics and Narcotic Addiction,* 3rd ed. Springfield, IL: Charles C. Thomas, 1967.

McEvoy, G., ed. "Opiate Agonists." In *American Hospital Formulary Service Drug Information.* Bethesda, MD: American Society of Hospital Pharmacists, 1991.

Meddis, S. "USA's Illegal Drug Bill: $40 Billion." *USA Today,* 20 June 1991, 1A.

Scott, J. M. *The White Poppy: A History of Opium.* New York: Funk & Wagnalls, 1969.

Sterne, A. E. "A Life of Opium Addiction." *Journal of Inebriety* 29 (Autumn 1907): 203–209.

Treaster, J. "Heroin Use Rises as Crack Wanes." *New York Times,* 18 June 1991.

Washington, A. M., M. S. Gold, and A. C. Pottard. "Opiate and Cocaine Dependencies." *Drug Dependencies* 5 (1985): 46–47.

Zinsberg, N. E. "Nonaddictive Opiate Use." In *Handbook on Drug Abuse,* edited by R. L. Dupont, A. Goldstein, and J. O'Donnell. Washington, D.C.: NIDA/Department of Health, Education, and Welfare, 1979.

Stimulants

CHAPTER OUTLINE

Major Stimulants ▪ Amphetamines ▪ Cocaine ▪ Use by Athletes /
Minor Stimulants ▪ Caffeinelike Drugs (Xanthines) ▪ OTC Sympathomimetics

LEARNING OBJECTIVES

On completing this chapter, you will be able to:

1. Explain how amphetamines work.
2. Identify the FDA-approved uses for the amphetamines.
3. Recognize the major side effects of amphetamines on brain and cardiovascular functions.
4. Discuss the current medical attitudes concerning amphetamine use and abuse.
5. Identify the terms *"speed," "ice,"* and *"run"* as they relate to amphetamine use.

6. Explain what "designer" amphetamines are.
7. Identify the three cocaine eras.
8. Explain how cocaine use in the United States has political implications in some South American countries.
9. Trace the changes in attitude toward cocaine abuse that occurred in the 1980s and explain why they occurred.
10. Compare the effects of cocaine to those of amphetamines.
11. Identify the four principal means of administering cocaine and their relative potencies.

12. Distinguish the properties of "crack" that make it unique from other cocaine forms.
13. Identify the different stages of cocaine withdrawal.
14. Discuss the different approaches to treating cocaine dependence.
15. Identify and compare the major sources of the caffeinelike drugs, the xanthines.
16. List the principal physiological effects of caffeine.
17. Compare caffeine dependence and withdrawal to that associated with the major stimulants.

Source: David Conklin/Monkmeyer

DID YOU KNOW THAT . . .

- The first therapeutic use of amphetamines was in inhalers to treat nasal congestion.
- Ritalin is a type of amphetamine used to treat hyperactive (attention deficit disorder) children.
- The most common FDA-approved use of amphetamines is as a diet aid to treat obesity.
- "Ecstasy" is a "designer" drug that is chemically and pharmacologically related to amphetamines.
- High doses of amphetamines can kill brain neurons, which produce dopamine and serotonin.
- Amphetamines and cocaine have similar pharmacological effects.
- The original Coca-Cola was a cocaine-containing tonic developed in the late 1800s.
- In the early 1980s, cocaine was viewed as a relatively harmless, glamorous substance by the media and some medical experts in this country.
- Smoking "freebased," or "crack," cocaine is more dangerous and more addicting than other forms of administration.
- Cocaine was the first local anesthetic used for surgery.
- Many persons who abuse cocaine are attempting to self-medicate mood disorders, such as depression.
- The majority of those dependent on cocaine are also dependent on alcohol.
- Caffeine is the most frequently used stimulant in the world.
- OTC decongestant drugs usually contain mild CNS stimulants.

Stimulants are substances that act on the central nervous system (CNS). The user experiences pleasant effects initially, such as a sense of increased energy and a state of euphoria, or "high." But he or she may also feel restless and talkative and have trouble sleeping. High doses used over the long term can produce personality changes, as well. Many users self-medicate psychological conditions such as depression with stimulants. Because the initial effects of stimulants are so pleasant, these drugs are frequently abused, leading to dependence.

In this chapter, we will examine the two major classifications of stimulant drugs. Major stimulants, including amphetamines and cocaine, will be addressed first, given their prominent role in current drug abuse problems in the United States. The chapter will conclude with a review of minor stimulants, such as caffeine and sympathomimetics, which are available over the counter (OTC) and thus used by the majority of people.

(Because nicotine has unique stimulant and depressant properties, it is covered in Chapter 10, "Tobacco.")

MAJOR STIMULANTS

All of the major stimulants cause increased alertness, excitation, and euphoria; thus, these drugs are referred to as **"uppers."** The major stimulants are classified as either Schedule I ("designer" amphetamines) or Schedule II (amphetamine and cocaine) controlled substances because of their abuse potential. Although these drugs have common properties, they also have unique features that distinguish them from each other. The similarities and differences of the major stimulants will be discussed in the following sections.

"uppers"
a slang term for CNS stimulants

AMPHETAMINES

Amphetamines can be taken legally under the supervision of a doctor; however, even though the drugs are obtained by prescription, many amphetamine users abuse these potent agents. Because of widespread misuse of stimulants by patients taking them as diet aids, it has become clear that dependence on amphetaminelike drugs can develop.

THE HISTORY OF AMPHETAMINES Amphetamine was first synthesized by the German pharmacologist L. Edeleano in 1887, but it was not until 1910 that this and several related compounds were tested in laboratory animals. Another 17 years passed before Gordon Alles, a researcher looking for a more potent substitute for ephedrine (used as a decongestant at the time), self-administered amphetamine and gave a first-hand account of its effects. Alles found that, when inhaled or taken orally, amphetamine dramatically reduced fatigue, increased alertness, and caused a sense of confident euphoria (Grinspoon and Bakalar 1978).

Alle's impressive findings were discovered by the drug company Smith, Kline & French and acknowledged as a potential bonanza. Smith, Kline & French purchased the patent rights for this ephedrine substitute from Alles, and in 1932, their Benzedrine (amphetamine) inhaler became available as a nonprescription medication in drugstores across America. The inhaler, marketed for nasal congestion, was widely abused. Amphetamine inhalers were available over the counter until 1949. Because of a loophole in a law that was passed later, one brand of nasal decongestant containing 150 milligrams (mg) of methamphetamine was available OTC until 1965. It was not until 1971 that all potent amphetaminelike compounds in nasal inhalers were withdrawn from the market (Grinspoon and Bakalar 1978).

Much of the early popularity for the Benzedrine product was due to an enthusiastic reception by the medical profession. The American Medical Association (AMA) was responsible for naming the drug *amphetamine* and mildly cautioned that "continued overdosage" might cause "restlessness and sleeplessness"; however, the AMA claimed that no "serious reactions" had been observed. In 1937, the AMA recognized the use of amphetamine as acceptable treatment of **narcolepsy** and a form of Parkinson's disease. The AMA also claimed that Benzedrine was useful in the treatment of depressive disorders and that, under the supervision of a physician, amphetamine could be used to achieve "a sense of increased energy or capacity for work, or a feeling of exhilaration" (American Medical Association Council, reported in Grinspoon and Bakalar 1978).

---

narcolepsy
a condition causing spontaneous and uncontrolled sleeping episodes

---

Because of the lack of restrictions during this period, amphetamines were sold for a variety of different ailments. Advertisements for amphetamine inhalers made claims that they could be used to treat obesity, alcoholism, bedwetting, depression, schizophrenia, morphine and codeine addiction, nicotinism, heart block, head injuries, sea sickness, persistent hiccups, and caffeine mania. Many physicians looked upon amphetamines as truly versatile remedies, second only to aspirin in terms of scope, efficacy, and safety. Today, most of these uses are no longer approved as legitimate therapeutics but would be considered forms of drug abuse.

World War II provided a setting in which both the legal and "black market" use of amphetamines flourished (Grinspoon and Bakalar 1978). The stimulating effects of amphetamines made them suitable for wide use in World War II to counteract fatigue. The Germans, Japanese, and British made extensive use of these drugs in the early 1940s. By the end of World War II, large quantities of amphetamines were readily available without prescription in seven different types of nasal inhalers. The inhalers were easily broken and the amphetamines removed and dissolved in coffee or alcohol for a stronger "kick." It was not until 1947 that the extent of inhaler abuse was finally documented in medical literature. Early reports cited abuse problems in the military, but it quickly became apparent that the problem was widespread.

In spite of warnings, the U.S. armed forces issued amphetamines on a regular basis during the Korean War. Korean veterans going back to college used amphetamine tablets to help cram for examinations, and other students quickly adopted the practice. Amphetamine use became widespread among truck drivers making long hauls; it is believed that among the earliest distribution systems for illicit amphetamines were truckstops along major U.S. highways. High-achievers under continuous pressure in the fields of entertainment, business, and industry often relied on amphetamines to counteract fatigue. Homemakers used them for weight control and to combat boredom from unfulfilled lives. At the height of the American epidemic in 1967, some 31 million prescriptions were written for **anorexiants** (diet pills) alone.

---

anorexiants
drugs that suppress the appetite for food

In sum, 6% to 8% of all U.S. adults could have been using legal, prescription amphetamines at this time. This figure does not include unknown illegal amphetamine use (Ellinwood 1974). About the same time, the Food and Drug Administration (FDA) estimated that more than 25 tons of legitimately manufactured amphetamine were diverted to illegal sales; at times, about 90% of the legal supply went into the illegal market.

In the late 1950s, some West Coast narcotic addicts used a combination of amphetamine and heroin to get an effect similar to that of heroin and cocaine. (Cocaine, for the most part, was unavailable at this time.) These addicts also used amphetamine alone when heroin could not be obtained. By the early 1960s, intravenous amphetamine was the first choice for a majority of drug users in West Coast cities. Individuals would get prescriptions for large amounts of methamphetamine for treatment of heroin addiction. The abuse of legally obtained methamphetamine became so prevalent that a number of physicians and pharmacists were prosecuted and convicted for encouraging this practice. And because of its abuse potential, injectable amphetamine was completely withdrawn from the market.

While amphetamine abuse is typically thought of as an American phenomenon, the drug has been abused in many other industrial nations, as well. Only Japan and Sweden have had largescale epidemics of amphetamine abuse comparable to the experience in the United States in the 1960s.

Although a variety of related drugs and mixtures currently exist, the most common amphetamine substances are dextroamphetamine (Dexedrine), methamphetamine (Desoxyn), and amphetamine itself. Generally, if doses are adjusted, the psychological effects of these various drugs are similar, so they will be discussed as a group. Other drugs with similar pharmacological properties are phenmetrazine (Preludin), and methylphenidate (Ritalin). Common slang terms for the amphetamines include speed, crystal, meth, bennies, dexies, uppers, pep pills, diet pills, jolly beans, copilots, hearts, footballs, white crosses, and ice.

HOW AMPHETAMINES WORK   Amphetamines are synthetic amines, chemicals with nitrogen in their molecules, which are similar to natural neurotransmitters such as norepinephrine (noradrenalin), dopamine, and the stress hormone epinephrine (adrenalin). The amphetamines exert their pharmacological effect by increasing the activity of these catecholamine substances and serotonin (see

Chapter 5), both in the brain and nerves associated with the sympathetic nervous system. Because amphetamines cause release of norepinephrine from sympathetic nerves, they are classified as *sympathomimetic* drugs. The amphetamines generally cause an arousal or activating response (also called the "fight-or-flight response") that is similar to your normal reaction to emergency situations or crises.

Amphetamines cause alertness by stimulating the reticular activating system (see Chapter 5). In addition, they activate other parts of the brain. The individual becomes aroused, hypersensitive to stimuli, and feels "turned on." These effects occur even without external sensory input. This activation may be a very pleasant experience in itself, but a continual high level of activation may convert to anxiety, severe apprehension, or a feeling of panic.

Amphetamines have potent effects on dopamine in the reward (pleasure) center of the limbic system (see Chapter 5). The "flash," or sudden feeling of intense pleasure that occurs when amphetamine is taken intravenously, probably results from a high dose of the drug quickly reaching the reward center in the brain. Some users describe the sensation as a "whole body orgasm," and many associate intravenous methamphetamine use with sexual feelings. Some report that use of amphetamines prolongs sexual activity, sometimes for hours. When orgasm finally is reached, it may be more pleasurable than usual. In contrast, others find that, while using amphetamines, they cannot reach orgasm under any circumstances. Although a minority of users actually report increased sexual activity while taking amphetamine, many users cite enhanced sexual pleasure as their principal reason for taking these stimulants (Jaffe and Martin 1990).

Amphetamines have three major actions on neurotransmission:

1. Amphetamines cause the release of the catecholamines and serotonin neurotransmitters, as described above. This release affects the next neuron across the synapse, as if a normal nerve message were being transmitted.
2. Amphetamines block the enzyme that me-

tabolizes these neurotransmitters (mono-amine oxidase), thereby prolonging their effects.

3. Amphetamines enhance their own effects as well as those resulting from normal stimulation by blocking the reuptake of these transmitters so that their effect on other neurons persists. (At least a third of these neurotransmitters normally are reabsorbed by the neurons, which stops their activity and allows them to be used again.)

A curious condition commonly reported with heavy amphetamine use is **behavioral stereotypy,** or getting "hung up." This refers to a simple activity that is done repeatedly. An individual who is "hung up" will get caught in a repetitious thought or act for hours. For example, he or she may take objects apart, like radios or clocks, and carefully categorize all the parts, or sit in a tub and bathe all day, persistently sing a note, repeat a phrase of music, or repeatedly clean the same object. This phenomenon seems to be peculiar to potent stimulants such as the amphetamines and cocaine.

---

behavioral stereotypy
meaningless repetition of a single activity

Behavioral stereotypy is said to occur in part because of the effects of amphetamines on dopamine in the brain. This neurotransmitter is associated with the complex controls for some of the body's motor functions. One theory is that, when dopamine activity is continually enhanced by amphetamine exposure, the associated neurons become sensitized so the effect of this transmitter becomes exaggerated and stereotypy occurs (Sulser and Sanders-Bush 1971). Similar patterns of repetitive behavior also occur in psychotic conditions, such as paranoid schizophrenia. This similarity suggests that the intense use of stimulants such as amphetamines or cocaine alters the brain in a manner like that which causes psychotic mental disorders.

Chronic use of high doses of amphetamines causes dramatic decreases in the brain content of the neurotransmitters dopamine and serotonin that persist for months, even after drug use is stopped (Jaffe and Martin 1990; Schmidt et al. 1985). These decreases have been shown to reflect the death of CNS neurons that release these transmitters. It is not clear why this neuronal damage occurs or how it affects behavior.

APPROVED USES Until 1970, amphetamines had been prescribed for a large number of conditions, including depression, fatigue, and long-term weight reduction. In 1970, the FDA, acting on the recommendation of the National Academy of Sciences, restricted the legal use of amphetamines to three medical conditions: (1) narcolepsy, (2) hyperkinetic (attention deficit disorder) behavior, and (3) short-term weight reduction programs.

Narcolepsy. Amphetamine treatment of narcolepsy is not widespread because this is a relatively rare disorder. *Narcolepsy* comes from the Greek words for "numbness" and "seizure." A person who has narcolepsy falls asleep as frequently as 50 times a day if he or she stays in one position very long. Taking low doses of amphetamines helps keep narcoleptic persons alert.

Hyperkinetic Behavior. This common behavioral problem in children and adolescents involves an abnormally high level of physical activity **(hyperkinesis)** and an inability to focus attention. About 4 out of every 100 grade school children and 40% of school children referred to mental health clinics because of behavioral disturbances are hyperactive. Boys are much more likely to be diagnosed as hyperactive than girls. Such children have short concentration spans, are aggressive, lack clear direction, and are hard to anticipate. Their aggressive, talkative, restless, and impulsive behavior disrupts the classroom and often home life, as well. Such behavior problems usually impede learning.

---

hyperkinesis
excessive movement

The drug commonly used to treat hyperkinetic (attention deficit disorder) children is the amphetamine-related methylphenidate or Ritalin. It is a mild stimulant of the central nervous system that counteracts physical and mental fatigue while having only slight effects on blood pressure and respiration. Its stimulant potency is intermediate between that of amphetamine and caffeine. Methylphenidate and amphetamine are about equally effective in treating hyperkinesis, but methylphenidate is thought to interfere with growth less than amphetamine (Weiner 1980) and to have less abuse potential. Stimulants have a paradoxical calming effect on children with hyperkinesis; the reason for this is unknown.

Similar attention deficit problems also appear in some adults. It is not clear if the mechanisms for the problem are the same in both children and adults, but Ritalin appears to be equally effective in the treatment of both populations.

Weight Reduction. By far the most common legal use of amphetamines is for the treatment of obesity. According to accepted medical and health standards, 24% to 45% of American adults are overweight (Appelt 1990). Amphetamines and chemically similar compounds are used as anorexiants to help such people control appetite. Amphetamines are thought to act by affecting the appetite center in the hypothalamus. They do not affect blood-sugar levels, but they do prompt a decrease in food intake. The FDA has approved short-term use of amphetamines for weight loss programs.

Unless the dose is continuously increased, the appetite-suppressing action of this drug, together with the pleasant stimulating effects, usually wear off after about two to four weeks of treatment. At high doses, the anorexic effect returns, but an even greater tolerance will result. Because of this buildup of tolerance, the FDA has issued a warning about the danger of long-term use of amphetamines.

Many experts feel that the euphoric effect of amphetamines is the primary motivation for their continued use in weight reduction programs. It is possible that many obese people have a need for gratification that can be satisfied by an amphetaminelike drug. If the drug is taken away, these individuals return to food to satisfy their need and sometimes experience "rebound," causing them to gain back more weight than they lost. Because of the particularly fragile psychological state of many obese patients and the potentially severe side effects of amphetamines, support for these drugs as diet aids is diminishing. Most clinicians who work with weight loss programs prefer to use nonmedicinal approaches, such as behavioral modification, counseling techniques, and support group therapy.

SIDE EFFECTS OF THERAPEUTIC DOSES   The two principal side effects of therapeutic doses of amphetamines include (1) abuse potential, which has already been discussed at length, and (2) cardiovascular toxicities. As early as 1935, reports in medical journals suggested that Benzedrine might cause serious cardiovascular problems (Grinspoon and Bakalar 1978). Many of these effects are due to the amphetamine-induced release of epinephrine from the adrenal glands and norepinephrine from the nerves associated with the sympathetic nervous system. The effects include increased heartrate, elevated blood pressure, and damage to vessels, especially small veins and arteries. In users with a history of heart attack, coronary arrhythmia, or hypertension, amphetamine toxicity can be severe or even fatal.

CURRENT MISUSE   Because amphetamine drugs can be readily synthesized in makeshift laboratories for illicit sales, accurate figures on the amount of illegal drugs manufactured and sold are not available. However, estimates run from 10% to 25% of the amount on the legal market. Surveys suggest that there was a decline in the abuse of amphetamines in the late 1980s (see Table 9-1), in parallel with the trend in cocaine abuse (*NIDA Notes* 1991).

Since the late 1970s, U.S. medical associations have asked all physicians to be more careful in the use of prescribed amphetamines. In fact, presently, use is recommended only for narcolepsy and some cases of hyperactivity in children. In spite of FDA approval, most medical associations do not recommend the use of amphetamines for weight loss. Probably less than 1% of all prescriptions now

TABLE 9-1 Prevalence of amphetamine abuse

Age Group	Prevalence*	
	1982	1988
High school seniors	20%	11%
College students	21%	6%

Source: NIDA Notes 6 (Spring 1991).
*Used during previous year.

written are for amphetamines, in contrast to 8% in 1970.

Amphetamine abusers commonly administer a dose of 10 to 30 mg. Besides the positive effects of this dose—the "high"—it can also cause hyperactive, nervous, or jittery feelings that encourage the use of a depressant such as benzodiazepine, barbiturate, or alcohol to relieve the discomfort of being "wired" (Jaffe and Martin 1990).

A potent and commonly abused form of amphetamine is **"speed,"** an illegal methamphetamine available as a white crystalline powder for injection. The profit for the speed manufacturer is substantial enough to make illicit production financially attractive. One estimate is that a pound of methamphetamine crystal can be made for about $100 and sold in quarter- or half-ounce amounts on the "street" for about $2,500. Methamphetamine is relatively easy to synthesize if the chemicals are available. In 1969, it was reported that a 9-year-old child synthesized speed in her home. Another 15-year-old "speed cook" admitted synthesizing methamphetamine with only a vacuum, a big glass, a cooking pan, a heater, and a hair dryer. Today, so-called "meth" or "speed labs" are frequently raided by law enforcement agencies across the country as local drug entrepreneurs try to get in on the profits. Due to the ease of production and the availability of chemicals used to prepare methamphetamine, there continues to be a constant supply of this drug. Consequently, while the use of other stimulants such as cocaine and most types of amphetamines has been substantially declining, the use of methamphetamine has stayed relatively constant.

"speed"
an injectable methamphetamine used by drug addicts

Patterns of High-Dose Use. Amphetamines can be taken orally, intravenously, or by smoking. The intensity and duration of effects vary according to the mode of administration. The "speed freak" uses chronic, high doses of amphetamines intravenously. Another approach to administering amphetamines is the use of **"ice,"** which can cause effects as potent but perhaps more prolonged than intravenous doses. The cycle or pattern of use often starts with several days of repeated administrations, usually of "speed," gradually increasing in amount and frequency. This pattern of intense stimulant use is called a **"run."** Some users inject up to several thousand milligrams in a single day. Initially, the user may feel energetic, talkative, enthusiastic, happy, confident, and powerful and may initiate and complete highly ambitious tasks. He or she will be unable to sleep and will usually eat very little. His or her pupils will be dilated, mouth dry, and body temperature elevated (**hyperpyrexia**).

"ice"
a smokable form of methamphetamine

"run"
intense use of a stimulant, consisting of multiple administrations over a period of days

hyperpyrexia
elevated body temperature

After the first day or so, unpleasant symptoms become prominent as the dosage is increased. Symptoms commonly reported at this stage are teeth-grinding, disorganized patterns of thought and behavior, stereotypy, irritability, self-consciousness, suspiciousness, and fear. Hallucinations and delusions can occur that are similar to a paranoid psychosis and indistinguishable from schizophrenia. The person is likely to show aggressive and antisocial behavior for no apparent reason. Severe chest pains, abdominal discomfort that mimics appendicitis, and fainting from overdosage are sometimes reported. "Cocaine bugs" is one bizarre effect of high doses of potent stimulants such as amphetamines: The user experiences strange feelings, like insects crawling under the skin. The range of physical and mental symptoms from low to high doses is summarized in Table 9-2.

Toward the end of the run, which usually lasts from three to five days, the adverse symptoms dominate. When the drug is discontinued because the supply is exhausted or the symptoms become too unpleasant, prolonged sleep follows, sometimes lasting several days. On awakening, the person is lethargic, hungry, and often severely depressed. The amphetamine user may overcome these effects with another smoke of ice or injection of speed, initiating a new cycle. Barbiturates, benzodiazepines, and opiate narcotics are sometimes used to ease the "crash" or to terminate an unpleasant run (see Chapter 6).

Continued use of massive doses of amphetamine often leads to considerable weight loss, sores in the skin, nonhealing ulcers, liver disease, hypertensive disorders, cerebral hemorrhage (stroke), heart attack, kidney damage, and seizures. Experiments in which rhesus monkeys received chronic intravenous injections of methamphetamine resulted in direct injury to the small arteries and veins, causing them to rupture and produce severe brain damage. Oral methamphetamine given to monkeys and rats can result in cerebral vascular changes and kidney damage as serious as that caused by intravenous methamphetamine (Rumbaugh 1977). For some of these effects, it is impossible to tell whether they are caused by the drug, poor eating habits, or other factors associated with the lifestyle of people who inject methamphetamine.

Speed freaks are generally unpopular with the rest of the drug-taking community, especially "acid-heads" (addicts who use LSD) because of the aggressive, unpredictable behavior associated with use of potent stimulants. In general, drug abusers who take high doses of these agents, such as amphetamines or cocaine, are more likely to be involved in violent crimes than those who abuse other drugs. Consequently, these individuals may live together in "flash houses" totally occupied by chronic amphetamine or stimulant addicts. Heavy

TABLE 9-2   Summary of the effects of amphetamine on the body and mind

	Body	**Mind**
Low dose	Increased heartbeat	Decreased fatigue
	Increased blood pressure	Increased confidence
	Decreased appetite	Increased feeling of alertness
	Increased breathing rate	Restlessness, talkativeness
	Inability to sleep	Increased irritability
	Sweating	Fearfulness, apprehension
	Dry mouth	Distrust of people
	Muscle twitching	Behavioral stereotypy
	Convulsions	Hallucinations
	Fever	Psychosis
	Chest pain	
	Irregular heartbeat	
High dose	Death due to overdose	

users are generally unable to hold steady jobs because of their drug habits and often have a parasitic relationship with the rest of the illicit drug-using community.

Although claims have been made that amphetamines do not cause physical dependence, it is almost certain that the depression (sometimes suicidal), lethargy, and abnormal sleep patterns occurring after high chronic doses are part of withdrawal. This type of rebound effect is opposite to those of drugs that are CNS depressants (see Chapter 6). Withdrawal from depressants causes severe and toxic overstimulation, even to the point of convulsions.

Amphetamine Combinations. Amphetamines are frequently used in conjunction with a variety of other drugs, such as barbiturates, benzodiazepines, alcohol, and heroin. About one-half of all regular users of amphetamine diet pills are also heavy users of alcohol (Chambers and Griffey 1975). Amphetamines intensify, prolong, or otherwise alter the effects of LSD, and the two drugs are sometimes combined. The majority of speed users have also had experience with a variety of psychedelic and other drugs. In addition, persons dependent on opiate narcotics frequently use amphetamines or cocaine. (The combinations are called **"speedballs."**)

"speedball"

a combination of amphetamine or cocaine with an opioid narcotic, often heroin

---

"Designer" Amphetamines. "Designer" drugs, as defined by Gary Henderson, a pharmacologist at the University of California at Davis, are drugs of abuse that are:

1. synthesized from common chemicals but retain abuse potential
2. exempt (at least initially) from control by Drug Enforcement Administration (DEA) regulations because of their novel chemical structures

3. skillfully marketed on the "street" under attractive, often exotic names (Henderson 1988)

Because the basic amphetamine molecule can be easily synthesized and readily modified, new amphetaminelike drugs occasionally appear on the streets. Although these designer amphetamines tend to be thought of as new drugs when they first appear, in fact, most were originally synthesized from the 1940s to the 1960s by pharmaceutical companies trying to find new decongestant and anorexiant drugs to compete with the other amphetamines. Some of these compounds were found to be too toxic to be marketed but have been rediscovered by "street chemists" and are being sold to unsuspecting victims trying to experience a new sensation. See Table 9-3 for a list of these designer amphetamines.

The box on page 257 presents an excerpt from San Francisco street literature promoting a designer amphetamine called "U4Euh." This drug was developed in the early 1960s as an appetite suppressant but was never marketed because it was found to cause serious damage to the lungs as well as seizures. Despite the known danger from this drug, it was sold illegally from 1987 to 1990 on the streets of several states, causing a number of deaths (Bunker et al. 1990).

Other drugs of abuse that are chemically related to amphetamine include DOM (STP), MDA, and MDMA (or methylenedioxymethamphetamine, called "Ecstasy" or "Adam"). All of these drugs are currently classified as Schedule I agents. MDMA has maintained its popularity in the United States, regardless of its controlled status, especially on college campuses and with the affluent. It has been described as a "smooth amphetamine" by abusers and does not appear to result in the severe depression, or "crash," often associated with frequent high dosing of the more traditional amphetamines. MDMA and related designer amphetamines are somewhat unique from other amphetamines in that, besides causing excitation, they have prominent hallucinogenic effects, as well. These drugs have been characterized as combining the properties of amphetamine and LSD. The psy-

TABLE 9-3 "Designer" amphetamines

Amphetamine Derivative	Properties
Methylenedioxy**methamphetamine** (MDMA, "Ecstasy")	Stimulant and hallucinogen
Methylenedioxy**amphetamine** (MDA)	More powerful stimulant and less powerful hallucinogen than MDMA
4-Ethoxy-2, 5-dimethoxy**amphetamine**	Effects like MDA (stimulant and hallucinogen)
4-Methylaminorex	CNS stimulant like amphetamine
3-, 4-Methylenedioxy-N, N-dimethyl**amphetamine**	Mild MDMA
N, N-Dimethyl**amphetamine**	One-fifth potency of amphetamine
4-Thiomethyl-2, 5-dimethoxy**amphetamine**	Hallucinogen
Para-methoxymeth**amphetamine**	Weak stimulant

Source: Sapienza et al. 1989.

chedelic effects of MDMA are likely caused by release of the neurotransmitter serotonin. After using hallucinogenic amphetamines, the mind is often flooded with a variety of irrelevant and incoherent thoughts and exaggerated sensory experiences and is more receptive to suggestion. In fact, some psychiatrists have proposed that drugs like MDMA are useful tools in psychoanalysis and have unsuccessfully requested that the FDA approve them for such use (see Chapter 11).

METHYLPHENIDATE: A SPECIAL AMPHETAMINE
Methylphenidate (Ritalin) is related to the amphetamines but is a relatively mild central nervous system stimulant that has been used to alleviate depression. Research now casts doubt on its effectiveness for treating depression, but it is effective in treatment of narcolepsy. As explained previously, methylphenidate has also been found to aid in calming children suffering from attention deficit disorder and is currently the drug of choice for this purpose. The potency of methylphenidate lies between that of caffeine and amphetamine. It is not used much on the street because, compared to other amphetamines, it has less abuse potential. Even so, methylphenidate has been classified as a Schedule II drug, like the other prescribed amphetamines.

T h i n k   A b o u t   I t . . .

1. Why do you think the FDA continues to approve amphetamines for treatment of obesity despite the potential for serious side effects and the lack of evidence that such treatment has long-term benefits?
2. Why do you think "speed freaks" are generally unpopular with LSD users?
3. Why are federal agencies so concerned about the "street" use of "designer" amphetamines?
4. As an adviser to the DEA, you are asked to propose a program that would address the problem of "designer" amphetamines. What steps would you suggest to prevent the development and sales of these drugs in the "streets"?

COCAINE

Over the last 10 to 15 years, cocaine abuse has become the greatest drug concern in U.S. society. In the so-called "war against drugs," cocaine eradication is considered to be a top priority. The tremendous attention recently directed at cocaine reflects the fact that, from 1978 to 1987, the United States experienced the largest cocaine epidemic in history. Antisocial and criminal activities related to the effects of this potent stimulant have become highly visible and widely publicized.

As recently as the early 1980s, cocaine use was not believed to cause dependency because it did not cause gross withdrawal effects like alcohol and narcotics (Gawin 1991). In fact, a 1982 article in *Scientific American* stated that cocaine was "no more habit forming than potato chips" (Van Dyck and Byck 1982). This has clearly been proven false: Cocaine is highly addictive. In the United States alone, 1 to 3 million people are dependent on cocaine and require treatment to eliminate the dependence. Studies suggest that at least 25 million Americans have tried cocaine sometime during their life (Green 1985).

There is no better substance than cocaine to illustrate the "love-hate" relationship that people can have with drugs. Many lessons can be learned by understanding the impact of cocaine and the social struggles that have ensued as people have tried to determine their proper relationship with this substance.

THE HISTORY OF COCAINE USE   Cocaine has been used as a stimulant for thousands of years. Its history can be classified into three eras, based upon geographical, social, and therapeutic considerations. Studying each era will help us understand current attitudes about cocaine.

The First Cocaine Era. The first cocaine era was characterized by an almost harmonious use of this stimulant by South American Indians living in the regions of the Andean Mountains. One record dates cocaine use back to about 2500 B.C. in Peru, where coca leaves and even a chewed quid (wad) of coca were found near gravesites. Natives of Peru, Bolivia, and Colombia have long chewed the leaves of the *Erythroxylon coca* shrub, found in the high altitudes of the Andean Mountains. Leaves of this coca plant contain up to 1% of the alkaloid stimulant cocaine.

Without written accounts, historians can only speculate as to the role and significance of coca to these early people. The environments of these pre–Columbian Indians were barren and inhospitable. Yet with few resources, the highlanders constructed irrigation aqueducts, stone temples, buildings, an incredible network of roads, and a very demanding farming system on mountain terraces.

It is believed that the stimulant properties of cocaine played a major role in the advancement of this isolated civilization, providing its people the energy and motivation to realize such dramatic achievements while being able to endure tremendous hardships. This hypothesis is supported by artifacts including monolithic idols (500 B.C. to 200 A.D.) with distended cheeks of coca chewers and ancient bells cast in the shape of human faces, showing prominent bulges in the cheeks (Aldrich and Barker 1976). These and many other Indian

This sculpture from ancient Colombian civilization (ca. 1300 A.D.) represents the head of a coca chewer.
Source: Courtesy of the Fitz Hugh Ludlow Memorial Library, San Francisco. Photo by Jeremy Bigwood.

artifacts underscore the religious reverence with which coca was held by these people until the time of the Spanish Conquistadors.

The first written description of coca chewing in the New World was by explorer Amerigo Vespucci (1499):

> They were very brutish in appearance and behavior, and their cheeks bulged with the leaves of a certain green herb which they chewed like cattle, so that they could hardly speak. Each had around his neck two dried gourds, one full of that herb in their mouth, the other filled with a white flour like powdered chalk. . . . [This was lime, which was mixed with the coca to enhance its effects.] When I asked . . . why they carried these leaves in their mouth, which they did not eat, . . . they replied it prevents them from feeling hungry, and gives them great vigor and strength (Aldrich and Barker 1976, 3).

When the Spanish conqueror Francisco Pizarro invaded Peru in the sixteenth century, he found coca to be the center of the Incan social and religious systems. According to legend, the coca plant was divine. The Incan word *coca* simply meant "the tree," and this plant was viewed as the source of power for the expanding Incan empire.

It is ironic that there are no indications that these early South American civilizations had any significant social problems with cocaine, considering the difficulty it has caused contemporary civilizations. The ancient Indians appeared to be able to live harmoniously with this drug and even take advantage of its unique pharmacological properties to advance their societies. There are three possible explanations for their positive experiences with coca:

1. The Andean Indians maintained control of the use of cocaine. For the Incas, coca could only be used by the conquering aristocracy, chiefs, royalty, and other designated honorables (Aldrich and Barker 1976). This rigid control prevented indiscriminate use of coca, which almost certainly would have led to abuse.
2. These Indians used the unpurified form of cocaine in the coca plant, while later civilizations purified the drug and thus dramatically increased its potency and the likelihood of abuse.
3. Chewing the coca leaf was a slow, sustained form of administering the drug; therefore, the effect was much less potent than snorting, intravenous injection, or smoking—techniques most often used today.

The Spanish conquerors forbade the use of coca at first because they did not understand its significance to the Indians. It was outlawed and declared to be a form of satanic idolatry. However, in the mid-1500s, Spanish commercialism took precedence when the conquistadores learned that coca helped their Indian laborers to endure and work harder; coca was then used to pay the slaves. Taxes were also paid in coca leaves as were tithes to the Catholic Church (Aldrich and Barker 1976).

The Second Cocaine Era. A second major cocaine era began in the nineteenth century. During this period, scientific techniques were used to elucidate the pharmacology of cocaine and identify its dangerous effects. It was also during this era that the threat of cocaine to society—both its members and institutions—was first recognized.

Reports from highly regarded naturalists of the virtues of coca leaves stirred the imagination of Europeans. In 1859, Paolo Mantegazza, an eminent Italian physician, wrote the following account after chewing an ounce of fresh coca leaves: "Borne on the wings of two coca leaves, I flew about in the spaces of 77,438 worlds, each one more splendid than the others. . . . I prefer a life of ten years with coca to one of a hundred thousand without it" (Gay et al. 1973). At about this time, scientists in North America and Europe began experimenting with a purified, white, powdered extract made from the coca plant.

In the last half of the nineteenth century, Corsican chemist Angelo Mariani removed the active ingredients from the coca leaf and identified cocaine. This purified cocaine was added into cough drops and into a special Bordeaux wine called *Vin Mariani*. The Pope gave Mariani a medal in appreciation for the fine work he had done. The cocaine extract was publicized as a magical drug that would free the body from fatigue, lift the spirits, and cause a sense of well-being, and the cocaine-laced wine became widely endorsed throughout the civilized world. Included in a long list of luminaries who advocated this product for an array of ailments were the Czar and Czarist of Russia; the Prince and Princess of Wales; the Kings of Sweden, Norway, and Cambodia; commanders of the French and English armies; President McKinley of the United States; H. G. Wells; August Bartholdi (sculptor of the Statue of Liberty); and some 8,000 physicians.

The astounding success of this wine attracted imitators, all making outlandish claims. One of these cocaine tonics was a nonalcoholic beverage named Coca-Cola, which was made from African kola nuts and advertised as the "intellectual beverage and temperance drink." By 1906, Coca-Cola no longer contained detectable amounts of cocaine, but caffeine had been substituted in its place. Today, this popular soft drink contains approximately 46 mg of caffeine per 12-ounce serving (Aldrich and Barker 1976).

In 1884, the esteemed Sigmund Freud published his findings on cocaine in a report called "Uber Coca." Freud recommended this "magical drug" for an assortment of medical problems, including depression, hysteria, nervous exhaustion, digestive disorders, hypochondria, "all diseases which involve degenerations of tissue," and drug addiction.

In response to a request by Freud, a young Viennese physician, Carl Koller, studied the ability of cocaine to cause numbing effects. He discovered that it was an effective local anesthetic that could be applied to the surface of the eye and permit painless minor surgery to be conducted.

The "refreshing" element in Vin Mariani was coca extract. *Source:* Courtesy of the Drug Enforcement Administration, Washington, D.C.)

POPULAR
FRENCH TONIC WINE
*Fortifies and Refreshes Body & Brain
Restores Health and Vitality*

Sigmund Freud was an early advocate of cocaine, which he referred to as a "cure-all." *Source:* © Key-stone/The Image Works

This discovery of the first local anesthetic had tremendous worldwide impact. Orders for the new local anesthetic, cocaine, overwhelmed pharmaceutical companies.

Soon after the initial jubilation over the virtues of cocaine came the sober realization that, with its benefits, cocaine also had severe disadvantages. As more people used more cocaine, particularly in tonics and patent medicines, the CNS side effects and abuse liability became painfully evident. By the turn of the century, cocaine was being processed from the coca plant and purified routinely by drug companies. In its purified form, people began to snort or inject the popular powder, which increased both the effects and the dangers. The controversy over cocaine exploded before the American public in newspapers and magazines. In subtle ways, cocaine use was even integrated into the literature of the day. The creator of Sherlock

Holmes, Arthur Conan Doyle, introduced cocaine use by the detective Holmes into his mystery books:

> Sherlock Holmes took his bottle from the corner of the mantelpiece, and his hypodermic syringe from its neat morocco case. With his long, white, nervous fingers he adjusted the delicate needle and rolled back his left shirt cuff. For some little time, his eyes rested thoughtfully upon the sinewy forearm and wrist, all dotted and scarred with innumerable puncture marks. Finally, he thrust the sharp point home, pressed down the tiny piston, and sank back into the velvet-lined armchair with a long sigh of satisfaction.*

In the early 1900s, anticocaine sentiment arose that resembled the racist attitudes of the Spanish conquistadores several hundred years earlier. At this time, black laborers in the South began using cocaine to help them endure heavy labor and long working days. Plantation owners encouraged such use by issuing cocaine rations to their black laborers to help increase their productivity. As cocaine use spread north, into black, urban slums, white lawmakers became frightened of cocaine-driven blacks and pushed to outlaw the use of this stimulant. As medical and police reports of cocaine abuse and toxicities escalated, public opinion demanded that cocaine be banned. In 1914, the Harrison Act incorrectly classified both cocaine and coca as narcotic substances (cocaine is a stimulant) and outlawed their uncontrolled use.

Although prohibited in patent and nonprescription medicines, prescribed medicinal use of cocaine continued into the 1920s. Medicinal texts included descriptions of therapeutic uses for cocaine to treat fatigue, vomiting, seasickness, melancholia, and gastritis. However, prescriptions also included lengthy warnings about excessive cocaine use, "the most insidious of all drug habits" (Aldrich and Barker 1976).

Little of medical or social significance occurred for the next few decades. The medicinal use of cocaine was replaced mostly by the amphetamines during World War II because cocaine could not be supplied from South America. (Co-

---

*Doyle 1938. Published with the permission of the copyright owner of the Sir Arthur Conan Doyle literary estate.

caine is not easily synthesized, so even today, the supply of cocaine, both legal and illegal, continues to come from the Andean countries of South America.) During this period, cocaine continued to be employed for its local anesthetic action, was available on the "black market," and was used recreationally by musicians, entertainers, and the wealthy. Because of the lack of availability, the cost of cocaine was prohibitive for most would-be consumers. Cocaine abuse problems were of minor concern until the 1980s.

The Third Cocaine Era. With the 1980s came the third major era of cocaine use. Interestingly, this era started much like the second in that the public and even the medical community were naive and misinformed about the drug. Cocaine was viewed as a glamorous substance and portrayed by the media as the drug of celebrities. Its use by prominent actors, athletes, musicians, and other fast-paced elite was common knowledge. By 1982, over 20 million Americans had tried cocaine in one form or another, compared to only 5 million in 1974 (Green 1985).

The following is an example of a report from a Los Angeles television station, which was typical of the misleading information being released to the public:

> Cocaine may actually be no more harmful to your health than smoking cigarettes or drinking alcohol; at least that's according to a six-year study of cocaine use. It concludes that the drug is relatively safe and, if not taken in large amounts, it is not addictive. The study appears in the new issue of *Scientific American* (Byck 1987).

With such visibility, an association with prestige and glamour, and what amounted to an indirect endorsement by medical experts, the stage was set for another epidemic of cocaine use. Initially, the high cost of this imported substance limited access. However, with increased demand came increased supply, and prices tumbled from an unaffordable $100 a "fix" to an affordable $10. The epidemic began.

By the mid-1980s, cocaine permeated all elements of society. No group of people or part of

In the early 1980s, cocaine was a glamorous drug used by glamorous people. This cover of *Time* magazine (July 6, 1981) depicts the public's cavalier attitude about cocaine use during that time. *Source:* Copyright 1981 Time Warner Inc. Reprinted by permission.

the country was immune from its effects. Many tragic stories were told of athletes, entertainers (see the box on John Belushi), corporate executives, politicians, fathers and mothers, high school students, and even children using and abusing cocaine. It was no longer the drug of the laborer or even the rich and famous. It was everybody's drug and everybody's problem.

COCAINE PRODUCTION Because cocaine is derived from the coca plant, which is imported from Andean countries, America's problems with this drug have had a profound effect on several South American countries. With the dramatic rise in U.S. cocaine demand in the early 1980s, coca production in South America increased just as dramatically. The coca crop is by far the most profitable

For You to Consider...

John Belushi: A Victim of Cocaine

"Television, Film Comedian, John Belushi Dies at 33" was the headline of a front-page article in the *Washington Post* on March 6, 1982. Like other newspapers across the country that day, the *Post* reported that this popular comedian had died from a cocaine overdose in a Los Angeles hotel the day before.

John Belushi had attracted many fans with his antics on the television show *Saturday Night Live* and performances in various movies, including *Animal House*. He was known as an uninhibited comedian who was unable to appease his appetites. Belushi was described as a strenuous and tireless partier who loved alcohol and drugs. His uncontrolled craving for these substances eventually killed him. The official cause of death was "a drug overdose due to intravenous injections of cocaine and heroin."

Source: © Marcia Resnick 1981

Source: "Television, Film Comedian, John Belushi Dies at 33," *Washington Post*, 6 March 1982, 1A.

agricultural venture in these countries (see Table 9-4). In addition, this crop is easily cultivated, easily maintained (the coca plant is a perennial and remains productive for decades), and can be harvested several times a year (on average, two to four). The coca harvest has brought many jobs and some prosperity to these struggling economies. According to *National Geographic*, coca exports bring between $0.5 and $1 billion to Bolivia annually. In U.S. terms, this is a relatively small amount, but for a country such as Bolivia, this money can be the difference between life and death for many impoverished families (Boucher 1991).

In 1988, 2,500 hectares (2.47 acres/hectare) of coca were eliminated in Bolivia in response to U.S. pressures, but 6,800 hectares of new coca took their place. In spite of U.S. efforts, coca production increased by 25% in Peru in 1989. The profits, combined with the traditional view held by the people in Latin American countries that coca is a desirable substance, have made it difficult to persuade farmers to change crops just to satisfy the demanding *gringos*.

In conjunction with local governments (and likely after a few bribes, possibly in the form of foreign aid), the United States has attempted to destroy coca crops directly by burning, cutting, and spraying herbicides. One recent novel approach is the use of a species of caterpillar that eats coca leaves and defoliates the plants. The United States Department of Agriculture (USDA) has spent over $6 million investigating the possibility of rearing these insects and dropping them

TABLE 9-4 Comparison cost of South American crops (1987)

Crop	Earnings per Hectare*
Coca	$6,400
Coffee	$1,500
Bananas	$600
Corn	$300

Source: Based on Boucher 1991.
*Approximately 2.5 acres.

en masse on coca-growing regions (Boucher 1991). It remains to be seen how practical this approach will be.

Obviously, attempts like these to eliminate the livelihood of coca farmers does not improve the image of the United States in foreign lands. Such strategies have turned many peasants against the United States and their own governments, as well. One result has been public support for political opponents, such as members of ruthless cocaine cartels and leftist guerrillas.

COCAINE PROCESSING Cocaine is one of several active ingredients from the leaves of *Erythroxylon coca* (its primary source). The leaves are harvested two or three times a year and used to produce coca paste, which contains up to 80% cocaine. The paste is processed in clandestine labs to form a pure, white hydrochloride salt powder. Often, purified cocaine is **adulterated** (or "cut") before it is sold on the "streets" with substances such as powdered sugar, talc, arsenic, lidocaine, strychnine, and methamphetamine. Adverse responses to administering street cocaine are sometimes caused by the additives, not the cocaine itself. The resultant purity of the cut material ranges from 10% to 60%. This technique of diluting the cocaine is intended to make the drug go farther and increase the profit margin for the "pusher" (Farrar and Kearns 1989).

adulterated
contaminating substances are mixed in to dilute the drugs

Cocaine is often sold in the form of little pellets, called "rocks," or as flakes or powder. If it is in pellet form, it must be crushed before used. Such exotic names as Peruvian rock and Bolivian flake are bandied about to convince the buyer that the "stash" is high grade. Other street names used for cocaine include blow, snow, flake, leaf, C, coke, toot, white lady, girl, cadillac, nose candy, gold dust, and stardust.

Some users have become quite proficient in testing cocaine for impurities. The bleach, melting-point, and combustion methods are common and rapid tests. For instance, if a small sample of cocaine is dropped into bleach, various patterns and colors are produced according to the cutting materials and adulterants (contaminating substances). In addition, each impurity has its own melting point. If the sample is burned, pure cocaine leaves very little residue. Although the information gained from these tests can provide clues about the purity of the drug, only a thorough analysis with professional laboratory methods will be

For centuries, the coca plant harvest has been an important part of South American rural life. *Source:* Courtesy of the Drug Enforcement Administration, Washington, D.C.)

accurate. Another form of this drug commonly used illicitly is **"freebased"** cocaine. Kits and paraphernalia can be obtained to convert the hydrochloride form of cocaine into the freebase product (see Figure 9-1).

"freebasing"
the conversion of cocaine to an alkaline form so it can be smoked

---

CURRENT ATTITUDES AND PATTERNS OF ABUSE
Given contemporary medical advances, we have greater understanding of the effects of cocaine and the toxicities and dependence it produces. The reasons for abusing cocaine are better understood, as well. For example, it is clear that as many as 30% of chronic cocaine users are self-medicating mental problems such as depression or attention deficit disorders. Such knowledge helps in identifying and administering effective treatment. Hopefully, society will never again be fooled into thinking that cocaine abuse is an acceptable form of entertainment.

Attempts are being made to use this understanding (some recently acquired, some merely relearned) to educate people about the true nature of cocaine. This is likely behind recent trends of declining cocaine use. A dramatic reversal in patterns of cocaine abuse occurred from 1987 to 1990. In winter 1991, the Secretary of the Department of Health and Human Services, Louis Sullivan, reported that those actively using cocaine had declined from 2.9 million to 1.6 million (Moore 1991). Decreases occurred in virtually every age group evaluated (see Figure 9-2). Recent surveys by the U.S. Department of Health and Human Services reveal that, in general, cocaine use is not acceptable to persons in high school or college; these changes in attitude almost certainly contributed to the dramatic reduction in use. A reduction in total money spent on the purchase of illicit cocaine also decreased from $22.5 billion in 1989 to $17.5 billion in 1990 (Meddis 1991) (see Figure 9-3).

Further evidence of the dramatic decline in cocaine abuse was reported in June 1991 by Herbert Kleber, the Deputy Director for Demand Reduction, with the Office of National Drug Control Policy (Kleber 1991). He announced that casual cocaine use was down 40% in 1990 compared to

FIGURE 9-1 Paraphernalia used for "freebasing" cocaine. *Freebase* refers to the alkaloid form of "street" cocaine. To manufacture freebase cocaine, the powder is mixed with ether in a container such as a beaker or flask and heated to evaporate the cocaine base. If this procedure is done carelessly, the very flammable ether can explode.

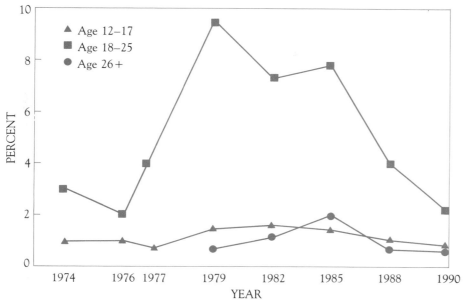

Note: Estimates are not available for the 26+ age group for 1974, 1976, and 1977.

FIGURE 9-2   Trends in Americans' cocaine use by age group, 1974–1990. These data represent the percentages of those surveyed who reported using cocaine 30 days before the survey. The information is from NIDA's 1990 National Household Survey, which had a sample of 9,259 Americans age 12 and over, living in the contiguous 48 states. *Source: NIDA Notes* 5 (Winter 1991): 22.

1987. Significant declines were observed in all ethnic groups, with the greatest change occurring in Caucasians and the least change in Hispanics. A decline of 25% occurred from 1989 to 1991 in the segment of the population involved in heavy cocaine abuse; this was reflected in a 50% reduction in cocaine-related calls to emergency hot-line services.

Cocaine is no longer viewed as a glamorous drug of the rich and the famous but as a potentially dangerous substance that can strike when least expected. This realization has changed attitudes and behaviors.

COCAINE ADMINISTRATION   Cocaine can be administered orally, inhaled into the nasal passages, injected intravenously, or smoked. The form of administration is important in determining the intensity of cocaine's effects, its abuse liability, and the likelihood of toxicity.

Oral administration of cocaine produces the least potent effects; most of the drug is destroyed in the gut or liver before it reaches the brain. The result is a slower onset of action with a milder, more sustained stimulation. This form is least likely to cause problems and dependence. South American Indians still take cocaine orally to increase their strength and for relief from fatigue. Administration is usually done by prolonged chewing of the coca leaf. Oral use of cocaine is not common in the United States.

"Snorting" involves inhaling cocaine hydrochloride powder into the nostrils, where deposits form on the lining of the nasal chambers and the drug passes through the mucosal tissues into the bloodstream. Substantial CNS stimulation occurs in several minutes, persists for 30 to 40 minutes, and then subsides. The effects occur faster and are shorter lasting and more intense than those achieved with oral administration, as more of the drug gets

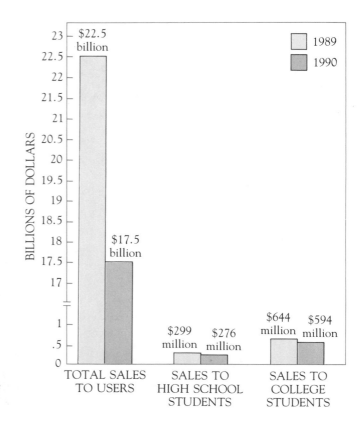

FIGURE 9-3 Money spent on cocaine in 1989 and 1990 by different age groups in the United States *Source:* Office of National Drug Control Policy

into the brain more quickly. Because concentrations of cocaine in the body are higher following snorting than after oral ingestion, the side effects are more severe. One of the most common consequences of snorting cocaine is rebound depression, or "crash," which is of little consequence after oral consumption. As a general rule, the intensity of the depression correlates with the intensity of the euphoria.

According to studies by the National Institute on Drug Abuse, about 10% to 15% of those who try intranasal (snorting) cocaine go on to heavier forms of dosing, such as intravenous (IV) administrations. Intravenous administration of cocaine is a relatively recent phenomenon because the hypodermic needle was not widely available until the late 1800s. This form of administration has contributed to many of the cocaine problems that appeared at the turn of the century. IV administration allows large amounts of cocaine to be introduced very rapidly into the body and causes severe side

effects and dependence. Within seconds after injection, cocaine users experience an incredible state of euphoria. The "high" is intense but short lived; within 15 to 20 minutes, the user experiences dysphoria and is heading for a "crash." In order to prevent these unpleasant rebound effects, cocaine is readministered every 10 to 30 minutes. Readministration continues as long as there is drug available.

This binge activity resembles that which occurs with the methamphetamine "run." When the cocaine supply is exhausted, the binge is over. Several days of abstinence may separate bingeing episodes; the average cocaine addict binges once to several times a week, with each binge lasting 4 to 24 hours. Cocaine addicts claim that all thoughts turn toward cocaine during binges; everything else loses significance. This pattern of intense use is how some people blow all of their money on cocaine.

"Freebasing" is a method of reducing impurities in cocaine and preparing the drug for smoking. It produces a type of cocaine that is more powerful than normal cocaine hydrochloride. In freebasing, the cocaine hydrochloride is treated with a liquid base such as sodium carbonate or ammonium hydroxide. The cocaine dissolves along with many of the impurities commonly found in it (such as amphetamines, lidocaine, sugars, and others). A solvent, such as petroleum or ethyl ether, is added to the liquid to extract the cocaine. The solvent containing the cocaine floats to the top and is drawn off with an eyedropper; it is placed in an evaporation dish to dry, and crystallized cocaine residue is then crushed into a fine powder, which can be smoked in a special glass pipe (see Figure 9-4).

The effects of smoked cocaine are as intense or greater than those achieved through intravenous administration. The onset is very rapid, the eu-

FIGURE 9-4 More "freebasing" paraphernalia. A water pipe is often used to smoke freebased cocaine, or "crack." Cocaine administered by smoking is very potent and fast acting; the effect lasts for 10 to 15 minutes, after which depression occurs. This is the most addicting form of cocaine. *Source:* W. R. Spence, *Cocaine, the Unseen Dangers* (Waco, TX: Health Edco, 1987). Reprinted with permission, HEALTH EDCO, © A Division of WRS Group, Inc.

phoria is dramatic, the depression is severe, the side effects are dangerous, and the chances of dependence are high. The reason for these intense reactions to inhaling cocaine into the lungs is that the drug passes rapidly through the lining of the lungs into the many blood vessels present; it is then carried almost directly to the brain.

Freebasing has become popular in the United States in the past few years due to the fear of diseases such as AIDS and hepatitis that are transmitted by sharing contaminated hypodermic needles. But freebasing involves other dangers. Because the volatile solvents required for freebasing are very explosive, careless people have been seriously burned or killed during processing (Siegel 1985). "Street" synonyms used for freebased cocaine include baseball, bumping, white tornado, world series, and snow toke.

"CRACK"   Between 1985 and 1986, a special type of freebased cocaine known as **"crack"** or "rock" appeared on the streets. By 1988, approximately 7% of the young adult population had tried crack. This cocaine product is inexpensive and can be smoked without the dangerous explosive solvents mentioned earlier in the discussion of freebasing. Crack is made by taking powdered cocaine hydrochloride and adding sodium bicarbonate (baking soda) and water. The paste that forms removes impurities as well as the hydrochloride from the cocaine. The substance is then dried into hard pieces called *rocks*, which may be as high as 90% pure cocaine. Other slang terms for "crack" include base, black rock, gravel, Roxanne, and space basing.

"crack"
already processed and inexpensive "freebased" cocaine, ready for smoking

---

Like freebased cocaine, crack is usually smoked in a glass water pipe. When the fumes are absorbed into the lungs, they act rapidly, reaching the brain within 8 to 10 seconds. An intense "rush" or "high" results, and later, a powerful state of depression, or "crash," occurs. The high may last only 3 to 5 minutes, and the depression may persist from 10 to 40 minutes or longer in some cases. As soon as crack is smoked, the nervous system is greatly stimulated by the release of dopamine, which seems to be involved in the rush. Cocaine prevents resupply of this neurotransmitter, which probably triggers the crash.

In New York and Los Angeles in 1986, 55% to 66% of all the cocaine arrests involved crack. This is probably the drug with the greatest potential for addiction. Crack is at least as addicting as freebased cocaine (Central Ohio Lung Association 1986).

Use of crack and other types of cocaine may be fatal (see the adjacent box). Death can result from a number of different reactions to the drug. Crack can cause high blood pressure that may lead to brain hemorrhage; it may block the heart's electrical system and cause the heart to stop; and it may cause lung failure associated with heart and blood vessel problems.

MAJOR EFFECTS OF COCAINE   As already mentioned, cocaine has profound effects on several vital systems in the body. With the assistance of modern technology, the mechanisms whereby cocaine alters body functions are better understood today. Such knowledge will hopefully lead to better treatment of cocaine dependence.

Most of the pharmacological effects of cocaine use stem from enhanced activity of the catecholamine (dopamine, noradrenalin, adrenaline) and serotonin transmitters. It is believed that the principal action of the drug is to block the reuptake of these substances following their release from neurons. The consequence of such action is to prolong the activity of these transmitter substances at their receptors and substantially increase their effects. The summation of cocaine's effects on these four transmitters causes CNS stimulation. The changes in the dopamine transmitter system result in an increase in locomotor activity, repetitive behavior (stereotypy), and elevation of mood. The increase of noradrenalin activity following cocaine

Let's Get the Facts

"Crack": A Nation's Emergency

How do emergency room nurses and doctors treat patients suspected of overdosing on "crack"? Judy Dixon, the associate head nurse in the emergency department at the University of Miami–Jackson Memorial Hospital, Miami, Florida, says, "You just treat the symptoms. . . . Patients often present with anxiety or paranoia, they may be combative, and at first we may not know exactly what's going on with them." These patients are so frightened that usually, if pressed, they admit that they have taken crack.

The first step in treatment, according to Dixon, is to begin intrave-

nous fluids; many of these patients are dehydrated because they have not taken any liquids for the several days they have been bingeing on crack. Next, the patients are controlled physically or even restrained if they come in showing violent or aggressive behavior. Usually, blood pressure and heartrate are elevated; drugs may be needed to correct these cardiovascular effects, although in some cases, just getting the patient to calm down will correct the problem. Crack increases body temperature. Patients who have overdosed can have temperatures as high as 106° to 108° F; according to Dixon, these patients usually die. Finally, crack users frequently have damaged their lungs

and may suffer difficulty in breathing, chest congestion, or even pneumonia.

It is impossible to predict how much crack will cause severe overdose reactions. Fatal doses can range from 20 mg to 500 mg. Oddly, some chronic users overdose while administering no more than their usual amount of crack. The wide variability in crack's effects makes this a particularly dangerous form of cocaine. As Dixon said, "Again, all we can do is treat the symptoms. . . . If they arrive in cardiac or respiratory arrest, if they come in and they're already seizing, then it's too late to help them."

Source: "Crack, the Nation's Emergency" 1990.

administration increases the effects of the sympathetic nervous system and alters cardiovascular activity (see below).

Central Nervous System. Because cocaine has stimulant properties, it has antidepressant effects, as well; however, its short-term action and abuse liability make cocaine unsatisfactory for the treatment of depression disorders. The effects of stimulation appear to increase both physical and mental performance while masking fatigue. High doses of cocaine cause euphoria (based on the form of administration) and enhance the sense of strength, energy, and performance. Because of these positive effects, cocaine has intense reinforcing properties, which encourage continual use and dependence. High chronic doses alter personality, frequently causing psychotic behavior that resembles paranoid schizophrenia. In many ways, the CNS effects of cocaine are like those of amphetamines although perhaps with a more rapid onset, a more intense high (this may be due partially to the manner in which the drugs are administered), and a shorter duration of action.

Beside dependence, other notable CNS toxicities that can be caused by cocaine use include headaches, temporary loss of consciousness, and seizures. Some of these effects may be due to the increased body temperature caused by this drug.

Cardiovascular System. Cocaine can cause pronounced changes in the cardiovascular system by enhancing the sympathetic nervous system, increasing the levels of adrenalin, and causing vasoconstriction. The initial effects of cocaine are to increase the heartrate and elevate blood pressure. At the same time that the heart is being stimulated and working harder, the vasoconstriction effects deprive the cardiac muscle of needed blood. Such a combination can cause severe heart arrhythmia (an irregular contraction pattern) or heart attack. This can happen to even the young user; a fatal cardiac response to cocaine has been reported in patients as young as 19 years of age (Weiss 1986). Other degenerative processes have also been described in the hearts and blood vessels of chronic cocaine users. In addition, the vasoconstrictive action of this sympathomimetic can cause damage

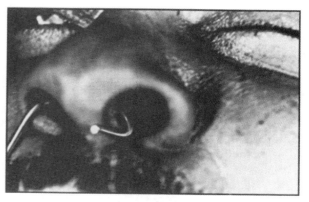

Nasal damage done by chronic "snorting" of cocaine. Because cocaine causes vasoconstriction, routine use can deprive the nasal tissues of blood and result in deterioration of the nasal cartilage (septum). In this patient, the septum is perforated, and a probe can be passed through. *Source:* From W. R. Spence, *Cocaine, the Unseen Dangers* [Waco, TX: Health Edco, 1987]. Reprinted with permission, HEALTH, EDCO, © A Division of WRS Group, Inc.

to other tissues, prompting a stroke, lung damage in those who smoke cocaine, destruction of nasal cartilage in those who snort the drug, and damage to the gastrointestinal tract.

Local Anesthetic Effect. Cocaine was the first local anesthetic used routinely in modern-day medicine. There is speculation that the ancient Andes Indians of South America used cocaine-filled saliva from chewing coca leaves as a local anesthetic for surgical procedures (Aldrich and Barker 1976). However, this assumption is contested by others (Byck 1987). Even so, cocaine is still a preferred local anesthetic for minor pharyngeal (back part of the mouth and upper-throat area) surgery due to its good vasoconstriction (reduces bleeding) and topical, local numbing effects. Although relatively safe when applied topically, significant amounts of cocaine can enter the bloodstream and, in sensitive people, cause CNS stimulation, toxic psychosis, or even on rare occasions, death.

COCAINE WITHDRAWAL There has been considerable debate as to whether cocaine withdrawal actually happens and if so, what it involves. With the most recent cocaine epidemic and the high incidence of intense, chronic use, it has become apparent that nervous systems do become tolerant to cocaine and that, during abstinence, withdrawal symptoms occur. In fact, because of CNS dependence, the use of cocaine is less likely to be stopped voluntarily than is the use of other illicit drugs (Schwartz et al. 1991). Certainly, if the withdrawal experience is adverse enough, a user will be encouraged to resume the cocaine habit.

The intensity of cocaine withdrawal is proportional to the duration and intensity of use. Short-term withdrawal symptoms include depression (chronic cocaine users are 60 times more likely to commit suicide than others), sleep abnormalities, craving for the drug, agitation, and anhedonia (inability to experience pleasure). The long-term withdrawal effects include a return to normal pleasures, accompanied by mood swings and occasional craving triggered by cues in the surroundings.

Of particular importance to treatment of the chronic cocaine user is that abstinence after binge-ing appears to follow three unique stages, each of which must be dealt with in a different manner if relapse is to be prevented. These phases are clas-sified as phase 1, or "crash" (occurs 9 hours to 4 days after drug use is stopped), phase 2, or withdrawal (1 to 10 weeks), and finally, phase 3, or extinction (indefinite). The basic features of these phases are outlined in Table 9-5 (Gawin 1991).

TREATMENT OF COCAINE DEPENDENCE   Treatment of cocaine dependence has improved as experience working with these patients has increased. Even so, success rates vary for different programs. From 30%–90% of the patients who persist in outpatient treatment programs are considered to be "successfully treated" (Gawin 1991). The problem with such assessments is that they do not take into account patients who drop out of programs. Also, there is no clear-cut criteria for qualifying success. For example, is success considered to be abstaining from cocaine for one year, two years, five years, or forever?

No one treatment technique has been found to be significantly superior to others; consequently, there is substantial disagreement as to what is the best strategy for treating cocaine dependency. Major differences in treatment approaches include (1) whether outpatient or inpa-

TABLE 9-5   Cocaine abstinence phases

	Phase		
	1—"Crash"	2—Withdrawal	3—Extinction
Time occurs after last binge	1 hour–4 days	1–10 weeks	Indefinite
Features	*Initial* Agitation, depression, anorexia, suicidal thoughts	*Initial* Mood swings, sleep returns, some craving, little anxiety	Normal pleasure, mood swings, occasional craving, cues trigger craving
	Middle Fatigue, no craving, insomnia	*Middle and Late* Anhedonia, anxiety, intense craving, obsessed with drug seeking	
	Late Extreme fatigue, no craving, exhaustion		

Source: Adapted from Gawin and Kleber 1988.

tient status is appropriate, (2) which drugs and what dosages should be used to treat patients during the various stages of abstinence, and (3) what length of time the patient should be isolated from cocaine-accessible environments. It is important to treat each individual patient according to his or her needs. Some factors that need to be considered when formulating a therapeutic approach include:

> Why did the patient begin using cocaine, and why has dependency occurred?
>
> What is the severity of abuse?
>
> How has the cocaine been administered?
>
> What is the psychiatric status of the patient; are there underlying or coexisting mental disorders, such as depression or attention deficit disorder?
>
> What other drugs are being abused with the cocaine?
>
> What is the patient's motivation for eliminating cocaine dependence?
>
> What sort of support system (family, friends, coworkers, etc.) will sustain the patient in the abstinence effort?

Outpatient versus Inpatient Approaches. The decision as to whether to treat a patient dependent on cocaine as an outpatient or inpatient depends on a number of issues. For example, inpatient techniques allow greater control than outpatient; thus, the environment can be better regulated, the training of the patient can be more closely supervised, and his or her responses to treatment can be more closely monitored. In con-

trast, the advantages of the outpatient approach are that supportive family and friends are better able to encourage the patient, the surroundings are more comfortable and natural, potential problems that might occur when the patient returns to a normal lifestyle are more likely to be identified, and treatment is less expensive.

Cocaine-dependent patients should be matched to the most appropriate strategy based on their personalities and the conditions of their addiction. For instance, a cocaine addict who lives in the ghettos, comes from a home with other drug-dependent family members, and has little support probably would do better in the tightly controlled inpatient environment. However, a highly motivated cocaine addict who comes from a supportive home and a neighborhood that is relatively free of drug problems would probably do better on an outpatient basis.

Therapeutic Drug Treatment. Several drugs have been used to treat cocaine abstinence. Table 9-6 lists those that have been used in each of the three principal phases of cocaine abstinence (Kosten 1989). Besides relieving acute problems of anxiety, agitation, and psychosis, drugs can also diminish cocaine craving; this is done by giving drugs such as bromocryptine or L-DOPA that stimulate the dopamine transmitter system. As mentioned, the pleasant aspects of cocaine likely relate to its ability to increase the activity of dopamine in the limbic system. When cocaine is no longer available, the dopamine system becomes less active, causing depression and anhedonia,

TABLE 9-6 Medications used in treatment of cocaine abstinence at various phases

Phase	Drug	Drug Group (Rationale)
1—Crash	Benzodiazepines	Depressants (relieve anxiety)
	Haloperidol	Antipsychotic (relieve psychosis)
2—Withdrawal	Bromocryptine, L-DOPA	Dopamine agonist (relieve craving)
3—Extinction	Desipramine, imipramine	Antidepressant (relieve depression and craving)

Source: Based on Kosten 1989.

which results in tremendous craving for cocaine. The intent of bromocriptine or L-DOPA is to stimulate dopamine activity and relieve the cravings. While this approach often works initially, it is temporary. In the third phase of cocaine abstinence, antidepressants such as desipramine are particularly effective in relieving the subtle mood problems and occasional cravings.

The beneficial effects of these drugs can persist for months but are not fully understood. There is some debate over their use. Drugs are, at best, only adjuncts in the treatment of cocaine dependence; they are never solutions by themselves. Successful resolution of cocaine abuse requires intensive counseling; strong support systems from family, friends, and coworkers; and a highly motivated patient.

Polydrug Use by Cocaine Abusers. Treatment of most cocaine abusers is complicated by the fact that they are polydrug (multiple-drug) users. It is unusual to find a person who only abuses cocaine. Greater than 50% of those dependent on cocaine are also dependent on alcohol. As with amphetamines, cocaine abusers also frequently coadminister narcotics, such as heroin (Kosten 1989). Cocaine users often take other depressants, such as benzodiazepines, to help reduce the severity of the crash after their cocaine binge. Codependence on cocaine and a CNS depressant can complicate treatment but must be considered.

COCAINE AND PREGNANCY   One of the tragic consequences of widespread cocaine abuse is that literally thousands of babies are born each year in the United States having been exposed to cocaine in the womb. The majority of these **cocaine babies** are abandoned by their mothers and become an incredible burden on the social welfare system.

---

cocaine babies
children exposed to cocaine while in the womb

Many of these children have been damaged physically and psychologically by cocaine. The damage done to the developing fetus may be due to vasoconstriction of placental vessels, thus interfering with oxygen and nutrient exchange between mother and child, or to cocaine-induced contraction of the uterine muscles, resulting in trauma or premature birth. Current data suggest that infants exposed to cocaine during pregnancy are at greater risk for congenital defects, premature delivery, and mortality (Cregler and Herbert 1986). Some cocaine-exposed babies experience strokes before birth or heart attacks after delivery. In addition, neurobehavioral problems can result from fetal exposure to cocaine; cocaine babies often do not cuddle or nurse well and suffer emotional problems throughout their lives (NIDA 1987).

Although the likelihood of these problems has not been well established, a recent report found that, of 56 women who used cocaine and no other drug of abuse during pregnancy, 21% had offspring with underdeveloped heads and 27% had children with other forms of growth retardation (Hadeed and Siegel 1989). Such observations suggest that, when a woman uses cocaine during pregnancy, there is about one chance out of four that permanent damage will be done to the child.

Think About It...

1. What have past experiences with cocaine taught us about this drug? How can we use that knowledge to deal with the current cocaine crisis and prevent future problems with this substance?
2. Why have anticocaine policies of the U.S. government had such an international impact?
3. Why do you believe that cocaine abuse has declined in the United States? Do you think we have finally learned to deal with this problem? Support your answer.
4. Hundreds of millions of dollars have been spent to develop drugs to treat cocaine addiction. What types of drugs would most likely be useful in treating cocaine dependence?
5. It has been proposed that the solution to the cocaine problem in the United States is to legalize its use. What are the advantages and disadvantages to this approach? Would you personally support such a policy? Why?

■ Pure cocaine hydrochloride is a white fluffy powder with a snowlike appearance.

■ Flower of the Erythroxylon coca shrub.

■ Leaf of the coca plant from which cocaine is derived.

■ The leaves from the coca plants, in fields such as this, are harvested two or three times a year and used to produce coca paste.

■ Baskets such as these are filled with coca leaves during the harvest.

■ Jungle maceration pit used for leaching coca leaves to extract the cocaine.

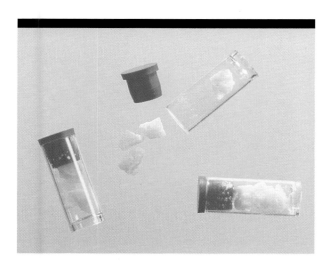

■ These vials contain crack, which is a form of cocaine that has been prepared for smoking.

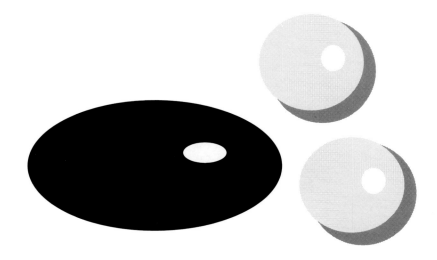

Marijuana can be grown almost anywhere in fields such as this.

In cultivated marijuana crops, male plants are removed in order to prevent pollination of female plants, such as this.

A manicured marijuana plant.

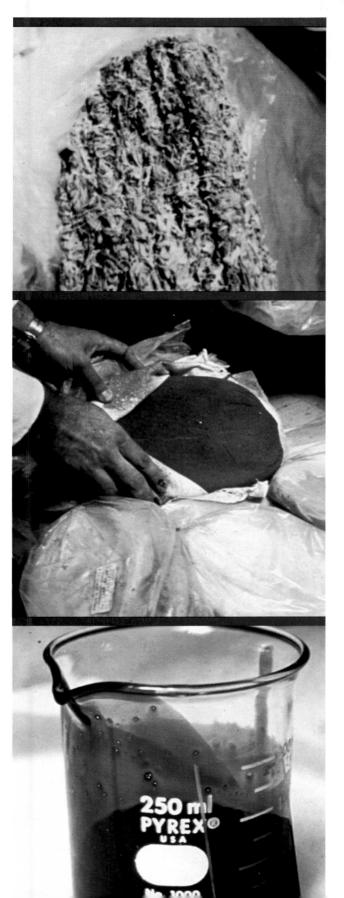

■ Thai sticks.

■ Hashish, such as that shown here, contains the purest form of resin and a THC content of 7%.

■ Oil extracted from hashish contains the hallucinogenic compound THC.

■ Mescaline is the most active hallucinogenic substance in a peyote cactus such as this.

■ Mushrooms similar to this *Psilocybe mexicana* have been used more than 2000 years by natives in Central America for their hallucinogenic properties.

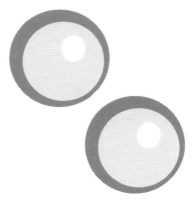

A unique form of administering LSD is achieved by adding the drug to absorbent paper such as these samples of blotter paper. The paper is divided into small decorated squares which are swallowed or chewed briefly. Each square represents a single dose.

PCP, such as that shown here, can cause a host of CNS actions such as hallucinations, stimulation, depression, anesthesia, and analgesia.

Illicit clandestine laboratories such as this are constructed by untrained drug chemists to crudely synthesize illicit drugs of abuse.

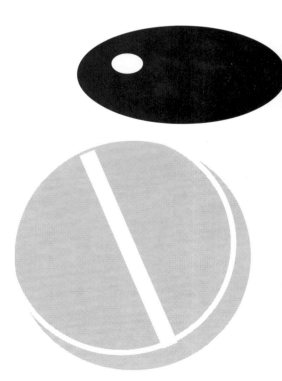

USE BY ATHLETES

A visible population frequently accused of abusing major stimulants are athletes, especially those at the professional and college levels. Barely a week passes that the media does not report of a football, basketball, or baseball player who has tested positive in a drug-screening evaluation or who has been suspended from competition due to stimulant abuse.

Sometimes the stories are more tragic. In 1986, reports of cocaine-related deaths of sports figures included basketball star Len Bias (see the box) and professional football player Don Rogers. Perhaps such tragedies helped to convince American youth of how lethal stimulant abuse can be. No one is immune from cocaine's dangers. Incidents such as these may be partially responsible for the subsequent decline in the incidence of stimulant abuse.

Amphetamines and cocaine are commonly abused to improve athletic skills. However, it is not clear if stimulants actually enhance athletic performance or only the athlete's *perception* of performance. A 1959 experiment is often cited by those that advocate the use of stimulants by athletes. This study examined the effects of amphetamine (at a dosage of 14 mg per 70 kg of body weight) on the performance of swimmers, runners, and weight throwers. It was found that the performance of highly trained athletes can be significantly improved in the majority of cases (about 75%) by the administration of amphetamine (Smith and Beecher 1959). A review of this area of research concluded:

> It is true that for a number of simple tasks there seemed to be little effect of amphetamine except in subjects whose performance had deteriorated as the result of prolonged work or sleep deprivation. On the other hand, data indicating a true enhancement are most convincing. Those on athletic performance obtained by Smith and Beecher . . . found that the effects of amphetamine were more apparent in rested than in fatigued subjects (Weiss 1969).

A more recent study has demonstrated that 48 to 96 mg doses of cocaine significantly improved the results on a digital performance behavioral test (measuring finger reactions) in rested subjects. Although the improvement (4%) was relatively small, it was suggested that such an effect could be significant in athletic competition (Higgins et al. 1990).

Amateur and professional athletic organizations are trying to control drug use among athletes. The Medical Commission of the International Olympic Organization conducted its first "doping" tests on a few athletes participating in the winter games at Grenoble in 1968. All tests proved negative. The Medical Commission defined *doping* as "the use of any drug with the aim of attaining an artificial and unfair increase of performance capacity in competition." Forbidden substances included psychomotor stimulant drugs, sympathomimetics (amphetamine, cocaine, and others),

---

For You to Consider...

Len Bias: A Story of Shattered Dreams and Cocaine Tragedy

Len Bias was an All-American basketball player from Maryland. In 1986, he was the number-one draft pick by the Boston Celtics of the National Basketball Association. Bias described the opportunity to play for the world champion Boston Celtics as a "dream within a dream." The day after signing the basketball contract, Bias made a lucrative deal to advertise Reebok athletic shoes.

The very next day, the dream was shattered. Len Bias was dead. The official statement by Maryland medical examiner John Smialek read: "Leonard Bias died of cocaine intoxication. This interrupted normal electrical control of his heartbeat, which resulted in sudden onset of seizures and cardiac arrest." The autopsy established that Bias had a strong, healthy heart and was not likely a chronic cocaine user. The cocaine levels in Bias' body were significant but not high enough to kill most people. Lester Grinspoon, a cocaine expert at Harvard Medical School, concluded that Bias was extremely sensitive to cocaine. Bias' death demonstrated to the nation that this drug can be unpredictable and deadly, even in society's healthiest and strongest members.

Source: Leo 1986.

central nervous system stimulants, narcotic analgesics (heroin and morphine), and anabolic steroids. In the 1968 summer games in Mexico, the Medical Commission broadened the list to include the use of any and all medication. As a result of this ruling, one of the American athletes in the 1972 summer Olympics forfeited his gold medal because ephedrine (an alkaloid similar in action to epinephrine), which he had been taking for asthma, was detected in his urine. A budget of $40 million was designated for doping control at the 1988 Olympics in Korea. In this competition, gold medal winner Ben Johnson from Canada, set a new world record for the 100-meter dash. A routine urine test revealed that he had used anabolic steroids, in violation of Olympic rules. Johnson lost his medal and millions of dollars in endorsements (which usually accompany such remarkable feats) and was suspended for two years from track-and-field competition. The abuse of performance-enhancing drugs continues to be a widespread problem in professional and amateur athletics.

MINOR STIMULANTS

Minor stimulants enjoy widespread use in the United States because of the mild lift in mood caused by their consumption. The most popular of these routinely consumed agents are methylxanthines (commonly called *xanthines*), such as caffeine, which are consumed in beverages made from plants and herbs. Other minor stimulants are contained in OTC medications, such as cold and hayfever products; these will be mentioned briefly in this chapter but discussed at greater length in Chapter 13. Because of their frequent use, some dependence on these drugs can occur; however, serious dysfunction due to dependence is infrequent. Consequently, abuse of xanthines such as caffeine is not viewed as a major health problem.

CAFFEINELIKE DRUGS (XANTHINES)

Caffeine is the world's most frequently used stimulant and perhaps its most popular drug. Beverages and foods containing caffeine are consumed by almost all adults and children living in the United States today (see Table 9-7). The most common sources of caffeine include coffee beans, tea plants, kola nuts, maté leaves, guaraná paste, and yoco bark.

Although the consumption of caffeine-containing drinks can be found throughout history, the active stimulant, caffeine, was discovered by German and French scientists in the early 1820s. Caffeine was described as a substance with alkaloid (basic) properties that was extracted from green

TABLE 9-7   Caffeine content of beverages and chocolate

Beverage	Caffeine Content (mg)	Amount
Brewed coffee	90–125	5 oz.
Instant coffee	14–93★	5 oz.
Decaffeinated coffee	1–6★	5 oz.
Tea	30–70	5 oz.
Cocoa	5 (but 100 of theobromine)	5 oz.
Coca-Cola	45	12 oz.
Pepsi-Cola	30	12 oz.
Chocolate bar	22	1 oz.

★The caffeine content of more than three dozen brands of instant coffee is given in the October 1979 issue of *Consumer Reports*.

coffee beans and referred to as *kaffebase* by Ferdinand Runge in 1820 (Gilbert 1984). In the course of the next 40 to 60 years, caffeine was identified in several other genera of plants, which were used as sources for common beverages. These included tea leaves (originally the drug was called *thein*); guaraná paste (originally the drug was called *guaranin*); Paraguay tea, or *maté*; and kola nuts. Certainly, the popularity of these beverages over the centuries attests to the fact that most consumers find the stimulant effects of this drug desirable.

THE CHEMICAL NATURE OF CAFFEINE   Caffeine belongs to a group of drugs that have similar chemical structures and are known as the xanthines. Besides caffeine, other xanthines are theobromine (means "divine leaf"), discovered in cacao beans (used to make chocolate) in 1842, and theophylline (means "divine food"), isolated from tea leaves in 1888. These three agents have unique pharmacological properties (which are discussed later), with caffeine being the most potent CNS stimulant.

BEVERAGES CONTAINING CAFFEINE   In order to understand the unique role that caffeine plays in U.S. society, it is useful to gain perspective on its most common sources: unfermented beverages. In 1986, caffeine consumption peaked, and Americans spent an estimated $5 billion on coffee imports, $200 million on tea, and about $1 billion on chocolate. Per capita consumption was an estimated 10.5 pounds of coffee, 1.2 pounds of tea, and 4.1 pounds of cocoa beans, all of which contain caffeine.

Coffee. Coffee is derived from the beans of several species of *coffea* plants. The *coffea arabica* plant grows as a shrub or small tree and is four to six meters high when growing wild. Coffee beans are primarily cultivated in South America and East Africa and constitute the major cash crop for exportation in several underdeveloped countries.

The name *coffee* was likely derived from the Arabian word *kahwa;* some argue it was named after the Ethiopian province *Kaffa,* the suggested site of origin for the coffee tree. From Ethiopia, the coffee tree was carried to Arabia and cultivated. The stimulant properties of coffee beans were known to original inhabitants of East Africa but were chewed dried rather than drunk. In Ethiopia, beans of the *coffea* plant were ground and mixed with animal fat and formed into small balls to be consumed on long trips as a food substitute. There is also evidence that natives of East Africa used the fruits of the coffee tree as money (Kihlman 1977).

Coffee became an important element in Arabian civilization. The Arabs first used beans in the preparation of beverages that became integrated into their social customs. An interesting Arabian legend is frequently recited concerning the so-called first use of coffee. It tells of Kaldi, the Arabian goatherder. It seems Kaldi noticed that his goats became lively and danced around after eating the berries of certain plants on the hillside. He followed the goats to the plants and ate some of the berries himself. He, too, danced and stayed up most of the night. A holy man was passing by and admired the alertness of the young man. Kaldi told him the secret of his energy. The monk ate the fruits and responded in a similar energetic fashion. Later, Mohammed instructed the holy man how to make a brew from the dried berries that would keep holy men awake to continue with their prayers. According to the legend, this brew soon became of great value to the Most Faithful in Mecca.

Coffee drinking was popular in Arabia and is mentioned in writings dating back to 900 A.D. In fact, in Mecca, coffee drinking was so popular that people spent more time in coffeehouses than in mosques, and the use of coffee was outlawed for a short period of time. However, illicit coffeehouses sprang up immediately, and the coffee prohibition was repealed.

Coffee probably reached Europe through Turkey and was likely used initially as a medicine. By the middle of the seventeenth century, there were coffeehouses in England and in France—places to relax and talk, to learn the news, to make business deals, and perhaps to hatch political plots. These coffeehouses turned into the famous "penny universities" of the early eighteenth century, where for a penny a cup, you could listen to some of the great literary and political figures of the day.

Coffee was originally consumed in the Americas by English colonists, although tea was initially

Gaucho offering maté from the saddle. *Source:* Peter Lang, The Photoworks/DDB

The Mayan Indians adopted the food and made a warm drink from the beans that they called *chocolatl* (meaning "warm drink"). The original chocolate drink was a very thick concoction that had to be eaten with a spoon. It was unsweetened because the Mayans apparently did not know about sugar cane.

Hernando Cortez, the conqueror of Mexico, took some chocolate cakes back to Spain with him in 1528, but the method of preparing them was kept a secret for nearly 100 years. It was not until 1828 that the Dutch worked out a process to remove much of the fat from the kernels to make a chocolate powder. This was the forerunner of the cocoa we know today. The cocoa fat, or *cocoa butter* as it is called, was later mixed with sugar and pressed into bars. In 1847, the first chocolate bars appeared on the market. By 1876, the Swiss had developed milk chocolate, which is so popular in today's confectionaries.

OTC DRUGS CONTAINING CAFFEINE Although the consumption of beverages is by far the most common source of xanthines, a number of popular OTC products contain significant quantities of caffeine. For example, many OTC analgesic products contain approximately 30 mg caffeine per tablet (Anacin, Excedrin). Higher doses of 100 mg to 200 mg per tablet are included in stay-awake (No-doz, Caffedrine) and "picker-upper" (Vivarin) products. The addition of caffeine to these OTC medications is highly controversial and has been criticized by clinicians who are unconvinced of caffeine's benefit in relieving pain or enhancing performance. Some critics believe that the presence of caffeine in these OTC medicines is nothing more than a psychological gimmick to entice customers because of the mild euphoric effects this stimulant provides.

PHYSIOLOGICAL EFFECTS OF THE XANTHINES The xanthines significantly influence several important body functions. Although the effects of these drugs are generally viewed as minor and short term, when used in high doses or by people who have severe medical problems, these drugs can be dangerous. The following sections summarize the responses of the major systems to xanthines.

CNS Effects. Of the common xanthines, caffeine has the most potent effect on the central nervous system, followed by theophylline; theobromine has relatively little influence. Because the CNS develops tolerance to the stimulant effects of caffeine, the brain's response to it depends on the frequency of consumption. In general, 100 mg to 200 mg of caffeine enhances a sense of alertness and diminishes the sense of fatigue. Caffeine is often used to block drowsiness and facilitate mental activity, such as when cramming for exams into the early hours of the morning. In addition, caffeine stimulates the formation of thoughts but does not improve intelligence. The effects of caffeine are most pronounced in unstimulated, drowsy consumers. The CNS effects of caffeine also diminish the sense of boredom. Thus, people engaged in dull, repetitive tasks, such as assembly-line workers, or nonstimulating and laborious exercises, such as listening to a boring professor, often consume caffeine beverages to help compensate for the tedium. Most certainly, xanthine drinks are popular because they cause these effects on brain activity.

Cardiovascular and Respiratory Effects. Drugs that stimulate the brain usually stimulate the cardiovascular system. The response of the heart and blood vessels to xanthines is dependent on dose and previous experience with these mild stimulants. With low doses (100 mg to 200 mg), heart activity can either increase, decrease, or do nothing; at higher doses (over 500 mg), the rate of contraction of the heart increases. Usually, xanthines cause minor vasoconstriction with a slight rise in blood pressure. The cerebral blood vessels are especially sensitive to the vasoconstrictive action of caffeine. In fact, cerebral vasoconstriction likely accounts for this drug's effectiveness in relieving some minor vascular headaches caused by vasodilation of the cerebral vessels.

Of the xanthines, theophylline has the greatest effect on the respiratory system, causing air passages to open and facilitating breathing. Because of this effect, tea has often been recommended to relieve breathing difficulties, and theophylline is frequently used to treat asthma-related respiratory problems.

Other Effects. The methylxanthines have noteworthy albeit mild effects on other systems in the body. They cause a minor increase in the secretion of digestive juices in the stomach, which can be significant to individuals suffering from stomach ailments such as ulcers. These drugs also increase urine formation (as any heavy tea drinker undoubtedly knows). In addition, consuming high doses of caffeine increases the metabolism of the body; the significance of this effect on body functions is not known.

Potentially Harmful Effects. Consuming occasional low doses of the xanthines (equivalent of 2 to 3 cups of coffee per day) is relatively safe (Rall 1990). However, frequent use of high doses causes psychological as well as physical problems called **caffeinism**. This condition is most often found in individuals who have developed CNS tolerance to caffeine and must substantially increase their consumption to regain the CNS stimulatory action; this includes about 10% of the adults who consume coffee (Greden 1979). Doses exceeding 1 gm (equivalent of 7 to 10 cups of coffee) per day can cause agitation, insomnia, tremors, visual flashes, and ringing (or buzzing) in the ears (tinnitus). Some researchers suggest consumption of large quantities of caffeine is associated with cancers of the bladder, ovaries, colon, and kidneys. These claims have not been reliably substantiated.

caffeinism
symptoms caused by taking high chronic doses of caffeine

One problem with many such studies is that they actually assess the effect of coffee consumption on cancers rather than caffeine. Because coffee contains so many different chemicals, it is impossible to determine specifically the effect of caffeine in such research (Bennett 1986). Other reports claim that caffeine promotes cyst formation in female breasts. Although these conclusions also have been challenged, many clinicians advise patients with mammillary cysts to avoid caffeine. Finally, there are reports that very high doses of caffeine given to pregnant laboratory animals can cause stillbirths or offspring with low birthweights or limb deformities. Even though studies of human mothers and their infants have not confirmed the teratogenic effects of caffeine seen in laboratory animals, mothers are usually advised to avoid or at least reduce caffeine use during pregnancy (Bennett 1986).

Based on the information available, there is no strong evidence that moderate use of caffeine leads to disease. There are, however, implications that people with existing severe medical problems—such as cardiovascular disease and possibly breast cysts—are at greater risk when consuming caffeine. Realistically, other elements—such as alcohol and fat consumption and smoking—are much more likely to cause serious health problems (Bennett 1986).

The severity of psychological dependence on caffeine is relatively minor compared to that of the potent stimulants; thus, the abuse potential of caffeine is also much less and dependence is less likely to interfere with normal daily routines. However, caffeine is so readily available and socially accepted (almost expected) that the high quantity of consumption has produced many modestly dependent users (Holtzman 1990). The degree of physical dependence on caffeine is related to dose but considerably less than that with the major stimulants. However, a recent study reported that caffeine doses as low as 100 mg/day can cause significant withdrawal effects, such as headaches, fatigue, mood changes, muscle pain, flulike symptoms, and nausea in some people (Holtzman 1990). With typical caffeine withdrawal, these effects can persist for several days (see Table 9-10). While these withdrawal symptoms are unpleasant, they usually are not severe enough to prevent most people from giving up their coffee or cola drinks, if desired.

TABLE 9-10   Caffeine withdrawal syndrome

Symptom	Duration
Headache	Several days to 1 week
Decreased alertness	2 days
Decreased vigor	2 days
Fatigue and lethargy	2 days
Nervousness	2 days

Source: Based on Holtzman 1990.

OTC SYMPATHOMIMETICS

Although often overlooked, the sympathomimetic decongestant drugs included in OTC products such as cold, allergy, and diet-aid medications have stimulant properties like those of caffeine. For most people, the CNS impact of these drugs is minor, but for those people who are very sensitive to these drugs, they can cause jitters and interfere with

TABLE 9-11   Common OTC sympathomimetics

Drug	OTC Product (form)
Phenylpropanolamine	Decongestant, diet aid (oral)
Ephedrine	Decongestant (oral, nasal spray or drops)
Levodesoxyephedrine	Decongestant (nasal inhalant)
Naphazoline	Decongestant (nasal spray or drops)
Oxymetazoline	Decongestant (nasal spray or drops)
Phenylephrine	Decongestant (oral, nasal spray or drops, eye drops)
Pseudoephedrine	Decongestant (oral)
Tetrahydozoline	Decongestant (eye drops)
Xylometazoline	Decongestant (nasal spray or drops)

Source: Based on Bryant and Lombardi 1990.

sleep. For such individuals, OTC products containing the sympathomimetics should be avoided prior to bedtime.

The common OTC sympathomimetics are shown in Table 9-11 and include ephedrine and phenylpropanolamine. In the past, these two OTC agents were packaged to look like amphetamine (called "look-alike drugs") and legally sold on the "streets," usually to children or high school–aged adolescents. Although much less potent than amphetamines, even these minor stimulants can be abused and have caused several deaths. Attempts to regulate look-alike drugs resulted in passage of the federal and state Imitation Controlled Substances Acts. These statutes prohibit the packaging of OTC sympathomimetics to appear like amphetamines.

These laws have not resolved the problem. New products called "act-alikes" have been created. While the packaging of the act-alikes does not resemble that of amphetamine capsules, these minor stimulants are promoted on the streets as "harmless speed" and "OTC uppers." It is likely that use of such products will lead to the abuse of more potent stimulants (Brown 1991).

Think About It . . .

1. How do you think reports in the media about the use of stimulants by athletes affect the popularity of these drugs?
2. Should athletes be tested for stimulant use? Defend your answer.
3. Do you believe that dependence on caffeine can lead to dependence on major stimulants? Explain.
4. Should the FDA restrict the use of nonprescription stimulants like they do the major stimulants?

K E Y   T E R M S

"uppers"
narcolepsy
anorexiants
behavioral stereotypy
hyperkinesis

"speed"
"ice"
"run"
hyperpyrexia
"speedball"

adulterated
"freebasing"
"crack"
cocaine babies
caffeinism

S U M M A R Y

1. Amphetamines were originally developed as decongestants and used in nasal inhalers. These potent stimulants enhance the activity of dopamine, norepinephrine, epinephrine, and serotonin by (a) increasing their release, (b) blocking their reuptake into neurons, and (c) blocking monoamine oxidase, a principal metabolizing enzyme for the catecholamines and serotonin.

2. Some amphetamines have been approved by the FDA (a) as diet aids to treat obesity, (b) to treat narcolepsy, and (c) to treat hyperkinetic problems (i.e., attention deficit disorder) in children.

3. In therapeutic doses, amphetamines can cause agitation, anxiety, and panic due to their effects on the brain; in addition, they can cause an irregular heartbeat, increased blood pressure, and heart attack or stroke. Intense, high-dose abuse of amphetamines can cause severe psychotic behavior, stereotypy, and seizures as well as the severe cardiovascular side effects mentioned above.

4. Most medical experts feel amphetamines have limited legitimate use. Because of their high abuse potential, only supervised use of low doses for treatment of narcolepsy and hyperkinetic disorders are viewed as acceptable by most clinicians. Tolerance and dependence develop quickly when these agents are used as diet aids.

5. "Speed" refers to the use of intravenous methamphetamine; this is a very addicting and dangerous form of amphetamine abuse. "Ice" is smoked methamphetamine; it is a more

potent and longer-acting form of amphetamine. A "run" is a pattern of intense, multiple dosing over a period of days that can cause serious neurological, psychiatric, and cardiovascular consequences.

6. "Designer" amphetamines are chemical modifications of original amphetamines. In spite of the chemical changes, designer drugs retain abuse potential and are often marketed on the "streets" using exotic and alluring names. Many of these so-called new amphetamines actually were developed years ago as decongestants or diet aids but were too dangerous to be marketed.

7. Cocaine was used by societies as early as 2500 B.C. The first cocaine era was characterized by harmonious use of the coca plant by ancient South American Indians living in the regions of the Andean Mountains. This era continued until the 1800s, when coca was introduced into Europe and North America. During this period, cocaine was extracted and purified from the coca plant, and scientific study of cocaine began. When the virtues and problems of cocaine became apparent during this era, its use was restricted in the United States by the Harrison Act. The final era began around 1980 and marks the greatest cocaine epidemic of all time. Use of cocaine became widespread, and the devastating effects of its uncontrolled use were abundant. "War" was declared against this drug, and its mechanism of action was identified. Cocaine use has reportedly declined in the late 1980s and early 1990s.

8. Coca crops are critical to the economies of several

impoverished Latin American countries. As part of the United States' attempt to resolve the cocaine problem, it has pressured these countries to destroy their coca crops, which means economic hardship for some. This policy has had political repercussions and resulted in some social unrest overseas.

9. In the late 1970s and early 1980s, cocaine was commonly viewed by the American public as a relatively safe drug with glamorous connotations. Medical experts did little to change this public opinion; some even claimed that cocaine had little abuse potential and was of little social concern. By the mid-1980s, it was apparent that cocaine was a very addicting drug with dangerous side effects. About this time, governmental and social agencies declared "war" on cocaine and tried to prevent distribution, discourage use, and educate people about its potential dangers. By 1988, use patterns had reversed and cocaine abuse was declining.

10. The CNS and cardiovascular effects of both amphetamines and cocaine are similar. However, cocaine's effects tend to occur more rapidly, be more intense, and wear off more quickly than those of amphetamines. The differences or similarities between the two depend on the user's previous experience with the drugs and the form of administration.

11. The intensity of the cocaine effect and the likelihood of dependence occurring are directly related to the means of administration. Going from least to most intense effect, the modes of cocaine administration include chewing,

"snorting," injecting, and smoking (or "freebasing").

12. "Crack" is cocaine that has been converted into its "freebase" form and is intended for smoking. Because inhaled cocaine rapidly enters the bloodstream and gets into the brain, crack has potent CNS effects, causes an intense "high," and is very addicting. Due to its potency, crack is also very dangerous, and the likelihood of severe side effects are significant.

13. Cocaine withdrawal goes through three main stages: (a) the "crash," the initial abstinence phase consisting of depression, agitation, suicidal thoughts, and fatigue; (b) withdrawal, including mood swings, craving, anhedonia, and obsession with drug seeking; and (c) extinction, when normal pleasure returns, cueing trigger craving and mood swings.

14. Treatment of cocaine dependence is highly individualistic and has variable success. The principal strategies include both inpatient and outpatient programs. Drug therapy often is used; this includes administration of dopamine agonists such as bromocryptine and L-DOPA to relieve short-term cocaine craving and use of antidepressants such as desipramine to alleviate mood problems and long-term craving. Psychological counseling and support therapy are essential components of treatment throughout.

15. Caffeine is the most frequently consumed stimulant in the world. It is classified as a xanthine (methylxanthine) and is found in a number of beverages, such as coffee, tea, guaraná, maté, and some soft drinks. It is also included in some OTC medicines such as analgesics and "stay-awake" products.

16. The principal physiological effects of caffeine include minor to moderate CNS stimulation, which causes an increased sense of energy and alertness, an improved sense of well-being, and a diminished sense of fatigue. These effects are most pronounced in users who are tired and drowsy; in such people, performance of mental and physical tasks can be improved. Caffeine causes minor stimulation of cardiovascular activity, kidney function (i.e., diuretic), and gastric secretion.

17. Dependence on caffeine can occur in persons who regularly consume large doses. Withdrawal can cause headaches, agitation, and tremors. Although unpleasant, withdrawal from caffeine dependence is much less severe than that from amphetamine and cocaine dependence. Consequently, persons dependent on caffeine are usually able to abandon their habits with little or no assistance; unassisted treatment of amphetamine or cocaine dependence is very difficult and frequently unsuccessful.

R E F E R E N C E S

Aldrich, M., and R. Barker. *Cocaine: Chemical, Biological, Social and Treatment Aspects,* edited by S. J. Mule. Cleveland, OH: CRC, 1976.

Appelt, G. "Weight Control Products." In *Handbook of Nonprescription Drugs,* 9th ed. Washington, D.C.: American Pharmaceutical Association, 1990.

Bennett, W., ed. "Coffee: Grounds for Concern." *Harvard Medical School Health Letter* 11 (October 1986): 1–4.

Boucher, D. "Cocaine and the Coca Plant." *BioScience* 41 (1991): 72–76.

Brown, M. *Guide to Fight Substance Abuse.* Nashville, TN: International Broadcast Services, 1991.

Bryant, B., and T. Lombardi. "Cold and Allergy Products." In *Handbook of Nonprescription Drugs,* 9th ed. Washington, D.C.: American Pharmaceutical Association, 1990.

Bunker, C., M. Johnson, J. Gibb, L. Bush, and G. R. Hanson. "Neurochemical Effects of an Acute Treatment with 4-Methlaminorex: A New Stimulant of Abuse." *European Journal of Pharmacology* 180 (1990): 103–111.

Byck, R. "Cocaine Use and Research: Three Histories." In *Cocaine: Chemical and Behavioral Aspects.* London: Oxford University Press, 1987.

Central Ohio Lung Association. *Crack—The Facts.* Columbus, OH: Central Ohio Lung Association, 1986.

Chambers, C. D., and M. S. Griffey. "Use of Legal Substances within the General Population: The Sex and Age Variables." *Addictive Diseases* 2 (1975): 7–19.

"Crack, the Nation's Emergency." *American Journal of Nursing* (April 1990): 42–43.

Cregler, L., and M. Herbert. "Special Report: Medical Complications of Cocaine Abuse." *New England Journal of Medicine* 315 (1986): 1495–1500.

Doyle, Arthur Conan. "The Sign of Four." In *The Complete Sherlock Holmes.* Garden City, N.Y., 1938.

Ellinwood E. H., Jr. "The Epidemiology of Stimulant Abuse." In *Drug Use—Epidemiological and Sociological Approaches,* edited by E. Josephson and E. E. Calls. Washington, D.C.: Hemisphere, 1974.

Farrar, H., and G. Kearns. "Cocaine: Clinical Pharmacology and Toxicology." *Journal of Pediatrics* 115 (1989): 665–675.

Gawin, F. "Cocaine Addiction: Psychology and Neurophysiology." *Science* 251 (1991): 1580–1586.

Gawin, F., and H. Kleber. "Evolving Conceptualizations of Cocaine Dependence." *Yale Journal of Biology and Medicine* 61 (1988): 123–136.

Gay, C. R., C. Sheppar, D. Inaba, and J. Newmeyer. "Cocaine in Perspective: 'Gift from the Sun God' to 'The Rich Man's Drug.'" *Drug Forum* 2 (1973): 409.

Gilbert, R. "Caffeine Consumption." In *The Methylxanthine Beverages and Foods: Chemistry, Consumption, and Health Effects.* New York: Alan R. Liss, 1984.

Greden, J. "Coffee, Tea and You." *The Sciences,* 1979, 6–11.

Green, E. "Cocaine, Glamorous Status Symbol of the 'Jet Set,' is Fast Becoming Many Students' Drug of Choice." *Chronicle of Higher Education,* 13 November 1985, 1, 34.

Grinspoon, L., and J. Bakalar. "The Amphetamines: Medical Use and Health Hazards." In *Amphetamines Use, Misuse and Abuse,* edited by D. Smith. Boston, MA: G. K. Hall, 1978.

Hadeed, A., and S. Siegel. "Maternal Cocaine Use during Pregnancy: Effect on the Newborn Infant." *Pediatrics* 84 (1989): 205–210.

Henderson, G. "Designer Drugs: Past History and Future Prospects." *Journal of Forensic Sciences* 33 (1988): 569–575.

Higgins, S., W. Bickel, J. Hughs, M. Lynn, M. Capeless, and J. Fenwick. "Effects of Intranasal Cocaine on Learning, Performance and Physiology." *Psychopharmacology* 102 (1990): 451–458.

Holtzman, S. "Caffeine as a Model Drug of Abuse." *Trends in Pharmacological Sciences* 11 (1990): 355–356.

Jaffe, J., and M. Martin. "Opioid Analgesics and Antagonists." In *The Pharmacological Basis of Therapeutics,* 8th ed., edited by A. Gilman, T. Rall, A. Nies, and P. Taylor. New York: Pergamon, 1990.

Kihlman, B. *Caffeine and Chromosomes.* Amsterdam, Netherlands: Elsevier, 1977.

Kleber, H. Keynote speaker, Committee on Problems of Drug Dependence, Fifty-Third Annual Scientific Meeting, June 16–20 1991, Palm Beach, FL.

Kosten, T. "Pharmacotherapeutic Interventions for Cocaine Abuse Matching Patients to Treatments." *Journal of Nervous and Mental Disease* 177 (1989): 379–390.

Leo, J. "How Cocaine Killed Leonard Bias." *Time,* 7 July 1986, 52.

Meddis, S. "USA's Illegal Drug Bill: $40 Billion." *USA Today,* 20 June 1990, 1A.

Moore, B. "NIDA Surveys Continuing Drop in Drug Use." *ADAMHA News* 4 (March-April 1991).

NIDA. *Cocaine/Crack. The Big Lie.* Publication number (ADM) 87-1427. Washington, D.C.: U.S. Department of Health and Human Services, 1987.

NIDA Notes (Spring 1991).

Rall T. "Drugs Used in the Treatment of Asthma." In *The Pharmacological Basis of Therapeutics,* 8th ed., edited by A. Gillman, T. Rall, A. Nies, and P. Taylor. New York: Pergamon, 1990.

Rumbaugh, C. L. "Small Vessel Cerebral Vascular Changes Following Chronic Amphetamine Intoxication." In *Cocaine and Other Stimulants,* edited by E. H. Ellinwood, Jr., and M. M. Kilbey. New York: Plenum, 1977.

Sapienza, F., H. McClain, M. Klein, and J. Tolliver. "New Controlled Substance Analogues of Interest to DEA." Abstract, Annual Meeting of the Committee on Problems of Drug Dependence. Washington, D.C.: Drug Enforcement Administration, Drug Control Section, 1989.

Schmidt, C., J. Ritter, P. Sonsalla, G. R. Hanson, and J. W. Gibb. "Role of Dopamine in the Neurotoxic Effects of Methamphetamine." *Journal of Pharmacology and Experimental Therapeutics* 233 (1985): 539–544.

Schwartz, R., M. Lyenberg, and N. Hoffman. "Crack Use by American Middle-Class Adolescent Polydrug Users." *The Journal of Pediatrics* 118 (1991): 150–155.

Siegel, R. K. "Treatment of Cocaine Abuse." *Journal of Psychoactive Drugs* 17(1985): 52.

Smith, G. M., and H. K. Beecher. "Amphetamine Sulfate and Athletic Performance. I. Objective Effects." *Journal of the*

American Medical Association 170 (1959): 542–557.

Sulser, F., and E. Sanders-Bush. "Effects of Drugs on Amines in the CNS." *Annual Review of Pharmacology* 11 (1971): 209–230.

Van Dyck, C., and R. Byck. "Cocaine." *Scientific American* 246 (1982): 128–141.

Van Dyke, C., P. Jatlow, J. Ungerer, P. G. Barash, and R. Byck. "Oral Cocaine: Plasma Concentrations and Central Effects. *Science* 200 (1978): 201–213.

Weiner, N. "Norepinephrine, Epinephrine, and the Sympathomimetic Amines." In *The Pharmacological Basis of Therapeutics,* 6th ed., edited by A. G. Gilman, L. S. Goodman, and A. Gilman. New York: Macmillan, 1980.

Weiss, B. "Enhancement of Performance by Amphetamine-Like Drugs." In *Abuse of Central Stimulants,* edited by F. Sjozvist and M. Tottie. New York: Raven, 1969.

Weiss, R. "Recurrent Myocardial Infarction Caused by Cocaine Abuse." *American Heart Journal* 111 (1986): 793.

Tobacco

CHAPTER OUTLINE

LEARNING OBJECTIVES

On completing this chapter, you will be able to:

1. Assess how addictive nicotine is.
2. Discuss the value of tobacco as a cash crop in the United States.
3. Explain how the quality of leaf tobacco has changed since the mid-1950s.
4. Name and briefly describe the two stages involved in processing tobacco.
5. Summarize the general history of tobacco use.

6. Report what the latest findings show regarding cigarette consumption in the United States.
7. Report what national health surveys reveal about tobacco use with regard to gender, education, and race and ethnicity.
8. Describe the relationship between "gateway" drugs and the use of licit and illicit drugs.
9. Define the following: *smokeless tobacco products; sidestream smoke;* and *second-hand smoke.*

10. Explain the effect of nicotine on the nervous system.
11. Report what research shows about health issues and the tar and nicotine contents of cigarettes.
12. Describe the two opposing groups that have come into existence as a result of the negative publicity regarding cigarette smoking.
13. List the three main types of behavioral treatments for the cessation of smoking.

Source: Fredrik D. Bodin/Stock, Boston

DID YOU KNOW THAT . . .

- Nicotine has been used as a lethal insecticide.
- Tobacco is the sixth largest cash crop in the United States.
- In 1988, the former U.S. Surgeon General publicly proclaimed that nicotine was as addictive as cocaine and heroin (Tolchin 1988).
- Over 4,000 substances have been identified in tobacco smoke, including several carcinogens.
- In the 1600s Turkey, Russia, and China all imposed the death penalty for smoking.
- Cigarette smoking has declined in the United States but risen in Third World countries.
- Daily cigarette smokers, as opposed to nonsmokers, are 10 times more likely to engage in the use of controlled substances, such as marijuana and cocaine.
- Uninhaled smoke from a lit cigarette has higher concentrations of carbon monoxide, nicotine, and ammonia than inhaled (mainstream) smoke.
- The American Cancer Society estimates that, on average, 90% of lung cancer deaths are caused by smoking.
- Health damage from smoking is estimated to cost Americans over $27 billion a year in medical care, absenteeism, decreased work productivity, and accidents.
- Nicotine kills over 300,000 Americans per year. This drug has the highest mortality rate, claiming more deaths than all other drugs combined.

Because tobacco has long been a legally authorized drug for adults—one that has been widely used and tolerated—many people are surprised to learn how harmful its effects can be. Many tobacco users are reluctant to admit how addictive the drug is, even though millions of Americans have become not only physically addicted but socially habituated and economically dependent on the continued use of this dangerous substance. Legal and social acceptance has made it easier for users to find acceptable reasons not to quit. Such acceptance has also made it harder to see how tobacco functions as a "gateway" drug, leading to other substance use. Because tobacco use is such an ingrained part of U.S. society, almost everyone will find some surprising information in a survey of the effects of tobacco.

This chapter begins with background information on the history of tobacco use. The properties of nicotine and its effects on the body are examined next, considering smoking as well as other forms of tobacco consumption. A review of methods of how to stop smoking includes discussion of behavioral elements, including the motivation to smoke. This leads into the question: Who smokes and why? The chapter ends with an analysis of social issues, such as smokers' rights in an increasingly vigilant society.

THE HISTORY OF TOBACCO USE

Tobacco was one of the New World's contributions to the rest of humanity. The word *tobacco* may have come from *tabacco*, which was a two-pronged tube used by the natives of Central America to take snuff. Columbus reported receiving tobacco leaves from the natives of San Salvador in 1492. However, the natives had been smoking the leaves for many centuries before Columbus arrived. Practically all the natives from Paraguay to Quebec used tobacco. The Mayas regarded tobacco smoke as divine incense that would bring rain in the dry season. The oldest known representation of a smoker is a stone carving from a Mayan temple, showing a priest puffing on a ceremonial pipe. The Aztecs used tobacco in folk medicine and religious ritual.

Indeed, Native Americans used tobacco in every manner known: smoked as cigars and cigarettes (wrapped in corn husks) and in pipes; as a syrup to be swallowed or applied to the gums; chewed and snuffed; and administered rectally as a ceremonial enema (Schultes 1978).

POPULARITY IN THE WESTERN WORLD

Tobacco reached Europe and was at first merely a curiosity, but its use spread rapidly. Europeans had no name for the process of inhaling smoke, so they called this "drinking" smoke. Perhaps the first European to inhale tobacco smoke was Rodrig de Jerez, a member of Columbus' crew. He had seen people smoking in Cuba and brought the habit to Portugal. When he smoked in Portugal, his friends, seeing the smoke coming from his mouth, believed he was possessed by the devil! He was placed in jail for several years (Heimann 1960).

In 1559, the French ambassador to Portugal, Jean Nicot, grew interested in this novel plant and sent one as a gift to Catherine de Medici, Queen of France. The plant was named **Nicotiana tabacum** after him.

Nicotiana tabacum
the tobacco primary plant species cultivated on the American continent

The next several hundred years saw a remarkable increase in the use of tobacco. Portuguese sailors smoked it and left tobacco seeds scattered around the world. Over the next 150 years, the Portuguese introduced tobacco to trade with India, Brazil, Japan, China, Arabia, and Africa. Many large tobacco plantations around the world were started by the Portuguese at this time.

An early Christian religious leader, Bishop Bartolome de las Casas (1474–1566), reported that Spanish settlers in Hispaniola (Haiti) smoked rolled tobacco leaves in cigar form like the natives. When the bishop asked about this disgusting habit, the settlers replied that they found it impossible to give up. The addictive qualities of tobacco were recognized even then (Corti 1931).

As the use of tobacco spread, so did the controversy about whether it was bad or good. Tobacco use was the first major drug controversy of global dimensions. As a medicine, tobacco was at first almost universally accepted. Nicholas Monardes, in his description of New World plants (dated 1574), recommended tobacco as an infallible cure for 36 different maladies. It was described as a holy, healing herb, a special remedy sent by God to humans.

Opponents of tobacco use disputed its medical value. They pointed out that tobacco was used in the magic and religion of Native Americans. (Monardes had also described ritual use by native priests.) Tobacco was attacked as an evil plant, an invention of the devil. King James I of England was fanatically opposed to smoking. In an attempt to limit tobacco use, he raised the import tax on tobacco and also sold the right to collect the tax (Austin 1978). (This may be the first example of indirect prohibition; see Chapter 12 on the Marijuana Tax Act.)

Nevertheless, tobacco use increased. By 1614, the number of tobacco shops in London had mushroomed to over 7,000, and demand for tobacco usually outstripped supply. Tobacco was literally worth its weight in silver, so to conserve, it was smoked in pipes with very small bowls (see Figure 10-1). Use of tobacco grew in other areas of the world, as well. West coast Africans captured and sold inland natives to the Portuguese for the equiv-

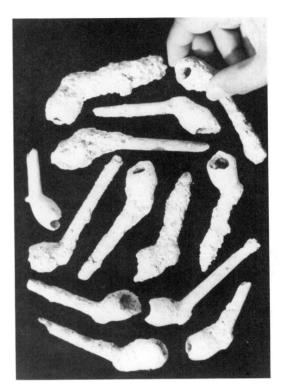

FIGURE 10-1 Clay pipes, part of the cargo for the American colonies, recovered from the wreck of the Virginia Merchant (1661) off the coast of Bermuda. *Source:* Reprinted with permission, Randy Witters, holder of the Weldon Witters literary estate.

alent of about 450 pounds of Brazilian tobacco per slave (Brooks 1952).

In 1642, Pope Urban VIII issued a formal decree forbidding the use of tobacco in church under penalty of immediate excommunication. Priests and worshippers had been staining church floors with tobacco juice. One priest in Naples sneezed so hard after taking snuff that he vomited on the altar in full sight of the congregation. Pope Innocent X issued another edict against tobacco use in 1650, but the clergy and the laity continued to take snuff and smoke. Finally, in 1725, Pope Benedict XIII, himself a smoker and "snufftaker," annulled all previous edicts against tobacco (Austin 1978).

In the 1600s, Turkey, Russia, and China all

imposed the death penalty for smoking. Sultan Murad the Cruel executed many of his subjects caught smoking. The Romanov tsars publicly tortured smokers and exiled them to Siberia. The Chinese decapitated anyone caught dealing in tobacco with the "outer barbarians." Yet smoking continued to grow to epidemic proportions. Despite their opposition to anything foreign, the Chinese became the heaviest smokers in Asia, thus facilitating the later spread of opium smoking (see Chapter 8) (Austin 1978). Thus, no nation whose population has learned to use tobacco products has been successful in outlawing use or getting people to stop.

Snuffing first became fashionable in France during the reign of Louis XIII and spread throughout European aristocracy. Snuffing was regarded as daintier and more elegant than constantly exhaling smoke. King Louis XIV, however, detested all forms of tobacco and would not permit its use in his presence. (He would have banned it, but he needed the tax revenue tobacco brought in.) His sister-in-law, Charlotte of Orleans, was one of the few at court who agreed with him. As she wrote to her sister: "It is better to take no snuff at all than a little; for it is certain that he who takes a little will soon take much, and that is why they call it 'the enchanted herb,' for those who take it are so taken by it that they cannot go without it." Napoleon is said to have used seven pounds of snuff per month (Corti 1931).

TOBACCO USE IN AMERICA

Tobacco played a significant role in the successful colonization of the United States (Langton 1991, 21). In 1610, John Rolfe was sent to Virginia to set up a tobacco industry. At first, the tobacco planted in Virginia was a native species, *Nicotiana rustica*, that was harsh and did not sell well. But in 1612, Rolfe managed to obtain some seeds of the Spanish tobacco species *Nicotiana tabacum*, and by 1613, the success of the tobacco industry and the Virginia colony was ensured.

The importance of tobacco as a substitute for money was noted by George Washington during the Revolutionary War: "I say, if you can't send money, send tobacco." (In World War I, General Pershing said, "You asked me what we need to win this war. I answer tobacco as much as bullets." General Douglas MacArthur said about the same thing in World War II because he believed tobacco was essential for good morale.) Tobacco played a strategic role in the Revolutionary War because of its value to the French, who loaned money to the colonists in exchange for tobacco. The British realized this, so General Cornwallis made the destruction of the Virginia tobacco plantations one of his major campaign objectives (Heimann 1960; Kaufman 1988).

The history of tobacco smoking in the United States is rich in terms of the tremendous number of laws, rules, regulations, and customs that have arisen out of the habit of smoking. Many states have had laws prohibiting the use of tobacco by young people as well as women. In the 1860s, for instance, it was illegal in Florida for anyone under the age of 21 to smoke cigarettes. A 20-year-old caught smoking could be taken to court and compelled to reveal his source (the cigarette "pusher"). In Pennsylvania, as in South Carolina, any child not informing on his or her cigarette supplier was a criminal.

Chewing and snuffing were the most common ways of using tobacco in the United States until fairly recently. In 1897, half of all tobacco was prepared for chewing. Law required that spittoons be placed in all public buildings until 1945.

Cigars became popular in the United States in the early 1800s. Cigar manufacturers fought the introduction of cigarettes for many years. They spread rumors that cigarettes contained opium, were made with tobacco from discarded cigar butts and with paper made by Chinese lepers, and so on (Heimann 1960). By about 1920, cigarette consumption started to exceed that of cigars. The introduction of the cigarette-rolling machine in 1883 spurred cigarette consumption because they became cheaper than cigars. By 1885, a billion cigarettes a year were being produced. Americans consumed over 615 billion cigarettes in 1978, or about 4,000 per person age 18 or older. More recent estimates claim that 50 to 60 million Americans continue to smoke (Henningfield and Nemeth-Coslett 1988; Siegel 1989).

TOBACCO PRODUCTION Tobacco farming is the sixth largest legal cash crop in the United States, ranking behind corn, soybeans, hay, wheat, and cotton (Foster et al. 1989, 121). North Carolina and Kentucky are the two leading growers of tobacco.

While there are over 60 species of plants, *Nicotiana tabacum* is the primary species of tobacco cultivated in the United States. The mature leaves are 1 foot to 2.5 feet long. The nicotine content is from 0.3% to 7%, depending on the variety, leaf position on the stalk (the higher the position, the more nicotine), and growing conditions. The flavor of tobacco comes from *nicotianin*, also called *tobacco camphor* (U.S. Surgeon General 1979).

After harvesting and drying, the tobacco leaves are shredded, blown clean of foreign matter and stems, remoisturized with glycerine or other chemical agents, and packed in huge wooden barrels called *hogsheads*. These barrels are placed in storehouses for one to two years to age, during which time the tobacco gets darker and loses moisture, nicotine, and other volatile substances. When aging has been completed, moisture is again added and the tobacco is blended with other varieties.

There are many types of tobacco, with varying characteristics of harshness, mildness, and flavor. *Bright*, also called *flue-cured* or *Virginia*, is the most common type used in cigarettes. (Flue-cured tobacco is heated in curing sheds to speed the drying process.) Developed just before the Civil War, this technique made tobacco smoke more readily inhalable. The exact blend proportions of various cigarettes are closely guarded trade secrets, but most cigarettes contain up to half of flue-cured bright, about one-third of burley, a small amount of Maryland type, and up to one-fifth of Turkish or Greek blends (Heimann 1960).

Interestingly, the amount of leaf tobacco in a cigarette has gone down about 25% since 1956. There are two reasons for this, not considering the introduction of filtertip cigarettes. (If a filtertip is the same size as a plain cigarette, it has about one-third less tobacco.) The first reason is the use of reconstituted sheets of tobacco. Parts of the tobacco leaves and stems that were discarded in earlier years are now ground up; combined with many other ingredients to control factors such as moisture, flavor, and color; and then rolled out as a flat, homogenized sheet of reconstituted tobacco. This sheet is shredded and mixed with regular leaf tobacco, thus reducing production costs. Nearly one-quarter of the tobacco in a cigarette comes from tobacco scraps made into reconstituted sheets.

A second technological advance further reduces the amount of tobacco needed. This process, called *puffing*, is based on freeze drying the tobacco and then blowing air or an inert gas, such as carbon dioxide, into it. The gas expands, or puffs up, the plant cells so they take up more space, are lighter, and can absorb additives better. The use of reconstituted sheets and puffing have reduced levels of tar and nicotine in cigarettes simply by reducing the amount of leaf tobacco they contain (U.S. Surgeon General 1979).

Tobacco additives are not controlled by the Food and Drug Administration (FDA) or any other government agency. Additives may include extracts of tobacco, as well as nontobacco flavors such as licorice, cocoa, fruit, spices, and floral compositions. (Licorice was first used in tobacco as a preservative around 1830 and became appreciated as a sweetener.) Synthetic flavoring compounds also may be used. The selection of tobacco-flavor additives from the "generally regarded as safe" (GRAS) list or natural extracts and the testing of their smoke decomposition products for toxicity or other biological activity are not required by law but are done voluntarily by manufacturers (U.S. Surgeon General 1981).

In the 1870s, a "cigarette girl" could roll about four cigarettes per minute by hand. When James Duke leased and improved the first cigarette-rolling machine in 1883, he could make about 200 cigarettes per minute. This was the last link in the chain of development leading to the modern American blended cigarette. Today's machines make over 3,600 uniform cigarettes per minute. Filtered cigarettes are made by a machine that attaches a double-size filter between two cigarettes and then cuts them apart (Heimann 1960).

Tar and nicotine levels in cigarettes have dropped considerably over the last 40 years (Palfai and Jankiewicz 1991). Most cigarettes today are low-tar and low-nicotine types. The filtertip, in which the filter is made of cellulose or charcoal, has also become common; over 90% of all cigarettes sold currently in the United States are filtertips (Stellman and Garfinkel 1986). The filter does help remove some of the substances in smoke, but most, such as carbon monoxide, pass through into the mouth and lungs. Over 4,000 substances have been identified in burning tobacco and paper. Many are known carcinogens, whereas the health consequences of many more have not been adequately analyzed.

The cost of making cigarettes (not counting the tobacco) is about three cents a pack. Total cost varies with the manufacturer but usually is not more than five to seven cents a pack. The total amount spent by the American consumer is about $25 billion a year for all tobacco products, with over 90% of that for cigarettes. In 1986, the tax revenue on all cigarettes to the U.S. government was about $4 billion, with over $1.5 billion more in state taxes.

GOVERNMENT REGULATION In the early 1960s, attitudes toward tobacco use began to change in the United States. Prior to this time, tobacco was perceived as being devoid of any negative consequences. After years of study and hundreds of research reports about the effects of smoking, the Advisory Committee to the U.S. Surgeon General reported in 1964 that "cigarette smoking is causally related to lung cancer in men; the magnitude of the effects of cigarette smoking far outweighs all

other factors." Congress passed legislation in 1965, setting up the National Clearinghouse for Smoking and Health. This organization has the responsibility of monitoring, compiling, and reviewing the world's medical literature on the health consequences of smoking.

Reports were published in 1967, 1968, and 1969. The statistical evidence presented in 1969 made it difficult for Congress to avoid warning the public that smoking was dangerous to their health. Since November 1, 1970, all cigarette packages and cartons have had to carry this label: "Warning: The Surgeon General Has Determined That Cigarette Smoking Is Dangerous to Your Health."

Further pressure on Congress prompted passage of laws that prohibited advertising tobacco on radio and television after January 2, 1971. The intent was to limit the media's ability to make smoking seem glamorous and sophisticated. The loss in revenue to radio and television was enormous.

The 1979 publication *Smoking and Health: A Report of the Surgeon General* gave up-to-date information on research about the effects of tobacco on cardiovascular disease, bronchopulmonary disease, cancer, peptic ulcer, and pregnancy. It also emphasized the increase in smoking by women and girls over the past 15 years. The 1981 U.S. Surgeon General's report, *The Changing Cigarette*, gave further information, and the 1985 report, *The Health Consequences of Smoking*, gave research findings showing the relationship of smoking, cancer, and chronic lung disease in the workplace. See Figure 10.2.

According to a 1985 federal law, cigarette containers are required to include a warning about the health hazards of tobacco. *Source:* George Gardner/Stock, Boston

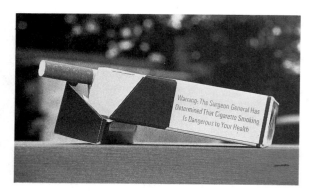

T h i n k   A b o u t   I t . . .

1. What would you say to someone who claims that it is okay to have an occasional cigarette to relieve tension? How about someone who says that their 70-year-old grandmother has smoked her entire life and never been sick?

2. An 11-year-old neighbor asks if you could buy her a pack of cigarettes. Your response is that smoking is harmful to her health and that it's illegal for anyone under age to purchase cigarettes. The 11-year-old responds, "I don't care

SURGEON GENERAL'S WARNING: Quitting Smoking Now Greatly Reduces Serious Risks to Your Health.

SURGEON GENERAL'S WARNING: Smoking By Pregnant Women May Result in Fetal Injury, Premature Birth, And Low Birth Weight.

SURGEON GENERAL'S WARNING: Smoking Causes Lung Cancer, Heart Disease, Emphysema, And May Complicate Pregnancy.

SURGEON GENERAL'S WARNING: Cigarette Smoke Contains Carbon Monoxide

FIGURE 10-2 Warnings on cigarette labels. Four warnings must be rotated on cigarette packages. They are rotated every three months; one warning must appear on every package. The messages are based on the reports of the U.S. Surgeon General on *The Health Consequences of Smoking* (1985) and went into effect on October 12, 1985.

about all that. Will you please buy me a pack?" What would you say? Why?

3. What would you say to someone who claimed that smoking is natural to humans, since it has been practiced by nature-loving Native Americans for centuries?

4. After having failed on numerous occasions, you have finally succeeded in getting a date with a certain member of the opposite sex. On the date, he or she pulls out and smokes a cigarette; you don't smoke. Would smoking be a major issue in continuing the relationship? Why?

SMOKING TOBACCO
THE PROPERTIES OF NICOTINE

The alkaloid **nicotine,** the main active ingredient in tobacco, was isolated in 1828. About 60 milligrams (mg) of nicotine is a lethal dose for an adult, although tolerance does build up rapidly. A cigar contains about 120 mg of nicotine, enough to kill the person who inhales the smoke as with a cigarette. The average cigarette delivers 0.05 to 2.5 mg of nicotine (1980 average contained less than 1 mg) (Jaffe 1980; U.S. Surgeon General 1981). The smoker who inhales gets about 90% of the nicotine in his or her bloodstream, compared to 20% to 50% from smoke taken into the mouth and then exhaled (Volle and Koelle 1975). The blood carries nicotine to the heart, which distributes the substance rapidly throughout the body. Nicotine from inhaled tobacco smoke reaches the brain in

seven seconds—twice as fast as from intravenous administration in the arm.

nicotine
the main active ingredient in tobacco

PHYSIOLOGICAL EFFECTS

In large doses, nicotine is highly toxic. It has been used as an insecticide, and at higher concentration levels, it has the same effects as a poison. The symptoms of nicotine poisoning are sweating, vomiting, mental confusion, diminished pulse rate, and breathing difficulty. Respiratory failure from the paralysis of muscles usually causes death to occur.

Nicotine is believed to be the substance in tobacco that causes dependence, based on how it is metabolized and the effects it produces. Regular users commonly smoke about 20 to 30 cigarettes per day, or one every 30 to 40 minutes. The biological half-life of nicotine in humans is approximately 20 to 30 minutes. Most nicotine is metabolized in the liver, producing inactive compounds that are removed through the kidneys. The rate of urinary excretion is faster when the urine is acidic.

Nicotine is a curious drug because it first stimulates and then depresses the nervous system. The stimulus effect is due to release of norepinephrine and the fact that nicotine mimics the action of acetylcholine. Nicotine thus stimulates cholinergic receptors (nicotinic type) first but is not removed from the receptors very rapidly; the next effect is depression, caused by blocked nerve activity. Nicotine increases the respiration rate at low dose levels because it stimulates the receptors in the carotid artery (in the neck) that monitor the brain's need for oxygen. Nicotine stimulates the cardiovascular system by releasing epinephrine, causing increases in coronary bloodflow, heartrate, and blood pressure. The effect is to increase the oxygen requirements of the heart muscle but not the oxygen supply. This may trigger heart attacks in susceptible persons.

Nicotine causes an initial stimulation of salivary and bronchial secretions, followed by inhibition. The excess saliva associated with smoking is caused by the irritating smoke, not the nicotine (Taylor 1980).

Nicotine and perhaps other substances in tobacco smoke tend to inhibit hunger contractions in the stomach for up to one hour. At the same time, it causes a slight increase in blood sugar and deadens the taste buds. These factors may be responsible for decreased feelings of hunger by many smokers. Smokers have often reported that they gain weight after they stop smoking and that their appetite increases. In addition, when someone who smokes one or more packs a day quits, there may be a decrease in heartrate (2 to 3 beats per minute) and up to a 10% decrease in basal metabolic rate (Jarvik 1979). The body is being stressed less, so it converts more food into fat.

Nicotine and other products in smoke, such as carbon monoxide, produce still other effects. Carbon monoxide is picked up by red blood cells, where it binds to the hemoglobin molecules and forms carboxyhemoglobin (Palfai and Jankiewicz 1991). Up to 10% of all the hemoglobin in smokers may be in the carboxyhemoglobin form. This form of hemoglobin cannot carry oxygen, so up to 10% of the smoker's blood is effectively out of circulation as far as normal oxygen-carbon dioxide exchange is concerned. This situation could easily cause a smoker to become out of breath from exertion. It is a factor in heart attacks and in the lower birthweight and survival rate of infants born to women who smoke during pregnancy (see also later in this chapter).

MORTALITY RATES

The risk of premature death is significantly higher (about 70%) for cigarette smokers than nonsmokers. According to the U.S. Surgeon General, estimates of premature deaths associated with cigarette smoking range from 320,000 to 400,000 per year, including 115,000 deaths from heart disease, 106,000 from lung cancer, 32,000 from other forms of cancer, 57,000 from chronic lung disease, 28,000 from stroke, and about 52,000 from other conditions.

A 35-year-old male who smokes two packs a day has a life expectancy that is 8.1 years shorter than his nonsmoking counterpart (U.S. Surgeon General 1985; Callahan 1987). The death rate increases with the amount smoked: A two-pack-a-day smoker has a mortality rate twice as high as a nonsmoker. Overall mortality rates are greater for those who smoke longer; death rates are directly proportional. Thus, the longer you smoke, the higher the mortality rate.

Various cigarettes have different tar and nicotine contents; this means that the effects they produce and thus the mortality rate vary, as well. Smokers of low-tar and -nicotine cigarettes have a mortality ratio 50% greater than that of nonsmokers but 15% to 20% less than that of cigarette smokers as a group (U.S. Surgeon General 1981; DeAngelis 1989). The mortality ratio is the number obtained by dividing the death rate of smokers by the death rate of nonsmokers.

Overall mortality ratios decline the longer exsmokers abstain from smoking. People who stop smoking before age 50 reduce their risk of dying over the next 15 years by 50%. The mortality rate for exsmokers is related to the *number* of cigarettes they used to smoke per day and the *age* at which they started to smoke. The mortality rate for cigar smokers is somewhat higher than that for nonsmokers and is related to the number of cigars smoked daily. The mortality rate for pipe smokers is slightly greater than that for nonsmokers.

CHRONIC ILLNESS

Not only do cigarette smokers tend to die at an earlier age than nonsmokers, but they also have a higher probability of contracting certain diseases (Schuckit 1984). Following the U.S. Surgeon General's report in 1964, the National Center for Health Statistics began collecting information on smoking. These findings have been helpful in assessing the relationships between tobacco use and illnesses, disability, and other health indicators. Among other things, the center found that men and women currently smoking cigarettes have more chronic health problems than persons who never smoked. What's more, there is a dose-response relationship between the number of cigarettes smoked per day and particular illnesses. For instance, men who smoke two packs of cigarettes a day have a four times higher rate of chronic bronchitis and/or **emphysema** compared to nonsmokers. The rate for women smoking two or more packs a day is nearly ten times higher.

emphysema
a common type of lung disease

Other indicators of sickness studied were workdays lost, days spent in bed because of illness, and days of limited activity resulting from chronic disease. Male smokers had a 33% excess and female smokers a 45% excess of workdays lost compared to nonsmokers. Male former smokers had a 41% excess and female former smokers a 43% excess of workdays lost. The 1974 survey calculated that more than 81 million workdays are lost in the United States every year by smokers compared to nonsmokers. This is a tremendous financial and productivity loss for the nation.

Data on disability and illness show continued high risk among former smokers. The most likely reason for this is that smokers quit because of a smoking-related illness that has already severely damaged the cardiovascular system or lungs. The data on workdays missed by former smokers need further analysis to determine the effects related to the length of time these people smoked and how many cigarettes they used per day.

CARDIOVASCULAR DISEASE   There is now overwhelming proof that cigarette smoking increases the risk of cardiovascular disease (Callahan 1987). Data collected from the United States, the United Kingdom, Canada, and other countries show that smoking is a major risk factor for heart attack. The probability of heart attack is related to the amount smoked, which has a synergistic relationship to other risk factors, like obesity.

Smoking cigarettes is a major risk factor for arteriosclerotic disease and for death from arteriosclerotic aneurysm of the aorta (Palfai and Jankiewicz 1991). (An *aneurysm* is a weakened area in a blood vessel that forms a blood-filled sac and may rupture.) Smokers have a higher incidence of atherosclerosis of the coronary arteries that supply blood to the heart (the arteries become blocked with fat deposits), and the effect is dose related. Both the carbon monoxide and the nicotine in cigarette smoke can precipitate angina attacks (painful spasms in the chest when the heart muscle does not get the blood supply it needs).

Smokers of low-tar and -nicotine cigarettes have less risk of coronary heart disease, but their risk is still greater than that of nonsmokers. The risk goes down if the person quits; after about 10 years, the risk of coronary disease in exsmokers approaches that of nonsmokers. Women who smoke and use oral contraceptives have a significantly higher risk of death or disability from stroke, heart attack, and other cardiovascular diseases than nonsmokers both on and off "the pill."

CANCER   Currently, lung cancer is the leading cause of cancer death in the United States, claiming 125,000 victims a year (American Cancer Society 1990). There were an estimated 460,000 deaths from all types of cancer in 1985, of which 125,600 were from lung cancer. Lung cancer is the most common type in men and in women. There has been a dramatic increase in lung cancer in women: fourfold in 25 years. Lung cancer mortality rates for women are increasing more rapidly than for men. Women who smoke die sooner, just as male smokers do; there is a direct relationship between smoking and lung cancer in both genders.

Astonishingly, approximately 85% of lung cancer cases in men and 75% in women are caused by cigarette smoking. Less than 10% of nonsmokers get lung cancer. What's more, 85% to 90% of all deaths from lung cancer are smoking related (Callahan 1987).

The risk of lung cancer increases with:

The amount smoked, as measured by the number of cigarettes smoked per day
The duration of smoking
The age at which the person started smoking
The degree of inhalation
The tar and nicotine content of the cigarettes

Use of filter cigarettes and of lower-tar and -nicotine cigarettes decreases the lung cancer mortality rate, but it is still significantly higher than that for nonsmokers. If a smoker quits, the lung cancer mortality rate goes down but will not approach the nonsmoker rate until 10 years of abstinence.

Pipe and cigar smokers are more likely to contract lung cancer than nonsmokers but less so than habitual cigarette smokers. Common types of cancers among cigar and pipe smokers include cancers of the mouth, larynx, and esophagus.

Exposure to certain air pollutants in the environment or in industry—especially the asbestos, uranium, nickel, and chemical industries—acts synergistically with cigarette smoking to increase lung cancer mortality rates far above what would be the rate for each separately.

Cancer of the larynx is significantly higher in smokers compared to nonsmokers and is related to the amount smoked. A compounding effect has also been shown to exist between smoking and alcohol consumption and between exposure to asbestos and smoking, increasing the likelihood of getting cancer of the larynx. The risk of laryngeal cancer goes down if the person stops smoking but like lung cancer, this form of cancer does not reach the level for nonsmokers for nearly 10 years.

There is also a causal relationship between smoking and cancers of the oral cavity, esophagus, urinary bladder, pancreas, and kidneys.

BRONCHOPULMONARY DISEASE   Cigarette smoking is the most important cause of bronchopulmonary disease, which includes a host of lung ailments. Cigarette smokers have higher death rates from pulmonary emphysema and chronic bronchitis and more frequently have impaired pulmonary function and other symptoms of pulmonary disease than nonsmokers (U.S. Surgeon General 1979; Callahan 1987).

Respiratory infections are more prevalent and more severe among cigarette smokers, particularly heavy smokers, than among nonsmokers. The risk of developing or dying from bronchopulmonary disease among pipe or cigar smokers is higher than that for nonsmokers but less than for cigarette smokers. Exsmokers have lower death rates from bronchopulmonary disease than do continuing smokers.

The cause of lung damage may be impaired immune system activity in lung tissue, genetic factors, and deficiencies in certain substances in the tissues. It is known that persons with a low amount of an enzyme called *alpha-1-antitrypsin* are more likely to develop emphysema. Smoking is especially dangerous for such people.

Smokers are more prone to develop bronchopulmonary disease in the presence of air pollutants, such as sulfur oxides and asbestos, than are nonsmokers. Coal dust, cotton dust, and chlorine have additive effects with cigarette smoking in damaging the lungs. Likewise, exposure to fumes and dust—especially talc and carbon black in the rubber industry and uranium and gold dust in the mining industry—acts synergistically with cigarette smoking in the development of bronchopulmonary disease.

It is now understood how cigarette smoking can cause one of the most common lung diseases, emphysema. Cigarette smoking produces inflammation of the lung tissue as well as an increase in the protein elastase in the tissue. Elastin, a structural material in the lungs, is broken down by elastase enzyme. Smoking inactivates alpha-1-antiprotease (also called alpha-1-antitrypsin, as noted previously), a protein capable of blocking the enzyme elastase. Because there is more elastase enzyme, there is a greater breakdown of lung elastin. In the long run, the lung tissue is damaged extensively, causing emphysema (U.S. Surgeon General 1984).

EFFECTS ON THE FETUS

Cigarette smoking during pregnancy has a significantly harmful effect on the development of the fetus, the survival of the newborn infant, and the continued development of the child. Adverse effects on pregnancy range from increased risk for spontaneous abortion, impaired fetal growth, stillbirth, premature birth, and neonatal death. Babies born to mothers who smoke have a lower average bodyweight and length and have a smaller head circumference. The amount a woman smokes will impact the size of the child she bears. If a smoking woman gives it up for the entire duration of the pregnancy, her child will probably be of normal size and strength.

The below-average weight of babies born to smokers is caused by carbon monoxide and nicotine. Carbon monoxide reduces the oxygen-carrying capacity of the fetus's blood, just as it does the mother's. Fetal growth is retarded because the tissue is starved for oxygen. Inhaled nicotine enters the mother's blood from her lungs and rapidly constricts the bloodflow to the placenta, reducing available oxygen and nutrients until the effect of the nicotine has worn off. In addition, nicotine crosses the blood-placental barrier to the fetal bloodstream. It has the same effects on the fetus's nervous system and blood circulation as on the mother's. However, the fetus cannot metabolize nicotine efficiently, so the effects last longer for the child than for the mother.

One known carcinogen in tobacco smoke, *benzo(a)pyrene*, crosses the placenta and enters the fetal blood. Experiments with pregnant mice exposed to benzo(a)pyrene showed that their offspring had a markedly higher incidence of cancer. The impact of smoking during pregnancy on the incidence of cancer in infants is not known.

Infants born to mothers who smoke have a reduced probability of survival. They are more likely to die from **sudden infant death syndrome (SIDS)** and other causes related to their retarded growth. Long-term effects may be observed in physical growth, mental development, and behavioral characteristics of those babies who survive the first four weeks of life. And it appears that children of mothers who smoke do not catch up with children of nonsmoking mothers in various stages of development, at least up to the age of 11. Smoking during pregnancy may also be a cause of hyperkinesis in children.

---

sudden infant death syndrome (SIDS)
unexpected and unexplainable death that occurs while infants are sleeping

---

If the father smokes even when the mother does not, the fetus may be affected through **second-hand smoke** or through damage to the sperm. There is a much higher mortality rate for newborn infants whose fathers smoke more than 10 cigarettes per day. Babies fathered by heavy smokers have twice the expected incidence of severe birth defects.

---

second-hand smoke
the smoke from burning tobacco that pollutes the air and is breathed by smokers and nonsmokers alike

---

TAKING TOBACCO WITHOUT SMOKING

While it is customary to associate the effects of tobacco use with smoking, there are in fact millions of nonsmokers who experience some tobacco effects, voluntarily or involuntarily, through **smokeless tobacco** products and exposure to second-hand smoke.

---

smokeless tobacco
two types of tobacco: chewing and snuff tobacco

SMOKELESS TOBACCO

Two types of tobacco products are classified as smokeless tobacco: chewing tobacco and snuff. Both are comprised of tobacco leaves that are shredded and twisted into strands and then either chewed or placed in the cheek between the lower lip and gum.

Interestingly, smokeless tobacco was used in the United States before cigarettes became popular. The use of smokeless tobacco declined until the early 1980s, when both chewing tobacco and snuff reemerged. The increase in use is partly due to more effective and persistent advertising campaigns, depicting famous athletes using such products. However, the perceived linkage between health hazards and the use of smokeless tobacco remains understated.

How many people use these products? The United Nations' World Health Organization views the use of smokeless tobacco as a threat to society. Estimates show that approximately 12 million Americans use smokeless tobacco, and between 6 million and 7 million either chew tobacco or **snuff** at least once a week (Wolfe 1987, 20).

Despite the well-known health hazards of tobacco products, athletes, such as this baseball player, often use smokeless tobacco. *Source:* Dean Abramson/Stock, Boston

snuff
powdered or finely cut tobacco leaves that are not chewed but instead placed between the lip or cheek and gum

Accelerated use is found in young males. In some areas of the country, between 25% and 35% of adolescent males use products such as Beech Nut or Red Man (both loose-leaf tobaccos) or Copenhagen or Skoal (canned, moist snuff). The U.S. Centers for Disease Control found that, in Alaska, 17% of five-year-old girls and 10% of five-year-old boys use smokeless tobacco (Wolfe 1987). Currently, 14 American states allow the sale of smokeless tobacco to minors.

How safe are smokeless tobacco products in comparison to cigarettes? A study conducted by the University of Southern California found that taking one pinch of snuff has effects equivalent to those of smoking three or four cigarettes. The likelihood of getting oral cancer increases significantly for anyone who uses smokeless tobacco daily for 3.5 years or more (Perry 1990, 20–23). Other evidence has shown that continued use of smokeless products can cause cancer of the pharynx and esophagus, as well. The incidence of developing these cancers is related to the duration of use and the type of product used (NIH 1986). Other less serious effects of using smokeless tobacco include severe inflammation of gum tissue, tooth decay, and receding gums.

Since the mid-1980s, sales of chewing tobacco have declined, primarily because of negative publicity, price hikes, and legislation. Recent laws require that rotating warning labels be placed on smokeless products, as they are on cigarettes. What's more, smokeless tobacco can no longer be advertised on television and radio.

SECOND-HAND AND "SIDESTREAM" SMOKE

Studies of smoking and its effects have given increased attention to what is termed *second-hand smoke*—the smoke from burning tobacco that pol-

BEETLE BAILEY *Source:* June 3, 1987, *Columbus Dispatch*, reprinted with special permission of King Features Syndicate, Inc.

lutes the air and is breathed in by smokers and nonsmokers alike. **"Sidestream" smoke**—that which comes directly from the lighted tip of a cigarette between puffs—is especially dangerous.

"sidestream" smoke
smoke released into the air directly from the lighted tip of a cigarette

---

"Sidestream" smoke has much higher concentrations of some irritating and hazardous substances—such as carbon monoxide, nicotine, and ammonia—than inhaled ("mainstream") smoke. If several people smoke in an enclosed area, the carbon monoxide (CO) level may exceed the safe limit recommended by the Environmental Protection Agency (EPA). Nine parts CO per million (ppm) parts air is the regulatory limit, but this can easily be exceeded. Under conditions of heavy smoking and poor ventilation, concentrations of CO as high as 50 ppm can occur from sidestream smoke. CO is a gas and is not removed by most standard air filtration systems. It can only be diluted by increasing ventilation with fresh air containing low levels of CO. Formation of CO can be reduced by increasing the amount of oxygen available during the burning of the tobacco. This can be done by using perforated cigarette paper and perforated filtertips. Regular and small cigars pro-

duce more CO than cigarettes because the tobacco leaf wrapper reduces the amount of oxygen available at the burning zone. The levels of CO created by smokers may cause nonsmokers with coronary disease to have angina attacks.

Nicotine from sidestream smoke has a tendency to settle out of the air. The body absorbs small amounts from heavily polluted air, which are probably not hazardous. Several carcinogens, such as benzo(a)pyrene and dimethylnitrosamine, are also absorbed in small amounts from sidestream smoke. The extent of the carcinogenic hazard is not known.

Irritation to the eyes, nose, and respiratory tract from sidestream smoke is probably caused by *acrolein.* Although acrolein is a toxic gas, levels from sidestream smoke are probably not hazardous to healthy nonsmokers—just irritating. However, the carbon monoxide and irritating substances are hazardous to nonsmokers with cardiovascular disease or bronchopulmonary disease and to young children. Children of smokers are more likely than children of nonsmokers to have bronchitis and pneumonia during the first year of life.

T h i n k   A b o u t   I t . . .

1. Are the warning labels on cigarette packages about the health hazards of smoking effective? Ask two or three smokers, and then ask several people who have recently quit smoking. Would you revise the warnings? If so, how?

2. What would you do if you won a scholarship from one of the major tobacco companies? Would you accept the money? Why or why not?
3. Assume that you are not a smoker. What would you do if, on your first day at a new job, a sizable group of fellow employees smoked in the lounge during break sessions?
4. Assume that you are a moderate smoker. What would you do if, while dining at a restaurant one evening, you light up a cigarette and a patron seated at the next table asks you not to smoke?

HOW TO STOP SMOKING

Since the U.S. Surgeon General's report in 1964, an estimated 50 million American men and women have stopped smoking. However, the current 54 million smokers in the United States consume over 615 billion cigarettes per year. The health damage has been estimated to cost the nation over $27 billion a year in medical care, absenteeism, decreased work productivity, and accidents. Cigarette smoking is the single most preventable environmental factor contributing to illness, disability, and death in the United States.

WITHDRAWAL AND READDICTION

When habitual smokers stop smoking, they may experience a variety of unpleasant withdrawal effects: craving for tobacco, irritability, restlessness, dullness, sleep disturbances, gastrointestinal disturbances, anxiety, and impairment of concentration, judgment, and psychomotor performance. The intensity of withdrawal effects may be mild, moderate, or severe and are not necessarily correlated with the amount the person smoked. The onset of these symptoms may occur within hours or days after quitting and may persist from a few days to several months. Frustration over these symptoms leads many people to start smoking again (Pomerleau 1979).

Even after the exsmoker has overcome withdrawal symptoms during the first few weeks, he or she is still at risk. Various internal and external stimuli may serve as triggers for craving or withdrawal symptoms. Stressful situations—such as an argument with a spouse, being with friends who smoke, and various types of social events—may cause a response similar to withdrawal. This sets the stage for readdiction.

BEHAVIORAL TREATMENTS

The behavioral modification approach has proven successful in helping people to quit smoking. In most nonbehavioral clinics, fewer than half of the smokers quit, and of those who do, only 25% to 30% are still not smoking 9 to 18 months later. The long-term abstinence rate is about 13% (Pomerleau 1979).

The three main types of behavioral treatment involve (1) punishment and aversive therapy, (2) stimulus control, and (3) substitute smoking procedures. Aversive conditioning techniques use cigarettes themselves to break the behavior pattern of smoking by making it so intense that it becomes unpleasant. A method called *rapid smoking* illustrates one successful use of aversive conditioning. The procedure is to have the person smoke cigarettes at a rapid rate, inhaling smoke about six seconds after each exhalation, until he or she cannot bear any more. Sessions are repeated daily until the person no longer desires to smoke. Follow-up sessions are held if the desire returns.

In a review of several studies using rapid smoking, the abstinence rate was 54% in short-term follow up and 36% in long-term follow up (two to six years after treatment) (Pomerleau 1979). The rapid smoking method essentially involves acute self-poisoning at a rate the person finds physiologically uncomfortable, compared to maintenance self-poisoning at the usual rate of smoking. This technique can be dangerously stressful for a person who has cardiovascular problems or reduced bronchopulmonary function.

Use of stimulus control is another approach to modification of smoking behavior. It is based on the assumption that smoking is associated with or controlled by environmental cues and that these cues contribute to the persistence of the habit. Programmed restriction of the stimuli that trigger smoking theoretically leads to a gradual elimination of smoking behavior. The person might be asked to keep a daily record of the circumstances in which he or she smokes each cigarette, which increases his or her awareness of smoking. Designated daily quotas can then be assigned as targets for reduction.

Generally, stimulus control by itself is not very effective. Better results are obtained when stimulus control procedures are combined with reward methods (e.g., deposited money is reimbursed for reaching a goal) and other techniques. Multiple-method approaches give results about equal to those of the rapid smoking method, with 61% of the participants quitting smoking after eight sessions of treatment and 32% remaining nonsmokers after a year. There is about a 50% return to addiction after treatment over longer periods of time (Pomerleau 1979).

The American Cancer Society has developed a list of alternative activities the new exsmoker might try as aids to get through the withdrawal period. When the craving for a cigarette arises the smoker may substitute these behaviors:

Sip a glass of water.
Nibble on fruit, celery, or carrots.
Chew gum or spices such as ginger, cinnamon bark, or clove.
Use nicotine replacements if necessary, such as lobeline sulphate tables (unless you have an ulcer) or nicotine-containing chewing gum.
Perform moderately strenuous physical activity, such as bicycling, jogging, or swimming (if the person's heart and lungs are not too damaged).
Spend as much time as possible in places where smoking is prohibited, such as movie theaters, libraries, and so on.
Use mouthwash after each meal.

To these might be added: Get rid of drug paraphernalia, such as ashtrays and lighters. How serious a person is about quitting can often be gauged by how willing he or she is to give up an expensive ashtray, cigarette box, or engraved lighter. If these things are kept on the rationalization that guests will expect such accessories, the person is setting himself or herself up for readdiction.

THE MOTIVATION NOT TO SMOKE

Although behavioral modification treatments are more effective than earlier methods, rates of 50% recidivism and 33% long-term abstinence leave considerable room for improvement. When relapse rates for heroin users, cigarette smokers, and alcoholics were plotted on graph paper, the curves for the percentage of relapse over a one-year period were virtually identical. However, these data were taken from persons who sought treatment. Heroin users and alcoholics who quit drugs on their own have much higher success rates.

We actually know very little about the success rate for the estimated 30 million American smokers who have quit on their own. It could be that those who seek treatment have a more severe form of dependence (Jaffe and Kanzler 1979). Mark Twain once said that he could give up smoking with ease and had in fact done so, "hundreds of times."

Many pleasant changes take place within a few weeks after you stop smoking. There is a reduction in coughing, nasal discharge, and saliva production. Shortness of breath usually improves rapidly. Food tastes better, sleep is sounder, fatigue diminishes, breath odor improves, and tobacco stains on the teeth and fingers disappear.

More effective methods of motivating smokers to quit and of discouraging teen-agers from starting are clearly needed. Changing social attitudes toward smoking are proving to have a strong effect. But what about youth? Nearly one-fifth (18.9%) of high school seniors are daily smokers, and 11.2% smoke one-half pack or more by the time they leave high school (NIDA 1990a). The harmful effects of tobacco are well established. What is needed is for smokers to start taking them personally!

Think About It...

1. Explain the three types of behavioral treatments used to help people stop smoking. Which do you think is most effective?

For You to Consider...

Profile of a Smoker

The following narrative, based on an interview with a 53-year-old man, illustrates some of the dilemmas faced by an older generation of smokers.

I guess I started smoking even before it was considered a drug! I was about 10, and we would steal cigarettes from our parents and smoke them in the back yard or away from our homes. At that age, we thought we were doing something against adults, and it felt fun to do something naughty. When we started, we didn't even know how to inhale.

Off and on until I was 17 or 18, I smoked occasionally, whenever my friends offered me a cigarette. I would follow the crowd. At 17 or so, I was buying cigarettes and carrying them around. I recall the menthols—Newport, Kool, Salem—also other non-menthol cigarettes.

No health hazards were publicized when I was a kid, as this was before the Surgeon General issued his famous finding that smoking is hazardous to your health. I remember that it was more common to find adults smoking than not smoking. Movies and television programs were filled with smokers. Smoking was as normal as wearing clothes! Over the years, I really got used to smoking. I tried quitting four times, and sometimes I stopped

for over two years. I switched to a pipe, then cigars, then cigarettes again. I think I tried smoking everything available in order to avoid any possible health hazards.

My health is fine, but I still worry whether I will ever develop cancer from smoking. I may have the beginnings of cancer right now and not even know it. I guess what you don't know, you don't worry about—until it's too late. Now I smoke about a pack of cigarettes per day, and just recently, I've been thinking about quitting again. I remember that, when I would go through weeks without smoking, I would slowly begin to feel better. No big change—just small things that add up to simply feeling better. I can usually breathe more clearly, my sinuses are not congested, and I don't have to look for out-of-the-way places to smoke so that people will not disapprove.

That's another thing: Today, society is against smoking. I never thought this would happen. I know several regular smokers who have to hide in their bedrooms or backrooms and offices with the doors shut in order to smoke a cigarette. This reminds me of the days when I use to smoke pot. Because it was illegal, we had to hide our smoking a joint. First spitting in public places became a violation of law when I was about 10 years old. Now, it

won't be long before smoking cigarettes will be against the law.

Quitting is very hard once you're addicted to nicotine. In a London subway, I once saw a sign that said, "Addiction to nicotine is worse than addiction to heroin." At the time I first read this sign, I thought it was a complete exaggeration. But now, eight years later, I am convinced it's true.

Whenever I quit smoking, I go through weeks of anguish and craving for just one more cigarette. Yeah, quitting is really tough, especially during the first few days. The desire to smoke is very strong at first. But then slowly, ever so so slowly, the craving begins to fade. After three months, the worst is over. Yet, even after a year, you can suddenly think of how great it would be to have just one cigarette.

Whenever I go back to smoking after having stopped for several months, I would always convince myself that I could easily stop again and that my health would be fine if I only had one to three cigarettes per day. Now that I think back, I realize that I am probably a life-addicted person. I'm a lifer! Don't let anyone kid you: Nicotine is really a "hard-core" drug, and it's horribly addictive.

Source: Interview conducted by Peter Venturelli, May 18, 1991.

2. How sincere do you think the 53-year-old male in the "For You to Consider" box is about wanting to quit smoking? What suggestions can you offer him?

WHO SMOKES AND WHY?

Given what we know today about the effects of smoking, it's hard to understand why people smoke. Lifetime users are understandably addicted; quitting is hard. But why would anyone start smoking?

CHARACTERISTICS OF SMOKERS

Recent surveys show that there has been a steady decline in tobacco use in the United States. Figure 10-3 illustrates a marked decline in the use of cigars, chewing tobacco, smoking tobacco (used largely in pipes), and cigarettes, particularly during the 1980s. Snuff consumption, on the other hand, increased dramatically in the early eighties after years of gradual decline. Reasons for this increase likely include the following: (1) snuff can be used anywhere, even in "no smoking" areas; (2) there has been an increase in outdoor advertising of the product; and (3) the fear associated with tobacco consumption has weakened somewhat in recent years (Foster et al. 1989, 124). As shown in Figure 10-3, however, the use of snuff has dropped off slightly in the last few years.

A long-term study on cigarette smoking found that, from 1944 to 1987, the percentage of American adults (18 years and older) who smoke dropped nearly 10% (see Table 10-1). (The decrease would have been 11% except for a slight increase reported in the last year of the study—see the table.) The data in this report also give revealing information about the nature of smokers and nonsmokers, examining factors such as sex, age, race, education level, household income, and so on. National health surveys have also found that gender, education, and race and ethnicity strongly affect who is most likely to smoke. But researchers believe that educational achievement levels are better predictors of who is likely to smoke than gender (Pierce 1989).

The data in Table 10-1 and Figure 10-4 support Pierce's finding, showing that college graduates are least likely to smoke when compared to people of other educational levels. Figure 10-4 also shows that people from higher household incomes are less likely to smoke. Other complementary findings indicate that smoking has declined across all educational levels; however, it has dropped five times faster among people who have attained some higher education.

When looking at gender and race, other findings are consistent. Men were more likely to smoke during the first half of this century. However, by 1964, when the U.S. Surgeon General warned about the likelihood of the ill effects of smoking, the rate of men smoking had begun to decline. Statistics reveal that the percentage of men smokers decreased from approximately 45% in 1974 to 33% in 1987. The percentage of women decreased at a slower rate, from approximately 36% in 1974 to 28% in 1987 (Fiore et al. 1989). In summary, men are more likely to smoke cigarettes than women. However, women are less likely to stop smoking.

Between 1974 and 1985, African-Americans were more likely to smoke than whites. In 1974, 44% of African-Americans and 36% of whites smoked. In 1987, 34% of African-Americans and 28% of whites smoked (Statistical Abstract 1990, 123). In comparing males to females, men of both races were more likely to smoke than females.

Trends in tobacco use among youth are not encouraging (see Table 10-2). Although the percentage of high school seniors who smoked cigarettes declined slowly from 1975 through 1989 (by about 8%), an alarming percentage of youth still do smoke. Approximately 66%—nearly two-thirds—smoked at least once in 1989. Given the addictive properties of tobacco, many of these youth will continue to use the drug throughout life.

The data in Table 10-3 give more specific insight into tobacco use by youth. Namely, in 1989, almost 19% of high school seniors smoked cigarettes daily; over 11% smoked a half-pack or more every day. These figures have declined since 1975, as well.

What these tables do not reveal is the likeli-

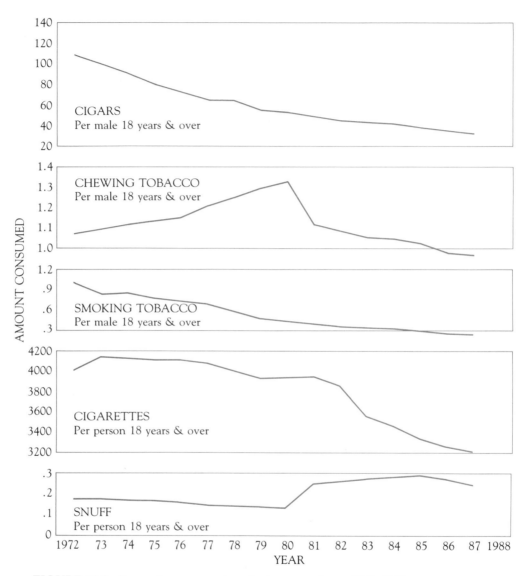

FIGURE 10-3   Per capita consumption of tobacco products: 1972–1982 *Source:* U.S. Department of Agriculture, *Annual Report on Tobacco Statistics* and *The Tobacco Outlook and Situation Report* (Washington, D.C.: U.S. Department of Agriculture, 1988).

hood that, within certain subgroups of high school seniors, tobacco use is actually increasing even though general use may be decreasing. Evidence from the National Institute on Drug Abuse (NIDA) (1991, 23) clearly shows that 55% of high school students who dropped out between the ages of 16 and 17 reported smoking cigarettes as compared

to 17.2% of those students who didn't quit school. Thus, while the level of education may be a precipitating factor in increased tobacco use, other underlying factors are responsible, as well. Family role models, peer influences, and the extent of attachment to such social institutions as the family, the school, and the economic system are all factors

TABLE 10-1 Cigarette Smoking Audit

QUESTION: Have you, yourself, smoked any cigarettes in the past week?

	July 1–7, 1988 (Telephone)		
	Yes	No	Number of Interviews
National	*32%*	*68%*	*1,000*
Sex			
Men	34	66	495
Women	30	70	505
Age			
18–29 years	28	72	248
30–49 years	35	65	399
50 & older	30	70	349
Region			
East	35	65	229
Midwest	31	69	271
South	31	69	323
West	28	72	176
Race			
Whites	32	68	911
Non-whites	26	74	86

	July 1–7, 1988 (Telephone)		
	Yes	No	Number of Interviews
Education			
College graduates	19	81	286
College incomplete	32	68	257
High school graduates	37	63	342
Not high school grads.	34	66	111
Politics			
Republicans	31	69	333
Democrats	32	68	340
Independents	29	71	294
Household Income			
$40,000 & over	24	76	270
$25,000–$39,999	37	63	285
$15,000–$24,999	32	68	190
Under $15,000	31	69	194
Religion			
Protestants	33	67	587
Catholics	28	72	266

Cigarette Smoking Audit (percent smokers)

	Total	Men	Women		Total	Men	Women
1988	32%	34%	30%	1972	43	48	38
1987	30	33	28	1971	42	47	37
1986	31	35	28	1969	40	44	36
1985	35	37	32	1958	45	NA	NA
1983	38	40	36	1957	42	52	34
1981	35	38	33	1954	45	57	32
1978	36	39	34	1948	44	54	33
1977	38	41	35	1944	41	48	36
1974	40	45	36				

NA = Not ascertained.

Source: The Gallup Report, Princeton, NJ.

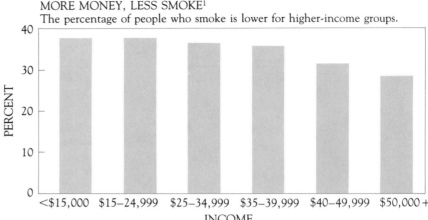

MORE MONEY, LESS SMOKE[1]
The percentage of people who smoke is lower for higher-income groups.

THE EDUCATION OF A SMOKER[2]
More than 30 percent of high school dropouts smoke.

FIGURE 10-4 Education and income levels of cigarette smokers *Source:* M. Gonzales and B. Edmondson, "The Smoking Class," *American Demographics* 10, no. 11 (November 1988): 34–37, 58.

[1]Based on "1986 Adult Use of Tobacco Survey," Centers for Disease Control, Rockville, MD.

[2]Based on Mediamark Research, Inc., Spring 1988.

responsible for experimentation and use of tobacco by youth.

REASONS FOR SMOKING

About 30% of Americans continue to smoke, even though they are aware of its many potentially detrimental effects. Nearly 25% smoke over a pack a day.

If you were to ask tobacco users why they smoke, their answers would be quite similar:

1. For relaxation and to enhance social interactions

2. To decrease the unpleasant effects of tension, anxiety, and anger
3. To satisfy the craving
4. It's a habit
5. For the stimulation, increased energy, and arousal
6. Manipulating objects is pleasing (the cigarette, pipe, and so on)

Not all tobacco smokers give all of these reasons for smoking. Pleasurable relaxation and reduction of tension and craving were rated as the most important. Habit, stimulation, and manipulation were of substantial but lesser significance (Jones et al. 1978).

TABLE 10-2 High school senior survey trends in lifetime prevalence: 1975–1989

Class of	Percentage Who Ever Used Cigarettes*
1975	73.6
1976	75.4
1977	75.7
1978	75.3
1979	74.0
1980	71.0
1981	71.0
1982	70.1
1983	70.6
1984	69.7
1985	68.8
1986	67.6
1987	67.2
1988	66.4
1989	65.7

Source: National Institute on Drug Abuse, *Monitoring the Future Study* (Ann Arbor, MI: Institute for Social Research, 1990).

Note: This information was gathered in annual nationwide surveys conducted for the National Institute on Drug Abuse by the University of Michigan Institute for Social Research. The 1989 survey involved more than 17,000 high school seniors from public and private schools.

*"Ever used" means "used at least one time."

TABLE 10-3 High school senior survey trends in daily use: 1975–1989

Class of	Percentage Who Used Cigarettes in the Last 30 Days*	
	Smoked Daily	Smoked Half-Pack or More Daily
1975	26.9	17.9
1976	28.8	19.2
1977	28.8	19.4
1978	27.5	18.8
1979	25.4	16.5
1980	21.3	14.3
1981	20.3	13.5
1982	21.1	14.2
1983	21.2	13.8
1984	18.7	12.3
1985	19.5	12.5
1986	18.7	11.4
1987	18.7	11.4
1988	18.1	10.6
1989	18.9	11.2

Source: National Institute on Drug Abuse, *Monitoring the Future Study* (Ann Arbor, MI: Institute for Social Research, 1990).

Note: This information was gathered in annual nationwide surveys conducted for the National Institute on Drug Abuse by the University of Michigan Institute for Social Research. The 1989 survey involved more than 17,000 high school seniors from public and private schools.

*"In the last 30 days" means "used at least once in the 30 days prior to the survey."

A high level of dependence on tobacco should be expected, for a number of reasons:

1. The habit can be rapidly and frequently reinforced by the inhalation of tobacco smoke (about 10 reinforcements per cigarette, or 200 with one pack).
2. The rapid metabolism and clearance of nicotine allows frequent and repeated use, which is encouraged by the rapid onset of withdrawal symptoms.
3. Smoking has complex pharmacological effects, both central and peripheral, that may satisfy a variety of the smoker's needs.
4. Some groups offer psychological and social rewards for use, especially the peer groups of young people.
5. Smoking patterns can be generalized; that is, the smoker becomes conditioned to continue smoking with other activities. For example, some smokers feel the need to smoke after a meal, when driving, and so on.

6. Smoking is reinforced by both pharmacological effects and ritual.
7. There is no marked performance impairment; in fact, smoking enhances performance in some cases. (Nicotine produces a state of alertness, prevents deterioration of reaction time, and improves learning.)
8. Cigarettes cost less and are more readily available than other psychoactive drugs (Jones et al. 1978).

These reasons may explain not only why people continue to smoke but also why it is hard for them to stop. A good deal of research suggests that nicotine is probably the reinforcing substance in tobacco. For example, experimental animals can discriminate between nicotine and other stimulant drugs, which implies that the drug affects the central nervous system. It can alter the emotional state, which might help maintain dependency. Rats and monkeys will self-administer nicotine intravenously, which shows that nicotine is a reinforcer; that is, it strengthens and maintains behaviors that lead to its availability and ingestion (Goldberg et al. 1981).

Smokers appear to regulate their intake of nicotine. The smoker with a low-nicotine cigarette is likely to smoke more and inhale more deeply. There appear to be specific nicotinic receptors in the brain that respond to nicotine. Consider that the average one-pack-a-day smoker is estimated to self-administer 70,000 pulses (one pulse per inhalation) of nicotine in a year. This surpasses by far the rate of any other known form of substance abuse. A habit that is reinforced as frequently and easily as smoking is very hard to break (Krasnegor 1979).

An incident that happened at Synanon, a treatment program for heroin addicts, illustrates how strong the smoking habit is. According to Synanon policy, addicts cannot use any drugs while being rehabilitated. In 1970, Synanon decided to ban cigarettes because of cost and because they seemed to serve as a crutch for people getting off other drugs. About 100 people left and chose possible readdiction to hard drugs rather than stay at Synanon without cigarettes. Residents of Synanon noted that the withdrawal symptoms for tobacco lasted much longer than those for other drugs, and they believed it was easier to quit heroin than cigarettes!

SOCIAL ISSUES: LOOKING TO THE FUTURE
ECONOMIC INTERESTS

The tobacco industry spends approximately $2.5 billion a year on advertising (Davis 1987)—more than any other industry. In fact, when the total spent on print and billboard advertising is broken down, the tobacco industry spends approximately $40 annually on every smoker in the United States (Liska 1990).

Although cigarette advertising was banned on television in 1971, it has increased in magazines oriented to youth and women. Ads portray smokers to be sexy, healthy, and adventurous, enjoying recreation and close relationships with lovers and friends. All of these themes are especially appealing to youth (Altman et al. 1987).

Interestingly, as the consumption of cigarettes has declined in the United States, new markets abroad have increased. Like the United States and Canada, other Western nations have been fairly successful in broadcasting that the use of tobacco is hazardous to your health. Per capita consumption in primarily nonindustrialized Third World countries has steadily increased with the availability of tobacco produced in the United States.

American-brand cigarettes hold prestige for middle- and lower-class groups in many foreign societies. In India, for example, along with English cigarettes, American cigarettes are considered superior in quality and are a status symbol for those who can afford to purchase such luxury items.

In some countries, like China, approximately 90% of the male population smokes. Nations like this represent an incredibly appealing market to American cigarette manufacturers. Given the shrinking market in the United States as well as in most modern industrialized nations, American manufacturers feel compelled to look overseas. They are finding lucrative markets in many Third World nations. Tobacco sales are becoming

For You to Consider...

A Moral Dilemma

Americans have had access to considerable research showing the health-related hazards of smoking. The U.S. government has responded to this research with attempts to protect or at least warn the public about the dangers of smoking. The result has been a steady decline in the number of Americans who smoke.

Should the U.S. government extend its warning to those Third World nations in which smoking is on the rise? What responsibility does the United States have as a world leader to protect humanity, particularly those who are uneducated and oppressed? What responsibility does the U.S. government have to American business interests, such as cigarette manufacturers?

teresting. "The decisions to use the tobacco or other gateway drugs set up **patterns of behavior** that make it easier for a user to go on to other drugs" ("Non-Smoking Youth" 1991). In other words, smokers have developed the behavioral patterns that may lead them to experiment and use other licit and illicit drugs.

> **patterns of behavior**
> consistent and related behaviors that occur together,
> such as marijuana use and euphoria, alcohol abuse
> and intoxication

How strong is this evidence? Figure 10-5 illustrates that daily smokers as opposed to non-smokers are much more likely to engage in the use of controlled substances such as marijuana and cocaine. The University of Michigan's Institute for Social Research (NIDA 1990) found that, of the high school seniors surveyed, cigarette smokers were 10 times more likely to use cocaine regularly than seniors who did not smoke. Also, the more a student smoked, the greater the likelihood of his or her marijuana and cocaine use.

stronger in certain foreign markets while becoming weaker in others.

TOBACCO AS A "GATEWAY" DRUG

Just recently, conclusive research findings have indicated that tobacco is more of a serious **"gateway" drug** than previously expected. For example, nearly all heroin addicts initially began using "gateway" drugs such as alcohol and/or tobacco products. (Granted, most people who drink alcohol and use tobacco do not become heroin addicts!)

> **"gateway" drugs**
> drugs whose use leads to the use of other drugs;
> alcohol, cigarettes, and marijuana are considered
> "gateway" drugs

Biochemical evidence proving that the use of "gateway" drugs leads to the abuse of others is currently weak. But other findings are quite in-

SMOKING PROHIBITION VERSUS SMOKERS' RIGHTS

In response to that part of the U.S. population that has effectively banned smoking from certain public facilities, people who desire to continue smoking have formed action groups to press their right to smoke. These groups have largely been organized by several tobacco companies. Through mailing lists, newsletters, and slick magazine promotions, the groups advocate and report:

1. How the rights of smokers have been eroded in public and private places
2. How to write to senators, congresspersons, and other political leaders, urging them to uphold smokers' rights
3. How to effectively lobby for smoking in the workplace
4. How the harmful effects of second-hand

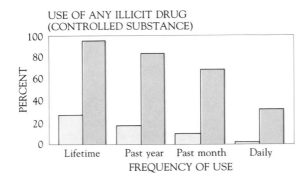

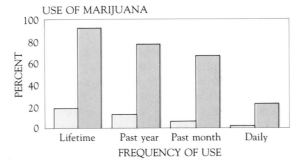

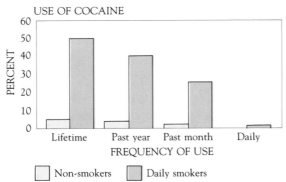

FIGURE 10-5 Use of illicit substances by daily tobacco users (high school seniors) *Source:* L. D. Johnston et al., *National Trends in Drug Use and Related Factors among American High School Students and Young Adults, 1975–1986* (Washington, D.C.: NIDA, 1987).

smoke have been exaggerated or remain unproven

5. How people who enjoy smoking have won major battles, preserving their right to smoke

While some modest gains have been made by these groups, the trend to restrict and ban cigarette smoking continues to be very strong. Antismoking groups have been highly successful in their efforts. Sixty percent of the population responding to a Gallup poll in July 1988 indicated that they would like to see laws that ban smoking in public places. Twenty-six percent of the smokers and 75% of the nonsmokers supported this view (Bezilla 1988). Increased sentiment in favor of more restrictions has even touched the heart of tobacco country, Raleigh, North Carolina! In short, the willingness of nonsmokers to speak up as firmly as necessary against being exposed to second-hand smoke is affecting smoking habits (Warner 1981).

A complete network of state laws restrict smoking (see Table 10-4). Interestingly, from a regional perspective, many states in the south (especially the "Deep South") are least restrictive, while many northeastern states are more restrictive. As of March 1989, 44 states restricted smoking in any public places, 27 limited smoking in restaurants, 32 limited smoking in public worksites, and 19 limited smoking in private worksites (see Table 10-4) (Foster et al. 1989, 135). Currently, all domestic airline flights ban smoking.

Several organized groups of nonsmokers have made quite an impact, including Action on Smoking and Health (ASH), the Group Against Smokers' Pollution (GASP), the American Lung Association, the American Cancer Society, and professional medical and dental associations. These groups have been instrumental in passing legislation restricting or banning smoking in public places; banning cigarette commercials on television; and prohibiting smoking on commercial aircraft, interstate buses, and in some restaurants, elevators, indoor theaters, libraries, art galleries, and museums. Table 10-5 summarizes the key events, regulations, and laws in the United States concerning smoking.

FUTURE SMOKERS

Not much research addresses who future smokers are likely to be. One study predicted that smokers will change because some subpopulations are not quitting (Coambs et al. 1988). This study surveyed 736 **"die-hard"** smokers, those who are defined as "least likely to quit." The respondents were divided into two groups: more and less likely to continue smoking. Based on a series of questions about attitudes toward smoking, the reluctant quitters had the following characteristics:

"die hards"
slang term for drug users who strongly resist quitting

1. They started smoking at a younger age.
2. They smoked the strongest brands.
3. They were not particularly concerned with the health-related effects of smoking.

Let's Get the Facts

Restrictions on Smoking Receive Strong Support

ATLANTA (AP)—Surveys from 10 U.S. cities—including one in the heart of tobacco country—show overwhelming sentiment for workplace smoking restrictions, government health officials said Thursday.

The surveys also found widespread support for outlawing tobacco advertising, the Centers for Disease Control reported.

Support for restricting smoking in the workplace ranged from 90 percent to 95 percent, the CDC said. From 47 percent to 73 percent of respondents called for a total ban on tobacco advertising.

But while large majorities favored restricting smoking in private workplaces, only 10 percent to 29 percent called for a total smoking ban there.

"The really compelling thing . . . is that we consistently got the same results. It shows this belief is nationwide," said Russell Sciandra, a Buffalo, N.Y.,

cancer researcher working with the survey project.

The survey results are similar to those in previous polls. A 1990 Gallup Poll report said 94 percent of Americans support workplace smoking restrictions, including 25 percent who support a ban.

Sciandra said researchers were particularly surprised by the numbers from Raleigh, N.C., the capital of a top tobacco-producing state.

There, 92 percent of the adults surveyed supported workplace smoking restrictions, including 14 percent who wanted it stopped entirely; 98 percent supported restrictions in restaurants; and 47 percent supported a ban on tobacco advertising.

"In the heart of tobacco country, even though the numbers tend to be lower than the rest of the country, we have strong support for smoking restrictions and restrictions on tobacco marketing," said Sciandra, associate director of the smoking control program at the Roswell Park Cancer Institute of Buffalo, N.Y.

"When you get almost a majority of the people in Raleigh saying tobacco advertising should be eliminated, that's pretty strong."

Walker Merryman, vice president of the Tobacco Institute, the industry's trade association, said other polls have shown most Americans opposed to a ban on cigarette advertising.

Other findings from the 10 surveys:

● A complete ban on cigarette sales was favored by 17 percent to 49 percent.

● From 62 percent to 74 percent supported smoking restrictions in bars.

● From 77 percent to 93 percent favored fining merchants selling tobacco to minors.

● And 31 percent to 56 percent thought tobacco companies should not be allowed to sponsor cultural or sports events.

Source: Associated Press 1991.

TABLE 10-4 State-by-state laws restricting smoking

A. Statewide law
B. Public transportation
C. Elevators
D. Indoor cultural & recreational facilities

E. Retail stores
F. Restaurants
G. Schools
H. Hospitals

I. Nursing homes
J. Government buildings
K. Public meeting rooms
L. Libraries

M. Other places[1]
N. Public worksites[2]
O. Private worksites[2]
P. Overall protection[3]

State	A	B	C	D	E	F	G	H	I	J	K	L	M[1]	N[2]	O[2]	P[3]
Alabama (AL)																0
Alaska (AK)	x	x	x	x	x	x	x	x	x	x	x	x	jk	d	a	3
Arizona (AZ)	x	x	x	x			x	x	x	x			k	bd		2
Arkansas (AR)	x	x					x	x					k	bd		2
California (CA)	x	x		x	x	x	x	x	x	x	x			b		3
Colorado (CO)	x	x	x	x			x	x	x		x			cd		2
Connecticut (CT)	x	x	x		x	x	x	x	x	x	x			c	c	4
Delaware (DE)	x	x														1
Dist. of Col. (DC)	x	x	x		x	x	x	x	x	x	x					3
Florida (FL)	x	x	x	x	x	x	x	x	x	x	x	x	jr	bd	bd	4
Georgia (GA)	x	x	x													1
Hawaii (HI)	x		x	x	x			x	x		x	x		bd	bdz	3
Idaho (ID)	x	x	x	x	x	x	x	x	x	x	x			d		3
Illinois (IL)																0
Indiana (IN)	x						x	x	x	x	x	x		cd		2
Iowa (IA)	x	x	x	x	x	x	x	x	x	x	x	x		d	d	4
Kansas (KS)	x	x	x	x	x	x	x	x	x	x	x	x		cd		3
Kentucky (KY)	x						x									1
Louisiana (LA)	x	= prohibits smoking in arena of Louisiana Superdome														1
Maine (ME)	x			x	x	x	x	x	x	x	x	x	jm	bd	bd	4
Maryland (MD)	x	x	x	x			x	x	x					b		2
Massachusetts (MA)	x	x	x	x	x	x	x	x	x	x	x	x	jkm	cd		3
Michigan (MI)	x	x	x	x	x	x	x	x	x	x	x		j	d		3
Minnesota (MN)	x	x	x	x	x	x	x	x	x	x	x	x	jk	cd	cd	4
Mississippi (MS)	x	x														1
Missouri (MO)																0
Montana (MT)	x	x	x	x	x	x	x	x	x	x	x			d	d	4

Source: Smoking and Health Review, "Action on Smoking and Health," in *Illegal Drugs and Alcohol*, edited by C. Foster, N. R. Jacobs, and M. A. Siegel (Wylie, TX: Information Plus, 1989), 232. Permission pending.

[1]j = jury rooms; k = day-care centers; m = mills, factories, barns, or stables; p = polling places; r = prisons; h = asbestos hazards.

[2]a = employer must post sign where smoking is prohibited; b = employer must have a written smoking policy; c = employer must have a policy that provides for a nonsmoking area; d = no smoking except in designated areas; z = govt. contractors only.

[3]Restrictiveness key, as adopted by U.S. Public Health Service: 0 = none; 1 = nominal; 2 = basic; 3 = moderate; 4 = extensive.

A. Statewide law
B. Public transportation
C. Elevators
D. Indoor cultural & recreational facilities
E. Retail stores
F. Restaurants
G. Schools
H. Hospitals
I. Nursing homes
J. Government buildings
K. Public meeting rooms
L. Libraries
M. Other places[1]
N. Public worksites[2]
O. Private worksites[2]
P. Overall protection[3]

State	A	B	C	D	E	F	G	H	I	J	K	L	M[1]	N[2]	O[2]	P[3]
Nebraska (NE)	x	x	x	x	x	x		x	x	x	x	x		d	d	4
Nevada (NV)	x	x	x	x	x	x	x	x	x	x	x	x	m		a	3
N Hampshire (NH)	x	x	x	x	x	x	x	x	x	x	x	x	p	d	b	4
New Jersey (NJ)	x	x	x	x	x	x	x	x	x	x	x	x		bc	bc	4
New Mexico (NM)	x		x							x	x	x		cd		2
New York (NY)	x	x		x								x	p		a	2
N Carolina (NC)																0
North Dakota (ND)	x	x	x	x			x	x	x	x	x	x		cd		3
Ohio (OH)	x	x	x	x			x	x	x	x	x		h	d		2
Oklahoma (OK)	x	x	x	x		x	x	x	x	x	x	x		cd		3
Oregon (OR)	x	x	x	x	x	x	x	x	x	x	x		j	d		3
Pennsylvania (PA)	x			x	x	x	x	x	x	x	x	x	r	d	abc	2
Rhode Island (RI)	x	x	x	x	x	x	x	x	x	x		x	m	b	b	4
South Carolina (SC)	x	x														1
South Dakota (SD)	x	x	x	x			x	x	x			x	l			2
Tennessee (TN)																0
Texas (TX)	x	x	x	x			x	x	x		x					2
Utah (UT)	x	x	x	x	x	x	x	x	x	x	x	x		d	d	4
Vermont (VT)	x		x						x		x		m	bd	bd	4
Virginia (VA)																0
Washington (WA)	x	x	x	x	x	x	x	x	x	x	x	x		d	d	4
West Virginia (WV)	x	x					x						m		a	1
Wisconsin (WI)	x	x	x	x	x	x	x	x	x	x				d		3
Wyoming (WY)																0
Total States #	44	36	32	30	25	27	33	34	32	31	29	20	18	32	19	

4. Smokers over the age of 40 were more physically dependent on nicotine than those under 40.

"Die-hard" smokers were believed to continue smoking because of denial rather than ignorance.

Think About It...

1. A recent national news telecast on CBS reported that one-third of high school students smoke cigarettes and that whites and young men (more than women) showed higher rates of smoking. Why do you think this is so?
2. Cite what you believe are three main reasons teen-agers begin smoking cigarettes.
3. Look through several magazines for cigarette advertisements. What themes do they attempt to associate with smoking?
4. Review the four characteristics of reluctant cigarette smokers discussed above. In light of these characteristics, how would you design a health education campaign to convince these "die-hard" smokers to stop?

TABLE 10-5 Key events in the United States concerning the regulation of smoking

Year	Event
1945	Mayo Clinic cautions against use of cigarettes by patients with cardiovascular disease. American Cancer Society announces parallelism between cigarette sales and lung cancer.
1957	American Cancer Society, National Cancer Institute, American Heart Association, and National Heart Institute issue report calling for government action regarding smoking and public health.
1958	Tobacco Institute formed by major cigarette manufacturers to counteract possible political effects of health studies.
1964	U.S. Surgeon General's report on smoking and health.
1965	National Clearinghouse for Smoking and Health (NCSH) established within the Public Health Service.
1966	Federal Cigarette Labeling and Advertising Act requires each package to present the statement: "Caution: Cigarette Smoking May Be Hazardous To Your Health."
1967	Federal Communications Commission rules that the Fairness Doctrine applies to cigarette advertising: television and radio must carry antismoking messages. Federal Trade Commission issues first report on tar and nicotine content.
1970	Cigarette package statement changed by law to: "Warning: the Surgeon General has determined that cigarette smoking is dangerous to your health."
1971	Radio and TV smoking commercials banned, and the Interstate Commerce Commission restricts smoking to the rear five rows of interstate buses.
1973	Arizona is the first state to prohibit smoking in all elevators, indoor theaters, libraries, art galleries, museums, concert halls, and buses. All airlines required to designate smoking and nonsmoking areas in planes.
1975	Minnesota passes Indoor Clean Air Act, which makes smoking illegal in all public places and public meetings except where otherwise designated.
1976	Superior Court of New Jersey decision in case of *Shimp v. New Jersey Bell Telephone Co.* Worker must be allowed to have a nonpolluted work environment.
1978	Civil Aeronautics Board bans cigar and pipe smoking on all American commercial airlines.
1984	The Comprehensive Smoking Education Act requires that cigarette packages and advertising carry new rotational warning labels as of October 12, 1985.
1988	Smoking banned on U.S. commercial flights under two hours in duration.

KEY TERMS

Nicotiana tabacum
nicotine
emphysema
sudden infant death syndrome
(SIDS)

second-hand smoke
smokeless tobacco
snuff
"sidestream" smoke

"gateway" drugs
patterns of behavior
"die hards"

SUMMARY

1. Nicotine is by far one of the most addictive drugs.
2. Interestingly, tobacco farming is the sixth-largest cash crop in the United States. Ranking ahead of it are corn, soybeans, hay, wheat, and cotton.
3. The quality of leaf tobacco has changed throughout years of production. Since 1956, the amount of leaf tobacco in a cigarette has gone down by approximately 25%. Most cigarettes today are low-tar and low-nicotine types, and 90% are filtertips.
4. Two stages are involved in processing tobacco: (a) the leaves are dried out, which is called *curing;* and (b) the harvest is aged for approximately two years.
5. It appears that the initial use of tobacco was on the South and North American continents. The early negative and positive views of tobacco were controversial. In this sense, tobacco was the first major drug controversy of global dimension. Tobacco also played a significant role in the successful colonization of the United States.
6. Cigarette consumption in the United States is declining while the exportation and use of cigarettes abroad is increasing. Latest surveys indicate that, while the percentage of teen-agers who try tobacco is slowly declining, a high percentage continue to try tobacco.
7. National health surveys found that gender, education, and race and ethnicity strongly affect who is most likely to smoke. Findings show that, the more education you have, the less likely you are to smoke. Men are more likely to smoke than women, and African-Americans are more likely to smoke than whites.
8. Users of such "gateway" drugs as alcohol and cigarettes are more easily allured than nonusers into experimenting with other licit and illicit drugs. Surprisingly, among youth cigarette smokers were 10 times more likely than nonsmokers to use cocaine regularly.
9. Tobacco products classified as *smokeless tobacco* include chewing tobacco and snuff. *"Sidestream"* smoke comes directly from the lighted tip of a cigarette between puffs and has much higher concentrations of irritating and hazardous substances. *Second-hand smoke* includes all smoke from tobacco products released into the air.
10. Nicotine is the substance in tobacco that causes dependence. This drug initially stimulates and then depresses the nervous system.
11. Research clearly shows that the tar and nicotine contents of cigarettes affect mortality rates. Cigarette smokers tend to die at an earlier age than nonsmokers. They also have a greater probability of contracting various illnesses: types of cancers; chronic bronchitis and emphysema; diseases of the cardiovascular system; and peptic ulcers. Finally, smoking also has adverse effects on pregnancy and may harm the fetus.
12. Because of all the negative publicity regarding cigarette smoking, prohibitionists versus smokers' rights groups are challenging one another.
13. The main types of behavioral treatment for the cessation of smoking are: (a) punishment and aversive therapy, (b) stimulus control, and (c) substitute smoking procedures.

R E F E R E N C E S

Altman, D. G., M. D. Slater, C.L. Albright, and N. Maccoby. "How an Unhealthy Product Is Sold: Cigarette Advertising in Magazines, 1960–1985." *Journal of Communication* 37 (1987): 95–106.

American Cancer Society. *Cancer Facts and Figures.* New York: ACS, 1990.

Associated Press. "Restrictions on Smoking Receive Strong Support." *Vidette* [Valparaiso, IN] *Messenger,* 31 May 1991, C1.

Austin, G. A. *Perspectives on the History of Psychoactive Substance Use.* Washington, D.C.: NIDA, 1978.

Bezilla, R., ed. *America's Youth 1977–1988.* Princeton, NJ: The Gallup Organization, 1988.

Brooks, J. E. *The Mighty Leaf: Tobacco through the Centuries.* Boston: Little, Brown, 1952.

Callahan, M. "How Smoking Kills You." *Parade,* December 1987, 209–211, 213.

Coambs, R. et al. "Characterizing Future Smokers." In *Problems and Drug Dependence, 1988,* edited by L. S. Harris. Washington, D.C.: NIDA, 1988.

Connolly, G. N., D. M. Werin, and S. S. Hecht. "The Reemergence of Smokeless Tobacco." *New England Journal of Medicine* 314 (1986): 1020–27.

Corti, E. C. *A History of Smoking.* London: G. G. Harrap, 1931.

Davis, R. M. "Current Trends in Cigarette Advertising and Marketing." *New England Journal of Medicine* 316 (1987): 725–732.

DeAngelis, T. "Behavior Is Included in Report on Smoking." *APA Monitor* 20, no. 3 (1989): 1, 4.

Fiore, M. C., T. E. Novotny, J. P. Pierce, E. J. Hatziandreau, K.M. Patel, and R. M. Davis, "Trends in Cigarette Smoking in the U.S.—The Changing Influence of Gender and Race." *Journal of the American Medical Association* 261 (January 1989): 49–56.

Foster, C. D., N. R. Jacobs, and M. A. Siegel, eds. *Illegal Drugs and Alcohol—America's Anguish.* Wylie, TX: Information Plus, 1989.

Goldberg, S. R., R. D. Spealman, and D. M. Goldberg. "Persistent Behavior at High Rates Maintained by Intravenous Self-Administration of Nicotine." *Science* 214 (1981): 573–575.

Gonzalez, M., and B. Edmondson. "The Smoking Class." *American Demographics* 10, no. 11 (November 1986): 34–37, 58.

Heimann, R. K. *Tobacco and Americans.* New York: McGraw-Hill, 1960.

Henningfield, J. E., and R. Nemeth-Coslett. "Nicotine Dependence." *Chest* 93, no. 2 (1988): 37S–55S.

Jaffe, J. H. "Drug Addiction and Drug Abuse." In *The Pharmacological Basis of Therapeutics,* edited by A. G. Gilman, L. S. Goodman, and A. Gilman, 6th ed. New York: Macmillan, 1980.

Jaffe, J. H., and M. Kanzler. "Smoking as an Addictive Disorder." In *Cigarette Smoking as a Dependence Process,* edited by N. A. Krasnegor. NIDA Research Monograph 23. Washington, D.C.: NIDA, 1979.

Jarvik, M. E. "Biological Influence on Cigarette Smoking." In *The Behavioral Aspects of Smoking,* edited by N. A. Krasnegor. NIDA Research Monograph 26. Washington, D.C.: NIDA, 1979.

Johnston, L. D., P. M. O'Malley, and J. G. Bachman. *National Trends in Drug Use and Related Factors among American High School Students and Young Adults, 1975–1986.* Washington, D.C.: NIDA, 1987.

Jones, R. T., T. R. Farrell III, and R. I. Herning. "Tobacco Smoking and Nicotine Tolerance." In *Self-Administration of Abused Substances: Methods for Study,* edited by N. A. Krasnegor. NIDA Research Monograph 20. Washington, D.C.: NIDA, 1978.

Kaufman, S. B. *Challenge and Change: The History of the Tobacco Workers International Union.* Urbana, IL: University of Illinois Press, 1988.

Krasnegor, N. A. "Introduction." In *The Behavioral Aspects of Smoking,* edited by N. A. Krasnegor. NIDA Research Monograph 26. Washington, D.C.: NIDA, 1979.

Langton, P. A. *Drug Use and the Alcohol Dilemma.* Boston, MA: Allyn and Bacon, 1991.

Liska, K. *Drugs and the Human Body.* New York: Macmillan, 1990.

National Institute on Drug Abuse. *Drug Use Among Youth: Findings from the 1988 Household Survey on Drug Abuse.* Department of Health and Human Services Publication no. (ADM) 91-1765. Rockville, MD: NIDA, 1991.

National Institute on Drug Abuse. *Capsules: Facts about Teenagers and Drug Abuse.* Rockville, MD: NIDA, January 1990a.

National Institute on Drug Abuse. *Monitoring the Future Study.* Ann Arbor, MI: Institute for Social Research, 1990b.

"Non-Smoking Youth Better Resist Other Drugs." *Prevention Newsline* 4, no. 3 (Spring 1991): 5.

Palfai, T., and H. Jankiewicz. *Drugs and Human Behavior.* Dubuque, IA: Wm. C. Brown, 1991.

Perry, S. "Recognizing Everyday Addicts." *Current Health* 2, no. 16 (May 1990): 20–23.

Pierce, J. P., M. C. Fiore, T. E. Novotny, E. J. Hatziandreu, and R. M. David. "Trends in Cigarette Smoking in the United States—Educational Differences Are Increasing." *Journal of the American Medical Association* 261 (6 January 1989): 56–60.

Pomerleau, O. F. "Behavioral Factors in the Establishment, Maintenance, and Cessation of Smoking." In *The Behavioral Aspects of Smoking,* edited by N. A. Krasnegor. NIDA Research Monograph 26. Washington, D.C.: NIDA, 1979.

Schuckit, M. A. *Drug and Alcohol Abuse: A Clinical Guide to Diagnosis and Treatment.* 2nd ed. New York: Plenum, 1984.

Schultes, R. E. "Ethnopharmacological Significance of Psychotropic Drugs of Vegetal Origin." In *Principles of Psychopharmacology,* edited by W. G. Clark and J. del Giudice. 2nd ed. New York: Academic, 1978.

Siegel, L. "Want to Take Risks? It Should be Your Choice." *Playboy* 36, no. 1 (1989): 37–44.

Smoking and Health Review. "Action on Smoking and Health." In *Illegal Drugs and Alcohol,* edited by C. Foster, N. R. Jacobs, and M. A. Siegel. Wylie, TX: Information Plus, 1989.

Statistical Abstract of U.S. *The National Data, 110 Edition.* Washington, D.C.: U.S.

Department of the Census, January 1990.

Stellman, S. D., and L. Garfinkel. "Smoking Habits and Tar Levels in a New American Cancer Society Prospective Study of 1.2 Million Men and Women." *Journal of the National Cancer Institute* 76 (1986): 1057–1063.

Taylor, P. "Ganglionic Stimulating and Blocking Agents." In *The Pharmacological Basis of Therapeutics,* edited by A. G. Gilman, L. S. Goodman, and A. Gilman. 6th ed. New York: Macmillan, 1980.

Tolchin, M. "Surgeon General Asserts That Smoking Is an Addiction." *New York Times,* May 17, 1988, 1, 26.

U.S. Department of Agriculture. *Annual Report on Tobacco Statistics.* and U.S. Department of Agriculture. *The Tobacco Outlook and Situation Report.* Washington, D.C.: U.S. Department of Agriculture, 1988.

U.S. Surgeon General. *The Health Consequences of Smoking: Cancer and Chronic Lung Disease in the Workplace.* Washington, D.C.: Government Printing Office, 1985.

U.S. Surgeon General. *The Health Consequences of Smoking,* Washington, D.C.: Government Printing Office, 1984.

U.S. Surgeon General. *The Changing Cigarette.* Publication no. 81-51056. Washington, D.C.: U.S. Department of Health, Education, and Welfare, 1981.

U.S. Surgeon General. *Smoking and Health: A Report of the Surgeon General.* Publication no. 79-50066. Washington, D.C.: U.S. Department of Health, Education, and Welfare, 1979.

Volle, R. L., and G. B. Koelle. "Ganglionic Stimulating and Blocking Agents." In *The Pharmacological Basis of Therapeutics,* edited by A. G. Gilman, L. S. Goodman, and A. Gilman. 6th ed. New York: Macmillan, 1975.

Warner, K. E. "Cigarette Smoking in the 1970s: The Impact of the Antismoking Campaign on Consumption." *Science* 211 (1981): 729–731.

Wolfe, R. "Smokeless Tobacco, the Fatal Pitch." *Multinational Monitor,* July/August 1987, 20–21.

Hallucinogens

CHAPTER OUTLINE

LEARNING OBJECTIVES

On completing this chapter, you will be able to:

1. Identify the three principal types of hallucinogens and their four principal hallucinogenic effects.
2. Explain why hallucinogens became so popular during the 1960s but are less commonly used today.
3. Describe the nature of the sensory changes that occur due to the influence of hallucinogens.

4. Outline how psychedelic, stimulant, and anticholinergic effects are expressed in the three principal types of hallucinogens.
5. Describe the rationale for using hallucinogens in psychotherapy.
6. Explain how the abuse liability of hallucinogens differs from that associated with other commonly abused drugs.
7. Describe what effects environment and personality have on the

individual's response to hallucinogens.
8. Discuss the occurrence of psychosis and "flashbacks" following LSD use.
9. Identify the problems of purity with "street" LSD.
10. Characterize how PCP differs from other hallucinogens.
11. Identify the abused inhalants, who uses them, and what hazards they cause.

Source: © Camerique

We have drunk the Soma and become immortal!
We have attained the light, we have found the Gods!
What can the malice of mortal man
or his spite, O Immortal, do to us now?
—*Rig Veda*, book VIII, 48 (Panikkar 1977)

This ancient Sanskrit hymn dates back to 1500 B.C. Some researchers believe *Soma* may have been the mushroom *Amanita muscaria* (see Figure 11-1), which causes hallucinations. Others believe Soma was hashish or even nutmeg preparations. People have known and written about hallucinations for centuries. Throughout the ages, individuals who saw visions or experienced hallucinations were perceived as being holy or sacred, receiving divine messages, or possibly as being bewitched and controlled by the devil. There are many indications that medicine men, shamans, witches, oracles, and perhaps mystics and priests of various groups were familiar with drugs and herbs that caused such experiences and today are known as *hallucinogens*.

In this chapter, we will begin with a brief historical review of the use of hallucinogens, tracing the trend in the United States from the 1960s to today. Next, the nature of hallucinogens and the effects they produce will be examined. The rest of the chapter addresses the various types of psychedelic agents: LSD types, phenylethylamines, anticholinergics, and other miscellaneous substances.

THE HISTORY OF HALLUCINOGEN USE

Through the years, peoples of the Americas have used over 130 psychoactive plants, but strangely enough, the rest of the world has used only about 20 such plants. Because there is no reason to believe that the Americas are richer in plants with psychoactive properties than the rest of the world, the reason for the extensive use of such plants may be cultural (Schultes and Hofmann 1973).

Probably the oldest record of **hallucinogens** in the Western hemisphere is a 4,500-year-old grave of a South American Indian, which contained a

hallucinogens
substances that alter sensory processing in the brain, causing perceptual disturbances, changes in thought processing, and depersonalization

snuff tube and some snuff (see Figure 11-2). This type of snuff—called *cohoba snuff*—is still being used today by some native tribes in that region. Its active ingredient is dimethyltryptamine (DMT), which is a fairly potent hallucinogen.

In the United States, hallucinogens came into their own in the 1960s when the general public became particularly aware of these drugs, especially lysergic acid diethylamide (LSD). By this time, psychiatrists and psychologists had been using such agents for years, extolling their virtues as aids in psychotherapy.

One of the early principal American proponents was Harvard psychology professor Timothy Leary, who, in the early 1960s, began giving graduate students hallucinogens such as psilocybin and LSD as a means of helping them to "get in touch with themselves."

Prior to this, several psychedelic substances, such as mescaline from the peyote cactus, could be obtained from chemical supply houses with no

FIGURE 11-1 The *Amanita muscaria*, sometimes called the *fly agaric*, mushroom yields hallucinogenic drugs. It may be the *soma* described in *Rig Veda*.

FIGURE 11-2 A South American Indian using a *tabaco*, or snuff tube.

restriction. Abuse was not a significant concern. That changed with the turbulent conditions of the 1960s, which set the stage for popularizing hallucinogens. This was the decade of racial struggles, the Vietnam War, and violent demonstrations. Many individuals were frustrated with the hypocrisy that appeared to permeate the sociological and political fiber of the country during this era. Some of those frustrated with "the establishment" tried to "turn on, tune in, and drop out" by using pharmacological crutches.

Psychedelic drugs became popular because medical professionals such as Leary reported that they allowed users to get in touch with themselves and achieve a peaceful inner serenity. At the same time, it became well publicized that the natural psychedelics (such as mescaline and peyote) were and had been for many years used routinely by some religious organizations of Native Americans for enhancing spiritual experiences. This contributed to the mystical, supernatural aura associated with hallucinogenic agents and added to their enticement to a so-called "drop-out" generation.

However, with widespread use of LSD, it was observed that this and similar drugs induced a form of psychosis like schizophrenia. The term **psychotomimetic** was coined to describe these compounds; it means "psychosis mimicking" and is still used in medicine today. The basis for the designation is the effects of these drugs to induce mental states that impair your ability to recognize and respond appropriately to reality.

psychotomimetic
substances that cause psychoticlike symptoms

A group of Kiowa Indian peyote worshippers are at an all-night ceremony. The *roadman*, or leader, in native dress, stands in the center. *Source:* R. Schultes and A. Hofmann, *The Botany and Chemistry of Hallucinogens*, 2nd ed. (Springfield, IL: Charles C. Thomas, 1980), figure 86, p. 198.

By the mid-1960s, federal regulatory agencies became concerned with the misuse of hallucinogens and the social impact of this growing problem. Access to hallucinogenic agents was restricted, and laws against their distribution were passed.

One strategy to preserve the right to use hallucinogens was based upon constitutional guarantees of freedom of religion. For example, peyote plays a central role in the ceremonies of Native Americans who follow a religion that is a combination of Christian doctrine and Native American religious rituals. They are located as far north as Canada. They believe that God made a special gift of this sacramental plant to them so that they might commune more directly with him. The first organized peyote church was the First-Born Church of Christ, incorporated in 1914 in Oklahoma. The Native American Church of the United States was chartered in 1918 and is the largest such group at present (approximately a quarter of a million members).

In 1918, bills were submitted to Congress to prohibit the use of peyote by Native Americans but were not passed. Federal and state legal battles over this issue ensued for half a century, until the Supreme Court finally heard the case of a Native American convicted of using peyote and ruled that Native Americans could use it within the confines of their religion.

In 1966, Timothy Leary attempted a similar constitutional strategy to retain legitimate access to LSD. He began a religion called The League of Spiritual Discovery; LSD was the sacrament. This unorthodox religious orientation to the LSD experience was presented in a manual called *The Psychedelic Experience*, which was based on the *Tibetan Book of the Dead* (Leary et al. 1964). It became the "bible" of the psychedelic drug movement.

The movement grew, but most members used "street" LSD and did not follow Leary's directions. Leary believed that the hallucinogenic experience was only beneficial under proper control and guidance. But the members of this so-called religion merely used the organization as a front to gain access to the drug. Federal authorities did not agree with Leary's *freedom of religion* interpretation and in 1969 convicted him for possession of mar-

Timothy J. Leary, one-time professor at Harvard University, shown here with his wife, experimented with various hallucinogenic drugs, including LSD. He asserted that the hallucinogenic experience was beneficial under proper control and guidance. *Source:* Rick Smolan/Stock, Boston

ijuana and LSD. Before being incarcerated, Leary escaped to Algeria and wandered for a couple of years before being extradited to the United States. He served several years in jail and was released in 1976, at which time he claimed to be totally rehabilitated and declared he would never again advocate the use of hallucinogens.

Today, the use of hallucinogens (excluding marijuana) is primarily a young adult phenomenon (Johnston et al. 1989) and has not returned to the high rate seen in the late 1960s and early 1970s. In 1990, 9% of high school seniors reported having ever used hallucinogens, compared to 16% in 1975 (NIDA 1991). Several factors have likely contributed to the decline of hallucinogen popularity in the United States.

1. In 1970, federal agencies included LSD in the same regulatory category as heroin (Jaffe 1990), making access to these drugs more difficult.

2. Relatively pure psychedelics do not tend to cause physical dependence, although minor psychological dependence might occur. Because severe addiction does not occur, discontinuation of hallucinogen use is not particularly problematic.

3. Social conditions in America are much different today than they were 20 to 30 years ago, when these agents were extremely popular. In the 1960s, there was great public agitation and discontentment concerning social and political issues. These frustrations encouraged many members of a socially conscious generation to turn to hallucinogens for relief. Recent generations appear to be less likely to feel alienated from social institutions and their government; as a result, they may have less inclination to turn to hallucinogens.

4. Concern about health issues relative to the use of the hallucinogens has contributed to the depopularization of these agents. For example, research conducted in the late 1960s suggested that LSD use caused chromosome breakage that could result in fetal damage if pregnancy were to occur. Federal agencies trying to control consumption of hallucinogens used these reports as part of their "education program" to convince young people to avoid using these compounds. Upon closer scrutiny of this early work and additional research, the validity and reliability of the initial studies have been seriously questioned (Dishotsky et al. 1971). Even so, the reports served their purpose and frightened many potential hallucinogen users (see later in this chapter). Another health concern for the potential user has been the presence of dangerous adulterant chemicals such as strychnine that are frequently used to "cut" hallucinogens.

THE NATURE OF HALLUCINOGENS

Agreement has not been reached on what constitutes a hallucinogenic agent (Glennon 1987), for several reasons. First, a variety of seemingly unrelated drug groups can all produce hallucinations, delusions, or sensory disturbances under certain conditions; for example, besides the traditional hallucinogens (such as LSD), anticholinergics, cocaine, amphetamines, and steroids can cause hallucinations.

What's more, responses to even the traditional hallucinogens can vary tremendously from person to person and experience to experience. It is apparent that multiple mechanisms are involved in the actions of these drugs, which contributes to the array of responses that they can cause. These drugs most certainly influence the complex inner workings of the human mind and have been described as **psychedelic, psychotogenic,** or (as already mentioned) *psychotomimetic.* The features of hallucinogens that distinguish them from other drug groups are their ability to alter perception, thought, and feeling in such a manner that does not normally occur except in dreams or during experiences of extreme religious exaltation (Jaffe 1990). We will examine these characteristics throughout this chapter.

psychedelic
substances that expand or heighten perception and consciousness

psychotogenic
substances that initiate psychotic behavior

PHYSIOLOGICAL EFFECTS

In general, LSD is considered the prototype agent by which other hallucinogens are evaluated. Typical users experience several stages of sensory experiences; they can go through all stages during a single "trip" or more likely, they will only pass through some. These stages include (a) heightened, exaggerated senses, (b) loss of control, (c) self-reflection, and (d) loss of identity and a sense of cosmic merging.

The following illustrations of the stages of the LSD experience are based primarily on an account by Solomon Snyder (1974), a highly regarded neuroscientist (one of the principal discoverers of endorphins; see Chapter 5), who, as a young man, personally experienced the effects of LSD.

HEIGHTENED SENSES   In his encounter with LSD, Snyder used a moderate dose of 100 to 200 micrograms and observed few discernible effects for the first 30 minutes except some mild nausea. After this time had elapsed, objects took on a purplish tinge and appeared to be vaguely outlined. Colors, textures, and lines achieved a beauty and richness Snyder had never before seen. Perception was so incisive that individual skin pores "stood out and

clamored for recognition" (p. 42). Objects became distorted; when Snyder focused upon his thumb, it began to swell, undulate, and then moved forward in a menacing fashion. Remarkable visions filled with vivid imagery occurred when his eyes were closed. The sense of time and distance changed dramatically; "a minute was like an hour, a week was like an eternity, a foot became a mile" (p. 43). The present seemed to drag on forever, and the concept of future lost its meaning. The exaggeration of perceptions and feelings gave the sense of more events occurring in a time period, giving the impression of time slowing.

An associated sensation described by Snyder is called **synesthesia,** a cross-over phenomenon between senses. For example, sound can take on visual dimensions and vice versa, enabling you to see sounds and hear colors. Snyder stated that, when he was under the influence of LSD, as people entered the room and clapped their hands, he could see sound waves undulating in the air before him. These altered sensory experiences are described as a heightened sensory awareness, often accompanied by enhanced clarity, and relate to the first component of the psychedelic state (Jaffe 1990).

---

synesthesia
a subjective sensation or image of a sense other than the one being stimulated, such as an auditory sensation caused by a visual stimulus

---

LOSS OF CONTROL   The second feature of LSD also relates to altered sensory experiences and a loss of control (Jaffe 1990). The user cannot determine whether the psychedelic trip will be a warm, comfortable experience or a "bad trip," with recollections of hidden fears and suppressed anxieties that can precipitate neurotic or psychotic responses. The frightening reactions may persist a few minutes or several hours and be mildly agitating or terrifyingly threatening (see the adjacent box). Some bad trips can include feelings of panic, confusion, suspiciousness, helplessness, and a total lack of control. Replays of these frightening

---

For You to Consider...

A "Bad Trip"

Boyard Taylor, an American author, wrote the following in 1855 about his hallucination while under the influence of hashish:

> I tore open my vest, placed my hand over the spot, and tried to count the pulsations; but there were two hearts, one beating at the rate of 1,000 beats a minute, and the other with a slow dull motion. My throat, I felt, was filled to the brim with blood, and streams of blood were pouring from my ears. I felt them gushing warm down my cheeks and neck. . . . My body seemed to shrink and grow rigid as I wrestled with the demon and my face to become wild, lean and haggard. . . . Oh horrors! The flesh had fallen from my bones, and it was a skeleton head that I carried on my shoulders. . . . I was sinking deeper and deeper into a pit of unutterable agony and despair. . . . Every effort to preserve my reason was accompanied by a pang of mortal fear, lest what I now experienced was insanity, and would hold mastery over me forever. The thought of death, which also haunted me, was far less bitter than this dread (Snyder 1974).

experiences can occur at a later time, even though the drug has not been taken again; such recurrences are referred to as **"flashbacks."**

"flashback"
the recurrence of an earlier drug-induced sensory experience in the absence of the drug

---

It is not clear what determines the nature of the sensory response. Perhaps it relates to the state of anxiety and personality of the user or of the nature of his or her surroundings. It is interesting that Timothy Leary tried to teach his "drug disciples" that "turning on correctly means to understand the many levels that are brought into focus; it takes years of discipline, training and discipleship" ("Celebration" 1966). He apparently felt that, with experience and training, you could control the sensory effects of the hallucinogens. This is an interesting possibility but has never been well demonstrated.

SELF-REFLECTION Snyder (1974) makes reference to the third component of the psychedelic response in his LSD experience. During the period when sensory effects predominate, self-reflection also occurs. While in this state, Snyder explains, the user "becomes aware of thoughts and feelings long hidden beneath the surface, forgotten and/or repressed" (p. 44). Giving a newfound clarity, the psychedelics allow the individual to have insight to true motives and relationships with the principal roleplayers in his or her life. Snyder claims that this clarity of perspective can lead to valid insights that are useful psychotherapeutic exercises.

Some psychotherapeutists have used or advocated the use of psychedelics for this purpose since the 1950s, as described by Sigmund Freud, to "make conscious the unconscious" (Snyder, 1974, 44). It should be noted that, while a case can be made for the psychotherapeutic use of this group of drugs, the Food and Drug Administration (FDA) has not approved any of these agents for psychiatric use. The psychedelics currently available are considered to be too unpredictable in their effects and possess substantial risks. Not only is their administration not considered to be significantly therapeutic, but their use is deemed a great enough risk that the principal hallucinogenic agents are scheduled as controlled substances.

LOSS OF IDENTITY AND COSMIC MERGING The final features that set the psychedelics apart as unique drugs are described by Snyder (1974) as the "mystical-spiritual aspect of the drug experience." He claims, "It is indescribable. For how can anyone verbalize a merging of his being with the totality of the universe? How do you put into words the feeling that 'all is one,' 'I am of the all,' 'I am no longer.' One's skin ceases to be a boundary between self and others" (p. 45). It is likely that this sense of cosmic merging and union with all humankind correlates to the exhiliratingly spiritual experiences described by mystics of many religions and from many different times and civilizations. The influence of hallucinogens in these historical experiences is unknown.

The loss of identity and personal boundaries caused by hallucinogens is not viewed as being so spiritually enticing by all. In particular, for individuals who have rigid, highly ordered personalities, the dissolution of a well-organized and -structured world is terrifying because the drug destroys the individual's emotional support. Such an individual finds that the loss of a separate identity can cause extreme panic and anxiety. During these drug-induced panic states, which in some ways are schizophreniclike, people have committed suicide or homicide. These tragic reactions are part of the risk of using hallucinogenics and explains some of the FDA's hesitancy to legalize or authorize them for psychotherapeutic use.

MECHANISMS OF ACTION

As with most drugs, hallucinogens represent the proverbial "two-edged sword." These drugs may cause potentially useful effects for many people. However, the variability in positive versus negative responses, coupled with lack of understanding as to what factors are responsible for the variables, have made these drugs dangerous and difficult to manage.

It has been suggested by researchers that all hallucinogens act at a common central nervous system (CNS) receptor to exert their psychedelic effects. Although this hypothesis has not been totally disproven, there is little evidence to support it. The fact that so many different types of drugs can cause hallucinogenic effects suggests that multiple mechanisms are likely responsible (Jacobs 1983). And because sensory processing by the brain involves multiple transmitter systems, it seems that those drugs that interfere with the normal functioning of such transmitter systems could alter routine interpretation of sensory input, causing hallucination.

The most predictable and typical psychedelic experiences are caused by LSD or similar agents. Consequently, these agents have been the primary focus of studies intended to elucidate the nature of hallucinogenic mechanisms. While LSD has effects at several CNS sites, from the spinal cord to the cortex of the brain, its effects on the neurotransmitter serotonin most likely account for its psychedelic properties. That LSD and similar drugs alter serotonin activity has been proven; how they affect this transmitter is not so apparent.

It appears as though LSD is an agonist that directly stimulates a subset of serotonin receptors of the serotonin type-2 variety (see Chapter 5). However, under some conditions, LSD can have antagonist (blocking) activity, as well. How these apparently contradicting effects relate to the psychedelic actions of LSD has yet to be determined (Jaffe 1990). The principal brain region(s) of these serotonin-directed effects are also not known. The neurons that release serotonin from their axon terminals (see Chapter 5) primarily originate in the brainstem but project their axons throughout the brain, making determination of the exact site of drug action very difficult.

Although many experts believe changes in serotonin activity are the basis for psychedelic properties of most hallucinogens, a case can be made for the involvement of norepinephrine, dopamine, acetylcholine, and perhaps other transmitter systems, as well. Only additional research will be able to sort out this complex but important issue.

T h i n k   A b o u t   I t . . .

1. Why were substances with hallucinogenic properties so popular with ancient religions and cults?
2. Why is personality so important in determining an individual's response to a hallucinogen?
3. Do you feel that a hallucinogenic experience would be enjoyable to the user? Why?

TYPES OF HALLUCINOGENIC AGENTS

Due to recent technological advancements, understanding of hallucinogens has advanced; even so, the classification of these drugs remains somewhat arbitrary. Many agents produce some of the pharmacological effects of the traditional psychedelics, such as LSD and mescaline.

A second type of hallucinogen includes those agents that have amphetaminelike molecular structures (referred to as *phenylethylamines*) and possess some stimulant action; this group includes drugs such as DOM (dimethoxymethyl*amphetamine*), MDA (methylenedioxy*amphetamine*), and MDMA (methylenedioxy*methamphetamine*). These agents vary in their hallucinogen/stimulant properties. MDA is more like an amphetamine (stimulant), while MDMA is more like LSD (hallucinogen). However, in large doses, each of the phenylethylamines causes substantial CNS stimulation.

The third major group of hallucinogens is the anticholinergic drugs, which block muscarinic receptors (see Chapter 5). Almost all drugs that antagonize the muscarinic receptors cause hallucinations in high doses. Many of these potent anticholinergic hallucinogens are naturally occurring and have been known, used, and abused for millennia.

TRADITIONAL HALLUCINOGENS: LSD TYPES

The LSD-like drugs are considered to be the prototypical hallucinogens and are used as comparison for other types of agents with psychedelic properties. Included in this group are LSD itself and some hallucinogens derived from plants, such as mescaline from the peyote cactus, psilocybin from mushrooms, dimethyltryptamine (DMT) from seeds, and myristicin from nutmeg. Because LSD is the principal hallucinogen, its origin, history, and properties will be discussed in detail, providing a basis for understanding the other psychedelic drugs.

LYSERGIC ACID DIETHYLAMIDE (LSD)   LSD is a relatively new drug, but similar compounds have existed for a long time. For example, accounts from the Middle Ages tell about a strange affliction that caused women to abort and others to develop strange burning sensations in their extremities. Today, we call this condition **ergotism** and know that it is caused by eating grain contaminated by the ergot fungus. This fungus produces compounds related to LSD called the *ergot alkaloids*. Besides the sensory effects, the ergot substances can also cause hallucinations, delirium, and psychosis.

ergotism
poisoning by toxic substances from the ergot fungus
Claviceps purpurea

Another possible example comes from Salem, Massachusetts, the site of the witch trials in 1692, in which several girls and women were condemned to death. The hallucinations and physical symptoms displayed by the so-called witches closely resemble those of ergotism. There may have been a reasonable explanation for this behavior. The farmers in Salem grew rye for breadmaking. Analysis of records of weather conditions from 1691 to 1692 shows that damp weather favored growth of the ergot fungus, which likely resulted in this tragedy (Caporael 1976).

In 1938, in the Sandoz Pharmaceutical Laboratories of Basel, Switzerland, Albert Hofmann worked on a series of ergot compounds in search for active chemicals that might be of medical value. Lysergic acid was similar in structure to a com-

pound called *nikethamide*, a stimulant, and Hofmann tried to create slight chemical modifications that might be worth further testing. The result of this effort was the production of lysergic acid diethylamide, or LSD. Hofmann's experience with this new compound gave insight to the effects of this drug and are detailed in the adjacent box.

Soon after LSD was discovered, the similarity of LSD experiences to the symptoms of schizophrenia were noted, which prompted researchers to investigate correlations between the two. The hope was to use LSD as a tool for producing an artificial psychosis to aid in understanding the biochemistry of psychosis. Interest in this use of LSD has declined because it is now generally accepted that LSD effects are different from natural psychoses.

The use of LSD in psychotherapy has also been tried in the treatment of alcoholism, autism, paranoia, schizophrenia, and various other mental and emotional disorders. Therapeutic use of LSD has not increased to any great extent over the years because of its limited success, legal aspects, difficulty in obtaining the pure drug, adverse reactions to the drug ("bad trips" can occur under controlled as well as uncontrolled conditions), and the problems of rapid tolerance build-up in some patients.

Nonmedical interest in LSD and related drugs began to grow during the 1950s, primarily among experimenters in the academic, professional, and artistic fields. As previously discussed, the drug gained public attention in the early 1960s as a result of experimentation by such individuals as Harvard University psychology professor Timothy Leary (see earlier in this chapter). Another significant influence on the LSD movement—one with considerably less religious orientation—was Ken Kesey's group, whose adventures are documented in a book called *The Electric Kool-Aid Acid Test* (Wolfe 1968).

As with other hallucinogens, the use of LSD has declined somewhat over the past two decades. Of high school seniors sampled in 1975 11% had ever used LSD; that number declined to 8% in 1990 (NIDA 1991). Similar declines were also observed in college and young adult populations (Johnston et al. 1989).

For You to Consider...

Albert Hofmann's Discovery

Following synthesis of the diethylamide derivative of lysergic acid in 1938, Hofmann noted nothing unusual about the product, so he stored it in a bottle on the laboratory shelf. In 1943, he checked over some of the synthetic compounds he had worked on and started making further tests of LSD. Most likely due to carelessness, a small amount must have entered his blood. Hofmann noted that:

> Last Friday, April 16, 1943, I was forced to stop my work in the laboratory in the middle of the afternoon and to go home, as I was seized by a peculiar restlessness associated with a sensation of mild dizziness. Having reached home, I lay down and sank in a kind of drunkenness which was not unpleasant and which was characterized by extreme activity of imagination. As I lay in dazed condition with my eyes closed (I experienced daylight as disagreeably bright), there surged upon me an uninterrupted stream of fantastic images of extraordinary plasticity and vividness and accompanied by an intense, kaleidoscope-like play of colors. This condition gradually passed off after about two hours.

Hofmann realized the experience was probably caused by the chemical he had been working with and decided to try a measured amount on himself. If the minute amount he had unwittingly taken caused the sensations he recorded, he thought 250 micrograms might be enough to prove the chemical's effects. Hofmann was to find out that LSD is one of the most potent drugs known. As low a dose as 50 micrograms can affect some people.

This is Hofmann's record of the first known deliberate LSD trip:

> 4:20 P.M.: 0.5 cc (0.25 mg LSD) ingested orally. The solution is tasteless.
>
> 4:50 P.M.: No trace of any effect.
>
> 5:00 P.M.: Slight dizziness, unrest, difficulty in concentration, visual disturbances, marked desire to laugh . . . [At this point, the laboratory notes are discontinued.]

The last words could only be written with great difficulty. I asked my laboratory assistant to accompany me home as I believed that my condition would be a repetition of the disturbance of the previous Friday. While we were still cycling home, however, it became clear that the symptoms were much stronger than the first time. I had great difficulty in speaking coherently, my field of vision swayed before me, and objects appeared distorted like images in curved mirrors. I had the impression of being unable to move from the spot, although my assistant told me afterwards that we had cycled at a good pace.

By the time the doctor arrived, the peak of the crisis had already passed.

> As far as I remember, the following were the most out-standing symptoms: vertigo; visual disturbances; the faces of those around me appeared as grotesque, colored masks; marked motor unrest, alternating with paresis; an intermittent heavy feeling in the head, limbs and the entire body, as if they were filled with metal; cramps in the legs, coldness and loss of feeling in the hands; a metallic taste on the tongue; dry, constricted sensation in the throat; feeling of choking; confusion alternating between clear recognition of my condition, in which state I sometimes observed, in the manner of an independent, neutral observer, that I shouted half insanely or babbled incoherent words. Occasionally I felt as if I were out of my body.
>
> Six more hours after ingestion of the LSD, my condition had already improved considerably. Only the visual disturbances were still pronounced. Everything seemed to sway and the proportions were distorted like the reflections in the surface of moving water. Moreover, all objects appeared in unpleasant, constantly changing colors, the predominant shades being sickly green and blue. When I closed my eyes, an unending series of colorful, very realistic and fantastic images surged in upon me. A remarkable feature was the manner in which all acoustic perceptions (for example, the noise of a passing car) were transformed into optical effects, every sound causing a corresponding colored hallucination constantly changing in shape and color like pictures in a kaleidoscope. At about 1 o'clock I fell asleep and awakened next morning somewhat tired but otherwise feeling perfectly well.

Source: Quotes from Albert Hofmann, "Psychotomimetic Agents" in *Drugs Affecting the Central Nervous System*, vol. 2, edited by A. Burger (New York: Marcel Dekker, 1968), pp. 169–235.

Methods of Administration. The physical properties of LSD are not distinctive. In its purified form, LSD is colorless, odorless, and tasteless. It can be purchased in several forms, including tablets, capsules, and even occasionally, a liquid. While LSD usually is taken by mouth, it is sometimes injected.

A somewhat unique form of administering LSD is achieved by adding the drug to absorbent paper, such as blotter paper, which can be divided into small decorated squares. Each square represents a single dose and can be stuck to the skin or applied to the surface of the eye, allowing the drug to transport into the body and exert its psychedelic effect (see Figure 11-3).

Physiological Effects. Like many hallucinogens, LSD is remarkably potent: One ounce contains about 300,000 adult human doses. However, at these low doses, LSD is rather low in toxicity. In monkeys, the lethal dose has been determined to be about 5 milligrams (mg) per kilogram (kg) of bodyweight. In rats, the lethal dose (expressed as LD-100, which means it kills 100% of the test animals) is about 20 mg/kg. The LD-50 (lethal dose for 50%) for humans is estimated at 150 to 200 times the hallucinogenic dose.

When taken orally, LSD is readily absorbed and diffused into all tissues. It will pass through the placenta into the fetus and through the blood-brain barrier. The brain receives about 1% of the total dose.

Within the brain, LSD is particularly concentrated in the hypothalamus, the limbic system, and the auditory and visual reflex areas. Electrodes placed in the limbic system show an "electrical storm," or a massive increase in neural activity, which might explain the overwhelming flood of sensations and the phenomenon of synesthesia reported by the user. LSD also activates the sympathetic nervous system; shortly after the drug is taken, body temperature and blood pressure rise, the person sweats, and the pupils of the eyes become dilated. Its effects on the parasympathetic nervous system cause an increase in salivation and nausea. These systemic effects do not appear to be related to the hallucinogenic properties of the drug.

Pharmacokinetic experiments with LSD show that about half of the substance is cleared from the body within 3 hours, and more than 90% is excreted within 24 hours. Tolerance to the effects of LSD develops more rapidly and lasts longer than tolerance to other hallucinogens. Tolerance develops very quickly to repeated doses, probably because of a change in sensitivity of the target cells in the brain rather than a change in its metabolism. Tolerance wears off within a few days after the drug is discontinued. Because there are no withdrawal symptoms, a person does not become physically dependent, but some psychological dependency on LSD can occur (Cohen 1978).

Behavioral Effects. Because LSD alters a number of systems in the brain, its behavioral effects are many and variable between individuals. The following sections address common CNS responses to this drug.

Creativity and Insight. A question often raised by researchers interested in experimenting with LSD is: Does it help expand the mind, increasing

FIGURE 11-3 LSD blotter paper. Small amounts of LSD are added to decorated, absorbent paper, such as this. Each small square represents a single dose, which is applied to the skin or surface of the eye, from where it is absorbed into the body.

This piece of sculpture was done by a university student while under the influence of LSD. *Source:* statue in possession of Dr. Glen Hanson.

insight and creativity? This is an extremely difficult question to answer because no one has ever determined the origin of insight and creativity. Moreover, each of us views these qualities differently.

Generally, subjects under the influence of LSD often express the feeling of being more creative, but creative acts such as drawing and painting are hindered by the motor impairment caused by LSD. The products of artists under the influence of the drug usually prove to be inferior to those produced prior to the drug experience. Paintings done in LSD creativity studies have been described as reminiscent of "schizophrenic art."

Creativity, attitude, and anxiety tests on 24 college students found that LSD had no objective effect on creativity, although many of the subjects said they felt they were more creative (McGlothin et al. 1967). This paradox is noted in several stud-

ies of LSD use: The subjects feel they have more insight and provide better answers to life's problems, but they do not or cannot demonstrate this increase objectively. Overt behavior is not modified, and these new insights are short lived unless they are reinforced by modified behavior (Cohen 1978).

In spite of these results, some researchers still contend that LSD can enhance the creative process. For example, Oscar Janigar, a psychiatrist at the University of California, Los Angeles, claims to have determined that LSD does not produce a tangible alteration in the way a painter paints; thus, it does not turn a poor painter into a good one. However, Janigar claims that LSD does alter the way the painter appraises the world and allows the artist to "plunge into areas where access was restricted by confines of perceptions" and consequently becomes more creative (Tucker 1987, 16).

Psychedelic Effects. It is important to remember that there is no typical pattern of response to LSD. It varies for each user as a function of the person's set, or expectations, and setting, or environment, during the experience. Some of the major responses are described as follows (Pahnke et al. 1970):

1. *The psychotic adverse reaction,* or *"freak out,"* is an intense, nightmarish experience. The subject may have complete loss of emotional control, paranoid delusions, hallucinations, and catatonic seizures. In rare instances, some of these reactions are prolonged, lasting days.

2. *The nonpsychotic adverse reaction* may involve varying degrees of tension, anxiety, fear, depression, and despair but not as intense a response as the "freak-out." A person with deep psychological problems or a strong need to be in conscious control or one who takes the drug in an unfavorable setting is more likely to have an adverse reaction than a person with a well-integrated personality.

3. *The psychedelic response* may consist of intensified and altered sensory impressions, accompanied by an impression of astonishingly clear thought and novel perspectives. Often periods of introspection ac-

company the sensory distortion, supposedly giving insight into personal motives and relationships.

4. *The psychedelic "peak"* relates to the cosmic or mystic experience, which transcends time and space. This "peak" is not achieved routinely; it is fast moving and the full intensity does not last long.

LSD behavioral toxicity can be treated with tranquilizers or a benzodiazepine (Jaffe 1990).

Perceptual Effects. Because the brain's sensory processing is altered by a hallucinogenic dose of LSD, many kinds of unusual illusions can occur. Some users report seeing shifting geometrical patterns mixed with intense color perception; others observe the movement of stationary objects, such that a speck on the wall appears as a large blinking eye or an unfolding flower. Interpretation of sounds can also be scrambled; a dropped ashtray may become a gun fired at the user, for instance. In some cases, LSD alters perceptions to the extent that people feel they can walk on water or fly through the air. The sensation that the body is distorted and even coming apart is another common effect, especially for novice users. Thoughts of suicide and sometimes actual attempts can be caused by use of LSD, as well.

Many LSD users find their sense of time distorted, such that hours may be perceived as years or an eternity. As discussed earlier, users may also have a distorted perception of their own knowledge or creativity; for instance, they may feel their ideas or work are especially unique, brilliant, or artistic. When analyzed by a person not on LSD, however, or explained after the "trip" is over, these ideas or creations are almost always quite ordinary.

In sum, LSD alters perception such that any sensation can be perceived in the extreme. An experience can be incredibly beautiful and uplifting or completely foul and disgusting.

The "flashback" is an interesting and poorly understood phenomenon of LSD use. Although usually thought of as being adverse, sometimes flashbacks are pleasant and even referred to as "free trips" (Nadis 1990). During a flashback, sensations caused by previous LSD use return, although the subject is not using the drug at the time.

There are three broad categories of LSD-related flashbacks:

1. *The "body trip"*—the recurrence of an unpleasant physical sensation
2. *The "bad mind trip"*—the recurrence of a distressing thought or emotion
3. *Altered visual perception*—the most frequent, consisting of seeing dots, flashes, trails of light, halos, false motion in the peripheral field, and other sensations (see the accompanying box for an example)

Flashbacks are most disturbing because they come on unexpectedly. Some have been reported as long as 20 years after use of LSD; for most people, however, flashbacks usually subside within weeks or months after taking LSD (Nadis 1990). The duration of a flashback is variable, lasting from a few minutes to several hours.

Although the precise mechanism of flashbacks is unknown, physical or psychological stresses and some drugs such as marijuana may trigger the experience. It has been proposed that flashbacks are an especially vivid form of memory that becomes seared into the subconscious mind due to the effects of LSD on the brain's transmitters. Treat-

---

For You to Consider...

The "After Flash"

As a teen-ager, John Doe took LSD approximately 30 times. Some 15 years later, he still sees grainy, photographic dots. He also sees "trails," blurred images associated with a moving object, such as a waving arm. "It's as if the lens of a camera were left open taking a time-lapse photograph." Doe also complains that the visual distortions also bring twinges of fear. "I have the feeling of coming on, a rush. It hits me in the gut, like going over the top of a hill. I take Valium, which stops it in its tracks" (Nadis 1990, 24).

ment consists of reassurance that the condition will go away and use of Valium if necessary to treat the anxiety or panic that can accompany the flashback experience (Nadis 1990).

Genetic Damage and Birth Defects. Experiments conducted in the mid-1960s suggested that LSD could cause birth defects, based on the observation that, when LSD was added to a suspension of human white blood cells in a test tube, the chromosomes of these cells were damaged. From this, it was proposed that, when LSD was consumed by humans, it could cause damage to the chromosomes of the male sperm, female egg, or the cells of the developing infant. Such damage theoretically could result in congenital defects in offspring (Dishotsky et al. 1971).

Carefully controlled studies conducted after news of LSD's chromosomal effects were made public have not supported this hypothesis. Experiments have revealed that, in contrast to the test tube findings, there is no chromosomal damage to white blood cells or any other cells when LSD is given to a human being (Dishotsky et al. 1971).

Studies have also shown that there are no carcinogenic or mutagenic effects from using LSD in experimental animals or humans, with the exception of the fruit fly. (LSD is a mutagen in fruit flies if given in doses that are equivalent to 100,000 times the hallucinogenic dose for humans.) Teratogenic effects occur in mice if LSD is given early in pregnancy. LSD may be teratogenic in rhesus monkeys if it is injected in doses (based on bodyweight) exceeding at least 100 times the usual hallucinogenic dose for humans. In other studies, women who took "street" LSD but not those given pure LSD had a higher rate of spontaneous abortions and births of malformed infants; this suggests that contaminants in adulterated LSD were responsible for the fetal effects and not the hallucinogen itself (Dishotsky et al. 1971).

Early Human Research. In the 1950s, the U.S. government—specifically, the Central Intelligence Agency (CIA) and the army—became interested in reports of the effects of mind-altering drugs, including LSD. Unknown to the public at the time, these agencies conducted tests on humans to learn more about such compounds and determine their usefulness in conducting military and clandestine missions. These activities became public when a biochemist, Frank Olson, killed himself in 1953 after being given a drink laced with LSD. Olson had a severe psychotic reaction and was being treated for the condition when he jumped out of a tenth-story window. His family was told only that he had committed suicide. The connection to LSD was not uncovered until 1975. The court awarded Olson's family $750,000 in damages in 1976.

In 1976, the extent of these studies was revealed: Nearly 585 soldiers and 900 civilians had been given LSD in poorly organized experiments in which participants were coerced into taking or not told that they were being given this drug. Powerful hallucinogens like LSD can cause serious psychological damage in some subjects, especially when they are unaware of what is happening.

Cases involving unwitting subjects are still being resolved. As recently as 1987, a New York judge awarded $700,000 to the family of a mental patient who killed himself after having been given LSD without an explanation of the drug's nature. The judge said that there was a "conspiracy of silence" between the army, the Department of Justice and the New York State Attorney General to conceal events surrounding the death of the subject, Harold Blauer.

MESCALINE (PEYOTE) Mescaline is one of approximately 30 psychoactive chemicals that have been isolated from the peyote cactus (see Figure 11-4) and used for centuries in the Americas. One of the first reports on the peyote plant was made by Francisco Hernandez of the court of King Philip II of Spain. King Philip was interested in reports from the earlier Cortez expedition about strange medicines the natives used and sent Hernandez to collect information about herbs and medicines. Hernandez worked on this project from 1570 to 1575 and reported the use of more than 1,200 plant remedies, as well as the existence of many hallucinogenic plants. He was one of the first to record the eating of parts of the peyote cactus and the resulting visions and mental changes.

FIGURE 11-4 The peyote cactus contains a number of drugs; the best known is mescaline.

In the seventeenth century, Spanish Catholic priests asked their Indian converts to confess to the use of peyote, which they believed was used to conjure up demons. However, nothing stopped its use. There is evidence that, by 1760, use of peyote had spread into what is now the United States.

Peyote has been confused with another plant, the mescal shrub, which produces dark red beans that contain an extremely toxic alkaloid called *cytisine*. This alkaloid may cause hallucinations, convulsions, and even death. There is also a mescal liquor, made from the agave cactus. Partly because of misidentification with the toxic mescal beans, the U.S. government outlawed the use of peyote and mescaline.

Mescaline is the most active drug in peyote; it induces intensified perception of colors and euphoria in the user. However, as Aldous Huxley said in *The Doors of Perception* (1954), his book about his experimentation with mescaline, "Along with the happily transfigured majority of mesca-

line takers there is a minority that finds in the drug only hell and purgatory." After Huxley related his experiences with mescaline, it was used by an increasing number of people.

Physiological Effects. The average dose of mescaline that will cause hallucinations and other physiological effects is from 300 to 600 mg. It may take up to 20 peyote (mescal) buttons (ingested orally) to get 600 mg of mescaline (see Figure 11-5).

Based on studies of animals, it is estimated that from 10 to 30 times the lowest dose that will cause behavioral effects in humans may be lethal. (About 200 mg is the lowest mind-altering dose.) Death in animals results from convulsions and respiratory arrest. Mescaline is perhaps 1,000 to 3,000 times less potent than LSD and 30 times less potent than another common hallucinogen, psilocybin (see later in this chapter).

Effects include dilation of the pupils (**mydriasis**), increase in body temperature, anxiety,

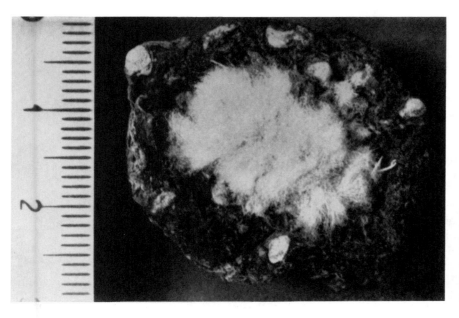

FIGURE 11-5 A mescal button, which is the dried head of a peyote cactus. *Source:* R. Schultes and A. Hofmann, *The Botany and Chemistry of Hallucinogens*, 2nd ed. (Springfield, IL: Charles C. Thomas, 1980), figure 87, p. 198.

visual hallucinations, and alteration of body image. The last effect is a type of hallucination in which parts of the body may seem to disappear or to become grossly distorted. Mescaline induces vomiting in many people and some muscular relaxation (sedation). Apparently, there are few after effects or drug hangover at low doses. Higher doses of mescaline slow the heart and respiratory rhythm, contract the intestines and the uterus, and cause headache, difficulty in coordination, dry skin with itching, and hypertension (high blood pressure).

mydriasis
pupil dilation

Mescaline users report that they lose all awareness of time. As with LSD, the setting for the "trip" influences the user's reactions. Most mescaline users prefer natural settings, most likely due to the historical association of this drug with Native Americans and their nature-related spiritual experiences (often under the influence of this drug). The visual hallucinations achieved depend on the

individual. Colors are at first intensified and may be followed by hallucinations of shades, movements, forms, and events. The senses of smell and taste are enhanced. Some people claim (as with LSD) that they can "hear" colors and "see" sounds, such as the wind. Synesthesia occurs naturally in a small percentage of cases.

At low to medium doses, an ecstatic state of euphoria is reported, often followed by a feeling of anxiety and less frequently by depression. Occasionally, users observe themselves as two people and experience the sensation that the mind and body are separate entities. A number of people have had cosmic experiences that are profound, almost religious, in which they discover a sense of unity with all creation. People who have this sensation often believe they have discovered the meaning of existence.

Mechanism of Action. Within 30 to 120 minutes after ingestion, mescaline reaches a maximum concentration in the brain and may persist for up to 9 or 10 hours. Hallucinations may last up to 2 hours and are usually affected by the dose level. About half the dose is excreted unchanged after 6 hours and can be recovered in the urine for reuse (if peyote is in short supply). A slow tolerance builds up after repeated use, and there is cross-tolerance to LSD. As with LSD, mescaline intoxication can be alleviated or stopped by taking a dose of chlorpromazine (Thorazine, a tranquilizer) and to a lesser extent with diazepam (Valium). Like LSD, mescaline likely exerts much of its hallucinogenic effects by altering serotonin systems (Jaffe 1990).

Analysis of "street" samples of mescaline in a number of U.S. cities over the past decade shows that the chemical sold rarely is authentic. Regardless of color or appearance, these street drugs are usually other hallucinogens, such as LSD, DOM, or PCP. Table 11-1 lists some typical "street" drugs, including what they were sold as and what they actually were. If a person decides to take hallucinogenic street drugs, "let the buyer beware." Not only is the actual content often different and potentially much more toxic than bargained for (they are frequently contaminated), but the dosage is usually unknown even if the drug is genuine.

PSILOCYBIN   The drug psilocybin has a long and colorful history. Its principal source is the *Psilocybe mexicana* mushroom (of the "magic" variety). It was first used by some of the early natives of Central America more than 2,000 years ago. In Guatemala, statues of mushrooms that date back to 100 B.C. have been found (see Figure 11-6). The Aztecs later used the mushrooms for ceremonial rites. When the Spaniards came into Mexico in the 1500s, the natives were calling the *Psilocybe mexicana* mushroom "God's flesh." Because of this seeming sacrilege, they were harshly treated by the Spanish priests.

Gordon Wasson identified the *Psilocybe mexicana* mushroom in 1955 (see Figure 11-7). The active ingredient was extracted in 1958 by Albert Hofmann, who also synthesized LSD. Doing research, Hofmann wanted to make certain he would feel the effects of the mushroom, so he ate 32 of them, weighing 2.4 grams (a medium dose by Indian standards) and then recorded his reactions (see the box on page 339). His experience illustrates how the personality of the drug taker and the setting can influence a drug's effects.

FIGURE 11-6   A stone effigy of a mushroom animal. *Source:* R. Schultes and A. Hofmann, *The Botany and Chemistry of Hallucinogens*, 2nd ed. (Springfield, IL: Charles C. Thomas, 1980), figure 18, p. 58.

Timothy Leary tried some psilocybin mushrooms in Mexico in 1960; apparently, the experience influenced him greatly. On his return to Harvard, he carried out a series of experiments using psilocybin with student groups. Leary was careless in experimental procedures and did some work in uncontrolled situations. This caused a major administrative upheaval, ending in his departure from Harvard.

One of Leary's questionable studies was the "Good Friday" experiment in which 20 theological students were given either a placebo or psilocybin in a double-blind (i.e., neither the researcher nor the subjects know who gets the placebo or the drug) study, after which all attended the same 2.5

TABLE 11-1 Sample of anonymous "street" drugs analyzed in 1986 by Street Pharmacologist Laboratories in Miami, Florida

Alleged Content	Actual Content	Description	Origin
Methadrine	Ephedrine	White powder	Los Angeles, CA
Methamphetamine	Methamphetamine	Cream powder	Eugene, OR
Cocaine	Cocaine, cinnamyl cocaine	White powder	Tucson, AZ
Cocaine	Cocaine, acetaminophen, procaine	White powder	Tucson, AZ
Cocaine	Cocaine, acetaminophen, lidocaine, procaine	White powder	Tucson, AZ
Cocaine	Cocaine, acetaminophen, lidocaine, procaine	White powder	Tucson, AZ
Cocaine	Cocaine, norcocaine	White powder	Miami, FL
Cocaine	Cocaine, norcocaine	White powder	Mansfield, OH
Cocaine	No drug detected	White powder	Boring, OR
Cocaine	Cocaine	Cream powder	Oakland, CA
Cocaine	Cocaine	White powder	Miami, FL
Cocaine	Cocaine, norcocaine, cinnamyl cocaine	White powder	San Francisco, CA
Cocaine, methadrine	Cocaine	White powder	Pleasant Hill, CA
Marijuana	Marijuana	Green plant material	Altoona, PA
MDMA	MDA	Clear cap, white powder	Unknown
MDMA	MDMA	Clear cap, white powder	Salt Lake City, UT
MDMA or MDA	MDA	White powder	Santa Barbara, CA
Unknown	Methaqualone	White tab, "Man"	Northern Virginia, VA
Unknown	No drugs detected	Pink tab	Bellwood, PA
Unknown	Benzocaine	White powder	Miami, FL
Unknown	Cocaine/benzocaine	White powder	Ft. Lauderdale, FL
Unknown	No drugs detected	Clear cap	Miami, FL
Unknown	Methaqualone	Scored tab, "714"	Los Angeles, CA
Unknown	PPA, lidocaine	White powder	Buffalo, NY
Unknown	Ephedrine	Red tab	Altoona, PA
Unknown	No drugs detected	Coarse granules	Los Angeles, CA
Unknown	No drugs detected	Pink capsule	Gainesville, FL
Prednisone	No drugs detected	White tab	Clackamas, OR
Prednisone	Chlorpheniramine (antihistamine)	Red tab	Clackamas, OR

Source: Courtesy of SP Labs.

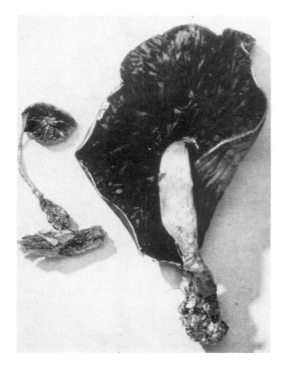

FIGURE 11-7 The *Psilocybe* mushroom, source of psilocybin and psilocin.

hour Good Friday service. The experimental group reported mystical experiences whereas the control group did not (Pahnke and Richards 1966). Leary believed that the experience was of value and that, under proper control and guidance, the hallucinatory experience could be beneficial.

Psilocybin is not very common on the "street." Generally, it is administered as a mushroom and either eaten fresh or dried. Accidental poisonings from these mushrooms are common for those who mistakenly consume poisonous mushrooms rather than the hallucinogenic variety.

The dried form of these mushrooms contains from 0.2% to 0.5% psilocybin. The hallucinogenic effects produced are quite similar to those of LSD, and there is a cross-tolerance between psilocybin, LSD, and mescaline. The effects caused by psilocybin vary with the dosage taken. Up to 4 mg will cause a pleasant experience, relaxation, and some body sensation. In some subjects, higher doses cause considerable perceptual and body-image changes, accompanied by hallucinations. Psilocybin stimulates the autonomic nervous system, dilates the pupils, and increases the body temperature. There is some evidence that psilocybin is metabolized into psilocin, which is more potent and may be the active ingredient. Psilocin is found in the mushroom but in small amounts. Like the other hallucinogens, psilocybin apparently causes no physical dependence.

DIMETHYLTRYPTAMINE (DMT) DMT is a short-acting hallucinogen found in the seeds of certain leguminous trees native to the West Indies and parts of South America (Schultes 1978). It is also prepared synthetically in illicit laboratories. For centuries, the powdered seeds have been used as a snuff called *cohoba* in pipes and snuffing tubes. The Haitian natives claim that, under the influence of the drug, they can communicate with their gods. Its effects may last under one hour, which has earned it the nickname "the businessman's lunch-break" drug.

DMT has no effect when taken orally; it is inhaled either as smoke from the burning plant or in vaporized form. DMT is sometimes added to parsley leaves or flakes, tobacco, or marijuana in order to induce its hallucinogenic effect. The usual dose is 60 to 150 mg. In structure and action, it is similar to psilocybin although not as powerful. Like the other hallucinogens discussed, DMT does not cause physical dependence.

NUTMEG High doses of nutmeg can be quite intoxicating, causing symptoms such as drowsiness, stupor, delirium, and sleep. Prison inmates have known about this drug for years, so in most prisons, use of spices such as nutmeg is restricted.

Nutmeg contains 5% to 15% myristica oil, which is responsible for the physical effects. Myristicin (about 4%), which is structurally similar to mescaline, and elemicin are probably the most potent psychoactive ingredients in nutmeg. Myristicin blocks release of serotonin from brain neurons. Some scientists believe that myristicin can be converted in the body to MMDA (a close relative of MDA, see below), which also affects the central

For You to Consider...

A Mexican "Trip"

Albert Hofmann recorded the following experience after ingesting psilocybin mushrooms:

> Thirty minutes after taking the mushrooms, the exterior world began to undergo a strange transformation. Everything assumed a Mexican character. As I was perfectly well aware that my knowledge of the Mexican origin of the mushroom would lead me to imagine only Mexican scenery, I tried deliberately to look on my environment as I knew it normally. But all voluntary efforts to look at things in their customary forms and colors proved ineffective. Whether my eyes were closed or open, I saw only Mexican motifs and colors. When the doctor supervising the experiment bent over to check my blood pressure, he was transformed into an Aztec priest, and I would not have been astonished if he had drawn an obsidian knife. In spite of the seriousness of the situation it amused me to see how the Germanic face of my colleague had acquired a purely Indian expression. At the peak of the intoxication, about 1½ hours after ingestion of the mushrooms, the rush of interior pictures, mostly abstract motifs rapidly changing in shape and color, reached such an alarming degree that I feared that I would be torn into this whirlpool of form and color and would dissolve. After about six hours the dream came to an end. Subjectively, I had no idea how long this condition had lasted. I felt my return to everyday reality to be a happy return from a strange, fantastic world into an old and familiar home.

Source: Quotes from Albert Hofmann, "Psychotomimetic Agents" in *Drugs Affecting the Central Nervous System,* vol. 2, edited by A. Burger (New York: Marcel Dekker, 1968), pp. 169–235.

---

nervous system. Mace, the exterior covering of the nutmeg seed, also contains the hallucinogenic compound myristicin.

Two tablespoons of nutmeg (about 14 g) taken orally cause a rather unpleasant "trip" with a dreamlike stage; rapid heartbeat, dry mouth, and thirst are experienced, as well. Agitation, apprehension, and a sense of impending doom may last about 12 hours, with a sense of unreality persisting for several days (Claus et al. 1970).

PHENYLETHYLAMINE HALLUCINOGENS

The phenylethylamine drugs are chemically related to amphetamines. Phenylethylamines have varying degrees of hallucinogenic and CNS stimulant effects, which are likely related to their ability to release serotonin and dopamine, respectively. Consequently, the phenylethylamines that predominantly release serotonin are dominated by their hallucinogenic action and are LSD-like, while those more inclined to release dopamine are dominated by their stimulant effects and are cocainelike.

DIMETHOXYMETHYLAMPHETAMINE (DOM OR STP) The basic structure of DOM is amphetamine. Nonetheless, it is a fairly powerful hallucinogen that seems to work through mechanisms similar to those of mescaline and LSD. In fact, the effects of DOM are similar to those caused by a combination of amphetamine and LSD, with the hallucinogenic effects of the drug overpowering the amphetaminelike physiological effects.

Doses of less than 3 mg produce pupil dilation and increases in heartbeat, blood pressure, and body temperature. DOM causes a mild euphoria that may last from 8 to 12 hours, with peak reactions occurring after 3 to 5 hours. "Street" doses of DOM have averaged 10 mg and are considered large. Such a dose would cause a "trip" lasting from 16 to 24 hours, which would likely cause a panic reaction by the user.

DOM produces a higher incidence of acute and chronic reactions than any of the other commonly used hallucinogens, with the possible exception of PCP (see later in this chapter). As with LSD and mescaline, the tranquilizer chlorpromazine (Thorazine) will rapidly ease the effects of the long "trip" but may also interfere with breathing. Bourne (1976) recommends using Valium because it causes fewer reactions than chlorpromazine.

"DESIGNER" AMPHETAMINES "Designer" amphetamines were discussed in Chapter 9 but are presented again here due to their hallucinogenic effects. Their hybrid actions as psychedelic stimulants not only make them a particularly fascinating topic for research but also provide a unique experience described by drug abusers as a "smooth amphetamine." This characterization likely accounts for the recent popularity of the designer amphetamines.

3,4-Methylenedioxyamphetamine (MDA).

MDA, first synthesized in 1910, is structurally related to both mescaline and amphetamine. Early research found that MDA is an anorexiant (causing loss of appetite) as well as a mood elevator in some persons. Further research has shown that the mode of action of MDA is similar to that of amphetamine. It causes extra release of the neurotransmitters serotonin, dopamine, and norepinephrine.

MDA has been used as an adjunct to psychotherapy. In one study, 8 volunteers who had previously experienced the effects of LSD under clinical conditions were given 150 mg of MDA. Effects of the drug were noted between 40 and 60 minutes following ingestion by all 8 subjects. The subjective effects following administration peaked at the end of 90 minutes and persisted for approximately 8 hours. None of the subjects experienced hallucinations, perceptual distortion, or closed-eye imagery, but they reported that the feelings the drug induced had some relationship to those previously experienced with LSD. The subjects found that both drugs induced an intensification of feelings, increased perceptions of self-

insight, and heightened empathy with others during the experience. Most of the subjects also felt an increased sense of aesthetic enjoyment at some point during the intoxication. Seven of the 8 subjects said they perceived music as "three dimensional." In an earlier study of patients taking this drug, the authors reported that nearly half had spontaneous reminiscences of childhood experiences but no hallucinations (Naranjo et al. 1967).

On the "street," MDA has been called the "love drug" because of its effects on the sense of touch and the attitudes of the users. Users often report experiencing a sense of well-being (likely a stimulant effect) and heightened tactile sensations (likely a hallucinogenic effect) and thus increased pleasure through sex and expressions of affection.

The MDA experience is often devoid of the visual and auditory distortions that mark the LSD experience. Those under the influence of MDA frequently focus on interpersonal relationships and demonstrate an overwhelming desire or need to be with or to talk to people. Some users say they have a very pleasant "body high"—more sensual than cerebral and more emphatic than introverted. The unpleasant side effects most often reported are nausea, periodic tensing of muscles in the neck, tightening of the jaw and grinding of the teeth, and dilation of the pupils.

"Street" doses of MDA range from 100 mg to 150 mg. Serious convulsions and death have resulted from larger doses, but in these cases, the quantity of MDA was not accurately measured. Ingestion of 500 mg of pure MDA has been shown to cause death. The only adverse reaction to moderate doses seems to be marked physical exhaustion, lasting as long as two days (Marquardt et al. 1978).

An unpleasant MDA experience should be treated the same as a "bad trip" with any hallucinogen. The person should be "talked down" (i.e., reassured) in a friendly and supportive manner. Usually, the use of other drugs is not needed, although medical attention may be necessary. Under the Comprehensive Drug Abuse Prevention and Control Act of 1970, MDA is classified as a Schedule I substance; illegal possession is a serious offense.

Methylenedioxymethamphetamine (MDMA). MDMA is a modification of MDA and in comparison is thought to have more psychedelic but less stimulant activity. MDMA is also structurally similar to mescaline, sharing some of that drug's euphoric effects. Thus, it has become known as "Ecstasy," "XTC" and "Adam."

MDMA was synthesized in 1960, but it has only become widely used in the last few years (Shulgin 1990). The unusual psychological effects it produces are part of the reason for increased popularity. The drug produces euphoria, increased sensitivity to touch, and lowered inhibitions. Many users claim it intensifies emotional feelings without sensory distortion and that it increases empathy and awareness both of your body and of the esthetics of the surroundings. Some consider MDMA an aphrodisiac. Because MDMA lowers defense mechanisms and reduces inhibitions, it has even been used during psychoanalysis.

MDMA has also been popularized by articles in *Newsweek* (Adler 1985), *Time* (Toufexis 1985), and other magazines, which have mentioned the euphoric effects, potential therapeutic value, and lack of serious side effects. MDMA is still popular with the affluent and college-age students. In some ways, it has replaced cocaine as the premier glamour drug in the United States (Peroutka 1990). Whether MDMA is truly such a "wonder drug" is debatable.

By 1985, there was widespread abuse of MDMA, and the Drug Enforcement Administration (DEA) prohibited use by placing it on Schedule I. At the time of the ban, it was estimated that up to 200 physicians were using the drug in therapy and an estimated 30,000 doses a month were being taken for nonmedical use (*American Medical News*, 1985).

MDMA is usually taken orally, but it is sometimes snorted. After the "high" starts, it may persist for minutes or even an hour, depending on the person, the purity of the drug, and the environment in which it is taken. When "coming down" from an MDMA-induced high, people will often take small oral doses known as "boosters" to get high again. If they take too many boosters, they become very fatigued the next day. The average dose is about 50 mg; a number of cases of toxic effects have been reported at higher doses.

There is disagreement as to the possible harmful side effects of MDMA. Some negative physiological responses include dilated pupils, dry mouth and throat, lower-jaw tension, clenching of teeth, agitation, and anxiety. Some of these reactions can be intense and unpredictable. A number of users report positive effects, which include a drop in defense mechanisms as well as a feeling of strength and stimulation, an enhanced pleasure from being touched, and a mild euphoria (Beck and Morgan 1986).

Several studies have demonstrated long-term damage to serotonin neurons in the brain following a single high dose of both MDMA and MDA (Stone et al. 1987; Gibb et al. 1990). Although the behavioral significance of this damage in humans is not clear, at the present time, caution using this drug is warranted. Whether MDMA is useful in psychotherapy remains to be proven; a number of therapists still believe it could be useful if administered under proper supervision (Greer and Tolbert 1990; Bakalar and Grinspoon 1990).

T h i n k   A b o u t   I t . . .

1. You are a back-to-nature person. You grow your own rye to make bread. The weather has been very wet this year, and fungus has grown in the grain. You decide to use the rye anyway and make a batch of bread. You notice that, after eating your homemade bread, members of your family start acting very strangely. What is the most likely explanation for their strange behavior? What could have been done to avoid it?

2. Do you feel that, in order to keep people from using LSD, the federal government would be justified in telling the public that this drug causes genetic damage, even though it was known that this was not true? Why?

3. Why do most mescaline users prefer natural settings when using the drug?

4. You are a psychiatrist who has successfully used MDMA during psychotherapy; you want to convince the FDA that this drug should be

available to clinicians. How would you defend your right to have access to this drug?

ANTICHOLINERGIC HALLUCINOGENS

The anticholinergic hallucinogens include naturally occurring substances, derived from plants and herbs found around the world, that have been used for many centuries (see Figure 11-8). These drugs are often mentioned in folklore and in early literature as being added to "potions." They are thought to have killed the Roman Emperor Claudius and to have poisoned Hamlet's father. Historically, they have been the favorite drugs used to eliminate inconvenient people. (However, one of the problems in using anticholinergic drugs to poison people is that the victim usually turns bright red.) Hallucinogens affecting the cholinergic neurons also have been used by South American Indians for religious ceremonies (Schultes and Hofmann 1980) and were probably used in witchcraft to give the illusion of flying, to prepare sacrificial victims for cutting out their hearts, and even to give some types of marijuana ("superpot") its kick (see Figure 11-8).

The potato family of plants (*Solanaceae*) contains most of these mind-altering drugs. Three potent anticholinergic compounds are commonly found in these plants: (1) scopolamine, or hyoscine; (2) hyoscyamine; and (3) atropine. Scopolamine may produce excitement, hallucinations, and delirium even at therapeutic doses; with atropine, doses bordering on toxic levels are usually required to obtain these effects (Schultes and Hofmann 1973). All of these active alkaloid drugs are acetylcholine antagonists (see Chapter 5). They occupy the acetylcholine (in particular, the muscarinic type) receptor site but do not activate it, which renders it nonfunctional or blocked.

Alkaloid drugs can be used as ingredients in cold-symptom remedies because they have a drying effect and block production of mucus in the nose and throat (see Chapter 13). They also prevent salivation, so that the mouth becomes uncommonly dry and perspiration may stop. Atropine may increase the heartrate by 100% and cause the pupils to dilate markedly, causing inability to focus on nearby objects. Other annoying side effects of these anticholinergic drugs include constipation and difficulty in urinating. These inconveniences usually discourage excessive abuse of these drugs for their hallucinogenic properties.

FIGURE 11-8 These plants belong to the species *Brugmansia* and contain anticholinergic hallucinogens. Native to South America, these plants have been used for centuries in Indian ceremonies and to induce visions. *Source:* R. Schultes and A. Hofmann, *The Botany and Chemistry of Hallucinogens*, 2nd ed. (Springfield, IL: Charles C. Thomas, 1980), figures of Brugmansia X insignis (p. 269), Brugmansia aurea (p. 265), and Figure 125, Brugmansis vulcanicola, page unknown.

Brugmansia aurea *Lagerh.*

Brugmansia X insignis

(B. Rodrigues) *Lockwood*

Anticholinergics depress the reticular activating system (see Chapter 5) and slow the brainwaves, as shown on an electroencephalogram (EEG). At large doses, a condition occurs that is similar to a psychosis, characterized by delirium, loss of attention, mental confusion, and sleepiness. Hallucinations may also occur at higher doses. At very high doses, paralysis of the respiratory system may cause death.

Although hundreds of plant species naturally contain anticholinergic substances and consequently can cause psychedelic experiences, only a few of the principal plants will be mentioned here.

ATROPA BELLADONNA: THE DEADLY NIGHTSHADE PLANT

Knowledge of this plant is very old, and its use as a drug is reported in early folklore. The name of the genus, *Atrop*, is the origin for the drug name *atropine*, and indicates the reverence the Greeks had for the plant. Atropos was one of the three Fates in Greek mythology, whose duty it was to cut the thread of life when the time came. This plant has been used for thousands of years by assassins and murderers. In the *Tales of the Arabian Nights*, unsuspecting potentates were poisoned with atropine from the deadly nightshade or one of its relatives. Fourteen berries of the deadly nightshade contain enough drug to cause death.

The species name, *belladonna*, means "beautiful woman." The early Roman and Egyptian women knew that girls with large pupils were considered attractive and friendly. To create this condition, they would put a few drops of an extract of this plant into their eyes, causing the pupils to dilate. Belladonna has also had a reputation as a love potion.

MANDRAGORA OFFICINARUM: THE MANDRAKE

The mandrake contains several active psychedelic alkaloids: hyoscyamine, scopolamine, atropine, and mandragorine. Mandrake has been used as a love potion for centuries but has also been known for its toxic properties. In ancient folk medicine, mandrake was used to treat many ailments in spite of its side effects. It was recommended as a sedative, to relieve nervous conditions, and to relieve pain (Schultes and Hofmann 1980).

The root of the mandrake is forked and, viewed with a little imagination, may resemble the human body (see Figure 11-9). Because of this resemblance, it has been credited with human attributes, which gave rise to many superstitions in the Middle Ages about its magical powers. Shakespeare referred to this plant in *Romeo and Juliet*. In her farewell speech, Juliet says, "And shrieks like mandrakes torn out of the earth, that living mortals hearing them run mad."

HYOSCYAMUS NIGER: HENBANE

Henbane is a plant that contains both hyoscyamine and scopolamine. In 60 A.D., Pliny the Elder spoke of henbane: "For this is certainly known, that if one takes it in drink more than four leaves, it will put him beside himself" (Jones 1956). Henbane was also

FIGURE 11-9 *Mandragora officinarum*, or the mandrake, another plant containing psychedelic alkaloids. *Source:* R. Schultes and A. Hofmann, *The Botany and Chemistry of Hallucinogens*, 2nd ed. (Springfield, IL: Charles C. Thomas, 1980), figure 135, p. 297.

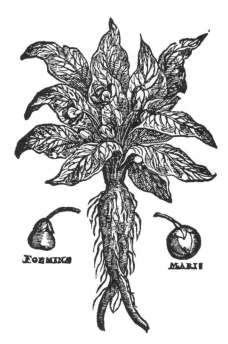

Mandragoras mas & fœmina.
The male and female Mandrake.

FOEMINA   MARIS

used in the orgies, or *bacchanalias*, of the ancient world:

> Thus at the Bacchanalia, when the wide-eyed Bacchantes with their flowing locks flung themselves naked into the arms of the eager men, one can be reasonably certain that the wine which produced such sexual frenzy was not a plain fermented grape juice. Intoxication of this kind was almost certainly a result of doctoring the wine with leaves or berries of belladonna or henbane. The orgiastic rites were never totally suppressed by the Church and persisted in secret forms through the Middle Ages. Being under the shadow of the Church's displeasure, they are inevitably associated with the devil, and those who took part in them were considered to be either witches or wizards (De Ropp 1975).

Although rarely used today, henbane has been given medicinally since early times. It was frequently used to cause sleep, although hallucinations often occurred if given in excess. It was likely included in witches brews and deadly concoctions during the Dark Ages (Schultes and Hofmann 1980).

***DATURA STRAMONIUM:* JIMSONWEED**   The *Datura* group of the Solanaceae family (see above) includes a large number of related plants found worldwide. The principal active drug in this group is scopolamine; there are also several less active alkaloids.

Throughout history, these plants have been used as hallucinogens by many societies. They are mentioned in early Sanskrit and Chinese writings and were revered by the Buddhists. There is also some indication that the priestess (oracle) at the ancient Greek temple of Apollo at Delphi was under the influence of *Datura* when she made prophecies (Schultes 1970). Prior to the supposed divine possession, she appeared to have chewed leaves of the sacred laurel. A mystic vapor was also reported to have risen from a fissure in the ground. The sacred laurel may have been one of the *Datura* species, and the vapors may have come from burning these plants.

Datura stramonium, also referred to as *jimsonweed*, was used by the Algonquin Indians of the

eastern woodlands of North America during a ceremony of entry into manhood (see Figure 11-10):

> The youths are confined for long periods, given no other substance but the infusion or concoction of some poisonous, intoxicating roots. . . . They became stark, staring mad, in which raving condition they were kept eighteen or twenty days. . . . Thus they unlive their former lives and commence manhood by forgetting that they ever have been boys (Schultes and Hofmann 1973).

Jimsonweed gets its name from an incident that took place in seventeenth century Jamestown. The British soldiers were trying to capture Nathaniel Bacon, who had made seditious remarks

For You to Consider...

Jimsonweed in Jamestown

The following account tells of the intoxicated antics of a group of British soldiers who ate some of the "James-Town Weed," or *jimsonweed*:

> The James-Town Weed . . . is supposed to be one of the greatest Coolers in the World. This being an early Plant, was gather'd very young for a boil'd Salad, by some of the Soldiers sent thither, to pacifie the Troubles of Bacon; and some of them eat plentifully of it, the Effect of which was a very pleasant Comedy; for they turn'd natural Fools upon it for several Days: One would blow up a Feather in the air; another wou'd dart Straws at it with much Fury; and another stark naked was sitting up in a Corner, like a Monkey, grinning and making Mows at them; a Fourth would fondly kiss, and paw his Companions, and snear in their Faces, with a Countenance more antick, than any in a Dutch Droll. In this frantick Condition they were confined, lest they should in their Folly destroy themselves; though it was observed, that all their Actions were full of Innocence and good Nature. Indeed, they were not very cleanly; for they would have wallow'd in their own Excrements, if they had not been prevented. A thousand such simple Tricks they play'd, and after Eleven Days, return'd to themselves again, not remembering any thing that had pass'd (Beverly 1947, 139).

FIGURE 11-10 *Datura stramonium*, or jimsonweed, a common plant that contains the hallucinogenic drug scopolamine.

about the king (see the adjacent box). Although still abused occasionally by adventuresome young people, the anticholinergic side effects of jimsonweed are so unpleasant that it rarely becomes a long-term problem.

OTHER HALLUCINOGENS

Technically, any drug that alters perceptions, thoughts, and feelings in a manner that is not normally experienced but in dreams can be classified as a hallucinogen. Because the brain's sensory input is complex and involves several neurotransmitter systems, drugs with many diverse effects can cause hallucinations. For example, CNS stimulants (e.g., amphetamines and cocaine), CNS depressants (e.g., sedatives/hypnotics or general anesthetics), and drugs that influence endocrine systems (e.g., steroids), under certain circumstances can all be hallucinogens (Jaffe 1990).

These major drug groups have already been discussed in detail. Three other agents that do not conveniently fit into the principal categories of hallucinogens will be discussed in the following sections.

PHENCYCLIDINE (PCP)   PCP was developed in the late 1950s as an intravenous anesthetic. Although it was found to be effective, it had serious side effects that caused it to be discontinued for human use. Sometimes when people were recovering from PCP anesthesia, they experienced delirium and manic states of excitation lasting 18 hours (Jaffe 1990). PCP is currently a Schedule II drug, legitimately available only as an anesthetic for animals. However, it has been banned from veterinarians since 1985 because of its high theft rate.

"Street" PCP is mainly synthesized from readily available chemical precursors in illicit laboratories. Within 24 hours, "cooks" (the makers of street PCP) can set up a lab, make several gallons of the drug, and destroy the lab before the police can locate them. Liquid PCP is then poured into containers and ready for shipment (Sanchez 1988).

PCP first appeared on the street drug scene in 1967 as the *"PeaCe Pill."* In 1968, it reappeared in New York as a substance called "hog." By 1969, PCP was found under a variety of guises. It was sold as "angel dust" and sprinkled on parsley for smoking. Other slang terms used for PCP include *loveboat, lovely, key to street E, greed, wacky weed, supergrass, rocket fuel, elephant tranquilizer, snorts, cyclone, cadillac, earth, killer weed,* and *flying saucers* (Sanchez 1988).

It was at this time that PCP began to find its way into a variety of street drugs sold as psychedelics. By 1970, authorities observed that phencyclidine was used widely as a main ingredient in psychedelic preparations. (It is still frequently substituted for and sold as LSD and mescaline.) Analysis of street drugs in 1970 showed that most mescaline and THC (active ingredient in marijuana) on the street was really PCP, in part or entirely. PCP is commonly found in preparations called *superpot, monkeyweed, horse tranquilizer, superweed,* and *crystal T* in amounts ranging from 2 to 110 micrograms a single dose.

One difficulty in estimating the effects or use patterns of PCP is caused by variance in drug purity. Also, there are about 30 **analogs** of PCP, some of which have appeared on the street. PCP has so many other street names that people may not know they are using it or they may have been deceived when buying what they thought was LSD or mescaline. Users may not question the identity of the substances unless they have a bad reaction.

analogs
drugs with similar structures

PCP is available as a pure, white crystalline powder, as tablets, or as capsules. It can be taken orally, smoked, sniffed, or injected. In the late 1960s through the early 1970s, PCP was mostly taken orally, but it is now commonly smoked or snorted. By smoking PCP, the experienced user is better able to limit his or her dosage to a desired level. After smoking, the subjective effects appear within 1 to 5 minutes and peak within the next 5 to 30 minutes. The "high" lasts about 4 to 6 hours, followed by a 6- to 24-hour "comedown." There is a 30-second to a 1-minute lag to onset of effects if the drug is snorted; the rest of the sequence of events is the same as when smoked. If the drug is taken orally, a longer period elapses before it takes effect; thus, users may take too much, causing more overdoses and adverse effects than if the drug is smoked or snorted (Petersen and Stillman 1978).

In the 1977 national drug survey taken by the National Institute on Drug Abuse, about 6% of 12- to 17-year olds and 14% of 18- to 25-year-olds had tried or were using PCP (Petersen and Stillman 1978). The popularity of PCP has declined dramatically since then. In 1990, only 3% of high school seniors reported having ever used this drug (NIDA 1991).

Physiological Effects. Although PCP may have hallucinogenic effects, it can also cause a host of other physiological actions, including stimulation, depression, anesthesia, and analgesia. The effects of PCP on the central nervous system vary greatly. At low doses, the most prominent effect is similar to that of alcohol intoxication, with generalized numbness. As the dose of PCP is increased, the person becomes even more insensitive and may become fully anesthetized. Large doses can cause coma, convulsions, and death.

The majority of peripheral effects are apparently related to activation of the sympathetic nervous system (see Chapter 5). Flushing, excess sweating, and a blank stare are common, although the size of the pupils is unaffected. The cardiovascular system reacts by increasing blood pressure and heartrate. Other effects include side-to-side eye movements, called *nystagmus;* muscular incoordination; double vision; dizziness; nausea;

and vomiting. These symptoms occur in many people taking medium to high doses.

Psychological Effects. PCP has unpleasant effects most of the time it is used. Why, then, do people use it repeatedly as their drug of choice?

PCP has the ability to alter markedly the person's subjective feelings; this may be reinforcing, even though the alteration is not always positive. There is an element of risk, not knowing how the "trip" will turn out. PCP may give the user feelings of strength, power, and invulnerability. One user describe the effects of PCP as follows: "I felt like I didn't have a care in the world. It made me feel like God, like I was powerful. I felt superhuman" (Sanchez 1988). Other positive effects include heightened sensitivity to outside stimuli, a sense of stimulation and mood elevation, and dissociation from surroundings. Also, PCP is a social drug; virtually all users report taking it in groups rather than during a solitary experience (Petersen and Stillman 1978).

PCP also causes serious perceptual distortions. Users cannot accurately interpret the environment and as a result may walk in front of moving cars or jump off buildings, feeling indestructible or weightless. In California, when many people were experimenting with PCP, drownings were frequent. A study found that, in 19 cases of death where PCP was present, 11 were due to drowning (one in the shower). Apparently, some PCP users lose their orientation while swimming or immersed in water and drown, sometimes in small amounts of water (Petersen and Stillman 1978). High oral doses have been used to commit suicide; respiratory depression is the specific cause of death.

Chronic users may take PCP in "runs" extending over two to three days, during which time they do not sleep or eat. In later stages of chronic administration, users may develop outright paranoia and unpredictable violent behavior, as well as auditory hallucinations. Law enforcement officers claim to be more fearful of suspects on PCP than of suspects on other drugs of abuse. Often such people appear to have superhuman strength and are totally irrational and very difficult, even dangerous, to manage.

The role of PCP in precipitating long-term psychosis is poorly understood. Many of those who become psychotic with PCP resemble those who become psychotic using LSD (Petersen and Stillman 1978). Evidence shows clearly that PCP can cause psychosis in some subjects (Jaffe 1990). During initial clinical trials of PCP as an anesthetic, one-sixth of the volunteers became severely psychotic for several hours after they woke up. Because of these postanesthetic reactions, the focus of investigation shifted from using PCP as an anesthetic to using it to produce model psychoses, until the drug was withdrawn from experimental use in humans.

PCP has no equal in its ability to produce brief psychoses nearly indistinguishable from schizophrenia. The psychoses—induced with moderate doses given to normal, healthy volunteers—last about two hours and are characterized by changes in body image, thought disorders, estrangement, autism, and occasionally rigid inability to move (**catatonia,** or catalepsy). Subjects report feeling numb, have great difficulty differentiating between themselves and their surroundings, and

For You to Consider...

The PCP Explosion

The following account relays a horrible incident involving a woman on PCP and law enforcement personnel who tried to subdue her:

> Before the Prince George's County police officer pumped three bullets into her, 26-year-old Sharon Araoye horrified neighbors in a Riverdale Hills apartment complex in July. Walking toward the officer in the parking lot, Araoye, who was nude, repeatedly plunged a butcher knife into her body—including her eye, chest, abdomen, and groin. She continued to stab herself even after the officer fired at her. She died five hours later.
>
> The reason for the fatal outburst; phencyclidine, PCP (Sanchez 1988).

complain afterward of feeling extremely isolated and apathetic. They are often violently paranoid during the psychosis. When PCP was given experimentally to hospitalized chronic schizophrenics, it made them much worse not for several hours but for six weeks. "PCP is not just another hallucinogen, to be warned about in the same breath as LSD. . . . PCP is far more dangerous to some individuals than the other abused drugs" (Luisada 1978).

---

catatonia
a period of physical rigidity, excitement, and stupor

Medical Management. The diagnosis of a PCP overdose is frequently missed because the symptoms often closely resemble those of an acute schizophrenic episode. Table 11-2 compares the symptoms commonly seen at low, moderate, and high doses of PCP.

Simple, uncomplicated PCP intoxication can be managed with the same techniques used in other psychedelic drug cases. It is important to have a quiet environment, limited contact with an empathic person capable of determining any deterioration in the patient's physical state, protection from self-harm, and the availability of hospital facilities. "Talking down" is not helpful; the patient is better off isolated from external stimuli as much as possible.

There is no specific antagonist to reduce the toxic effects of PCP. Treatment is basically symptomatic. Because PCP tends to stay in the body, removal should be accelerated by acidification of the urine with substances like citric acid and ammonium chloride. Valium is often used for its sedating effect to prevent injury to self and to staff and also to reduce the chance for severe convulsions. A drug that blocks dopamine, such as the antipsychotic agents (e.g., Haldol), is used to make the patient manageable (Jaffe 1990).

The medical management of a comatose or convulsing patient is more difficult. The patient may need external respiratory assistance and external cooling to reduce fever. Blood pressure may

TABLE 11-2 Comparison of symptoms commonly seen in emergency room patients having taken low, moderate, and high doses of PCP

Low Dose (under 5 mg)	Moderate Dose (5 to 10 mg)	High Dose (over 10 mg)
Agitation	Coma or stupor	Long coma (12 hours to days)
Serious incoordination	Eyes remain open	Eyes closed
Blank stare	Pupils in middle and reactive	High blood pressure
Catatonic rigidity	Vomiting	Muscular rigidity
Unable to speak	Extreme salivation	Convulsions
Lessened response to pinprick	Repetitive motor movements	No peripheral sensation
Flushed	Profuse sweating	Profuse sweating
Profuse sweating	Shivering	Decreased corneal and gag reflexes
Sensitive to sound	Nystagmus	Hypersalivation
Nystagmus	Flushing	Fever
	Fever	Repetitive motor movements
	Insensitive to pain, touch	Posture may be bowed (abdomen out)

Source: Based on Petersen and Stillman 1978.
Note: Oral sedative dose 1–5 mg; subanesthetic dose 7.5 mg.

have to be reduced to safe levels and convulsions controlled. Restraints and four to five strong hospital aides are often needed to prevent the patient from injuring himself or herself or the medical staff. After the coma lightens, the patient typically becomes delirious, paranoid, and violently assaultive (Petersen and Stillman 1978).

Effects of Chronic Use. Chronic PCP users develop a tolerance to the drug; thus, a decrease in behavioral effects and toxicity can occur with frequent administration. Different forms of dependence may occur when tolerance develops. Users may complain of vague cravings after cessation of the drug. In addition, long-term difficulties in memory, speech, and thinking persist for 6 to 12 months in the chronic user (Jaffe 1990). These functional changes are accompanied by personality deficits such as social isolation, states of anxiety, nervousness, and extreme agitation.

MARIJUANA Marijuana, discussed at length in Chapter 12, will only be briefly mentioned here because of its psychedelic properties. In high doses, marijuana use can result in image distortions and hallucinations. Some users claim that marijuana can enhance hearing, vision, and skin sensitivity, but these claims have not been confirmed in controlled laboratory studies. The most frequent complaint when using marijuana is the development of anxiety sometimes accompanied by paranoia that can range from mild suspicions to fear of insanity. The effects are most likely to occur to the novice user and are short term. Usually, simple reassurance and a friendly environment are sufficient treatments.

Although marijuana itself does not appear to cause severe emotional disorders like the other hallucinogens, it can aggravate underlying mental illness such as depression. Each month, an estimated 5,000 people seek professional treatment due to marijuana-related problems (Brown 1991). In contrast to other hallucinogens that have a combination of stimulant and psychedelic effects, marijuana causes a combination of depression and hallucinations. Because of the usual level of CNS depression, this drug causes drowsiness and enhances the appetite.

INHALANT Inhalants are **volatile** drugs (exist as a gas) and can be introduced into the body through the pulmonary (lungs) route. This category of drugs includes an array of different compounds with very distinct pharmacological properties; however, most are able to cause hallucinations as well as create intoxicating and euphorigenic effects.

---

volatile
readily evaporated at low temperatures

Many of these substances were never intended to be used in humans; consequently, they are often not thought of as having abuse potential. For example, inhalants include some solvents, glue, paint thinner, aerosols from paints, hairsprays, cookware coating agents, liquid-paper correction fluid, nail polish remover, lighter and cleaning fluids, and gasoline. These chemicals are not regulated like other drugs of abuse, so they are readily available to young people. Consequently, children and teen-agers (7 to 17 years) are most likely to abuse inhalants. Parents should be particularly cautious about making sure their children are not inadvertently exposed to these chemicals.

The effects of the volatile chemicals and aerosols that are commonly abused include initial nausea with some irritation of the airways, resulting in coughing and sneezing. With continued use, inhalants have an anesthetic effect. At low doses, there may be some mild stimulation followed by a loss of control, lack of coordination, and disorientation accompanied by dizziness and possible hallucinations. With higher doses, violent behavior may occur; ultimately, the user may become unconscious.

Several potential toxicities may result from inhaling substances. Many of these chemicals can cause heart arrhythmia, the principal cause of death from inhalant exposure (Jaffe 1990). In some cases, the abuser inhales the vapors from a plastic bag to maximize the dose. If continued for a long period, dangerous **hypoxia** may occur and cause brain damage or death. Other potential toxic consequences of inhaling such substances include hy-

Let's   Get   the   Facts

Specific Signs of Inhalant Use

1. Uncommon collection of glues, paints, lacquer thinners, cleaning fluid, gasoline, ether, and nail polish.
2. Sniffles similar to common cold without illness present.
3. Smell similar to the inhalable substances on the breath.

Source: L.A.W. Publications, "Let's All Work To Fight Drug Abuse," new ed. (Addison, TX: C & L Printing Company, Inc., 1985), p. 39. Used with permission of the publisher.

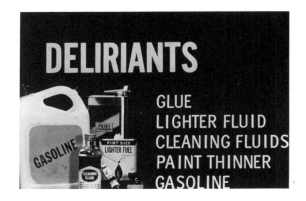

hypoxia
a state of oxygen deficiency

pertension and damage to the cardiac muscle, peripheral nerves, brain, and kidneys.

When used properly, other forms of inhalants with abuse potential are important therapeutic agents. Included in this category are the general anesthetics. Although all of the anesthetic gases work much like the CNS depressants, only nitrous oxide (laughing gas) is available enough to be a significant abuse concern. Nitrous oxide is frequently used for minor outpatient procedures in offices of both physicians and dentists. Consequently, the most likely abusers of this substance are health professionals themselves or their staff. Nitrous oxide does not pose a significant abuse problem for the general public.

Think   About   It . . .

1. Cultivating plants that contain anticholinergic drugs is not restricted, while cultivating marijuana, another hallucinogenic substance, is. Why do you think federal agencies are not as concerned about vegetation that contains anticholinergic drugs as they are about marijuana?
2. In the Middle Ages, consumption of mandrake could get you burned at the stake. Why?
3. If you were a regular hallucinogen abuser, why would you be more inclined to use LSD than PCP?
4. As a director at the Drug Enforcement Administration, you have been assigned to develop a plan to deal with the persistent abuse of inhalants. What would you propose?

K E Y   T E R M S

hallucinogens

psychotomimetic

psychedelic

psychotogenic

synesthesia

"flashback"

ergotism

mydriasis

analogs

catatonia

volatile

hypoxia

S U M M A R Y

1. Many drugs can exert hallucinogenic effects. The principal hallucinogens include LSD-types, phenylethylamines, and anticholinergic agents. Of these, LSD is the prototypical drug. The four major effects that occur from administering LSD include (a) heightened senses, (b) a loss of sensory control, (c) self-reflection or introspection, and (d) a loss of identity or sense of cosmic merging.

2. The popularity of the classical hallucinogens, such as LSD, has diminished substantially since the turbulent times of the 1960s. Some of the explanations for their diminished popularity include increased federal regulation, lack of physical dependence resulting from their use, changes in social climate, and concern about dangerous side effects.

3. By definition, hallucinogens affect sensory input to the brain. They alter perceptions, thoughts, and feelings in such a manner that does not normally occur except in dreams or during experiences of extreme religious exaltation. Sensory input is exaggerated, resulting in vivid and unusual visual and auditory effects. The hallucinogen user becomes a passive observer, unable to prolong an enjoyable experience or terminate a "bad trip."

4. Because sensory perception is a complex process, involving several brain regions and several transmitter systems, a number of distinct drug groups are capable of altering sensory processing and causing hallucinations. The classical hallucinogens, such as LSD, cause predominantly psychedelic effects. Phenylethylamines are related to amphetamines and cause varying combinations of psychedelic and stimulant effects; CNS stimulation results in increased energy and a sense of euphoria. Anticholinergic drugs are also psychedelic in high doses; in addition, they tend to cause lethargy or drowsiness with a host of other annoying side effects: dry mouth; constipation; blurred vision; flushed, hot skin; and an inability to urinate.

5. One of the prominent effects of hallucinogens is to cause self-reflection. The user becomes aware of thoughts and feelings that had been forgotten or repressed. Such experiences help to clarify motives and relationships and cause periods of greater openness. These effects have been claimed by some psychiatrists to provide valid insights useful in psychotherapy.

6. The classical hallucinogens are distinct from other commonly abused drugs in that they do not cause physical dependence.

Although some tolerance can occur to the hallucinogenic effects of drugs like LSD, withdrawal effects are usually minor. Consequently, hallucinogens tend to be less abused than other scheduled drugs. Another reason for less abuse problems with hallucinogens is that some of these drugs, such as anticholinergic substances, cause very unpleasant side effects.

7. Because the major effect of hallucinogens is to alter perception, the environment plays a major role in determining the sensory response to these agents. Environments that are warm, comfortable, and hospitable tend to create a pleasant sensory response to the psychedelic effects of these drugs. In contrast, threatening, hostile environments are likely to lead to intimidating, frightening "bad trips." Knowing this, experienced hallucinogen users carefully select their surroundings when they use these drugs.

8. In some users, high doses of LSD can cause a terrifying destruction of identity, resulting in panic and severe anxiety that resembles schizophrenia. However, close scrutiny has revealed some major differences between the drug-induced and the naturally occurring psychoses. Another

psychological feature commonly associated with LSD is the "flashback" phenomenon. The mechanism is not known, but LSD use can cause recurring, unexpected visual and time distortions that last a few minutes to several hours. Flashbacks can occur months to years after use of the drug.

9. Hallucinogens purchased on the "street" are usually poorly prepared and contaminated with adulterant substances. For example, pure LSD or mescaline are rarely available; they are often diluted with other hallucinogens, such as PCP, or "cut" with toxic chemicals, such as strychnine. Because of such contamination, it is often difficult to determine if side effects caused by street drugs are due to the hallucinogens themselves or some unknown additive. This practice of cutting with other substances also makes use of street hallucinogens very dangerous.

10. PCP differs from the other traditional hallucinogens in several ways: (a) It is a general anesthetic in high doses, although it is no longer used in humans for this purpose. (b) It causes a psychosis that more closely resembles that of schizophrenia than any of the other drugs of abuse. PCP can cause incredible strength and extreme violent behavior, making users very difficult to manage. (c) Management of the severe psychological reactions to PCP requires drug therapy, whereas treatment of other hallucinogens often only requires reassurance, "talking down," and supportive therapy. (d) Reactions to overdoses include fever, convulsions, and coma.

11. The commonly abused inhalants are volatile substances that can cause hallucinations, intoxication, and euphoria. These substances include chemicals used as solvents, glue, paint thinner, aerosols from spray paint, hairsprays, cookware coating agents, paper-correction fluid, nail polish remover, and lighter and cleaning fluids. These chemicals are typically abused by children and teen-agers due to their availability. The effects of inhalant drugs are mild stimulation, lack of motor control, dizziness, and hallucinations. High doses can cause violent behavior, heart arrhythmia, unconsciousness, and even death.

R E F E R E N C E S

Adler, J. "Getting high on Ecstasy." Newsweek, 15 April 1985, 15.

American Medical News, 14 June 1985.

Bakalar, J. B., and L. Grinspoon. "Testing Psychotherapies and Drug Therapies: The Case of Psychedelic Drugs. In Ecstasy: The Clinical Pharmacological and Neurotoxicological Effects of the Drug MDMA, edited by S. J. Peroutka. Boston: Kluwer, 1990.

Beck, J., and P. A. Morgan. "Designer Drug Confusion: A Focus on MDMA." Journal of Drug Education 16, no. 3 (1986): 23–26.

Bourne, P. G., ed. Acute Drug Emergencies: A Treatment Manual. New York: Academic, 1976.

Brown, M. Guide to Fight Substance Abuse. Nashville, TN: International Broadcast Services, 1991.

Caporael, L. R. "Ergotism: The Satan Loosed in Salem?" Science 192 (1976): 21–26.

"Celebration #1." The New Yorker 42 (1966): 43.

Claus, E. P., V. E. Tyler, and L. R. Brady. Pharmacognosy, 6th ed. Philadelphia: Lea & Febiger, 1970.

Cohen, S. "Psychotomimetics (Hallucinogens) and Cannabis." In Principles of Psychopharmacology, edited by W. G. Clark and J. del Giudice. 2nd ed. New York: Academic, 1978.

De Ropp, R. S. Drugs and the Mind. New York: Grove, 1975.

Dishotsky, N. I., W. D. Loughman, R. E. Mogar, and W. R. Lipscomb. "LSD and Genetic Damage." Science 172 (1971): 431–440.

Gibb, J. W., D. Stone, M. Johnson, and G. R. Hanson. "Neurochemical Effects of MDMA." In Ecstasy: The Clinical, Pharmacological and Neurotoxicological Effects of the Drug MDMA, edited by S. J. Peroutka. Boston: Kluwer, 1990.

Glennon, R. "Psychoactive Phenylisopropylamines." In Psychopharmacology, edited by H. Meltzer. New York: Raven, 1987.

Greer, G., and R. Tolbert. "The Therapeutic Use of MDMA." In Ecstasy: The Clinical, Pharmacological and Neurotoxicological Effects of the Drug MDMA, edited by S. J. Peroutka. Boston: Kluwer, 1990.

Hofmann, A. "Psychotomimetic Agents." In Drugs Affecting the Central Nervous System, edited by A. Burger. Vol. 2. New York: Marcel Dekker, 1968.

Huxley, A. The Doors of Perception. New York: Harper and Brothers, 1954.

Jacobs, B. "Mechanism of Action of Hallucinogenic Drugs: Focus upon Postsynaptic Serotonergic Receptors." In Preclinical Psychopharmacology, Part 1, edited by D. Grahame-Smith. Amsterdam: Excerpta Medica, 1983.

Jaffe, J. "Drug Addiction and Drug Abuse." In The Pharmacological Basis of Therapeutics, edited by A. Gilman, T. Rall, A. Nies, and P. Taylor. 8th ed. New York: Pergamon: 1990.

Johnston L., P. O'Malley, and J. Bachman. Drug Use, Drinking, and Smoking: National Survey Results from High School, College and Young Adult Populations. Washington, D.C.: NIDA, 1989.

Jones, W. H. S. *Natural History.* Cambridge, MA: Harvard University Press, 1956.

Leary, T., R. Metzner, and R. Alpert. *The Psychedelic Experience.* New Hyde Park, NY: University Books, 1964.

Luisada, P. V. "The Phencyclidine Psychosis: Phenomenology and Treatment." In *Phencyclidine (PCP) Abuse: An Appraisal,* edited by R. C. Petersen and R. C. Stillman. Washington, D.C.: NIDA Research Monograph no. 21, Department of Health, Education, and Welfare. Washington, D.C.: NIDA, 1978.

McGlothin, W., S. Cohen, and M. S. McGlothin. "Long-Lasting Effects of LSD on Normals." *Archives of General Psychiatry* 17 (1967): 521–532.

Marquardt, G. M., V. DiStefano, and L. L. Ling. "Pharmacological Effects of (±)-, (S)-, and (R)-MDA." In *The Psychopharmacology of Hallucinogens,* edited by R. C. Stillman and R. E. Willette. New York: Pergamon, 1978.

Nadis, S. "After Lights." *Omni,* February 1990, 24.

Naranjo, C., A. T. Shulgin, and T. Sargent. "Evaluation of 3, 4-Methylenedioxyamphetamine (MDA) as an Adjunct to Psychotherapy." *Medicina et Pharmacologia Experimentalis* 17 (1967): 359–364.

National Institute on Drug Abuse. *NIDA Notes* 6 (Spring 1991): 35.

Pahnke, W. N., A. A. Kurland, S. Unger, C. Savage, and S. Grof. "The Experimental Use of Psychedelic (LSD) Psychotherapy." In *Hallucinogenic Drug Research: Impact on Science and Society,* edited by J. R. Gamage and E. L. Zerkin. Beloit, WI: Stash, 1970.

Pahnke, W. N., and W. A. Richards. "Implications of LSD and Experimental Mysticism." *Journal of Religion and Health* 5 (1966):175–208.

Panikkar, R., trans. *Rig Veda, Book VIII, 48. (Sanskrit hymns, 1500 B.C.).* Los Angeles: University of California Press, 1977.

Peroutka, S. "Recreational Use of MDMA." In *Ecstasy: The Clinical, Pharmacological and Neurotoxicological Effects of the Drug MDMA,* edited by S. J. Peroutka. Boston: Kluwer, 1990.

Petersen, R. C., and R. C. Stillman. "Phencyclidine: An Overview." In *Phencyclidine (PCP) Abuse: An Appraisal,* edited by R. C. Petersen and R. C. Stillman. NIDA Research Monograph no. 21, Department of Health, Education, and Welfare. Washington, D.C.: NIDA, 1978.

Sanchez, E. "PCP Users Are Courting Fire." *Washington Post,* 7 March 1988, A-1.

Schultes, R. E. "Ethnopharmacological Significance of Psychotropic Drugs of Vegetal Origin." In *Principles of Psychopharmacology,* edited by W. G.

Clark and J. del Giudice. 2nd ed. New York: Academic, 1978.

Schultes, R. E. "The Plant Kingdom and Hallucinogens (Part III)." *Bulletin on Narcotics* 22, no 1 (1970): 25–53.

Schultes, R., and A. Hofmann. *The Botany and Chemistry of Hallucinogens.* 2nd ed. Springfield, IL: Charles C. Thomas, 1980.

Schultes, R. E., and A. Hofmann. *The Botany and Chemistry of Hallucinogens.* Springfield, IL: Charles C. Thomas, 1973.

Shulgin, A. "History of MDMA." In *Ecstasy: the Clinical, Pharmacological, and Neurotoxicological Effects of the Drug MDMA,* ed. by S. J. Peroutka. Boston: Kluwer, 1990.

Snyder, S. H. *Madness and the Brain.* New York: McGraw-Hill, 1974.

Stone, D., M. Johnson, G. R. Hanson, and J. W. Gibb. "A Comparison of the Neurotoxic Potential of Methylenedioxyamphetamine (MDA) and N-Methylated and N-Ethylated Derivatives." *European Journal of Pharmacology* 134 (1987): 245–248.

Toufexis, A. "A Crackdown on Ecstasy." *Time,* 10 June 1985, 64.

Tucker, R. "Acid Test." *Omni,* November 1987, 16.

Wolfe, T. *The Electric Kool-Aid Acid Test.* New York: Farrar, Straus, and Giroux, 1968.

Marijuana

CHAPTER OUTLINE

LEARNING OBJECTIVES

On completing this chapter, you will be able to:

1. Explain what *marijuana* refers to and what it consists of.
2. Describe the effects that high- and low-dose levels of marijuana have on the body.
3. Define *hashish* (or *hasheesh*), *ganja, sensimilla,* and *bhang.*
4. Cite the amount of THC present in marijuana sold on the "streets" in the United States.

5. Discuss whether the potency of marijuana has changed over the last 10 years.
6. Cite world and U.S. use estimates for marijuana.
7. Give a brief history of marijuana use.
8. Summarize how THC affects the body overall and in particular, the respiratory system, blood pressure, sexual behavior, and growth and development.

9. Discuss the link between marijuana use and progression to other more serious drugs.
10. Explain whether increased use of marijuana is necessary in order to maintain the euphoric effects.
11. Describe how marijuana has been prescribed for therapeutic purposes.

Source: Charles Gatewood/Stock, Boston

DID YOU KNOW THAT . . .

- Over 66 million Americans have used marijuana, which represents 32% of the population. World-wide estimates suggest that 200 to 250 million people have tried marijuana.
- The extent of marijuana use is strongly affected by age differences, gender differences, and peer influences.
- In some states, marijuana is one of the largest cash-producing crops.
- The first known record of marijuana use is in the *Book of Drugs* written in 2737 B.C. by the Chinese.
- Since marijuana plants are so abundant and grow easily, the earliest uses of this plant were in making rope and cloth.
- The potency of marijuana varies enormously.
- THC, the main psychoactive chemical in marijuana, is what produces the "high."
- THC remains stored for a long period in body fat; complete elimination can take up to 30 days.
- THC reaches the brain within 14 seconds after inhalation.
- A typical "high" from one marijuana cigarette lasts two to three hours.
- Findings from surveys indicate that 60% to 80% of marijuana users sometime drive when "high."
- Cannabis has been used to treat extreme nausea and glaucoma.
- Government-grown marijuana cigarettes can be purchased from drugstores when prescribed by physicians.

Perhaps no other substance has been the object of so much research and controversy as marijuana. It is a vegetable substance called *Cannabis sativa,* the hemp plant, and grows wild in most temperate and tropical climates. It is also a money-making cash crop in parts of the world, including the United States. When prepared as a drug, marijuana consists of dried and crushed leaves, flowers, stems, and seeds. At low dose levels, usually when smoked or eaten, marijuana has sedative effects; at higher doses, the effects are similar to those of mind-expanding hallucinogens. The potency of marijuana varies tremendously, depending on the source and selectivity of plant materials.

In this chapter, we will begin with a review of current attitudes toward marijuana use. The history of marijuana use will be considered next, tracing its roots to ancient civilizations. The physiological and behavioral effects of marijuana will be examined in some detail, along with known therapeutic uses. The chapter concludes with a look at use trends. The role of marijuana as a "gateway" drug is considered, as well.

ATTITUDES TOWARD MARIJUANA USE

There are several interesting ironies connected with marijuana use. One is that marijuana continues to be perceived as a mild substance and one of the least seriously addictive, yet statistics indicate that it is the most widely used illicit (illegal) substance in the United States, used by almost 66 million Americans (Foster et al. 1989). Thirty-two percent of the population has tried marijuana at least once in their lives: four million youths (age 12–17 years), 17 million young adults (age 18–25 years), and over 45 million adults (age 26 and older) (NIDA 1991). Of the 21 million people who used marijuana at least once in the past year, almost one-third, or 6.6 million, used the drug once a week or more. On the other hand, since 1979, the use of marijuana has continuously decreased for all age groups (NIDA 1990b). The number of current users declined from 18 million (9%) in 1985 to 12 million (6%) in 1988.

Another irony is that, in some states, marijuana is one of the largest cash-producing crops. Law enforcement efforts to eliminate the production and distribution of this illegal substance have not been successful.

Estimates are that 200 million to 250 million people throughout the world have used marijuana. While more users live in Africa and Asia, use among Western populations has increased in the last two years. By the 1970s, as many as 24 million Americans had tried marijuana and about 8 million continued to use it on either an occasional or regular basis. In 1978, more than half the population of 18- through 25-year-olds in the United States had used cannabis.

Even the origin of the word *marijuana* (or *marihuana*) is debatable. It may come from either a Portuguese or Spanish word for "intoxicating."

THE HISTORY OF MARIJUANA USE

In many societies, marijuana has historically been a valued crop. It is called *hemp* because the woody fibers of the stem yield a fiber that can be made into cloth and rope. The term *Cannabis* comes from the Greek word for *hemp.*

Cannabis was apparently brought to the Western hemisphere by the Spaniards as a source of fiber and seeds. For thousands of years, the seeds have been pressed to extract a red oil used for medicinal and nonmedical uses. The plant (both male and female) also produces a resin with active

Marijuana leaves from home-grown plants. *Source:* © Jerry Howard/Stock, Boston

ingredients that affect the central nervous system (CNS). Marijuana contains hundreds of chemical compounds, but only a few found in the resin are responsible for producing the euphoric "high."

The first known record of marijuana use is the *Book of Drugs* written about 2737 B.C. by the Chinese Emperor Shen Nung; he prescribed marijuana for treating gout, malaria, gas pains, and absent mindedness. The Chinese apparently had much respect for the plant. They obtained fiber for clothes and medicine from it for thousands of years. The Chinese named the plant *ma (maw)*, which means "valuable" or "endearing." In the 1930s, marijuana was still called *ma*.

Around the year 500 B.C., another Chinese book of treatments referred to the medical use of marijuana. Nonetheless, the plant got a bad name from the moralists of the day, who claimed that youngsters became wild and disrespectful from the recreational use of *ma*. They called it the "liberator of sin" because under its influence, the youngsters refused to listen to their elders and did other scandalous things. Marijuana was banned in China but later legalized.

India also has a long and varied history of marijuana use. It was an essential part of early Indian religious ceremonies for thousands of years. The well-known *Rig Veda* and other chants de-scribe the use of *soma*, which some believe was marijuana. (As mentioned earlier, in Chapter 11, others believe it was the *Amanita* mushroom.) Early writings describe a ritual in which resin was collected from the plants. After fasting and purification, certain men ran naked through the cannabis fields. The clinging resin was scraped off their bodies, and cakes were made from it and used in feasts. For centuries, missionaries in India tried to ban the use of marijuana, but they were never successful; its use was heavily ingrained in the culture.

Records from Assyria in 650 B.C. refer to a drug called *azulla* that was used for making rope and cloth and was consumed to experience euphoria. The ancient Greeks also knew about marijuana. Galen described the general use of hemp in cakes, which when eaten in excess were narcotic. Herodotus described the Scythian custom of burning marijuana seeds and leaves to produce a narcotic smoke in steambaths. It was believed that breathing the smoke from the burning plants would cause frenzied activity. Groups of people stood in the smoke and laughed and danced as it took effect. Pliny the Elder related that the sails and cordage of the Roman galleys were made of hemp. In the nineteenth century, the explorer Burton mentioned that African natives burned plants and inhaled the smoke, which seemed to intoxicate them.

One legend about cannabis is based on the travels of Marco Polo in the twelfth century. Marco Polo told of the legendary Hasan Ibn-Sabbah, who terrorized a part of Arabia in the early 1100s. His men were some of the earliest political murderers and were supposed to kill under the influence of hashish, a strong, unadulterated cannabis derivative. The cult was called the *hashishiyya*, from which came the word *hashish*. (The word *assassin* may be derived from the name of *Sheik Hasan*, who was a political leader in the tenth century.)

It is unlikely, however, that using hashish can turn people into killers. Experience suggests that people tend to become sleepy and indolent rather than violent after eating hashish or another of the strong cannabis preparations available in Arabia. Hasan's men were probably given the drug to relax after they had done their deeds. Authorities on Islamic history say there is no basis for the colorful stories about the use of hashish to turn young men into killers (Abel 1980).

Napoleon's troops brought hashish to France after their campaign in Egypt at the beginning of the nineteenth century, despite Napoleon's strict orders to the contrary. By the 1840s, the use of hashish, as well as opium, was widespread in France, and efforts to curb its use were unsuccessful. One famous novel of the time, *The Count of Monte Cristo* by Alexandre Dumas, mentions the use of hashish. Dumas, who experimented with drugs, recounts the story of the assassins and their use of hashish in the novel. By the 1850s, marijuana use was so prevalent that psychiatrist Moreau de Tours advocated its use by students to help them gain insight into mental conditions that he believed were similar to the state of marijuana intoxication.

In North America, hemp was planted near Jamestown in 1611 for use in making rope. By 1630, half the winter clothing at this settlement was made from hemp fibers. There is no evidence of the medicinal use of hemp. Hemp was also valuable as a source of fiber for clothing and rope for the Pilgrims at Plymouth. To meet the demand for fiber, a law was passed in Massachusetts in 1639, requiring every household to plant hemp

seed. However, it took much manual labor to get the hemp fiber into usable form, resulting in a chronic shortage of fiber for fish nets and the like (Abel 1980).

George Washington had a field of hemp at Mount Vernon, and there is some indication that it was used for medicine as well as for making rope. Washington once mentioned that he forgot to separate the male and female plants, a process usually done because the female plant gave more resin if unpollinated.

In the early 1800s, U.S. physicians used marijuana extracts to produce a tonic used for both medicinal and recreational purposes. This changed in 1937 with passage of the Marijuana Tax Act, which prohibited its use as an intoxicant and regulated its use as a medicine.

Most of the abuse of marijuana in the United States during the early part of the twentieth century occurred near the Mexican border and in the ghetto areas of major cities. Cannabis was mistakenly considered a narcotic, like opium, and legal authorities treated it as such. In 1931, Harry Anslinger, who was the first appointed head of the Bureau of Narcotics and later would become responsible for the enforcement of marijuana laws, thought that the problem was slight. But by 1936, he claimed that the increase in the use of marijuana was of great national concern (Anslinger and Cooper 1937). Anslinger set up an informational program that finally led to the federal law that banned marijuana. The following sensationalized statement was part of Anslinger's campaign to outlaw the drug:

> What about the alleged connection between drugs and sexual pleasure? . . . What is the real relationship between drugs and sex? There isn't any question about marijuana being a sexual stimulant. It has been used throughout the ages for that: in Egypt, for instance. From what we have seen, it is an aphrodisiac, and I believe that the use in colleges today has sexual connotations (Anslinger and Cooper 1937).

Also during this time, some usually accurate magazines reported that marijuana was partly responsible for crimes of violence. In 1936, *Scientific American* reported that "marijuana produces a wide variety of symptoms in the user, including hilarity, swooning, and sexual excitement. Combined with intoxicants, it often makes the smoker vicious, with a desire to fight and kill'' (''Marijuana Menaces Youth'' 1936). A famous poster of the day, called ''The Assassination of Youth,'' was effective in molding attitudes against drug use (see Figure 12-1).

Largely because of the media's effect on public opinion, Congress passed the Marijuana Tax Act in 1937. However, it was declared unconstitutional in 1969. (In 1969, the tax levied on all transactions involving marijuana was declared self-incriminating—see Chapter 3.) Marijuana has not been classified as a narcotic since 1971.

Marijuana still grows wild in many American states today. Curiously, one reason for this is that, during World War II, the fiber used to make rope (sisal) was hard to import, so the government subsidized farmers to grow hemp. Much of today's crop comes from these same plants. Another reason for the spread of the plants is that, until recently, the seeds were used in birdseed. Canaries sing better after eating a little marijuana. Leftover seed was discarded in the garbage and thus spread to landfill dumps, where it sprouted. Birdseed containing marijuana seeds is still available, but the seeds are sterilized so they cannot germinate.

The Indian Hemp Drug Commission Report in the 1890s and the 1930s Panama Canal Zone Report on marijuana stressed that available evidence did not prove marijuana to be as dangerous as it was popularly thought; these reports were given little publicity, however, and were forgotten. In 1944, a report was issued by the LaGuardia Committee on Marijuana, which consisted of 31 qualified physicians, psychiatrists, psychologists, pharmacologists, chemists, and sociologists appointed by the New York Academy of Medicine. They stated in one key summary that marijuana was not the killer many thought it to be:

> It was found that marijuana in an effective dose impairs intellectual functioning in general. . . . Marijuana does not change the basic personality structure of the individual. It lessens inhibition and this brings out what is latent in his thoughts and emotions but it does not evoke responses that would otherwise be totally alien to him. . . . Those who have been smoking marijuana for years showed no mental or physical deterioration that may be attributed to the drug (Solomon 1966).

Much of the early research conducted did not analyze the potency of marijuana. As a result, findings from various studies are difficult to compare. Because the quality of marijuana varies so greatly, it is impossible to know the amount of drug taken without analyzing the original material and the leftover stub, or ''roach.'' Conditions like soil moisture and fertility, amount of sunlight, and

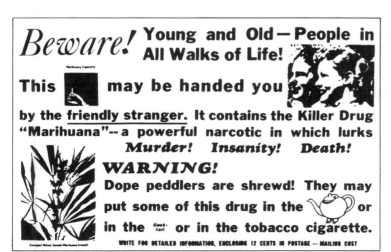

FIGURE 12-1 This antimarijuana poster was distributed by the Federal Bureau of Narcotics in the late 1930s.

temperature all have an effect on the amounts of active ingredients found in the resulting marijuana plant.

CHARACTERISTICS OF CANNABIS

In 1753, Carolus Linnaeus, a Swedish botanist, classified marijuana as **Cannabis sativa.** *Cannabis sativa* is a plant that grows readily in many parts of the world. Most botanists agree that there is only one species *(sativa)* and that all the variants *(indica, americana,* and *africana)* belong to that species; others believe that the variants are three distinct species (Schultes 1978). *Indica* is considered to have the most potent resin, but climate, soil, and selective plant breeding all influence potency.

Cannabis sativa
the hemp plant marijuana

Cannabis is *dioecious,* meaning that there are male and female plants (see Figure 12-2). After the male plant releases its pollen, it usually dies. Cultivators of marijuana often eliminate or remove the male plants once the female plant has been pollinated. The world's record marijuana plant was 39 feet tall, and its woody stem was nearly 3 inches in diameter.

There are more than 400 different chemicals in the cannabis plant, many of which have not yet been identified. Delta-9-tetrahydrocannabinol, or THC, is the primary mind-altering (psychoactive) agent in marijuana. THC is most highly concentrated in the flowering tops and upper leaves of the female plant. When crushed or eaten, these flowering tops produce a resin in which the psychoactive ingredient THC is found. The potency of the resin depends on which part of the plant is consumed. For example, less resin exists in the lower leaves and the stems than in the flowers and upper leaves.

In cultivated marijuana crops, male plants are

eradicated from the growing fields so that they cannot pollinate the female plants, which makes the potency of female plants increase dramatically. In the United States, this method produces a type of marijuana known as **sinsemilla** (meaning "without seeds" in Spanish). This type of marijuana is one of the most potent varieties available.

sinsemilla
one of the most potent types of marijuana available; means "without seeds"

Native U.S. cannabis is considered inferior because of a low concentration of THC, usually less than 0.5%. THC levels in Jamaican, Colombian, and Mexican varieties range between 0.5% and 7%.

In the United States, the amount of THC found in "street"-sold marijuana ranges broadly from 0.5% to 11%. Reports that the amount of THC in marijuana has risen dramatically since the 1960s appear to be false (Mijuriya and Aldrich 1988). Rather, the quantities of other more potent types of marijuana like sinsemilla are more readily available in illegal drug markets. The actual potencies of the more generic types of marijuana have remained the same in the last 30 years.

As mentioned earlier, *hashish* (or *hasheesh*), is another cannabis derivative that contains the purest form of resin. THC content in hashish averages from 7% to 14%. Historically, hashish users have represented a somewhat small percentage of the cannabis user population in the United States. Generally, this derivative is more widely used outside the United States; it is generally produced in Lebanon, Afghanistan, and Pakistan.

A third derivative of the cannabis plant is *ganja* in India. This preparation consists of the dried tops of female plants.

Finally, the weakest form of marijuana is known as *bhang;* it is made from parts of the cannabis plant that contain the least amount of THC. Often, these dried parts are ground into a powder and mixed into drinks, teas, and candies. Bhang is rarely found in the United States, largely be-

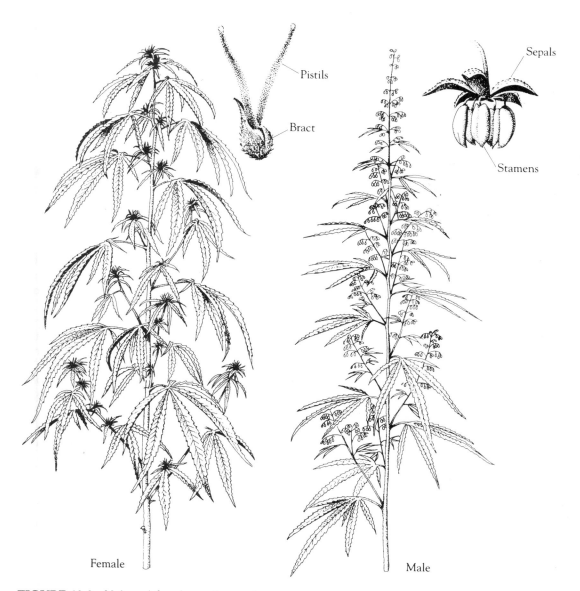

FIGURE 12-2   Male and female marijuana plants.

cause it is very weak and considered low grade, usually containing less than 1% or 2% THC.

T h i n k   A b o u t   I t . . .

1. Speculate on one of the ironies about marijuana use in the United States.
2. Why is the use of marijuana for recreational purposes so controversial? Cite arguments both for and against recreational use.
3. As a result of your expertise about the use and abuse of marijuana, a local group of cancer patients undergoing chemotherapy has asked you to help them write a letter to the president of the United States, asking for repeal of the law against marijuana use for cancer patients suffer-

ing from the side effects of chemotherapy treatment. What would you say in this letter of support?

4. Young teenagers in your neighborhood are smoking marijuana. What would you tell them about this drug? What advice would you give?

THE PHYSIOLOGICAL EFFECTS OF MARIJUANA USE

When marijuana smoke is inhaled into the lungs, THC, the psychoactive ingredient, leaves the blood rapidly through metabolism and through efficient uptake into the tissues. THC and its metabolites tend to bind to proteins in the blood and remain stored for long periods in body fat. Five days after a single injection of THC, 20% remains stored, whereas 20% of its metabolites remain in the blood. Complete elimination of a single dose can take up to 30 days. Measurable levels of THC in blood from chronic users can often be detected for several days or even weeks after their last marijuana cigarette.

In smokers, lung absorption and transport of THC to the brain are rapid; THC reaches the brain within as little as 14 seconds after inhalation. Marijuana is metabolized more efficiently through smoking than intravenous injection or oral ingestion. It is also three to five times more potent (Jones 1980).

Some effects of cannabis described in the following sections are unquestionably toxic in that they can either directly or indirectly produce adverse health effects. Other effects may be beneficial in treating some medical conditions. The uses of marijuana, THC, and synthetic cannabinoids, either alone or in combination with other drugs, are currently being investigated for use in treating an array of seemingly unrelated medical problems.

EFFECTS ON THE CENTRAL NERVOUS SYSTEM

The primary effects of marijuana—specifically, THC—are on CNS functions. The precise CNS effects of consuming marijuana or administering THC can vary according to the expectations of the user, the social setting, the route of administration, and previous experiences (Jaffe 1990). Smoking a marijuana cigarette can alter mood, coordination, memory, and self-perception. Usually, such exposure causes relaxation and a sense of well-being. Marijuana smokers often claim heightened sensory awareness, **altered perceptions** (particularly a slowing of time) associated with hunger (the **"munchies"**), and a dry mouth.

---

altered perceptions
changes in the interpretation of stimuli, as resulting from marijuana use

the "munchies"
hunger experienced while under the effects of marijuana

High doses of THC or greater exposure to marijuana can cause hallucinations, delusions, and paranoia. Some users describe anxiety developing into panic after high-dose exposure. Due to the availability and widespread use of marijuana, extreme dysphoria and psychiatric emergencies from marijuana overdose are becoming somewhat common. Long-term users often show decreased interest in personal appearance or goals as well as an inability to concentrate, make appropriate decisions, and remember.

The mechanism whereby THC alters CNS activity is not readily apparent. Even the precise classification of this drug is uncertain. The responses to marijuana are highly variable and appear to have elements of all three major groups of drugs of abuse. Consequently, marijuana use can cause euphoria and paranoia (like stimulants), drowsiness and sedation (like depressants), and hallucinations (like psychedelics). It is possible that THC alters several receptor or transmitter systems in the brain; this would account for its diverse and somewhat unpredictable effects. It has been speculated that THC alters the lipid membrane in all neurons and interferes with the normal functions of these brain cells; such a nonspecific action would account for the varied effects of this drug, as well.

In contrast to the theory of a general, nonselective action for marijuana is the recent dramatic discovery of a specific receptor site in the brain for THC. Researchers now believe that a selective endogenous marijuana system exists in the brain and is activated by THC when marijuana is consumed. Some researchers speculate that an endogenous THC-like substance (perhaps an unidentified neurotransmitter) naturally works at these marijuana sites; efforts are being made to identify this substance. It is possible that, from this discovery, a group of new therapeutic agents will be developed that can selectively interact with the marijuana receptors, resulting in medical benefits without the side effects that generally accompany marijuana use (Hudson 1990).

EFFECTS ON THE RESPIRATORY SYSTEM

Marijuana is often smoked like tobacco. It would be unusual if there were not some effects from its repeated inhalation, such as those caused by the inhalation of any combustible product. When smoking tobacco, for example, nearly 70% of the total suspended particles in the smoke are retained in the lungs. There is reason to believe that, because marijuana smoke is inhaled more deeply than tobacco smoke, more tar residues are retained.

Smoke is a mixture of tiny particles suspended in gas, mostly carbon monoxide. These solid particles combine to form a residue called *tar*. Cannabis produces more tar (up to 50% more) than an equivalent weight of tobacco and is smoked in a way that increases the accumulation of tar (Jones 1980).

Over 150 chemicals have been identified in marijuana smoke and tar. A few are proven carcinogens; however, many have not yet been tested for carcinogenicity. The carcinogen benzopyrene, for example, is 70% more abundant in marijuana smoke than in tobacco smoke. When cannabis tar is applied to the skin of experimental animals, it causes precancerous lesions similar to those caused by tobacco tar. Similarly, whenever isolated lung tissue is exposed to these same tars, precancerous changes result (Jones 1980; Turner 1980; Hollister 1986).

Special white blood cells in living lung tissue—*alveolar macrophages*—play a role in removing debris from the lungs. When exposed to smoke from cannabis, these cells are less able to remove bacteria and other foreign debris.

Smoking only a few marijuana cigarettes a day for six to eight weeks can significantly impair pulmonary function. Laboratory and clinical evidence often indicates that heavy use of marijuana causes cellular changes and that users have a higher incidence of such respiratory problems as laryngitis, pharyngitis, bronchitis, asthmalike conditions, cough, hoarseness, and dry throat (Jones 1980; Hollister 1986). Recent reports emphasize the potential damage to pulmonary function that can occur from chronic marijuana use (NIDA 1991).

Most marijuana users in the United States inhale much less smoke than tobacco smokers do, resulting in less exposure to tar. As a result, any comparative pathology between cannabis and tobacco is difficult to make; the detection of pathology in comparing the two is virtually impossible. However, evidence suggests that many 20-year-old smokers of both hashish and tobacco have lung damage comparable to that of heavy tobacco smokers over 40 years of age. It is believed that the tar from tobacco and marijuana have damaging effects, but it is not known whether smokers who use both products suffer synergistic or additive effects (Jones 1980; Hollister 1986).

EFFECTS ON THE CARDIOVASCULAR SYSTEM

In humans, cannabis causes both an increase in heartrate related to the amount of THC consumed and a reddening of the eyes. In physically healthy users, these effects, as well as slight changes in heart rhythm, are transitory and do not appear to be significant. In patients with **angina pectoris,** however, the increased oxygen requirement due to the accelerated heartrate can cause pain more readily in response to exercise. The effect of can-

angina pectoris
severe chest pain and feelings of suffocation associated with diminished blood supply to the heart

nabis on people with heart rhythm irregularities is not known.

Marijuana use may also cause changes in blood pressure. Abnormally low pressure in a standing position is most frequently observed. Users sometimes mention that they feel lightheaded when they stand up after smoking. Chronic administration of large doses of THC to healthy volunteers shows that they adapt to the increase in heartrate, the decrease in blood pressure, and the increase in blood volume.

People with angina and some other cardiovascular problems seem to be at an increased risk when smoking marijuana (Hollister 1986). Marijuana products also bind hemoglobin, limiting the amount of oxygen that can be carried to the heart tissue. This deficiency could trigger heart attacks in susceptible people (Palfai and Jankiewicz 1991). The National Academy of Science's Institute of Medicine recommends that persons with cardiovascular disease avoid marijuana use because there are still many unanswered questions about its effects on the cardiovascular system.

EFFECTS ON SEXUAL PERFORMANCE AND REPRODUCTION

Drugs may interfere with sexual performance and reproduction in several ways. Drugs may alter sexual behavior, affect fertility, damage the chromosomes of germ cells in the male or female, or adversely affect fetal growth and development.

The Indian Hemp Commission, which wrote the first scientific report on cannabis, commented that it had a sexually stimulating effect, like alcohol. However, the report also said that cannabis was used by Asian Indian ascetics to destroy the sexual appetite. This apparent discrepancy may be a dose-related effect. Used occasionally over the short term, marijuana may act as an **aphrodisiac** by releasing CNS inhibitions. In addition, the al-

---

aphrodisiac
a substance that stimulates or intensifies sexual desire

---

tered perception of time under the influence of the drug could make the pleasurable sensations appear to last longer than they actually do.

Marijuana affects the sympathetic nervous system to increase vasodilatation in the genitals and to delay ejaculation (Harclerode 1980). High doses over a period of time lead to depression of libido and impotence, possibly due to the decreased amount of testosterone, the male sex hormone.

Cannabis has several effects on semen. The total number of sperm cells and the concentration of sperm per unit volume is decreased during ejaculation. Moreover, there is an increase in the proportion of sperm with abnormal appearance and reduced motility. These qualities are usually associated with low fertility and a higher probability of producing an abnormal embryo should fertilization take place.

As of 1987, there were no documented reports of children with birth defects in which the abnormality was linked to the father's smoking marijuana. It is possible that damaged sperm cells are incapable of fertilization (so that only normal sperm cells reach the egg) or that the abnormal sperm appearance is meaningless in terms of predicting birth defects. When marijuana use stops, the quality of the semen gradually returns to normal over several months (Harclerode 1980; NAS 1982).

Less reliable data are available on the effects of cannabis on female libido, sexual response (ability to respond to sexual stimulation with vaginal lubrication and orgasm), and fertile reproductive (menstrual) cycles ("Marijuana" 1987). Preliminary data from the Reproductive Biology Research Foundation show that chronic smoking of cannabis (at least three times per week for the preceding six months) adversely affects the female reproductive cycle. Results with women were correlated with work in rhesus monkeys; it was found that THC blocks ovulation (due to effects on female sex hormones).

Data on effects of marijuana use during pregnancy and lactation are inconclusive. Some evidence exists that the use of this drug by pregnant women can result in intrauterine growth retardation, which is characterized by prolonged labor, low birthweight, and behavioral abnormalities in newborns (Nahas 1986, 83; Roffman and George 1988).

Pregnant rhesus monkeys treated with THC levels equivalent to those associated with moderately heavy marijuana use (according to U.S. standards) had an abortion and fetal death rate about four times higher than the drug-free control monkeys. THC and other cannabinoids pass through the blood-placental barrier and concentrate in the fetus's fatty tissue, including its brain. Ethical considerations prevent duplication of the experiment in humans.

Often, women who smoke marijuana during pregnancy also use other drugs—such as alcohol, tobacco, and cocaine—which are known to have adverse effects on the developing fetus. Like many other substances, THC is taken up by the mammary glands in lactating females and is excreted in the milk. Effects on human infants have not been determined (Petersen 1980).

In studies on mice and rats (but not humans), the addition of THC to pregnant animals lowered litter size, increased fetal reabsorption, and increased the number of reproductive abnormalities

in the surviving offspring (Dewey 1986). The offspring of the drug-treated animal mothers had reduced fertility and more testicular abnormalities. The dose of cannabinoids used in these studies was proportionally higher than that used by humans. Again, this points to the need for added caution by pregnant women using marijuana, even though there is no explicit proof of its prenatal effects (Dewey 1986).

EFFECTS ON THE IMMUNE SYSTEM

Animal experiments have shown that THC, cannabis extracts, and marijuana smoke in doses comparable to those associated with typical use by humans suppress the immune system reactions. In humans, some studies but not all indicate that heavy use of marijuana may interfere with the T-lymphocyte part of the immune system, the component that plays a role in resistance to viral infection and cancer. The combination of inhaled carcinogens and depressed T-lymphocyte function could mean a greater risk of cancer for marijuana users.

An increased frequency of cancer has not been apparent in countries where cannabis use is traditional and extensive (for example, Jamaica, India). However, in many of these countries, people have relatively shorter life spans; thus those persons who might have developed cancer may not have lived to the age when cancers commonly develop. The question of decreased immunity in chronic users must be determined in countries where the lifespan is longer. Cancer often takes 20 to 30 years to develop from the time of beginning exposure to carcinogens. Marijuana has nearly twice as much benzopyrene, a proven carcinogen, as tobacco.

TOLERANCE AND DEPENDENCE

It has been known for many years that tolerance to some effects of cannabis builds rapidly in animals; namely, the drug effect becomes less intense with repeated administration. Frequent use of high doses of marijuana or THC in humans produces similar tolerance. For example, increasingly higher

---

Let's Get the Facts

The Link between Marijuana Use and Pregnancy

How does the use of marijuana affect fetal growth and development? Findings from Zuckerman et al. (1989) indicate that infants born to mothers using marijuana weighed an average of 79 g less and were an average of 0.5 cm shorter than infants of nonusers. Another finding is that children born to women who smoked marijuana just prior to or during pregnancy were 10 times more likely to develop a rare form of leukemia than were children born to drug-free women (Robison et al. 1989).

Pregnant women should be warned that marijuana use impairs fetal growth. The cause is believed to be the combined biochemical effects on the fetus and indirect effects of such factors as changes in blood oxygenation, blood pressure, and heartrate.

doses must be given to obtain the same intensity of subjective effects and increased heartrate that occur initially with small doses.

Frequent high doses of THC also can produce mild physical dependence. Healthy subjects who smoke several "joints" a day or who are given comparable amounts of THC orally experience irritability, sleep disturbances, weight loss, loss of appetite, sweating, and gastrointestinal upsets when drug use is stopped abruptly. This mild form of withdrawal is not experienced by all subjects, however. It is much easier to show psychological dependence in heavy users of marijuana (Jones 1980; Hollister 1986).

Psychological dependence involves an attachment to the euphoric effects of the THC content in marijuana. The subjective effects of marijuana intoxication include a heightened sensitivity to and distortion of sight, smell, taste, and sound; mood alteration; and diminished reaction time.

Think About It...

1. A local high school teacher has asked you to come and speak to her biology class on how marijuana affects the body. What topics would you cover? Briefly summarize what you would say.
2. The amount of effect that THC will have on the central nervous system varies according to the expectations of the user, the social setting, the route of administration, and previous experiences. Discuss these four factors in some detail.
3. A friend of yours says that, after reading this chapter, he will continue to smoke a "joint" or two once or twice a week because it appears that smoking marijuana is safer than smoking cigarettes. Given your understanding, what would you say to this individual?

THERAPEUTIC USES

Cannabis had been used to treat a variety of human ills in folk and formal medicine for thousands of years in South Africa, Turkey, South America,

and Egypt as well as such Asian countries as India, the Malays, Burma, and Siam. As recently as 1937, tinctures of cannabis were still cited in the *U.S. Pharmacopeia and National Formulary*, which listed current therapeutic drugs.

Physicians have had difficulty with cannabis dosage because the effectiveness of this substance decreases with repeated use; also, the inhalation route requires experience with smoking. After marijuana was legally classified as a narcotic and the Marijuana Tax Act of 1937 required that its use be reported, medical use effectively ceased. Only in the past decade has there been renewed interest in possible medical uses for cannabis. A few potentially valuable uses are now known, and others are being investigated to a limited extent.

The use of marijuana, THC, or related drugs for treatment of the extreme nausea and vomiting that often accompany cancer chemotherapy is an example of a promising application of this drug. In fact it is the only use authorized by the Food and Drug Administration (FDA). Cannabis is not always effective but can sometimes help when other antinauseant drugs have failed. THC-treated chemotherapy patients show improved appetite and diminished weight loss. THC has an antiemetic effect (prevents vomiting) and stimulates appetite. In 1985, the FDA approved and licensed the Unimed drug company to produce a THC capsule under the name of **Marinol** (dronabinol) for cancer patients experiencing nausea from chemotherapy.

Marinol
FDA approved THC in capsule form (dronabinol)

Another well-publicized therapeutic use of marijuana is in reducing the vision-destroying intraocular pressure that occurs in the eye disease known as **glaucoma.** Marijuana lowers intraocular pressure in the eye, even though it does not cure the condition and eliminate blindness (Petersen 1980; NAS 1982). Use of marijuana to treat this eye illness is not widespread, since other medicines are as effective and are not illegal substances.

glaucoma
an eye disease manifested by increased intraocular pressure

Other possible medical uses of the THC ingredient found in *cannabis* include:

1. *Antiasthmatic effect*—Some research indicates that short-term smoking of marijuana has improved breathing for asthma patients. Marijuana smoke dilates the lung's air passages (bronchodilation). Findings also show, however, that the lung-irritating properties of marijuana smoke seem to offset its benefits. Regardless, marijuana may still prove useful when other drugs are not effective because of a different mode of action in causing bronchodilation.

2. *Muscle-relaxant effect*—Some studies also indicate that muscle spasms are relieved when patients with muscle disorders use marijuana.

3. *Antiseizure effect*—Marijuana has both convulsant and anticonvulsant properties and has been considered for use in preventing seizures associated with epilepsy. In animal experimentation, the cannabinoids reduced or increased seizure activities, depending on how the experiments were conducted. One or more of the marijuana components may be useful in combination with other standard antiseizure medication, although at present their value seems limited. A survey of young epileptics who smoked marijuana did not show a change in seizure patterns, but caution is advised ("Pot Kills" 1981).

4. *Antidepressant effect*—Cannabis and the synthetic cannabinoid synhexyl have been used successfully in Great Britain as specific euphoriants for the treatment of depression. In South Africa, native women smoke cannabis to dull the pain of childbirth. As an analgesic, cannabis has the advantage of not depressing the respiratory center, unlike the opioid narcotics (Solomon 1966).

Whether cannabis, one of its synthetic constituents, or a chemically related compound is accepted as a legitimate medicine depends on several considerations. For example, it must be determined whether the pharmaceutically desirable effects are useful for treating chronic conditions. Tolerance develops rapidly when THC is used; this is also true for new, chemically related compounds. Like any other medication, marijuana and related products must be carefully tested for toxicity and therapeutic effectiveness. This process is time consuming as well as expensive. Further, unless a marijuana-related chemical is shown to be significantly better than current alternatives, it is unlikely to reach the market.

THE BEHAVIORAL EFFECTS OF MARIJUANA USE

In the 1930s, it was believed that the acute effects of marijuana were very devastating on the user and that marijuana use could suddenly lead to violent and even promiscuous behavior. Publications forecasted that marijuana use would lead to madness (Rowell and Powell 1939) and that it was the "assassin of youth" (Anslinger and Cooper 1937).

These beliefs are no longer accepted with regard to casual or occasional use. In most individuals, low to moderate doses of cannabis produce euphoria and a pleasant state of relaxation. This state is usually mild and short lived; a typical "high" from one "joint" may last from two to three hours. The user experiences altered perception of space and time, impaired memory of recent events, and impaired physical coordination. An occasional "high" is not usually hazardous unless the person attempts to drive a car, operate heavy machinery, fly a plane, or function in similar ways requiring coordination, good reflexes, or quick judgment. Even low doses of marijuana adversely affect perception, such as being able to judge the speed of an approaching vehicle or how much to slow down on an exit ramp.

An acute dose of cannabis can produce adverse reactions, ranging from mild anxiety to panic

Let's Get the Facts

Specific Signs of Marijuana Use

1. A sweet odor similar to burnt rope in room, on clothes, etc.
2. Roach—small butt end of a marijuana cigarette.
3. Joint—looks like a hand-rolled cigarette, usually the ends are twisted or crimped.
4. Roach clips—holders for the roach. These could be any number of common items such as paper clips, bobby pins or hemostats. They could also be of a store-bought variety in a number of shapes and disguises.
5. Seeds or leaves in pockets or possessions.
6. Rolling papers or pipes, usually hidden somewhere.
7. Eye drops—for covering up red eyes.
8. Excessive use of incense, room deodorizers or breath fresheners.
9. Devices for keeping the substance such as boxes, cans or even con-

Marijuana paraphernalia. *Source:* © Judith Kramer/The Image Works

cealed containers like a soft drink can with a screw-off lid.
10. Eating binges—an aftereffect in some marijuana users.
11. Appearance of intoxication yet no smell of alcohol.
12. Excessive laughter.

13. Yellowish stains on finger tips from holding the cigarette.

Source: L.A.W. Publications. "Let's All Work To Fight Drug Abuse," rev. ed. Addison, TX: C & L Printing, 1985, p. 39. Used with permission of the publisher.

and paranoia in some users. A few rare cases exhibit psychoses characterized by detachment from reality, delusional and bizarre behavior, and hallucinations. These reactions occur most frequently in individuals who are under stress, or who are anxious, depressed, or borderline schizophrenic; such effects may also be seen in normal users who accidentally take much more than their usual dose.

Extreme reactions also can occur as a result of ingesting marijuana treated (or "laced") with such things as LSD, PCP, or other additives, like *Datura* (jimsonweed) leaves. Based on limited evidence from survey studies, mild adverse reactions

are experienced on one or more occasions by more than one-half of regular users; they are mainly self-treated and usually go unreported. The small number of users who experience severe adverse reactions usually respond well to psychiatric treatment and recover in one or two days (Jones 1980; Hollister 1986).

DRIVING PERFORMANCE

Evidence shows that the ability to drive is strongly impaired while under the influence of marijuana. This effect has been demonstrated in laboratory assessments of driving-related skills such as eye-hand coordination and reaction time, in driver simulator studies, in test course performance, and in actual street-driving situations.

In limited surveys, from 60% to 80% of marijuana users indicate that they sometimes drive while high! A study of drivers involved in fatal accidents in the greater Boston area showed that marijuana smokers were overrepresented in fatal highway accidents as compared to a control group of nonusers of similar age and gender. A 1989 study found that, of nearly 1,800 blood samples taken from drivers arrested for driving while intoxicated, 19% tested positive for marijuana.

One recent study tested subjects on the effects of known amounts of marijuana, alcohol, or both on driving. The subjects drove a course rigged with various traffic problems. There was a definite deterioration in driving skills among those who had used either drug, but the greatest deterioration was in subjects who had taken both. In another test, 59 subjects smoked marijuana until they were high and then were given sobriety tests on the roadside by highway patrol officers. Overall, 94% of the subjects didn't pass the test 90 minutes after smoking, and 60% failed at 150 minutes, even though the blood THC was much lower at this time (Hollister 1986). Other studies on driving show this same inability to drive for as long as 12 to 24 hours after marijuana use.

Because some perceptual or other performance deficits resulting from marijuana use may persist for some time after the high, users who attempt to drive, fly, operate heavy machinery, and so on may not recognize their impairment because they do not feel intoxicated (NIDA 1980). States such as California are setting up testing procedures for the presence of THC in urine or blood samples from apparently intoxicated drivers.

Future trends regarding driving while under the influence of marijuana are not promising. As the use of marijuana becomes more socially acceptable (or perhaps even legal) and penalties for simple possession become more lenient, it is likely that individuals will feel less inclined to hide their drug use. Unfortunately, it follows that these individuals may also be more inclined to drive while high.

CHRONIC USE

With regard to chronic use of marijuana, early research findings reported (1) chromosomal damage (Stenchever et al. 1974), (2) cerebral atrophy (shrinking of the brain) (Campbell et al. 1971), and (3) lowered capacity of white blood cells to fight disease (Nahas et al. 1974). To date, these findings have all been contradicted or otherwise refuted by subsequent research. The only finding that appears credible is that chronic use of marijuana impairs lung capacity (Oliwenstein 1988; Bloodworth 1987).

Other evidence indicates that chronic, heavy use of cannabis can lead to lasting behavioral changes in some users. Apathy, such as a lack of concern for the future and a general loss of motivation, has been observed in some heavy users, and psychotic and paranoid symptoms have been seen in others. These symptoms usually disappear when regular drug use is discontinued and recur when use is resumed.

In fact, such reactions are somewhat rare, although case studies suggest that certain cannabis users may be more susceptible than others (NAS 1982; Petersen 1980; Hollister 1986). Many psychiatrists are concerned about such reactions in youthful drug users (11 to 15 years of age) because of the possibility that regular use may produce adverse effects on psychological as well as physical maturation. (This concern involves all psychoactive drugs, including alcohol.)

A few cannabis users experience spontaneous recurrences of the symptoms of acute intoxication days or weeks later, similar to LSD "flashbacks." These recurrences are not common and do not require treatment. Because THC is stored in body fat, it is possible that flashbacks might be triggered by something that causes THC to be released from the fat cells where it has accumulated. This has not been proven, however.

Do other changes in brain function persist after a marijuana-induced high? Limited clinical evidence suggests that some long-term users do not recover completely when they discontinue drug use. Psychological functioning—which includes perception, coordination, intelligence, and other factors—has been tested in heavy users in Jamaica,

Costa Rica, Greece, Egypt, and India. The conclusions from these studies conflict and in some cases are difficult to interpret accurately because of poor experimental methods and possibly biased investigators. Studies with the largest groups of subjects done in Egypt and India show significant differences between users and matched nonusers, whereas the studies using much smaller samples in Jamaica and Costa Rica do not show any significant differences between users and nonusers (Jones 1980; Hollister 1986).

We are led to the conclusion that, with regard to chronic effects, there is very little reliable information. Cannabis appears to be a relatively safe substance. Even in large doses, it is impossible to have a lethal dose of cannabis. To date, there is no evidence that anyone has ever died from an acute overdose of marijuana alone.

THE AMOTIVATIONAL SYNDROME

Amotivational syndrome characterizes regular users of marijuana who experience a lack of motivation and reduced productivity. Specifically, users show apathy, difficulty in concentration, and a lingering disinterest in pursuing goals.

This syndrome has received a considerable amount of attention. People who are high, or "stoned," lack the desire to perform hard work and are not interested in doing difficult tasks (Miranne 1979). There is some evidence of this behavior ("Pot Kills" 1981). Overall, chronic users

For You to Consider...

Chronic Marijuana Use

The following comments show how marijuana use can become a destructive habit:

I guess you could say it was peer pressure. Back in 1969, I was a sophomore in college, and everyone was smoking "dope." The Vietnam War was in progress, and most students on college campuses were heavily involved in the drug scene. I first started smoking marijuana when my closest friends did. I was taught by other students who already knew how to enjoy the effects of "pot."

I recall that one of my fellow students used to supply me with "nickel bags," and many of us nicknamed him "God." How did he get such a name? Because he sold some very potent marijuana that at times caused us to hallucinate.

I used pot nearly every day for about a year and a half, and hardly an evening would pass without smoking dope and listening to music. Smoking marijuana became as common as drinking alcohol. I used it in the same manner a person has a cocktail after a long day. At first, I liked the effects of being "high," but later, I became so accustomed to the stuff that life appeared boring without it.

After graduating, my college friends went their separate ways, and I stopped using marijuana for a few years. A year later, in graduate school, a neighborhood friend reintroduced me to the pleasure of smoking pot. I began using it again but not as often. Whenever I experienced some pressure, I would use a little to relax.

After finishing my degree, I found myself employed at an institution that at times was boring. Again, I started using pot at night to relax, and somehow it got out of control. I used to smoke a little before work and sometimes during lunch. I thought all was going well until one day I got fired because someone accused me of being high on the job.

Soon afterward, I came to the realization that the use of marijuana can be very insidious. It has a way of becoming psychologically addictive, and you don't even realize it. When I was high, I thought that no one knew and that I was even more effective with others. Little did I know, I was dead wrong and fooling no one.

I do not oppose someone else using marijuana, but I learned my lesson seven years ago. Since then, I have smoked dope only three times.

Source: Interview with a 39-year-old male, Peter Venturelli, May 1990.

have lower grades in school, are more likely to be absent from classes, and are likely not to complete assignments and to drop out of school (Liska 1990). In terms of age, the earlier someone begins smoking marijuana, the more likely the amotivational characteristics will prevail and the more difficult it will be to cease using this drug.

While the effects of marijuana per se are somewhat responsible for creating this syndrome, other factors contribute, as well. For instance, marijuana users are more likely to associate with peers who are also users. Surveys show that members of these peer groups tend to be alienated from society and are likely to be classified as nonconformers or re-

Let's Get the Facts

Marijuana Use and Crime

How prevalent is marijuana use among arrestees? The graph shows the percentages of male arrestees from 11 locales who tested positive for marijuana during April through June 1988. (Information from Washington, D.C., does not appear because the D.C. Pretrial Testing Program does not test for marijuana.)

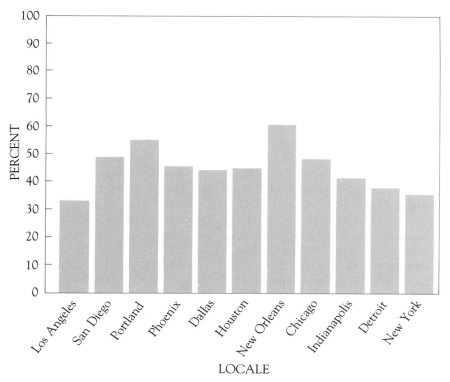

Source: National Institute of Justice 1988.

bellious youths. Imagine how an entire group of marijuana users can exert a profound effect on one another. They perpetuate a subculture emphasizing pleasure and nonconformity rather than hard work and success. The amotivational syndrome also dictates a noncaring attitude toward others and prompts subjective pleasure and alienation. Close ties with such a group desensitizes the individual about the negative aspects of drug abuse.

SUBJECTIVE EXPERIENCES

How does it feel to experience a cannabis high? There is a general sense of relaxation and tranquility, coupled with heightened sensitivity toward sound, touch, and taste (a typical hallucinogenic effect). Users report that their thinking wanders and short-term memory does not function very well. A brochure from the National Institute on Drug Abuse (NIDA) states that "the effects of marijuana can interfere with learning by impairing thinking, reading comprehension, and verbal and mathematical skills. Research shows that students do not remember what they have learned when they are 'high' " (NIDA 1990a, 37).

One marijuana user reported, "When I am high, things just simply flow differently. It's not like being high on alcohol. An alcohol high is a body high, while a pot high is more of a head experience" (Venturelli). Users report feeling "mellow" and believe that everything is fine. Other marijuana users cite feelings of euphoria and satisfaction with themselves. Another user said, "Being high can become habit forming, simply because it feels so good" (Venturelli). Marijuana is considered a recreational drug because it often intensifies pleasure and is used in conjunction with other pleasurable activities: eating, listening to music, meeting friends, and having sex.

TRENDS IN MARIJUANA USE

AGE DIFFERENCES

The data in Table 12-1 shows that marijuana use is strongly related to age. For individuals 12 to 13 years old (4.2%), lifetime rates were very low.

Lifetime rates were sharply higher in successive ages—15% among 14- to 15-year-olds and 30.3% among 16- to 17-year-olds. Lifetime rates of marijuana use steadily increased with age and reached a peak among those 26 to 29 years old. From the highest rate of 64%, the lifetime rates steadily decreased to 8.1% among those aged 50 and older (NIDA 1988).

Likewise, use during the past year steadily increased with age until the group of 18 to 21 years (30.6%) and then steadily decreased. Those 22 to 25 years old were most likely to report marijuana use during the past month (15.9%) (NIDA 1990a, 37).

PEER INFLUENCES

As discussed in the early chapters of this text, the mass media and parental role models have a significant impact on the attitudes that youth develop regarding drug use. However, peers may exert the most influence of all (Tec 1974; Tudor et al. 1987; Norem-Hebeisen and Hedlin 1983).

Research shows that it is very unlikely that an individual will use drugs when his or her peers do not use drugs. Marijuana use, in particular, is a group occurrence and thus strongly affected by peer pressure and influence. Learning theory (see Chapter 2) shows how peers can influence one another; drug-using peer members serve as role models, legitimizing this form of deviant behavior. Peers in such groups are in effect saying, "It's OK to use drugs," and they make drugs available. Heavy drug users are likely to belong to drug-using groups; in contrast, people who don't use drugs belong to groups where drug use is perceived as a very deviant form of social recreation.

OTHER RESEARCH FINDINGS

The following current trends regarding marijuana use were identified in a NIDA survey (1990a):

1. In the survey, people 26 to 34 and 18 to 25 years old were more likely to use marijuana than those 12 to 17 or 35 and older.
2. Among the respondents 12 years and older, it initially appears that males were more likely than females to use marijuana. While

TABLE 12-1 Marijuana use reported by Americans during lifetime, past year, and past month; expressed as percent (by age): 1988

Age	(Unweighted *N*)	Time Period		
		Lifetime	Past Year	Past Month
Total	*(8,814)*	*33.1*	*10.6*	*5.9*
12–17 years old	*(3,095)*	*17.4*	*12.6*	*6.4*
12–13	(925)	4.2	2.8	1.5
14–15	(1,060)	15.0	10.6	4.9
16–17	(1,110)	30.3	22.4	11.8
18–25 years old	*(1,505)*	*56.4*	*27.9*	*15.5*
18–21	(759)	50.3	30.6	15.0
22–25	(746)	62.1	25.3	15.9
26–34 years old	*(1,987)*	*62.1*	*17.6*	*10.8*
26–29	(899)	64.0	20.5	12.4
30–34	(1,088)	60.4	15.1	9.5
35 years and older	*(2,227)*	*19.6*	*3.2*	*1.4*
35–39	(419)	48.0	10.3	5.2
40–44	(342)	31.3	2.5	⋆
45–49	(265)	17.4	⋆	⋆
≥50	(1,201)	8.1	1.4	0.8

Source: NIDA 1988.
⋆Low precision; no estimate reported.

this was true in the 1960s, it is not any longer. Beginning in the 1980s, an increasing number of high school seniors of both sexes are likely to have tried marijuana: 53% of the males versus 48% of the females. These figures are very close when *casual* use is examined for males and females. When *compulsive* use is examined separately, however, use by males exceeds that of females 6% to 2% (Johnston et al. 1987).

3. The proportion of whites and blacks 12 years and older who ever used marijuana was about one-third. This was higher than the proportion of Hispanics (27.9%).

4. Residents of large metropolitan areas were more likely to use marijuana when compared to residents of small metropolitan or nonmetropolitan areas.
5. Southerners were less likely and Westerners were most likely to have used marijuana.
6. With regard to respondents 18 years and older, those who had completed more years of education were more likely to have used marijuana than those who had completed less years of education.
7. The unemployed were more likely to use marijuana than those employed full- or part-time.

8. Black males were slightly more likely to have used marijuana when comparisons were made to other males. White females were more likely than black females and Hispanic females to have ever used marijuana.

Radosevich et al. (1980) have highlighted three different factors related to marijuana use: (1) structural factors, such as age, gender, social class, and ethnicity/race; (2) social-interactional factors, such as type of interpersonal relationships, friendship cliques, and drug use within the peer-group setting; and (3) attitudinal factors, personal attitudes toward the use of drugs. Keep in mind that these factors can easily overlap; they are not separate and distinct.

THE ROLE OF MARIJUANA AS A "GATEWAY" DRUG

The adage that marijuana use leads to the use of other more serious drugs, such as heroin, is without foundation. While it is true that many heroin addicts began drug use with marijuana, it is also true that many, if not most, also used coffee and cigarettes. What's more, there are thousands of marijuana users who never go beyond this drug. As one study reports, "There are only a few thousand opiate addicts in Great Britain, yet there are millions who have tried cannabis" (Gossop 1987).

Nevertheless, some explanation is needed for the small percentage of marijuana users who do progress to such hard drugs as heroin. Possibly, the explanation may lie not in the use or nonuse of marijuana per se but in the type of person who is likely to experiment with and eventually abuse drugs. As we saw in Chapter 1, youth who turn to drugs are usually slightly to seriously alienated individuals. Thus, progression from marijuana to other drugs is more likely to depend on sociocultural factors such as peer-group composition, family relationships, social class, and the age at which drug use begins.

Let's Get the Facts

Fewer High School Seniors Using Marijuana?

The 1988 national survey of drug abuse given to high school seniors showed that drug use was at its lowest level since 1975 (NIDA 1990a). With regard to marijuana, 33.1% reported having used the drug during the previous year. In 1979, 50.8% reported having used marijuana during the previous year.

Some of the reasons cited for the decline in use are changing peer-group attitudes regarding drug use, increased effectiveness of antidrug advertising, and grim television coverage of drug use. Also consider that, given current U.S. demographics, there are fewer youth in the total population.

Think About It . . .

1. A young, marijuana-smoking couple you know has two children. The female partner approaches you and says that she is pregnant again; she goes on to explain that, because smoking "pot" during the previous pregnancies did not have any negative effects on her unborn children, she will probably continue to use the drug during this pregnancy. What advice would you give?

2. List and briefly discuss three therapeutic uses of marijuana.

3. A good friend has just started using marijuana to help him relax on weekends. He asks you to join him. How would you answer? Why?

4. Have a habitual marijuana user read the For You to Consider box on page 368. Ask him or her to answer the following questions: What is his or her overall impression regarding the interview? Is it believable or exaggerated? How safe is marijuana use? Additional comments?

K E Y   T E R M S

Cannabis sativa
sinsemilla
altered perceptions

the "munchies"
angina pectoris
aphrodisiac

Marinol
glaucoma

S U M M A R Y

1. Marijuana, or *Cannabis sativa*, consists of the dried and crushed leaves, flowers, stems, and seeds of this plant. THC (delta-9-tetrahydrocannabinol) is the primary mind-altering (psychoactive) ingredient in marijuana.

2. At low dose levels, such as when smoked or eaten, marijuana has a sedative effect. At higher dose levels, it produces hallucinations.

3. *Hashish, ganja, sinsemilla,* and *bhang* are all derivatives of the cannabis plant. Hashish (or hasheesh) is the strongest derivative. Its THC content is usually much higher than that of marijuana. *Ganja* consists of the dried tops of female plants. *Sinsemilla* is produced from unpollinated female marijuana plants and is one of the most potent forms. Finally, *bhang* is the weakest form of cannabis because it is made from parts of the plant that have the least THC.

4. In the United States, the amount of THC found in marijuana sold on the "streets" averages between 0.5% and 11%.

5. There is no evidence that the amount of THC present in marijuana is continually rising. The potency of generic "street"-sold marijuana has remained the same over the years. However, strong varieties are more readily available today.

6. World estimates show that 200 million to 250 million people have used cannabis. Thirty-two percent of the U.S. population has used marijuana at least once in their lives. While this number is high, since 1979, marijuana use has continued to decrease for all age groups.

7. Historically, few drugs have been the object of so much controversy as marijuana. Carolus Linnaeus, a Swedish botanist, classified marijuana as *Cannabis sativa* in 1753. In many societies, marijuana has been a valued crop, used often to make rope and cloth. The first known record of marijuana use is the *Book of Drugs*, written about 2737 B.C. by Chinese Emperor Shen Nung, who prescribed the drug for medicinal purposes. Other countries with a history of cannabis use include India, Assyria, Rome, Arabia, Egypt, and France. Early North American settlers grew marijuana, as well. Even George Washington had a field of hemp at Mount Vernon. It is important to be aware that cannabis use has met with both favor and disfavor over the years. Most cultures have gone through periods when marijuana use was considered legitimate, followed by periods in which the plant was banned and its growth, cultivation, and sale were prohibited by law.

8. THC is difficult to eliminate from the body; most of it is stored in body fat and takes up to 30 days to eliminate completely. Physiological evidence indicates that marijuana affects the respiratory system, as smoke from marijuana is carcinogenic. Marijuana use also causes changes in blood pressure, which can produce serious risk for people with cardiovascular problems. Sexual behavior and performance are affected, as well; fertility levels may be lowered and chromosomes may be damaged. Fetal growth and development may be adversely affected. In short-term use, marijuana may act as an aphrodisiac. In animal studies, THC suppresses immune system reactions.

9. No direct evidence suggests that marijuana is a "gateway" drug and leads to the use of other more addictive drugs, like heroin or cocaine. While most hard-core drug users start with alcohol, cigarettes, and marijuana, thousands of cannabis users do not progress to more serious drugs. Correlation does not mean causation.

10. The effectiveness of marijuana decreases with repeated use. Users must increase their dosages in order to maintain the same "high."

11. Marijuana is prescribed in many

countries, including the United States, to treat such illnesses as glaucoma, as well as the extreme nausea and vomiting that often

accompany chemotherapy. Marijuana has also been used as a sedative and muscle relaxant. Primarily in Great Britain, it has

been used as a remedy for depression, too.

R E F E R E N C E S

Abel, E. L. *Marijuana: The First Twelve Thousand Years.* New York: Plenum, 1980.

Anslinger, H. J., and C. R. Cooper. "Marijuana: Assassin of Youth." *The American Magazine* 124 (July 1937): 18–19, 150–153.

Bloodworth, R. C. "Major Problems Associated with Marijuana Use." *Psychiatric Medicine* 3, no. 3 (1987): 173–184.

Campbell, A. G., M. Evans, J. L. Thomson, and M. J. Williams. "Cerebral Atrophy in Young Cannabis Smokers." *The Lancet* (1971): 1219–1225.

Cohen, S. "Therapeutic Aspects." In *Marijuana Research Findings: 1980,* edited by R. C. Petersen. NIDA Research Monograph no. 31. Washington, D.C.: NIDA, 1980.

Dewey, W. L. "Cannabinoid Pharmacology." *Pharmacological Reviews* 38, no. 2 (1986): 48–50.

Foster, C. D., N. R. Jacobs, and M. A. Siegel, eds. *Illegal Drugs and Alcohol—America's Anguish.* Wylie, TX: Information Plus, 1989.

Gossop, M. *Living with Drugs.* 2nd ed. Aldershot, England: Wildwood House, 1987.

Harclerode, J. "The Effect of Marijuana on Reproduction and Development." In *Marijuana Research Findings: 1980,* edited by R. C. Petersen. NIDA Research Monograph no. 31. Washington, D.C.: NIDA, 1980.

Hollister, L. E. "Health Aspects of Cannabis." *Pharmacological Reviews* 38 (1986): 39–42.

Hudson, R. "Researchers Identify Gene That Triggers Marijuana's 'High'." *The Wall Street Journal,* 9 August 1990, B-2.

Jaffe, J. H. "Drug Addiction and Drug Abuse." In *The Pharmacological Basis of Therapeutics,* edited by A. Gilman, T. Rall, A. Nies, and P. Taylor. 8th ed. New York: Pergamon, 1990.

Jaffe, J. H. "Drug Addiction and Drug

Abuse." In *The Pharmacologial Basis of Therapeutics,* edited by L. S. Goodman, A. G. Gillman, and A. Gilman. 6th ed. New York: Macmillan, 1980.

Johnston, L. D., P. M. O'Malley, and J. G. Bachman. *National Trends in Drug Use and Related Factors among American High School Students and Young Adults, 1975–1986.* Department of Health and Human Services Publication no. 87-1535. Washington, D.C.: Government Printing Office, 1987.

Jones, R. T. "Human Effects: An Overview." In *Marijuana Research Findings.* NIDA Research Monograph no. 31. Washington, D.C.: NIDA, 1980.

L.A.W. Publications. *Let's All Work to Fight Drug Abuse,* rev. ed. Addison, TX: C & L Printing, 3rd ed. 1985.

Liska, K. *Drugs and the Human Body.* 3rd ed. New York: Macmillan, 1990.

"Marijuana." *The Harvard Medical School Mental Health Letter* 4, no. 5 (November 1987): 1–4.

"Marijuana Menaces Youth." *Scientific American* 154 (1936): 151.

Mijuriya, T. H., and M. R. Aldrich. "Old Drug, New Dangers—The Potency Question." *Journal of Psychoactive Drugs* 20 (1988): 47–55.

Miranne, A. C. "Marijuana Use and Achievement Orientation." *Journal of Health and Social Behavior* 20 (1979): 194–199.

Nahas, G. G. *The Treatment of Alcoholism.* New York: Brunner/Mazel, 1986.

Nahas, G. G., et al. "Inhibition of Cellular Immunity in Marijuana Smokers." *Science* 183 (1 February 1974): 419–420.

National Academy of Sciences, Institute of Medicine. *Marijuana and Health.* Washington, D.C.: National Academy Press, 1982.

National Institute on Drug Abuse. *Drug Abuse and Drug Abuse Research.* De-

partment of Health and Human Services Publication no. 91-1704. Washington, D.C.: NIDA, 1991.

National Institute on Drug Abuse. "Capsules: Facts about Teenagers and Drug Abuse." No. 17. Rockville, MD: NIDA, January 1990a. (Photocopy)

National Institute on Drug Abuse. *National Household Survey on Drug Abuse: Main Findings 1988.* Department of Health and Human Services Publication no. 90-1882. Washington, D.C.: NIDA, 1990b.

National Institute on Drug Abuse. *National Household Survey on Drug Abuse: Main Findings 1985.* Department of Health and Human Services Publication no. 88-1586. Rockville, MD: NIDA, 1988.

National Institute on Drug Abuse. *Marijuana and Health.* Eighth Annual Report to the U.S. Congress from the Secretary of Health and Human Services. Washington, D.C.: NIDA, 1980.

National Institute of Justice. *Drug Use Forecasting (DUF).* Washington, D.C.: NIJ, 1988. (Photocopy)

Norem-Hebeisen, A., and D. P. Hedlin. "Influences on Adolescent Problem Behavior: Causes, Connections, and Contexts." In *Adolescent Substance Abuse: A Guide to Prevention and Treatment,* edited by R. Isralowitz and M. Singer. New York: Haworth, 1983.

Oliwenstein, L. "The Perils of Pot." *Discover* 9, no. 6 (1988): 18.

Palfai, T., and H. Jankiewicz. *Drugs and Human Behavior.* Dubuque, IA: William C. Brown, 1991.

Petersen, R. C. "Marijuana and Health." In *Marijuana Research Findings: 1980.* NIDA Research Monograph no. 31. Washington, D.C.: NIDA, 1980.

"Pot Kills Motivation, Impairs Cognitive Functioning." *U.S. Journal* 12 (May 1981): 97–103.

Radosevich, M., L. Lanza-Kaduce, R. L. Akers, and M. D. Krohn. "The Sociology of Adolescent Drug and Drinking Behavior: Part II." *Deviant Behavior* 1 (January-March 1980): 145–169.

Robison, L. L., J. D. Buckley, A. E. Daigle, G. D. Hammond, R. Wells, D. Benjamin, and D. C. Arthur. "Use and Risk of Childhood Nonlymphoblastic Leukemia Among Offspring." *Cancer* 63 (15 May 1989): 1904–1911.

Roffman, R. A., and W. H. George. "Cannabis Abuse." In *Assessment of Addictive Behaviors*, edited by D. M. Donovan and G. A. Marlatt. New York: Guilford, 1988.

Rowell, E., and R. Powell. *On the Trail of Marijuana: The Weed of Madness.* Mountain View, CA: Pacific, 1939.

Schultes, R. E. "Exhnopharmacological Significance of Psychotropic Drugs of Vegetal Origin." In *Principles of Psychopharmacology*, edited by W. G. Clark and J. del Giudice. 2nd ed. New York: Academic, 1978.

Solomon, D., ed. *The Marihuana Papers.* New York: New American Library, 1966.

Stenchever, M. A., T. J. Kunysz, and M. A. Allen. "Chromosome Breakage in Users of Marijuana." *American Journal of Obstetrics and Gynecology* 118 (January 1974): 106–113.

Tec, N. *Grass Is Green in Suburbia.* Roslyn Heights, NY: Libra, 1974.

Tudor, C. G., D. M. Petersen, and K. W. Elifson. "An Examination of the Relationships between Peer and Parental Influences and Adolescent Drug Use." In *Chemical Dependencies: Patterns,* Costs, and Consequences, edited by C. D. Chambers, J. A. Inciardi, D. M. Petersen, H. A. Siegal, and O. Z. White. Athens, OH: Ohio University Press, 1987.

Turner, C. E. "Chemistry and Metabolism." In *Marijuana Research Findings: 1980.* NIDA Research Monograph no. 31. Washington, D.C.: NIDA, 1980.

Venturelli, P. Unpublished interviews with college students, 1983 to date.

Zuckerman, B., D. A. Frank, R. Hingson, H. Amaro, S. M. Levenson, H. Kayne, S. Parker, R. Vinci, K. Aboagye, L. E. Fried, H. Cabral, R. Timperi, and H. Bauchner. "Effects of Maternal Marijuana and Cocaine Use on Fetal Growth." *The New England Journal of Medicine* 320 (1989): 762–768.

Nonprescription (OTC) Drugs

CHAPTER OUTLINE

Federal Regulation of OTC Drugs / **Public Use and Misuse** ▪ Common Misconceptions / **Types of OTC Drugs** ▪ Internal Analgesics ▪ External Analgesics ▪ Cold, Allergy, and Cough Remedies ▪ Sleep Aids ▪ Stimulants ▪ Gastrointestinal Medications ▪ Diet Aids ▪ Skin Products / **Rules for OTC Drug Use**

LEARNING OBJECTIVES

On completing this chapter, you will be able to:

1. Outline the general differences between prescription and nonprescription drugs.
2. Explain the rationale for the switching policy of the Food and Drug Administration (FDA).
3. Identify some of the drugs that the FDA will likely make available over the counter (OTC) in the future.

4. Discuss the potential problems of making more effective OTC drugs available to the public.
5. Classify the principal drug groups that are available OTC.
6. Identify the type of information that is included on the labels of nonprescription medicines.
7. Discuss the three types of OTC analgesics and their principal uses.
8. Identify the major drugs in OTC cold products and their

effectiveness in relieving cold symptoms.
9. Discuss the use of stimulants and depressants in OTC products.
10. Explain when individuals should not self-medicate with OTC antacids.
11. Identify the major types of OTC drugs used to treat skin problems.
12. Cite the rules for safe use of nonprescription drugs.

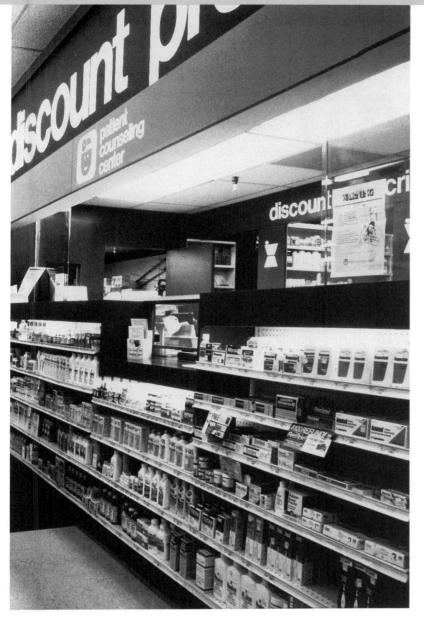

Source: © Camerique

Over $10 billion is spent each year in the United States on drug products that are purchased over the counter (OTC), and this market is increasing at the rate of 20% each year. Today, more than 300,000 different OTC products are available to treat everything from age spots to halitosis.

OTC substances are nonprescription drugs that may be obtained and used without the supervision of a physician. Regardless, some may be dangerous when used alone or in combination with other drugs. While some are very beneficial in the self-treatment of minor to moderate uncomplicated health problems, many others are of questionable therapeutic value and their usefulness is overstated by manufacturers.

In this chapter, we will review over-the-counter/nonprescription drugs. The first topic is policies regarding OTC drug regulation and actual public use and misuse. Common types of OTC products will then be considered individually: internal and external analgesics; cold, allergy, and cough remedies; sleep aids; stimulants; gastrointestinal medications, such as antacids and laxatives; diet aids; and skin products. The chapter concludes with a list of guidelines for using OTC products.

FEDERAL REGULATION OF OTC DRUGS

The Food and Drug Administration (FDA) is responsible for regulating nonprescription drugs. However, many critics claim that federal agencies, for the most part, have ignored their regulatory responsibility in regard to these products (Schwartz and Rifkin 1991). The history of OTC drug regulation is summarized in Table 13-1. (See also Chapter 3 for a detailed discussion.)

As previously discussed, the active ingredients in these products have been evaluated and classified according to their effectiveness and safety. At this time, almost all active ingredients still included in OTC drugs are category I. Also, as discussed in Chapter 3, the FDA is attempting to switch frequently used and safe prescription drugs to OTC availability. This policy is in response to public demand to make more effective medications available without a prescription. It is also an attempt by the FDA to help cut medical costs to the public. By making these drugs available OTC, the need for costly visits to health providers can be reduced. A few of the more notable drugs that have been made nonprescription as a consequence of this switching policy are ibuprofen (NSAIDS—

Advil, Nuprin); diphenhydramine (antihistamine—Benadryl); hydrocortisone (corticosteroid—Cortaid); loperamide (antidiarrheal—Imodium); fluoride (mouth rinses—Fluorigard); clotrimazole (vaginal antifungal—Gyne-Lotrimin); and adrenaline (bronchodilator—Bronkaid Mist) (see Table 13-2).

One of the major concerns of health professionals is that reclassification of safe prescription drugs to OTC status will result in overuse or misuse of these agents and perhaps encourage individuals to self-medicate rather than seek medical care for potentially serious health problems. However, the FDA has proceeded cautiously, and no major problems have yet been identified.

It is likely that switching will continue to occur, and hopefully, the public will be prepared to make good use of the new and effective drugs made available. In fact, another 57 drugs currently available by prescription are expected to be given OTC status in the next several years (Siegelman 1990). Included in those drugs currently being considered for switching by the FDA are Tagamet and Zantac (for treatment of ulcers), Naprosyn (analgesic/antiinflammatory, like ibuprofen), Seldane (nonsedating antihistamine), and Phenergan (sedative).

TABLE 13-1 History of OTC drug legislation and policy in the United States

Date	Event	Result
1906	Pure Food and Drug Act	Drugs must meet standards of purity and strength claimed by manufacturer. Must list opiate, cocaine, alcohol, and cannabis contents.
1912	Sherley Amendment	Cannot make false or fraudulent therapeutic claims about a product. Difficult to enforce.
1938	Food, Drug, and Cosmetic Act	New products judged safe before marketing.
1951	Humphrey-Durham Amendment	Drugs divided into prescription and nonprescription types.
1962	Kefauver-Harris Amendments	Manufacturer must establish safety and effectiveness of all drugs manufactured after 1938.
1966	NAS/NRC–FDA Study of Drugs	National Academy of Sciences/National Research Council evaluates 3,400 new drugs marketed between 1938 and 1962, including 512 OTC drugs. Only 15% of OTC products judged effective.
1972	FDA OTC Drug Products Evaluation Program	17 panels of experts to review all OTC drugs (over 300,000 on market).

Source: Copyright 1982 by the American Pharmaceutical Association, *Handbook of Nonprescription Drugs*, 7th ed. Reprinted with permission of the American Pharmaceutical Association, 2215 Constitution Ave., NW, Washington, D.C. 20037, (202) 628-4410.

TABLE 13-2 Major drug classes approved by the FDA for OTC status

Drug Class	Effects
Analgesics and antiinflammatories	Relieve pain, fever, and inflammation
Cold remedies	Relieve cold symptoms
Antihistamines and allergy products	Relieve allergy symptoms
Stimulants	Diminish fatigue and drowsiness
Sedatives and sleep aids	Promote sleep
Antacids	Relieve indigestion from rebound acidity
Laxatives	Relieve self-limiting constipation
Antidiarrheals	Relieve minor, self-limiting diarrhea
Emetics and antiemetics	Induce or block vomiting (respectively)
Antimicrobials	Treatment of skin infections
Bronchodilators and antiasthmatics	Assist breathing
Dentifrices and dental products	Promote oral hygiene
Acne medications	Treat and prevent acne
Sunburn treatments and sunscreens	Treat and prevent skin damage from ultraviolet rays
Dandruff and athlete's foot medications	Treat and prevent specific conditions
Contraceptives and vaginal products	Prevent pregnancy and treat vaginal infections
Ophthalmics	Promote eye hygiene and treat eye infections
Vitamins and minerals	Provide diet supplements
Antiperspirants	Promote body hygiene

Source: Gilbertson 1990.

For You to Consider...

Misuse of OTC Medication: Case Studies

The following cases illustrate the inappropriate use of OTC drugs and the potential problems that can result.

Case 1

Parents of a young child were going out for the evening. Their child often fussed when they were gone, so they decided to do something to keep the child from hassling the babysitter. They knew that cough syrup with antihistamine caused drowsiness, so they gave the child Benylin Cough Syrup (containing the antihistamine diphenhydramine) prior to the arrival of the babysitter in order to make the child fall asleep (Popovich 1991).

Case 2

An elderly woman experiencing delusions and hallucinations was admitted to the hospital. Laboratory tests revealed very high levels of calcium in her body. When questioned, the woman explained that she consumed a few TUMS antacids each day. With further probing, it was discovered that she actually had been consuming 200 TUMS tablets every week for 9 years (Popovich 1991).

Case 3

A four-year-old patient with juvenile rheumatoid arthritis experienced a severe chemical burn inside her mouth. It was discovered that she was given chewable aspirin every night to relieve the pain associated with her disease. One night, she fell asleep with the aspirin still in her mouth. Because of the caustic properties of this drug, the lining of her cheek was burned (Popovich 1991).

Case 4

A 34-year-old woman suffered blood clots during the delivery of her last child. She was put on the anticlotting drug warfarin to prevent additional clots. The following week, the patient experienced a headache and treated it with aspirin. She was not aware that aspirin also interferes with the formation of blood clots. The next morning, the patient slipped and fell but did not appear to be significantly injured. Later that day, she noticed large amounts of blood in her urine. Her husband rushed her to the hospital, where she was diagnosed with serious internal bleeding due to the interaction of warfarin and aspirin (Popovich 1991).

PUBLIC USE AND MISUSE

A lack of understanding about the nature of the OTC products—what they can and cannot do—and their potential side effects can result in harmful misuse. For this reason, it is important that those who consume OTC medications thoroughly analyze the benefits and risks in advance. Information about proper use of OTC medications is required to be cited on the drug label and is regulated by the FDA (see Figure 13-1 for an example). Required label information includes (1) approved uses of the product, (2) detailed instructions on safe and effective use, and (3) cautions or warnings to those at greatest risk when taking the medication (Gilbertson 1990).

Unfortunately, many consumers either choose to ignore the warnings on OTC labels or simply do not bother to read them. For example, excessive or inappropriate use of some nonprescription drugs can cause drug dependence. Consequently, persons who are always dropping medication in their eyes "to get the red out" or popping antacids like dessert after every meal are likely addicted. They continue to use OTC products to avoid unpleasant eye redness or stomach acidity, which are actually withdrawal consequences of excessive use of these medications.

COMMON MISCONCEPTIONS

It is extremely important that consumers be given accurate information concerning the OTC drugs they purchase. There are many examples of inaccurate or incorrect assumptions about OTC drugs that have led to problems.

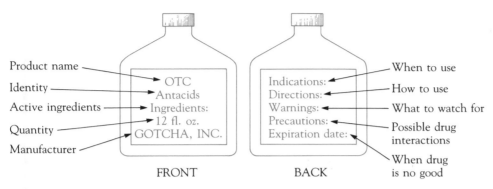

FIGURE 13-1 Label information controlled by the FDA

One of these misconceptions is that the government would not let the manufacturers of OTC products make inaccurate claims. While the U.S. Federal Trade Commission (FTC) does prosecute manufacturers for making fraudulent statements, the process is excruciatingly slow and of limited success. A company can tie up legal proceedings for years. For example, it took the FTC 16 years to get the word *liver* removed from the name *Carter's Little Liver Pills*, even though this medication had no association with or effect on the liver.

Another incorrect assumption involves whether a medication cures or just *relieves* symptoms. Drugs such as cold remedies are often used by people to cure colds; however, there is no cure for the common cold. The vast majority of OTC products are **symptomatic** medications.

---

symptomatic
drugs that relieve symptoms but not causes of medical problems

---

TYPES OF OTC DRUGS

INTERNAL ANALGESICS

In 1990, the American public spent more than $2 billion on internal (taken by mouth) analgesics, the largest sales category of OTC drugs. Most of the money was for salicylates (aspirin products—

Anacin, Bayer), acetaminophen (Tylenol, Datril, Pamprin, Panadol), and ibuprofen (Advil, Nuprin). The compositions of common OTC internal analgesics are given in Table 13-3. As explained in Chapter 8, the choice of an analgesic depends on the condition being treated. Besides their pain-relieving effects, these drugs can also be used as antipyretics (to reduce fever) or antiinflammatories (to relieve symptoms of inflammation). These products vary considerably in toxicity and interaction with other drugs (see Chapter 8 for details).

Aspirin and other OTC nonnarcotic analgesics (NSAIDS) are effective in treating mild to moderate musculoskeletal (somatic) pain and headaches and can be used to treat other discomforts such as toothaches, sore throats, sunburns, and menstrual pain (VanTyle 1990). However, these drugs are ineffective in relieving discomfort from abrasions, cramps, and pain from internal organs.

CAFFEINE AND OTHER ADDITIVES   A number of OTC analgesic products contain caffeine. There is no conclusive evidence that caffeine relieves pain, although its stimulant effect may be perceived as pleasant and encourage use. The combination of caffeine with OTC analgesics may be useful in treating vascular headaches because of the vasoconstrictive properties on cerebral blood vessels caused by this stimulant. In most OTC analgesic products, the amount of caffeine is less than that found in one-fourth to one-half cup of coffee (about 30 mg/tablet; e.g., Anacin, Excedrin). Other in-

TABLE 13-3   Compositions of OTC internal analgesics (dose/unit)

Product	Salicylate	Acetaminophen	Ibuprofen	Other
Anacin	400 mg	—	—	caffeine
Anacin (Maximum Strength)	500 mg	—	—	caffeine
Bayer	325 mg	—	—	—
Empirin	325 mg	—	—	—
Alka-Seltzer	325 mg	—	—	antacid
Ascriptin A/D	325 mg	—	—	Maalox
Ecotrin	325 mg	—	—	coated tablet
Excedrin Extra Strength	250 mg	250 mg	—	caffeine
Anacin 3-Regular	—	325 mg	—	—
Datril-Extra Strength	—	500 mg	—	—
Tylenol	—	325 mg	—	—
Tylenol, Junior Strength	—	160 mg	—	—
Advil	—	—	200 mg	—
CoAdvil	—	—	200 mg	decongestant
Haltran	—	—	200 mg	—
Medipren	—	—	200 mg	—
Nuprin	—	—	200 mg	—

Source: Physician's Desk Reference for Nonprescription Drugs 1991.

gredients—such as antacids, antihistamines, and decongestants—sometimes included in OTC pain-relieving products also have little or no analgesic action and usually add little to the therapeutic value of the medication.

EXTERNAL ANALGESICS

A large number of OTC drugs are used externally in the form of liniments, gels, lotions, and ointments to relieve pain in muscles, organs, and joints. This type of pain is often called *deep-seated pain.* The products are used topically (applied to the surface of the skin) and work by counter-irritant action rather than direct internal analgesic action. That is, these products have irritants that stimulate sensory receptors in the skin and increase bloodflow to the painful area, causing redness and a warm sensation. The counter-irritants take your mind off the original pain and focus it on a different type of skin sensation caused by the irritants.

Most of the drugs employed as counter-irritants are volatile substances that have a medicinal odor. These antiseptic smells may have a placebo effect, bringing pain relief to many people. It is possible that the physical massage given as the counter-irritant is applied and the resultant increased bloodflow help relieve muscle tension, but the drugs themselves do not cure the muscle, joint, or ligament damage that often causes these aches and pains. Sometimes, counter-irritants can give temporary pain relief to persons with neuralgia (nerve pain), rheumatoid arthritis, bursitis (inflammation in the joints), and some muscle cramps. However, relief should not be confused with effective treatment.

Volatile substances employed as counter-irritants include methyl salicylate, menthol, camphor, thymol, allyl isothiocyanate, capsicum oleoresin, turpentine oil, cinnamon oil, clove oil, chloroform, methacholine chloride, and histamine dihydrochloride. Methyl salicylate is the most commonly used and is found in ointments such as Ben-Gay. This external analgesic is quickly absorbed through the skin. Infants and small children are more sensitive to the toxic effects of salicylates, and care must be taken to prevent accidental ingestion. The wintergreen odor of this drug can be attractive to children, who mistake it for candy. One teaspoon of methyl salicylate can seriously poison a young child.

Menthol is different from the other counterirritants because it has a mild anesthetic action as well as being an irritant. This drug also stimulates the nerve receptors that perceive cold but depresses those that send out pains.

Clove oil is another highly irritating substance. The chief constituent is eugenol. Clove oil or pure eugenol are often used as a temporary pain reliever for toothache.

Another compound familiar to many people is allyl isothiocyanate, or oil of mustard. This drug is a powerful irritant and may cause blisters on the skin if the substance used is too concentrated. Oil of mustard is the active ingredient in the old-fashioned mustard plaster remedy used to treat chest congestion.

COLD, ALLERGY, AND COUGH REMEDIES

The common cold accounts for 20% of all acute illness in the United States. It is also the single most expensive ailment in the country (Sause and Manigione 1991). More time is lost from work and school due to the common cold than from all other diseases combined. About one-half of all absences and approximately one-fourth of total work time lost each year in industry is due to cold symptoms. Americans spent nearly $2 billion in 1990 for cough, cold, allergy, hay fever, and sinus products. These medications represent the second largest sales category of OTC drugs.

The incidence of the common cold varies with age. Children between 1 and 5 years are most susceptible; each child averages 6 to 12 respiratory illnesses per year, most of which are common colds. Individuals 25 to 30 years old average about 6 respiratory illnesses a year, and older adults average 2 or 3. The declining incidence of colds with age is due to the immunity that occurs after each infection with a cold virus; thus, if reinfected with the same virus, the microorganism is rapidly destroyed by the body's defense and the full-blown symptoms of a cold do not occur (Sause and Mangione 1991).

Most colds have similar general symptoms: the first stage, in which the throat and nose are dry and scratchy, and the second stage, in which secretions accumulate in the air passages, nose, throat, and bronchial tubes. The second stage is marked by continuous sneezing, nasal obstruction, sore throat, coughing, and nasal discharge. There may be watering and redness of the eyes and pain in the face (particularly near the sinuses) and ears. One of the most bothersome symptoms of the common cold is the congestion of the mucous membranes of the nasal passages, due in part to capillary dilation, which causes them to enlarge and become more permeable. Such vascular changes allow fluids to escape, resulting in drain-

The common cold accounts for 20 percent of all acute illnesses in the United States. *Source:* © W. Hill, Jr./ The Image Works

age and also inflammation due to fluid-swollen tissues (Bryant and Lombardi 1990).

DECONGESTANTS Cold and allergy products are formulated with such drugs as decongestants (sympathomimetics), antihistamines (chlorpheniramine or pheniramine), analgesics (aspirin or acetaminophen), and an assortment of other substances (vitamin C, alcohol, caffeine, etc.). Table 13-4 lists the ingredients found in many common OTC cold and allergy products.

Antihistamines reduce congestion caused by allergies, but they are relatively ineffective in the case of virus-induced colds. In high doses, the anticholinergic action of antihistamines (see Chapter 5) also decreases mucus secretion, relieving the runny nose; however, this action is probably insignificant at the lower recommended doses of OTC preparations (Sause and Mangione 1991). An anticholinergic drying action may actually be harmful because it can lead to a serious coughing response. Due to anticholinergic effects, antihistamines also may cause dizziness, drowsiness, impaired judgment, constipation, and dry mouth. Because of the limited usefulness and the side effects of antihistamine for treating colds, decongestant products without such agents should be selected for these viral infections (e.g., Sudafed Sinus Caplets or Contac Non-Drowsy Formula).

In contrast, antihistamines are very useful in relieving allergy-related congestion and symptoms.

The sympathomimetic drugs used as decongestants cause nasal membranes to shrink because of their vasoconstrictive effect, which reduces the congestion caused by both colds and allergies. Such drugs can be used in the form of sprays or drops (topical decongestants) or systemically (oral decongestants) (see Table 13-5). Ephedrine is a natural product sometimes found in OTC cold medicines that is similar to the neurotransmitter norepinephrine. Other FDA-approved sympathomimetics include pseudoephedrine, phenylpropanolamine, phenylephrine (probably the most effective topical), naphazoline, oxymetazoline, and xylometazoline.

Frequent use of decongestant nasal sprays can cause *congestion rebound* due to tissue dependence. After using a nasal spray regularly for longer than the recommended period of time, the nasal membranes adjust to the effect of the vasoconstrictor and become very congested when the drug is not present. The person becomes "hooked" and uses the spray more and more with less and less relief, until the tissue does not respond and the sinus passages become almost completely obstructed. Allergists frequently see new patients who are addicted to nasal decongestant sprays and are desperate for relief from congestion (Bryant and

TABLE 13-4 Compositions of common OTC cold and allergy products (dose/tablet)

Product	Sympathomimetic	Antihistamine	Analgesic
Actifed	pseudoephedrine (60 mg)	triprolidine (2.5 mg)	—
Allerest		triprolidine (2.5 mg)	—
Benadryl	pseudoephedrine (60 mg)	diphenhydramine (25 mg)	—
Chlortrimeton	—	chlorpheniramine (4 mg)	—
Contac	phenylpropanolamine (75 mg)	chlorpheniramine (12 mg)	—
Contac Non-Drowsy Formula	pseudoephedrine (30 mg)	—	acetaminophen (500 mg)
Dimetapp	phenylpropanolamine (75 mg)	brompheniramine (12 mg)	—
Dristan	phenylephrine (5 mg)	chlorpheniramine (2 mg)	acetaminophen (325 mg)
Sudafed Sinus	pseudoephedrine (60 mg)	—	acetaminophen (500 mg)

Source: Physician's Desk Reference for Nonprescription Drugs 1991.

TABLE 13-5 Compositions of OTC topical decongestants (drug concentrations)

Product	Sympathomimetic	Other
Afrin Nasal Spray	oxymetazoline (0.25%)	—
Dristan Nasal Spray	phenylephrine (0.5%)	antihistamine
Neo-Synephrine	phenylephrine (0.125–1.0%)	—
Vicks Sinex, Long-acting	oxymetazoline (0.05%)	—

Source: Physician's Desk Reference for Nonprescription Drugs 1991.

Lombardi 1990). This problem can be prevented by using nasal sprays sparingly and for no longer than the recommended time.

Orally ingested sympathomimetic drugs give less relief from congestion than the topical medications but do not cause rebound effects. In contrast, systemic administration of these drugs is more likely to cause cardiovascular problems (i.e., stimulate the heart, cause arrhythmia, and increase blood pressure).

ANTITUSSIVES Other drugs used to relieve the common cold are intended to treat coughing. The cough reflex is an essential means to clear the lower respiratory tract of foreign matter, particularly in the later stages of a cold. There are two types of cough: productive and nonproductive. A *productive* cough clears mucous secretions and foreign matter so that breathing becomes easier and the infection clears up. A *nonproductive* cough causes throat irritation and is often self-perpetuating because of the irritation; this type of cough is of little cleansing value. Some types of cough suppressant (**antitussive**) medication are useful for treating a nonproductive cough but should not be used to suppress a productive cough (Sause and Mangione 1991).

Two kinds of OTC preparations are available to treat coughing:

antitussives
drugs that block the coughing reflex

1. *Antitussives*—such as codeine, dextromethorphan, and diphenhydramine (an antihistamine)—which act on the central nervous system (CNS) to raise the threshold of the cough-coordinating center, thereby reducing the frequency and intensity of a cough
2. **Expectorants**—such as guaifenesin and terpin hydrate—which theoretically (but not very effectively) increase and thin the respiratory tract fluids in order to soothe the irritated respiratory tract membranes and decrease the thickness of the accumulated congestion so that coughing becomes more productive.

expectorants
substances that stimulate mucus secretion and diminish mucus viscosity

Table 13-6 lists commonly used OTC antitussives and their compositions.

Often, the tickling sensation in the throat that triggers a cough can be eased by sucking on a cough drop or hard candy, which stimulates saliva flow to soothe the irritated membranes. Unless the cough is severe, sour hard candy often works just as well as more expensive cough lozenges.

Cough remedies, like other medications, have a psychological value. Many patients with respiratory tract infections claim they cough less after using cough remedies, even when it is objectively

TABLE 13-6 Compositions of common OTC antitussives (dose/unit)

Product	Dextromethorphan	Expectorant	Other
Cheracol plus	20 mg	—	antihistamine; alcohol
Cheracol D	10 mg	guaifenesin	alcohol
Hold	5 mg	—	—
Novahistine DMX	10 mg	guaifenesin	sympathomimetic; alcohol
Triaminic Multisymptom	10 mg	—	sympathomimetic; antihistamine
Robitussin CF	10 mg	guaifenesin	sympathomimetic
NyQuil	30 mg	—	sympathomimetic; antihistamine; alcohol (25%)

Source: Physician's Desk Reference for Nonprescription Drugs 1991.

demonstrated that the remedies reduce neither the frequency nor the intensity of the cough. Cough remedies work in part by reducing patients' anxiety about the cough and causing them to believe that their cough is lessening. If a person believes in the remedy, he or she often can get as much relief from a simple, inexpensive product as from the most sophisticated and costly one. If a cough does not ease in a few days, the person should consult a doctor.

VITAMIN C   Vitamin C is found in some OTC cold remedies, although there is little evidence that it has a beneficial or preventive effect. Even so, Linus Pauling, a Nobel laureate, advocates using large doses of vitamin C (Bryant and Lombardi 1990). It should be noted that doses of 4 to 12 grams daily of this acidic vitamin (technically known as *ascorbic acid*) can cause kidney stones and that high levels can cause unreliable glucose tests in diabetics. Those who believe in taking vitamin C should use supplements instead of buying it mixed with a cold remedy. Better still, drinking lots of orange juice may help. Even if vitamin C does not relieve the cold, the increase in liquid intake might.

WHAT REALLY WORKS?   Unfortunately, modern medicine and pharmacology have no cure for the common cold. In most cases, the best treatment is still lots of rest, increased fluid intake to prevent dehydration and to facilitate productive coughing,

humidification of the air if it is dry, gargling with diluted salt water (2 tsp. per quart), an analgesic to relieve the accompanying headache or muscle ache, and perhaps an occasional decongestant if nasal stuffiness is unbearable.

Allergy symptoms, on the other hand, can often be relieved by antihistamines or by desensitization injections, depending on what the person is allergic to. Allergies can also be relieved by eliminating the allergens from the environment as much as possible.

Think About It...

1. You work for the FDA and have been asked to identify prescription drugs that you would recommend be switched to OTC status. What types of drugs would be appropriate for nonprescription use? Why?

2. OTC cold medicines almost always have two or more active ingredients. Why are they formulated as combination drug products? What are the advantages and disadvantages of this drug approach?

3. Actually, only three different active internal analgesics can be purchased OTC, but hundreds of different products contain these three types of drugs. Why does the FDA allow so much duplication in the OTC market? Is this good or bad for the consumer? Why?

SLEEP AIDS

An estimated 50% of the American population experiences insomnia (the inability to get to sleep or stay asleep) at some time, and 33% complain of sleep difficulties on a continuing basis. The millions of people having sleep difficulties spend millions of dollars on OTC products (e.g., Nytol, Sleep-eze, Sominex) advertised as inducing a "safe and restful sleep." Described as nonbarbiturate and non–habit forming, these are low-potency products that have a minimal action on the sleep and wakefulness centers of the brain, controlled through the reticular activating system (see Chapter 5).

The drugs commonly used in OTC sleep aids are antihistamines, particularly diphenhydramine (Caro and Dombrowski 1990). Although antihistamines have been classified as category I sleep-aid ingredients (see Chapter 3), their usefulness in treating significant sleep disorders is highly questionable. At best, some people who suffer mild,

temporary sleep disturbances caused by problems such as physical discomfort, short-term disruption in daily routines (such as jet lag), and extreme emotional upset might experience relief. However, even for those few who initially benefit from these agents, tolerance develops within two to four days. For most sleep problems, OTC sleep aids are of no therapeutic value and are rarely recommended by health professionals. Actually, their placebo benefit is likely more significant than their actual pharmacological benefit.

Because antihistamines are CNS depressants, in low doses, they can cause sedation and antianxiety action (see Chapter 6). Although in the past, some OTC products containing antihistamines were promoted for their relaxing effects (e.g., Quietworld, Compoz), currently, no sedatives are approved for OTC marketing. The FDA decided that the earlier products relieved anxiety by causing drowsiness, so in fact, they were not legitimate sedatives (Caro and Dombrowski 1990). Because of this ruling, medications that are promoted as

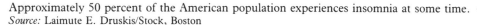

Approximately 50 percent of the American population experiences insomnia at some time.
Source: Laimute E. Druskis/Stock, Boston

antianxiety products are no longer available without a prescription.

STIMULANTS

Some OTC drugs are promoted as stay-awake (No Doz) or energy-promoting (Vivarin) products. In general, these medications contain high doses of caffeine (100 mg/tablet to 200 mg/tablet). (Caffeine and its pharmacological and abuse properties were discussed at length in Chapter 9.) While it is true that CNS stimulation by ingesting significant doses of caffeine can increase the state of alertness during periods of drowsiness, the usefulness of such an approach is often highly suspect. For example, the use of these products to suppress highway fatigue following a full day of driving is frequently ineffective and can lull the user into a false sense of alertness. Routine use of stay-awake or energy-promoting products to enhance performance at work or in school can lead to dependence, resulting in withdrawal upon cessation of use of the drug. Most health professionals agree that there are more effective and safer ways to deal with fatigue and drowsiness; for example, get plenty of rest.

"LOOK-ALIKE" AND "ACT-ALIKE" DRUGS   Mild OTC stimulants have been marketed as safe substitutes for more potent and illicit stimulants of abuse. Known as "look-alike" stimulants, these products have been made to appear as real amphetamines and are intended to give a mild lift or sense of euphoria. The principal drugs found in the look-alikes are phenylpropanolamine, ephedrine, and caffeine. The same drugs are routinely found in OTC decongestants and diet aids.

As mentioned in Chapter 9, some states have outlawed look-alike medications, but new products, called "act-alikes," have taken their place. Act-alikes do not resemble the restricted amphetamine drugs. Even so, these minor stimulants are sold on the "streets" as "speed" and "uppers," especially to young users, and are promoted by drug dealers as being legal and harmless.

Although much less potent than amphetamines, look-alikes and act-alikes, used in high doses, can cause anxiety, restlessness, throbbing headaches, breathing problems, and tachycardia (rapid heartbeat). There have even been reports of death due to heart arrhythmia and cerebral hemorrhaging. The availability of these drugs encourages their routine use and the development of dependence. Thus, they can serve as "gateway" drugs, leading to abuse of more potent compounds.

The manufacturers of the look-alike and act-alike drugs unscrupulously advertise in college newspapers, handbills posted at truckstops, and unsolicited literature from mail-order companies. Occasionally, these products are even promoted by sending free samples in the mail (Brown 1991).

GASTROINTESTINAL MEDICATIONS

The gastrointestinal (GI) system consists principally of the esophagus, stomach, and intestines and is responsible for the absorption of nutrients and water into the body, as well as the elimination of body wastes. The function of the GI system can be altered by changes in eating habits, stress, infection, and organic disorders, such as ulcers and cancers. Such problems may affect appetite, cause discomfort or pain, result in nausea and vomiting, and alter the formation and passage of stools from the intestines.

A variety of OTC medications are available to treat some of these GI symptoms. However, before individuals self-medicate with nonprescription drugs, they should be certain that the cause of their problem is minor, self-limiting, and does not require professional care.

ANTACIDS   In 1990, close to $1 billion was spent on antacid preparations that claim to give relief from indigestion caused by excessive eating or drinking, and heartburn and for long-term treatment of chronic peptic ulcer disease (Garnett 1990). It is estimated that as much as 50% of the population has had one or more attacks of **gastritis,** often referred to as acid indigestion, heartburn, upset stomach, and sour or acid stomach. This gastric discomfort is most often due to acid rebound, occurring one to two hours after eating; by this time, the stomach contents have passed into the small intestines, leaving the gastric acids to irritate or damage the lining of the empty stomach.

gastritis
inflammation or irritation of the gut

Some cases of severe, chronic acid indigestion may progress to peptic ulcer disease. Peptic ulcers (open sores) most frequently affect the duodenum (first part of the intestine) and the stomach. Although this condition is serious, it can be treated effectively with drugs such as cimetidine (Tagamet), ranitidine (Zantac), and famotidine (Pepcid), often combined with antacids. A person with acute, severe stomach pain; chronic gastritis; blood in the stools (common ulcer symptoms); diarrhea; or vomiting should see a physician promptly and not attempt to self-medicate with OTC antacids.

Most bouts of acid rebound, however, are associated with overeating or consuming irritating foods or drinks; these are self-limiting cases and can usually be managed with OTC antacids. Because of their alkaline (opposite of acidic) nature, the nonprescription products neutralize gastric acids and give relief.

There are four principal active ingredients found in OTC antacids:

1. *Sodium bicarbonate* is a potent and fast-acting acid neutralizer, and it is inexpensive. However, it has a high sodium content that can be harmful to those who should restrict sodium intake. In addition, frequent use of sodium bicarbonate can severely disrupt the metabolic balance of the body; this should be discouraged, especially for children. It is also of social significance to remember that bicarbonate interaction with gastric acid generates the gas carbon dioxide. Accumulation of this gas in the gastrointestinal tract can result in belching and other gaseous activities that are not socially ingratiating. Products with sodium bicarbonate include baking soda, Alka-Seltzer, and Soda Mint.

2. *Calcium carbonate*, an alkaline substance, is also commonly used in OTC antacid products. Cal-

cium carbonate rapidly neutralizes acid, but it can cause a rebound effect, so that after the chemical leaves the stomach, even more gastric acid is secreted than before. Calcium carbonate may also make kidney stones worse for people who have this problem. Calcium-containing OTC antacids have been recommended for women to prevent osteoporosis. However, this practice has been questioned. Some experts argue that calcium carbonate is not the best form of calcium for treatment of this disease. OTC products containing this calcium compound are Alka-Mints, Di-Gel, and Rolaids-Calcium Rich.

3. *Aluminum hydroxide* and related compounds are used in Gaviscon, Gelusil, Maalox, and Mylanta. Because of their low neutralizing action, aluminum salts are almost always used in combination with magnesium salts. The constipating effect of

For You to Consider...

FDA Guidelines for Antacid Use

1. For relief of indigestion, antacids should not be taken for longer than two weeks. If the user still isn't relieved, a physician should be consulted.
2. The user should know that antacids may cause diarrhea (magnesium salts) or constipation (aluminum salts).
3. Patients with restricted salt intake because of blood pressure problems and the like should be aware that many antacids contain sodium; these people should select a product that does not.
4. The tablet forms of antacids are less effective than liquid preparations. If tablets are preferred, they should be chewed thoroughly and followed with a full glass of water. Effervescent tablets are supposed to be dissolved in a glass of water first; most of the bubbles should be allowed to subside before swallowing the preparation.
5. The user should be aware that significant drug interactions may occur; in such cases, a pharmacist or physician should be consulted for further information (Garnett 1990, 24).

aluminum salt is counterbalanced by the laxative effect of magnesium salt.

4. *Magnesium salts,* taken in low doses, are effective albeit slow antacids and safe for chronic use. In higher doses, magnesium salts stimulate the passage of feces and are even promoted as a laxative (see the label of Milk of Magnesia). Due to the slow onset of action and laxative tendency, magnesium salts are usually combined with either calcium carbonate (Di-Gel, Camalox) or aluminum hydroxide (Gelusil, Maalox, Mylanta).

Table 13-7 lists common OTC antacids and their compositions.

Some antacid products have antiflatulent ingredients to provide relief from gastric gas (e.g., Di-Gel, Mylanta). The most commonly used, simethicone, breaks up gas bubbles and thus relieves pressure by facilitating belching and passing gas. Alginic acid, bismuth salts, and other substances are similarly used in some products. None of these ingredients is classified as an antacid, as they are not effective in neutralizing acid.

Generally speaking, OTC antacid preparations are safe for occasional use at low recommended doses, but some warnings must be considered (see the adjacent box). Aluminum-magnesium hydroxide gels have low toxicity and an adequate neutralizing capacity. But all antacids can interact with other drugs; they may alter the gastrointestinal absorption or renal elimination of other medications. For example, some antacids inhibit the absorption of tetracycline antibiotics; thus, these products should not be taken at the same time. Antacids also can decrease both the absorption of iron and the absorption of the major tranquilizer chlorpromazine, which is used to treat schizophrenia. On the other hand, antacids can increase absorption of some drugs from the GI system, such as levodopa (used in treating Parkinson's disease) and the anticoagulant dicumarol. (When increased in blood levels by 50%, this effect can be lethal.) Consequently, patients using prescription drugs should consult with their physicians before taking OTC antacids.

INTESTINAL PROBLEMS Millions of people use OTC drugs to treat constipation and diarrhea. Over

TABLE 13-7 Compositions of common OTC antacids (dose/unit)

Product (form)	Magnesium Salt	Calcium Carbonate	Aluminum Hydroxide	Other
Ascriptin	50 mg		50 mg	aspirin
Di-Gel (tablets/liquid)	128 mg	280 mg	—	simethicone
Gelusil (liquid)	200 mg	—	200 mg	—
Gaviscon	20 mg		80 mg	
Maalox (tablets/liquid)	300 mg	—	600 mg	—
Mylanta (tablets/liquid)	200 mg	—	200 mg	simethicone
Rolaids (tablets)	—	—	334 mg	—
Phillips Milk of Magnesia (liquid)	405 mg	—	—	—
Alka-Mints (tablets)	—	850 mg	—	—
Rolaids—Calcium Rich (tablets)	—	550 mg	—	—
TUMS (liquid/tablets)	—	500 mg	—	—
Camalox (liquid)	200 mg	250 mg	225 mg	—
Alka-Seltzer (dissolving tablets)	—	—	—	sodium bicarbonate

Source: Physician's Desk Reference for Nonprescription Drugs 1991.

$0.5 billion was spent in 1990 for OTC drugs classified as laxatives or cathartics as well as antidiarrheals.

Intestinal problems are common in the United States. The typical Western diet includes little fiber but many highly processed foods that interfere with the passage of food through the GI system. Instead of altering lifestyles or eating habits, many people self-medicate to correct their problems. This solution often leads to the abuse of drugs that either accelerate or retard the passage of stools in the intestines. Some of these people have taken either laxatives or antidiarrheals on a long-term basis and must continue to do so because they have a bowel addiction. This type of **iatrogenic** illness is not uncommon.

iatrogenic
illness caused by the treatment

For You to Consider...

Factors That Cause Constipation

1. Not responding to the defecation urge can weaken the normal defecation reflexes and prevent regular defecation.
2. Poor eating habits—such as insufficient bulk in the diet, low fluid intake, and excessive ingestion of foods like processed cheese—may interfere with normal passage of food through the GI system.
3. Mental stress and change of environment may alter GI function.
4. Prolonged use of certain drugs can cause constipation, including aluminum hydroxide and calcium carbonate (antacids), opiates, anticholinergic drugs, and laxatives.
5. Organic problems in the GI system—such as growths, damage to intestinal sphincter valves, and so on—can cause constipation, as well (Darlington and Curry 1979).

Laxatives. A variety of factors can cause constipation (see the adjacent box). Treatment of constipation without using drugs is usually possible and almost always preferred. Switching to a high-fiber diet, drinking plenty of water, and getting regular exercise are all safe and effective ways to treat this problem (Curry and Tatum-Butler 1990). Dietary fiber is that portion of vegetables, grains, fruit, and other plant products that the human gastrointestinal system cannot digest. It absorbs water and adds bulk to the intestinal contents.

Adding fiber to the diet often works to correct chronic constipation, whereas laxatives sometimes alleviate the immediate problem. Several classes of laxatives are available:

1. *Bulk-forming laxatives* provide the bulk necessary to stimulate the defecation reflex. These substances will create bulk by absorbing fluid and swelling and include dietary fiber, semisynthetic cellulose (methylcellulose), and polyacrylic resins (polycarbophil). An example of an OTC bulk-forming laxative is Metamucil. These drugs require 12 to 72 hours to take effect.

2. *Stimulant laxatives* act on the intestine to reduce absorption of **electrolytes** and water and to stimulate the propulsive activity of the intestine. These substances are not recommended if the person has abdominal pain, nausea, or vomiting because these can be symptoms of appendicitis. Most of the drugs in this category require 6 to 8 hours to take effect. Examples include Castor oil, phenolphthalein, and bisacodyl. OTC stimulant laxatives include Carter's Little Pills (notice: no more "Liver"), Dulcolax, Feen-a-Mint, and Phenolax. Stimulant laxatives are effective but are probably the most abused of all laxatives. They are not recommended for simple constipation, and they should never be used for more than one week of regular treatment.

electrolytes
charged molecules—such as sodium, potassium, calcium, bicarbonate, and chloride—that dissolve in body fluids

3. *Emollients* are surfactants (wetting agents) and emulsifiers (substances allowing the mixing of fats

and water) that soften the fecal mass. These laxatives require about 12 to 72 hours to act and should not be used any longer than a week without consulting a physician. Correctol and Colace are OTC laxatives that contain emollient ingredients.

4. *Lubricants*, such as mineral oil and olive oil, penetrate and soften fecal matter and are useful for people who should avoid straining when passing stools (e.g., following hemorrhoid surgery). Repeated, prolonged use of mineral oil can cause problems because absorbed oil accumulates in the body. Lubricants also impair absorption of fat-soluble vitamins A and D. Lubricants require about 6 to 8 hours to take effect. Haley's M-O is an example of an OTC lubricant laxative.

5. *Saline laxatives* pull water from the body tissue, adding bulk and encouraging **peristaltic** action of the intestine. These agents are used when patients are preparing for a bowel exam or to eliminate drugs in suspected cases of food or drug poisoning. Saline laxatives are used in large doses so the body can purge and empty the large intestine. Examples include magnesium salts and sodium phosphate. Milk of Magnesia is an example of such an OTC laxative.

---

peristaltic
wavelike contraction of muscles

Regular use of most laxatives, particularly the stimulant preparations, can result in abuse. In fact, excessive use of laxatives can cause diarrhea and vomiting, leading to fluid and electrolyte losses and muscular weakness. Heavy use of laxatives over a long period of time can also cause structural damage to the intestines and kidney problems, as well.

These are some of the long-term effects suffered by *bulimic* individuals, who consistently use laxatives to purge their bodies of food after binges of overeating. Young women are most likely to be bulimic. In fact, bulimia often accompanies a psychosomatic eating disorder known as *anorexia nervosa*, in which the individual refuses to eat and/or

takes extreme measures to induce weight loss (e.g., purging via vomiting or taking laxatives). Athletes who must meet weight requirements in certain sports (e.g., wrestlers, jockeys) have been known to purge, as well. Clearly, purging is not a healthy approach to weight control. Over the long term, serious intestinal and kidney problems may result.

Antidiarrheals. Millions of Americans use antidiarrheal compounds on occasion. However, some people take such preparations routinely, as you would consume an after-dinner mint.

Diarrhea has various causes. It is not unusual for travelers to come down with diarrhea, typically caused by new types of bacteria being introduced in the intestines due to changes in diet, even water. The intestines respond by producing large quantities of fluid and increasing intestinal motility to flush out the microorganisms (like bacteria), causing diarrhea. "Traveler's trot" is bothersome but usually of short duration and treatable. Diarrhea can also be caused by psychogenic factors, such as stress and anxiety; hormonal factors; allergic responses; consumption of irritating food or drink; and some drugs (Longe 1990).

Many antidiarrheal drugs are available on the market. Some work against the symptoms of the affliction, some against the cause, and others against the effect of the disease—that is, loss of nutrients or electrolytes. The categories of drugs used include opiates, adsorbents, astringents, electrolytes, nutrients, bulk laxatives (as absorbents), antibiotics, digestive enzymes, sedatives, tranquilizers, smooth muscle relaxants, and anticholinergics. Many of these, such as the pure opiate preparations and tranquilizers, are not available OTC in the United States, although they can often be purchased without a prescription in foreign countries.

Even though a prescription is usually required, the opiates are relatively safe and effective. All derivatives of opium tend to cause constipation. Pure paregoric (contains some morphine) is a Schedule II prescription drug; sometimes paregoric is combined with other antidiarrheal drugs (e.g., DIA-quel). OTC paregoric cannot contain more than 100 mg of opium (about 25 ml of paregoric) per 100 ml of liquid. Imodium A-D is the

Types of OTC Drugs

ULA 13-4
Approximately 35–50 percent of the people in the United States are obese and 50 percent are overweight. *Source:* © M. Siluk/The Image Works

liquid form of loperamine, which was switched to OTC status in 1988. Loperamide is classified as a nonabusing narcotic. It is an effective drug and should only be used to treat acute, nonspecific diarrhea associated with a self-limiting condition.

Polycarbophil (Sorboquel) is the only OTC preparation (other than low-dose opiates) that has been found by the FDA to be safe and an effective antidiarrheal. It is an adsorbent and has a marked capacity to take up free water in the bowels, thus drying up the stools.

Drugs such as aluminum hydroxide, attapul-gite, bismuth compounds, kaolin, magnesium tri-silicate, and pectin are the most frequently used adsorbents in OTC antidiarrheal preparations. The FDA says adsorbents are safe to use in recommended doses, but their usefulness as antidi-arrheals is questionable. In other words, the user should not expect a dramatic response. Adsorbents appear to work by adsorbing toxins, bacteria, and various noxious materials that irritate the intestine and cause diarrhea. They will adsorb nutrients and some drugs, like the tetracycline antibiotics, as well. Bismuth subsalts, like Pepto-Bismol, will turn the stools dark. Kaopectate and Diatrol are examples of adsorbent antidiarrheals that contain no other active ingredients.

The anticholinergics, such as the belladonna alkaloids, are prescription antidiarrheal drugs. Combination OTC antidiarrheal preparations that contain anticholinergic compounds (such as atropine) are available, but the low dosage is ineffective. When combined with adsorbents, anticholinergics may also be adsorbed, thus making them even less likely to be effective. Donnagel is an example of an OTC adsorbent-anticholinergic combination.

DIET AIDS

In American society, being slim and trim are prerequisites to being attractive. It is estimated that approximately 25%–30% of the people in the United States are obese (with body fat in excess of 20% of normal) and 50% are overweight. Being obese is pathological and has been linked to cardiovascular disease, some cancers, diabetes, chronic fatigue, and an array of aches and pains, not to mention psychological disorders such as depression. Popular remedies for losing weight often come as fad diets advertised in supermarket journals, expensive weight-loss programs, or the use of OTC diet aids.

Using drugs as diet aids is highly controversial. Most experts view them as useless or even dangerous. These drugs are supposed to depress the appetite, which helps users maintain low-calorie diets. The most effective of these are called **anorexiants.** Potent anorexiants, such as amphetaminelike drugs, can cause dangerous side effects (see Chapter 9) and are only available by prescription. The appetite suppression effects of prescription anorexiants only last for two to four weeks, after which time tolerance occurs. Thus, even pre-

Acne is due to chronic inflammation caused by bacteria trapped in plugged sebaceous glands or hair follicles. *Source:* Custom Medical Stock Photos

scription diet-aid drugs are only useful for a short period.

The most potent and most frequently used OTC diet-aid ingredient is the sympathomimetic phenylpropanolamine (Acutrim, Appedrine, Dexatrim). Estimates show that the best of the OTC products significantly reduce appetite in less than 30% of the users, and tolerance occurs in one to three days of use. Clearly, such products are of no value in the treatment of obesity.

Other ingredients found in OTC diet aids include benzocaine (to numb the taste buds and take the fun out of eating—Spantrol, Slim-Lin Gum) and methylcellulose (to give a stuffed feeling—Diet-Trim). None of these ingredients have been shown to be particularly effective in the treatment of obesity.

SKIN PRODUCTS

Because the skin is so accessible and readily visible, most people are sensitive about its appearance. These cosmetic concerns are motivated by attempts to look good and preserve youth. Literally thousands of OTC skin products with cosmetic and health objectives are available to consumers. In this summary, only a few of the most commonly used products will be mentioned: acne medications, sun products, and basic first-aid products.

---

anorexiants
drugs that suppress the activity of the brain's appetite center, causing reduced food intake

ACNE MEDICATIONS Acne is a universal skin problem that occurs most frequently during puberty in response to the secretion of the male hormone androgen (both males and females have this hormone) (Billow 1990). Acne is due to chronic inflammation caused by bacteria trapped in plugged sebaceous (oil) glands and hair follicles. This condition consists of whiteheads, pimples, nodules, and in more severe cases, pustules, cysts, and abscesses. Moderate to severe acne can cause unsightly scarring on the face, back, chest, and arms and should be treated aggressively by a dermatologist with drugs such as antibiotics (tetracycline) and potent **keratolytics,** such as Retin A (retinoic acid or vitamin A) or Accutane (isotretinoin). Usually, minor to moderate acne does not cause permanent skin damage or scarring and often can be safely self-medicated with OTC acne medications (Billow 1990).

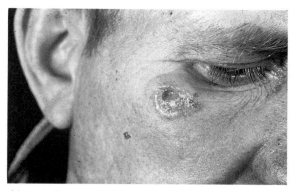

Almost all cases of skin cancer in this country are a direct consequence of exposure to ultraviolet light. *Source:* Custom Medical Stock Photo

---

keratolytics
caustic agents that cause the keratin skin layer to peel

Several nonprescription approaches to treating mild acne are available:

1. *Sebum removal*—Oil and fatty chemicals (sebum) can accumulate on the skin and plug the sebaceous glands and hair follicles. Use of OTC products such as alcohol wipes can help remove such accumulations (e.g., Noxema Antiseptic Skin Cleanser).

2. *Peeling agents*—The FDA found several keratolytic agents safe and effective for treatment of minor acne: benzoyl peroxide (Oxy 5 and Oxy 10), salicylic acid (Stri Dex), resorcinol, and sulfur (Clearasil Adult Care), alone or in combination. These drugs help to prevent acne eruption by causing the **keratin layer** of the skin to peel or by killing the bacteria that cause inflammation associated with acne. If multiple concentrations of a keratolytic are available (e.g., Oxy 5 and Oxy 10), it is better to start with a lower concentration and move up to the higher one, allowing the skin to

become accustomed to the caustic action of these products. The initial exposure may worsen the appearance of acne temporarily; however, with continual use, the acne usually improves.

---

keratin layer
the outermost protective layer of the skin

SUN PRODUCTS The damaging effects of sun exposure on the skin have been well publicized in recent years. It is now clear that the ultraviolet (UV) rays associated with sunlight have several adverse effects on the skin. It has been demonstrated that almost all 600,000 to 700,000 cases of skin cancer each year in the United States are a direct consequence of exposure to UV rays. Presently, almost 1 of 7 persons will experience some form of skin cancer during his or her lifetime.

The majority of these will be cancers of skin cells called *basal cell* or *squamous cell carcinomas* (Rigel 1991). These usually are easily excised by minor surgery and have a good prognosis for recovery. About 0.5% of the population will suffer a much more deadly form of skin cancer called *melanoma*. It is estimated that, because people today tend to spend so much time outdoors, by the year 2000, the risk of this cancer will reach 1 in

75 Americans (Ritter 1991). Melanomas are cancers of the pigment-forming cells of the skin, called *melanocytes*, and spread rapidly from the skin throughout the body, frequently causing death.

Another long-term concern (to some people worse than cancer) related to UV exposure is premature aging. Skin frequently exposed to UV rays, such as during routine tanning, experiences deterioration associated with the aging process. Elastin and collagen fibers are damaged, causing a loss of pliability and elasticity in the skin and resulting in a leathery, wrinkled appearance (DeSimone 1990).

Because of these damaging effects of sun exposure, an array of protective sunscreen products are available OTC. They are formulated to screen out the shorter, more dangerous UV-B rays and allow in varying amounts the passage of the longer, less dangerous UV-A rays. The screening potential of these products is designated by an SPF (sun protection factor) or PF (protection factor) number. The higher the number, the greater the protection; SPF numbers range from 2 to 45. Because the natural pigment in the skin affords some UV protection, people with fair complexions (less skin pigmentation) require products with higher SPF numbers than do dark-skinned people. Sunscreen chemicals found in these sun-protection products are shown in Table 13-8.

Individuals who want complete protection from UV exposure can use OTC sunblockers, which prevent any tanning. Sunscreen ingredients in high concentrations essentially become sunblockers (e.g., Coppertone Sunblock Lotion SPF 45). In addition, an opaque zinc oxide ointment

is a highly effective and inexpensive sun-blocking product and is available OTC.

SKIN FIRST-AID PRODUCTS   A variety of unrelated OTC drugs are available as first-aid products for the self-treatment of minor skin problems. Included in this category of agents are

1. *Local anesthetics*, such as benzocaine (e.g., Americaine First Aid Spray or Solarcaine), to relieve the discomfort and pain of burns or trauma
2. *Antibiotics and antiseptics*, such as bacitracin (Polysporin), neomycin (Neosporin), betadine, and tincture of iodine to treat or prevent skin infections
3. *Antihistamines* (Benadryl) or corticosteroids (hydrocortisone—Cortaid and Lanacort) to relieve itching or inflammation associated with skin rashes, allergies or insect bites

These first-aid skin products can be effective when used properly. In general, side effects to such topical products are few and minor when they occur.

RULES FOR OTC DRUG USE

The OTC marketplace for drugs operates differently than does its prescription counterpart. The use of OTC drugs is not restricted, and consumers are responsible for making correct decisions about these products. Thus, the consumer sets policy and determines use patterns.

TABLE 13-8   Selected approved OTC sunscreen ingredients

Ingredient	Brand	Concentration
para aminobenzoic acid (PABA)	PreSun	5%–15%
homosalate	Shade Sunblock Stick 30	8%–15%
oxygenzone	Coppertone, Shade Sunblock	2%–6%
padimate	Aquaray, NiveaSun	1%–4%

Source: DeSimone 1990.

Because there are no formal controls over the use of OTC drugs, abuse often occurs. In extreme situations, the abuse of OTC medication can be very troublesome, resulting in structural damage to the body and dependence, tolerance, and withdrawal responses. Proper education about the pharmacological features of these agents is necessary if consumers are to make intelligent and informed decisions about OTC drug use.

When used properly, nonprescription drugs can be effective in treating many minor to moderately severe health problems. Because of rising medical costs and in response to public demand, even more effective OTC drugs will be available in the future. To reduce the incidence of problems, the following rules should be observed when using nonprescription products:

1. *Always know what you are taking.* Identify the active ingredients in the product.
2. *Know the effects.* Be sure you know both the desired and potential undesired effects of each active ingredient.
3. *Read and heed the warnings and cautions.* The warnings are not intended to scare but to protect.
4. *Don't use anything for more than one to two weeks.* If the problem being treated persists beyond this time, consult a health professional.

5. *Be particularly cautious if also taking prescription drugs.* Serious interactions between OTC and prescription medications frequently occur. If you have a question, be sure to find the answer.
6. *If you have questions, ask a pharmacist.* Pharmacists are excellent sources of information about OTC drugs. They possess up-to-date knowledge of OTC products and can assist consumers in selecting correct medications for their health needs. Ask them to help you.
7. Most importantly: *If you don't need it, don't use it!*

Think About It...

1. Do you think look-alike or act-alike stimulants should be made illegal? Why do you think the FDA doesn't eliminate these products from the marketplace?
2. What are the major dangers of using OTC antacids to self-medicate indigestion? Should the FDA do more to prevent misuse of OTC drugs such as antacids?
3. Can pharmacists help the public to better utilize OTC drugs, particularly as the FDA switches more effective drugs from prescription to nonprescription status? How?

KEY TERMS

symptomatic	**iatrogenic**	**keratolytics**
antitussives	**electrolytes**	**keratin layer**
expectorants	**peristaltic**	
gastritis	**anorexiants**	

S U M M A R Y

1. Prescription drugs are available only by recommendation of a physician. Nonprescription (OTC) drugs are available upon request and do not require approval by a health professional. In general, OTC medications are safer than their prescription counterparts but often less effective, as well.

2. The switching policy of the FDA is an attempt to make available more effective medications to the general public on a nonprescription basis. This policy has been implemented in response to the interest in self-treatment by the public and in an attempt to reduce health care costs.

3. Drugs currently under review by the FDA for switching to OTC status include ulcer medications, such as Tagamet and Zantac; antiinflammatory drugs, such as Naprosyn; a nonsedating antihistamine, such as Seldane; and a sedative, such as Phenergan.

4. Potential problems with making more effective drugs available OTC include overuse and inappropriate use, leading to dependence and other undesirable side effects. These more effective drugs could encourage self-treatment of medical problems that require professional care.

5. The principal drug groups available OTC are used in the treatment of common, minor medical problems and include analgesics, cold remedies, allergy products, mild stimulants, sleep aids, antacids, laxatives, antidiarrheals, antiasthmatics, acne medications, sunscreens, contraceptives, and nutrients.

6. Information on OTC product labels is critical for proper use of these drugs and thus regulated by the FDA. Product labels must list the active ingredients and their quantities in the product. Labels must also provide instructions for safe and effective treatment with the drug as well as cautions and warnings.

7. The three principal OTC analgesic drugs are the salicylates (aspirinlike), acetaminophen, and ibuprofen. They are recommended for treatment of mild to moderate musculoskeletal pain as well as fever and inflammation. Acetaminophen has few side effects, while salicylates and ibuprofen are much better antiinflammatory drugs.

8. OTC cold products often consist of multiple drugs and are intended to relieve the major symptoms associated with this viral infection. Cold remedies often contain decongestants that can counter nasal stuffiness; analgesics are also present to relieve cold-related headaches and muscle aches. Other common ingredients in cold medications are antitussive drugs to block the coughing reflex. Less effective drugs found in these products include antihistamines (good for allergies but not colds) and expectorants.

9. Many OTC products contain mild CNS stimulants and depressants. The use of these drugs in nonprescription medications is usually considered controversial, as it is argued that these drugs are of little therapeutic value in OTC products. As with the more potent stimulants and depressants, continual use of the OTC counterparts leads to tolerance, dependence, and abuse. It is possible that some of these nonprescription products serve as "gateway" drugs to more potent and dangerous stimulants and depressants.

10. Antacids often are used to self-medicate gastrointestinal problems that actually require professional care. Symptoms that suggest self-treatment with OTC drugs should not be attempted are cramps, vomiting, diarrhea, blood in the stools, or persistent upset stomach. These complaints are often associated with potentially dangerous conditions, such as ulcers, cancers, or other organic diseases.

11. OTC skin products are used to treat a variety of minor, uncomplicated skin disorders—such as acne and minor cuts, abrasions, and burns—and to prevent damage done by exposure to sunlight.

12. Although OTC drug products can be useful for treatment of many minor to moderate, self-limiting medical problems, when used without proper precaution, they can cause problems. In order to optimize benefits and minimize risks when taking OTC medications, the following rules should be observed: always know what you are taking; know the effects; follow the warnings; don't use anything for a long period; be especially cautious if also taking prescription drugs; ask the pharmacist when you have questions; and don't use these drugs unless you need to.

R E F E R E N C E S

Billow, J. "Acne Products." In *Handbook of Nonprescription Drugs.* 9th ed. Washington, D.C.: American Pharmaceutical Association, 1990.

Brown, M. *Guide to Fight Substance Abuse.* Nashville, TN: International Broadcast Services, 1991.

Bryant, B., and J. Lombardi. "Cold and Allergy Products." In *Handbook of Nonprescription Drugs.* 9th ed. Washington, D.C.: American Pharmaceutical Association, 1990.

Caro, J., and C. Walker. "Sleep Aid and Stimulant Products." In *Handbook of Nonprescription Drugs.* 8th ed. Washington, D.C.: American Pharmaceutical Association, 1986.

Caro, J., and S. Dombrowski. "Sleep Aid and Stimulant Products." In *Handbook of Nonprescription Drugs.* 9th ed. Washington, D.C.: American Pharmaceutical Association, 1990.

Curry, C., and D. Tatum-Butler. "Laxative Products." In *Handbook of Nonprescription Drugs.* 9th ed. Washington, D.C.: American Pharmaceutical Association, 1990.

Darlington, R. C., and C. E. Curry, Jr. "Laxatives Products." In *Handbook of Nonprescription Drugs.* 7th ed. Washington, D.C.: American Pharmaceutical Association, 1979.

DeSimone, E. "Sunscreen and Suntan Products." In *Handbook of Nonprescription Drugs.* 9th ed. Washington, D.C.: American Pharmaceutical Association, 1990.

Garnett, W. "Antacid Products." In *Handbook of Nonprescription Drugs.* 9th ed. Washington, D.C.: American Pharmaceutical Association, 1990.

Gilbertson, W. "The FDA's OTC Drug Review." In *Handbook of Nonprescription Drugs.* 9th ed. Washington, D.C.: American Pharmaceutical Association, 1990.

Longe, R. "Antidiarrheal and Other Gastrointestinal Products." In *Handbook of Nonprescription Drugs.* 9th ed. Washington, D.C.: American Pharmaceutical Association, 1990.

Physician's Desk Reference for Nonprescription Drugs. 12th ed. Oradell, NJ: Medical Economics Data, 1991.

Popovich, N. "Not All Over-the-Counter Drugs Are Safe." *American Journal of Pharmaceutical Education* 55 (1991): 166–172.

Rigel, D. "Malignant Melanoma in the 1990s." *Pharmacy Times,* May 1991, 33–39.

Ritter, M. "Risk of Sometimes-Fatal Skin Cancer Rising." *The Salt Lake Tribune,* 13 June 1991, D10.

Sause, R., and R. Mangione. "Cough and Cold Treatment with OTC Medicine." *Pharmacy Times,* February 1991, 108–117.

Schwartz, R., and S. Rifkin. "No More Paper Tiger." *American Druggist,* June 1991, 26–34.

Siegelman, S. "The Coming Wave of Rx-to-OTC Switches." *American Druggist,* August 1990, 37–42.

VanTyle, K. "Internal Analgesics Products." In *Handbook of Nonprescription Drugs.* 9th ed. Washington, D.C.: American Pharmaceutical Association, 1990.

Drugs and Psychiatric Disorders

LEARNING OBJECTIVES

On completing this chapter, you will be able to:

1. Explain the similarities between the effects of drugs of abuse and characteristics of psychiatric disorders.
2. Describe the features that characterize psychotic disorders.
3. Compare and distinguish the principal types of affective disorders.
4. Explain the mechanisms that account for the similarities between psychiatric disorders and the psychiatric effects of drugs of abuse.
5. Describe, in general, why psychotherapeutic drugs are effective in relieving the symptoms of psychiatric diseases.
6. Describe which group of drugs relieves each major category of psychiatric disorder and why it works.
7. Recognize the major side effects of the principal psychotherapeutic agents, including benzodiazepines, antipsychotic agents, MAO inhibitors, tricyclic antidepressants, Prozac, and lithium salts.
8. Describe the connections between Parkinson's disease, schizophrenia, antipsychotic agents, and cocaine use.
9. Explain why treatment of depression is often unsuccessful.

Source: Frances M. Cox/Stock, Boston

DID YOU KNOW THAT . . .

- During the Middle Ages, people who were mentally ill often were thought to be possessed by evil spirits.
- Almost all drugs of abuse can cause symptoms that mimic some form of psychiatric disorder.
- Drug abuse is classified as a form of psychiatric disorder.
- Mental illness is caused by an imbalance of neurotransmitters in the brain.
- Even though drug treatment is often successful in relieving psychiatric disorders, because of negative side effects, many patients often do not take their medication.
- Tranquilizers are effective in relieving schizophrenia.
- Long-term use of some tranquilizers can cause permanent facial motor problems, or *tardive dyskinesia.*
- Relief from major depression usually requires several weeks of drug treatment.
- Patients suffering severe depressive disorders sometimes use their antidepressant medication to attempt suicide.
- Cocaine has a mechanism of action similar to those of some of the antidepressant drugs.
- About 30% of those individuals who abuse cocaine do so to relieve depression.
- For most depressed patients, Prozac is safer than other antidepressant medications.
- Some drugs of abuse can be used to create animal models for the study of psychiatric disorders.

Only recently have we begun to appreciate the nature of psychiatric disorders and to use that understanding to develop effective treatments. Complicated and often conflicting attitudes have evolved concerning the significance of mental illness, primarily because of ignorance. Many of these archaic and erroneous misconceptions still influence current attitudes of educated and uneducated people alike. For example, to some individuals, a visit to a psychiatrist or other therapist means that you have a serious character flaw.

In this chapter, we will examine the use of drugs to treat psychiatric disorders, beginning with a brief history. The review of various types of psychiatric disorders will be general, given the complexity of the topic. Most of the chapter addresses the primary types of psychotherapeutic drugs: anxiolytics, antipsychotics, and antidepressants. The chapter concludes with an analysis of the association between drug abuse and mental disorders.

THE HISTORY OF MENTAL ILLNESS

Actually, mental illness has been recognized for thousands of years as being a significant health problem. **Psychiatric disorders** were referred to in the ancient Egyptian medical records known as the *ebers papyrus* (1900 B.C.), which describe in detail mental problems such as depression. Centuries later, during the enlightened period of the Greeks and Romans, it was widely accepted that mental disorders were caused by physical problems. Hippocrates argued that emotional functions and associated difficulties originated in the brain, although he knew little about how it functioned. Because of these enlightened attitudes, those with serious mental illnesses were usually treated in a humane fashion, which often included rest and peaceful surroundings.

---

psychiatric disorder
inappropriate behavior due to abnormal transmission, processing, or responding by the brain to sensory input

---

After the fall of Roman civilization, enlightened attitudes toward psychiatric disorders disappeared. With the destruction of classical scientific knowledge, new theories of mental illness developed during the Dark Ages. These theories were based on religious superstition and proposed that mentally ill individuals were possessed by the devil; they were often considered to be witches or warlocks. Emotional and physical suffering experienced by the mentally infirmed were viewed as just punishments for sinful behavior. Because of these spiritual explanations, the mentally ill were dealt with by the Church rather than by medicine. The ecclesiastical approach to treatment included torture and burning at the stake. The destruction of these oddly behaving individuals was viewed as necessary to protect society. The violent elimination of witches continued in England until 1684 and in the United States into the eighteenth century.

Even though, during the Renaissance, classical attitudes about mental illness were rekindled, how to deal with afflicted people was still a difficult problem. Burning or hanging no longer were accepted as appropriate forms of therapy, so special hospitals or asylums were constructed in the seventeenth and eighteenth centuries to care for mentally ill patients. Actually, these institutions were little more than prisons with appalling conditions. Patients were frequently locked in cells or chained to walls for the rest of their lives. In some ways, burning or hanging would have been more humane.

It was not until the nineteenth century that

Trial and execution of persons accused of witchcraft continued in England until 1684 and in America into the 18th century. *Source:* North Wind Picture Archives

treatment of the psychiatric population became more therapeutic and less punitive. During this time, improved psychiatric facilities were created throughout Europe and the United States to deal with the mentally ill in a kind and decent manner. It was during this era that Sigmund Freud developed the psychoanalytic method of treatment for psychiatric disorders.

Even so, understanding of the brain and its functions remained quite elementary into the early twentieth century. Consequently, treatment of brain-related dysfunction, such as mental illness, was far from satisfactory. Only within the past 30 to 40 years has science truly begun to understand the intricacies of the human mind and its neurochemical principles. Such understanding has made

possible exciting new discoveries in psychiatric therapeutics that have meant a much brighter future for the mental patient than ever before (Andreason and Black, 1991).

It is now known that the central nervous system (CNS) controls mood and behavior by receiving, processing, and coordinating responses to sensory information. Conditions that interfere with normal functioning can scramble the perception of the external world (e.g., cause hallucinations) or alter the way in which someone responds to sensory information. In either case, the behavior of the individual would appear to be inappropriate for the situation and would be attributed to a psychiatric disorder. Given that diagnosis—namely, that a psychiatric problem exists—the more dif-

For You to Consider...

Case Histories: Comparing Naturally Occurring (A) and Drug-Induced (B) Psychotic Symptoms

A. This case relates the effects of taking a large quantity of amphetamine on William Burroughs, Jr.:

> I started seeing faces everywhere. No matter where I looked someone was there. Tiny people slept in my ashtray and the giant slouched, sulking, against the Chrysler Building. The trees in Washington Square were filled with faces from the past that blew in the breeze, even though I am still young. In the mirror, my own face crawled with a dozen others making positive identification impossible, but none of this was anything to worry about (Snyder 1974, 203).

B. In this case, Norma McDonald describes a natural psychotic episode she experienced:

> At first it was as if parts of my brain *awoke* which had been dormant, and I became interested in a wide assortment of people, events, places and ideas which normally would make no impression on me. Not knowing that I was ill, I made no attempt to understand what was happening. But there was overwhelming significance in all this, produced either by God or Satan and I felt that I was duty bound to ponder on each of these new interests, and the more I pondered, the worse it became. The walk of a stranger on the street could be a "sign" to me which I must interpret. Every face in the windows of a passing streetcar would be engraved on my mind, all of them concentrating on me and them concentrating on me and trying to pass me some sort of message (Snyder 1974, 68).

ficult task would remain: to determine what causes the mental disorder.

For example, in earlier chapters, we discussed that drugs, particularly those with abuse potential, can cause psychiatric problems that are indistinguishable from disorders that occur naturally (i.e., not induced by any external forces). Without knowing the drug history of the patient, the clinician would find it difficult to make a diagnosis. Interestingly, similar treatments can be used successfully for naturally occurring psychiatric disorders and drug-induced types. This suggests that similar brain mechanisms are involved in both dysfunctions and that the study of causative factors for drug-induced mental disorders could help in understanding naturally occurring psychiatric problems and vice versa. For example, a comparison of the two accounts contained in the adjacent box will help you appreciate the similarities between these disorders. In fact, many researchers in the field of mental illness or psychiatry use animal models that have been treated with high doses of drugs of abuse to study schizophrenia (PCP, cocaine, or amphetamine), depression (barbiturates or benzodiazepines), and anxiety and panic (CNS stimulants).

TYPES OF PSYCHIATRIC DISORDERS

Psychiatric disorders are comprised of a variety of distinct but sometimes overlapping dysfunctions that are characterized by abnormal mental states. The incidence of psychiatric disorders is startling. For example, sometime during their lives, approximately 80% of all Americans will suffer from a psychiatric disturbance severe enough to require psychiatric assistance; almost 25% of the population will require hospitalization for a serious, debilitating mental illness.

The abbreviated listing of psychiatric disorders in Table 14-1 is referred to as the *DSM-III-R classification*, meaning it is derived from the

TABLE 14-1 Abbreviated DSM-III-R classification of psychiatric disorders

Disorders usually first evident in infancy, childhood, or adolescence
Developmental disorders (e.g., mental retardation)
Disruptive behavior disorders
Anxiety disorders
Eating disorders
Gender identity disorders
Tic disorders
Elimination disorders
Speech disorders
Organic mental disorders
Dementias
Psychoactive substance-induced organic disorders*
Psychoactive substance use disorders*
Schizophrenia
Delusional (paranoid) disorder
Mood disorders
Bipolar disorders
Depressive disorders
Anxiety disorders
Dissociative disorders
Sexual disorders
Sleep disorders
Adjustment disorders
Personality disorders

Source: Adapted from APA, *Diagnostic and Statistical Manual of Mental Disorders*, 3rd ed., rev.
*Psychiatric disorders caused by drugs of abuse.

Diagnostic and Statistical Manual of Mental Disorders (3rd ed., revised). This is the authoritative publication on psychiatric disorders and is used by professionals in many fields. Note that disorders caused by psychoactive substances (including drugs of abuse) are considered as a classification of psychiatric disorder (APA 1987). This chapter discusses the most common of these psychiatric problems.

THE NEUROTRANSMITTER THEORY

Cumulative evidence suggests that many forms of mental disorders are due to brain biochemical factors. This is consistent with the fact that some drugs of abuse mimic psychiatric problems. Because such drugs dramatically alter the transmitter systems of the brain, it is almost certain that, in psychiatric disorders, these same transmitter systems are impaired and do not function in a balanced fashion. For example, just as imbalances in the neurotransmitters of the brain can cause motor impairments associated with neurological disorders such as Parkinson's disease, chemical imbalances can also interfere with normal thought processes and result in abnormal behavior. The ability of psychotherapeutic drugs to restore normal thought to most sufferers of psychiatric disorders suggests that these agents help to reestablish neurotransmitter balance.

ANXIETY DISORDERS

At extreme levels of expression, anxiety disorders are referred to as *neuroses* and can occur in anyone. They are usually associated with fear, restlessness, increased heartrate, and perspiration. In 2% to 5% of the population, anxiety becomes so extreme that it interferes with routine, daily activities. Such anxiety can focus on a variety of factors, ranging from a fear of being trapped in enclosed places or situations from which you cannot escape to a fear of doing things that could be embarrassing. Anxiety disorders can also focus on specific objects or environments, such as animals, heights, or water (Bond 1991), and be expressed as intense, uncontrollable fear, such as the panic attack. Bizarre behavior may result, such as extreme avoidance (person won't fly in an airplane or take a bath) or escape (person rushes out of a confining room without a logical explanation).

PSYCHOSIS

Psychotic disorders are characterized by the individual's inability to recognize reality. Thought

2. *Bipolar disorder* is commonly referred to as *manic-depressive illness* and includes episodes of both depression and an exaggerated state of elevated mood (i.e., a manic phase). The depression associated with bipolar disorder is similar to that which occurs with major depressive disorder.

3. Cyclothymia is characterized by numerous mood fluctuations that persist for more than two years but are not as extreme or debilitating as those that occur with bipolar disorder.

---

cyclothymia

high to low mood swings with chronic, mild mood instability; the patient usually remains functional

---

4. Dysthymia is a mild depressive disorder that persists for at least two years but does not include the extreme fluctuations present in the other three categories of depression. Dysthymia is not classified as major depression; it will be experienced by 3% of the population. Dysthymic patients rarely benefit from drug therapy and are best helped by **psychotherapy** (Grinspoon 1991). Take for example, Donna, a middle-aged female who experienced chronic anxiety and fatigue. She had come to resent her professional responsibilities and experienced occasional crying spells. Her emotional fluctuation interfered with both professional and personal relationships. After two years of minor depression associated with these emotional problems, Donna sought psychiatric help. Her affective disorder was relieved by counseling, which helped identify the underlying causes of her frustration. Drug therapy was unnecessary (Beahrs 1986, 47).

---

dysthymia

a mild, chronic depressive disorder, causing persistent unhappiness

psychotherapy

treatment of psychiatric disorders primarily based on verbal (counseling) or nonverbal communication

---

Everyone experiences some degree of what is known as **reactive depression,** which is induced by a specific unpleasant or stressful external situation or experience. For instance, depression usually follows the loss of a loved one or getting laid off from work. Such depression usually subsides when the crisis is resolved or the individual has had a chance to adjust to the tragedy. Compared to the treatment of endogenous depression, the approach to treating reactive depression tends to be more psychotherapeutic (counseling) and less pharmacotherapeutic (drugs). However, there are many exceptions to this rule, and the two forms of depression may occur simultaneously (i.e., a tragedy may set off an episode of endogenous depression). In fact, some common mechanisms may prompt both reactive and endogenous depression, and similar drugs can sometimes provide relief from both mood disorders.

---

reactive depression

depression that occurs in response to unpleasant or stressful stimuli

---

Think About It . . .

1. Identify some of the misconceptions about psychiatric disorders that influence attitudes today.
2. A new drug of abuse is being sold illegally on the "streets." One of its effects is that it causes extreme mood swings. How could this drug be used to develop treatments for bipolar mood disorders?
3. Why do you think that psychoactive substance use disorders are included in the DSM-III-R classification of psychiatric disorders (see Table 14-1)? How does this classification affect the way the public or health professionals deal with drug addicts?
4. A murderer is diagnosed as having a psychotic disorder. How should this person be handled, considering his or her individual needs as well as societal interests?
5. Your friend encourages you to move from

your apartment because your neighbor is a "crazy" psychotic who is being treated by a "shrink." How would you respond to this advice? How would you qualify your friend's attitudes toward people with psychiatric problems and psychotherapy in general?

USING PSYCHOTHERAPEUTIC DRUGS TO TREAT PSYCHIATRIC DISORDERS

Treatment for psychiatric disorders can be very complex and frustrating. For example, approximately 30% of all psychiatric patients have two or even more concurrent mental illnesses; a patient might have a combination of schizophrenia and severe depression, for example. In such cases, the important questions are: Which are the best drugs for therapy? Should drug combinations be used? What are the potential interactions between the drugs and the underlying problems?

Another frustrating therapeutic issue is the high rate of drug noncompliance. Many mental patients stop taking their medications. Actually, some enjoy the euphoria, energy, and grandiose sensation frequently associated with manic episodes. (Consider that thousands of drug addicts risk health, wealth, and arrest trying to achieve the same feelings by taking illicit drugs.) A similar compliance problem is seen with schizophrenics, who sometimes prefer their fantasy, psychotic world to the harsh, cruel reality in which they live. It often is not easy to convince such patients that they are better off taking drugs that deprive them of their mental escape and in addition expose them to annoying drug side effects (see box).

Because the different types of mental disorders are distinct from each other and likely involve different brain transmitter systems, it is not surprising that no single class of psychoactive drugs is effective in treating all forms of psychiatric problems. It is imperative that a proper diagnosis be made if appropriate drug therapy is to be rendered. In addition, behavior modification through psychotherapy has been shown to be very effective

For You to Consider...

Case Histories: Treatment Dilemmas

A. Multiple Mental Disorders

A 38-year-old male nurse who worked in an operating room was diagnosed as having a major depression disorder. He was treated successfully with antidepressants. While on the medication, he began to demonstrate psychotic behavior in that he believed that people at work were trying to hurt him. The psychosis appeared to be independent of the depression. The psychotic impressions developed into derogatory auditory hallucinations about some of

his associates. He became particularly angry at other nurses but claimed to feel comfortable with the surgeons. Because of his hallucinations, he suddenly discontinued use of the antidepressant medication, although he accepted a prescription for antipsychotic medication and said that he might have it filled sometime in the future (Reiser et al. 1987).

B. Noncompliance by Psychiatric Patients

Clarence was an intense person who displayed wide mood swings, ranging from grandiose self-perception to angry self-incrimination. He was diagnosed as having bipolar disorder and put on lithium, which returned mood and thinking to normal. He was maintained on lithium for several weeks, during which time he became fed up with the frequent urination and mild tremors caused by the medication. Clarence decided that the lithium was not helping, so he stopped taking it. Within a month, Clarence was hospitalized after getting into a fight and separating from his significant other. The lithium treatment was resumed, and within weeks, he was again under control (Beahrs 1986).

in treating many forms of mental disorders and can often be used instead of or in conjunction with drugs.

Psychoactive agents can only be given under the direction of a physician. As a rule, the physician who practices general medicine can effectively deal with mild forms of mental illness (e.g., anxiety) but has little experience in the treatment of severe psychiatric disorders. Such patients require the expertise of a psychiatrist, who is a physician with specialized training in dealing with mental disorders.

It should be realized that, as with other types of drug therapy, the use of chemical agents to treat a psychiatric ailment is not always 100% satisfactory. However, effective drug therapy has revolutionized approaches to dealing with the mentally ill. A high rate of therapeutic success has brought new hope and productivity to a majority of those who suffer from psychiatric problems.

The principal categories of psychoactive drugs commonly used in psychotherapy are discussed in the following sections (see also Table 14-2). In cases in which patients suffer from two or more different types of psychiatric disorders, a combination of psychotherapeutic drugs is often used (e.g., an antipsychotic in combination with an antidepressant). However, as with other drug combinations, the psychiatrist must be very cautious with psychoactive drugs to avoid negative interactions.

ANXIOLYTICS

Anxiolytics, for the most part, cause CNS depression. Thus, the effects that these drugs have on behavior are related to the degree of CNS depression they exert and are highly dose dependent (see Chapter 6.)

> **anxiolytic**
> drugs used to relieve anxiety

The benzodiazepines are particularly useful for the treatment of anxiety disorders; in general,

TABLE 14-2   Principal psychotherapeutic drugs

Psychiatric Disorder	Drugs Used for Treatment
Anxiety	benzodiazepines (e.g., Valium, Librium, Xanax)
	buspirone (BuSpar)
Panic attack	alprazolam (Xanax)
Depression	
Monopolar disorder	tricyclic antidepressants (e.g., Tofranil, Elavil) MAO inhibitors (e.g., Nardil, Parnate) fluoxetine (Prozac) trazodone (Desyrel) bupropion (Wellbutrin)
Bipolar disorder	lithium (Eskalith)
Psychosis (schizophrenia)	phenothiazines (e.g., Thorazine) butyrophenones (e.g., Haldol) clozapine (Clozaril)

Source: Medical Letter 1991a.

all of these agents are effective anxiolytics. They appear to relieve fear and anxiety by enhancing the activity of the inhibitory brain transmitter GABA (see Chapter 5). Another drug more recently approved by the Food and Drug Administration (FDA) for treatment of simple anxiety conditions is buspirone (BuSpar); it is postulated that this drug relieves fear by reducing the excessive activity of the serotonin neurons. Buspirone has several advantages over benzodiazepines in that it has no known potential for abuse; what's more, because it is not a CNS depressant, it does not cause sedation (*Medical Letter* 1991b). Benzodiazepines are also useful in treating drug-induced anxiety, such as that caused by stimulants of abuse.

One form of anxiety disorder that has received considerable public attention recently is known as the **panic attack,** a sudden, irrational feeling of incredible fear and impending doom. An attack is frequently accompanied by increased autonomic symptoms, such as a stimulated cardiovascular system (*Medical Letter* 1991a). The only approved drug for treatment of this disorder is a benzodiazepine called alprazolam (Xanax) (Bond 1991). Many patients suffering from panic attacks require long-term drug treatment. The exact mechanism of this disorder is not known.

---

panic attack

an episode of intense fear or discomfort accompanied by physiological symptoms such as dizziness, increased heartrate, shortness of breath, and shaking

---

ANTIPSYCHOTICS

Tranquilizers are the antipsychotic agents generally used to treat schizophrenia and acute psychosis. In fact, they have been extremely valuable in controlling psychotic episodes of schizophrenia. (It should be remembered, however, that they are not a cure but only relieve the symptoms and assist in therapy.) These antipsychotic agents are also very effective in therapy for acute psychotic responses to amphetamines, cocaine, and PCP. Tranquilizers themselves are not abused to any significant extent because of the potential for serious side effects.

Phenothiazines are an important class of antipsychotics used in the treatment of schizophrenia. Chlorpromazine (Thorazine), the first phenothiazine, was synthesized in 1950 during a search for anesthetic drugs. It was discovered that chlorpromazine by itself did not induce anesthesia but potentiated anesthetic properties of other drugs and decreased the patient's interest in his or her surroundings. As a result of this finding, chlorpromazine was tried to treat patients suffering psychotic episodes. Its effect was to reduce anxiety and relieve the psychosis itself. Chlorpromazine was first used in the United States in 1954 for the treatment of psychomotor excitement. Another antipsychotic, haloperidol (Haldol), became available for clinical use in psychiatry in 1958. It is not a phenothiazine but is classified as a butyrophenone. Other antipsychotic drugs have also been developed and are currently being used as antipsychotic agents, including Stelazine, Prolixin, and Mellaril.

All of these antipsychotic drugs exert their therapeutic effects because of their ability to block dopamine receptors in the limbic region of the brain (see Chapter 5). This activity also accounts for what is referred to as **extrapyramidal side effects.** These drugs compromise motor responses by blocking dopamine receptors in extrapyramidal brain structures; the results resemble the symptoms seen in Parkinson's disease. This is to be expected, as Parkinson's disease is the result of damage to the dopamine system in the brain; thus, drugs that are dopamine antagonists can mimic this neurological disorder.

---

extrapyramidal side effects

effects caused by drugs that interfere with functioning of the extrapyramidal motor system, including tremors, stooped posture, shuffling of feet, and unusual extreme facial grimacing and tongue protrusions

---

A number of nontraditional antipsychotics are being developed because they do not cause the same motor side effects as traditional tranquilizers. This group of new drugs includes clozapine (Clozaril), which was recently approved by the FDA for treatment of schizophrenia (*Medical Letter* 1991b). The uniqueness of this antipsychotic agent probably accounts for the fact that schizophrenics who do not respond to traditional drugs might respond to treatment with clozapine. Although this drug is still very expensive and can cause severe side effects (e.g., depress the patient's ability to fight infections), it has enabled some uncontrolled schizophrenic patients to return to a normal life.

Antipsychotic drugs have revolutionized the treatment of psychotic patients and dramatically reduced the residential patient population in mental hospitals. In the first half of the twentieth century, the inpatient population of state mental facilities quadrupled, from 113,000 to over 500,000. From 1945 to 1955, there was an average increase each year of about 13,000 patients. The first antipsychotic drugs were introduced in 1955. If the

1945 to 1955 rate of increase had continued to the present, there would be over 1 million hospitalized psychotic patients today. Instead, the number has decreased each year, so that in 1985, there were an estimated 475,000 fewer patients in mental hospitals than in 1955 (see Figure 14-1).

It is especially noteworthy that this decline has occurred in spite of an increase in the number of admissions to psychiatric hospitals. How can this be? First of all, the length of hospitalization has decreased remarkably. In 1955, the average stay was about six months; in 1966, it was two months and in 1985, about 21 days. In addition, more patients are being treated on an outpatient basis rather than being institutionalized. The increase in the number of after-care facilities has also been significant in the continuing treatment of persons with psychiatric problems. The case history in the adjacent box illustrates the improvement that usually occurs after antipsychotic therapy.

Traditional antipsychotic drugs are most ef-fective in the treatment of acute psychosis with positive symptomology (i.e., agitated, violent, aggressive, paranoid behavior). Patients with these symptoms usually respond rapidly and dramatically. In contrast, patients with chronic schizophrenia with negative symptoms (**catatonic, nonresponsive**) improve much more slowly, requiring weeks of treatment for a response, and the likelihood of success is diminished. Nonresponsive patients are maintained for long periods on antipsychotics, which increases the chances and severity of motor-related side effects. The new nontraditional antipsychotic drugs, such as clozapine, have been found to be useful in treating these types of schizophrenic patients (*Medical Letter* 1991b).

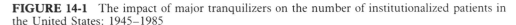

catatonia
a state of physical rigidity with stuporous periods

FIGURE 14-1 The impact of major tranquilizers on the number of institutionalized patients in the United States: 1945–1985

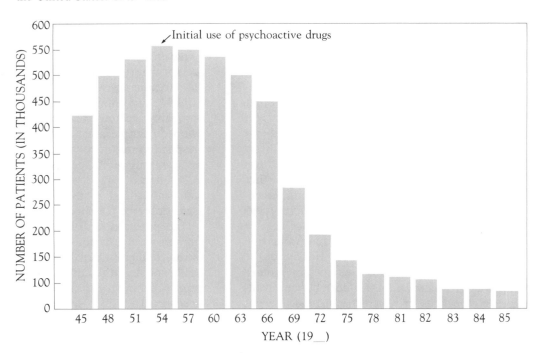

For You to Consider...

Case History:
Successful Antipsychotic Therapy

When Joan was first hospitalized, she was described as being totally distracted by messages directed at her from the TV, radio, and computer. She experienced several hallucinations each day. She was placed on oral fluphenazine (an antipsychotic). By the time Joan was released, all symptoms had subsided, except receipt of an occasional message from the radio. Joan was able to ignore the radio messages and claimed that they did not interfere with her functioning; these minor delusions persisted for four weeks of treatment. Over the next several weeks, different doses and administration forms of fluphenazine were tried until the delusions disappeared and Joan was able to think and function in a normal fashion (Liberman 1988).

SIDE EFFECTS   Although antipsychotic agents are not addictive, they can cause a host of annoying or dangerous side effects: low blood pressure (which can cause fainting, especially upon standing up too quickly), skin rashes, and sensitivity to the sun. Of particular concern are the abnormal motor activities that occur with chronic exposure to some of these agents. Involuntary muscle activity can include nervous tremors, rigidity of limbs, and a shuffling walk. Other motor effects include **akathisia** and **tardive dyskinesia.** Because most patients in psychiatric hospitals have been on antipsychotic drugs for long periods of time,

akathisia
a syndrome characterized by motor restlessness and an inability to remain sitting associated with a feeling of muscle quivering

tardive dyskinesia
a syndrome characterized by involuntary movement of tongue, lips, and jaw

40% to 50% have some degree of tardive dyskinesia. Some of the drug-induced movement abnormalities are permanent and will persist even after drug treatment is stopped. The dosage of antipsychotic drug used should always be the lowest effective level in order to avoid these annoying and sometimes devastating side effects (Baldessarini 1990).

MECHANISMS OF ACTION   Antipsychotics are characterized by their ability to decrease the agitation, hostility, and hallucinations associated with psychotic illnesses. These tranquilizers help the psychotic to think in a well-ordered and logical manner, enabling him or her to return to a productive life, enjoying normal interpersonal relationships.

As mentioned above, antipsychotic agents universally antagonize the actions of the neurotransmitter dopamine in the forebrain, particularly in those areas associated with the limbic systems. The more potent the antipsychotic drug, the more tightly it binds to a particular type of dopamine receptor (called the D-2 subtype) and blocks its function. This finding, which revolutionized antipsychotic drug development, led to formulation of the *dopamine theory of psychotic behavior.* Based on this theory, schizophrenia is due to excessive dopamine activity on the D-2 receptor. The blockade of dopamine receptors by these drugs also accounts for the involuntary motor movements described above (Baldessarini 1990). Because intense use of stimulants of abuse can cause schizophrenialike behavior, it is likely that drugs such as cocaine and amphetamines also enhance D-2 receptor activity.

ANTIDEPRESSANTS

Antidepressant drugs are capable of elevating mood in the severely depressed patient. Because of their potency and unpleasant side effects, however, use must be closely supervised by specially trained physicians. Interestingly, weeks of treatment with antidepressants are generally required before significant improvement in the depression is observed. The explanation for this delay in therapeutic action is not known but obviously can be very frustrating to discouraged patients. Consequently, both patients and physicians frequently dismiss an antidepressant agent as being ineffective before allowing sufficient time to make an accurate evaluation.

One of the most effective treatments for depressed patients is **electroconvulsive** therapy, sometimes called "shock treatment." It involves placing electrodes on the head and shocking the brain with electricity. Even though it may be equivalent in therapeutic value to antidepressant drugs, there are social stigmas against this technique. It seems inhumane to many people who do not understand the process. Nonetheless, electroshock treatment can be effective with depressed patients who do not respond to conventional antidepressant drugs and can elevate mood much more rapidly than drugs. This may be especially important for severely depressed patients (e.g., with suicidal tendencies), for whom immediate relief from the mood disorder is essential (Baldessarini 1990).

Information on antidepressant drugs first came from clinical reports on the treatment of tuberculosis. Until 1955, the incidence of tuberculosis was widespread in the United States. In 1952, drugs were found to be effective in treating this respiratory disease. Two of these agents were isoniazid and iproniazid. Iproniazid was chosen for widespread use because, of the two drugs, it was found to be least toxic. Clinical reports soon mentioned that patients receiving this drug had unusually high spirits and extremely elevated mood. In 1955, iproniazid was first used extensively as an antidepressant drug (Baldessarini 1990).

Iproniazid is a monoamine oxidase (MAO) inhibitor. MAO is an enzyme involved in the metabolism of the transmitters serotonin, norepinephrine, epinephrine, and dopamine; thus, blockage of this enzyme increases the levels of these transmitters and enhances their activity. Unfortunately, MAO inhibitors cause serious side effects, particularly in combination with substances that affect the heart or cause vasoconstriction and are metabolized by this MAO enzyme. An example of such a substance is the chemical tyramine. It can have sympathomimetic effects and is found in sufficiently high quantities in some foods (e.g., aged cheese, chocolate, raisin, chianti, and beer) to cause problems in patients using an MAO inhibitor. Iproniazid was removed from the market in 1961 after 54 deaths from such interactions. Because of this and other toxic effects, MAO inhibitors are usually not the first agents of choice in treating severe depression.

A second group of drugs, the tricyclic antidepressants, came into use about this time. They work by blocking the reuptake of transmitters such as serotonin and norepinephrine back into the neuron after being released. Such an effect allows the transmitters to remain active for longer periods of time. Interestingly, cocaine acts by a very similar mechanism. (A significant number of individuals who abuse this stimulant are trying to self-medicate a depression problem.)

Even though the tricyclic antidepressants have a cocainelike mechanism, they do not have cocainelike abuse potential. The likely reason is that cocaine also blocks the reuptake of the transmitter dopamine (the substance that most likely accounts for drug abuse potential) while the tricyclic antidepressants do not. Another possible reason for the lack of abuse of these agents is their prominent anticholinergic activity. Some very annoying side effects are associated with their ability to block the muscarinic receptor, including drowsiness, dry mouth, constipation, blurred vision, and others. These definitely are not the kind of drug effects that encourage abuse.

SIDE EFFECTS   Although relatively safe, tricyclic antidepressants cause cardiovascular problems in some patients. (Remember that norepinephrine, which is enhanced by these drugs, is the transmitter for the sympathetic nervous system.) These drugs can also cause patients with bipolar depression to switch abruptly from depression to manic excitement with delirium. Impaired sexual function as well as weight gain have been reported for both men and women using these drugs. Antidepressant drugs are commonly used in suicide attempts by severely depressed patients (Baldessarini 1990). For this reason, special efforts are made by psychiatrists to restrict the number of antidepressant pills available to the patient. Even so, patients sometimes hoard the medication and accumulate tablets until they have saved a sufficient number for a suicide attempt.

Withdrawal effects from tricyclic antidepressants have been reported when the medication is discontinued abruptly after chronic use. The most common symptoms include upset stomach, dizziness, headaches, nightmares, and salivation. Such withdrawal problems can best be avoided by tapering the antidepressant doses when treatment is to be discontinued (*Medical Letter* 1991b).

CONTINUED DEVELOPMENTS New antidepressant drugs are being introduced on a regular basis and have proven successful for some patients who did not find relief with older drug treatment. Some of these newer drugs have become particularly popular due to their relative lack of serious or annoying side effects.

One such drug, fluoxetine (Prozac), was approved for marketing as an antidepressant in 1988. It is currently the most popular antidepressant agent, due to its apparent wide margin of safety. There are currently no verified cases of death from an overdose of this agent by itself. In addition, Prozac lacks the troublesome anticholinergic side effects routinely associated with tricyclic antidepressants or the cardiovascular reactions caused by MAO inhibitors. One side effect commonly reported by users of Prozac is appetite suppression; for many, this is viewed as being a positive feature of the drug. In fact, Prozac is currently being evaluated by the FDA for use as an anorexiant in the treatment of obesity. Other reported side effects of Prozac include insomnia, nausea, and mild tremors. Moreover, Prozac does not seem to have abuse potential; consequently, it would be a good substitute for the abuse-promoting amphetamines as an appetite suppressant. It appears that Prozac exerts its antidepressant effects by selectively blocking the reuptake of serotonin into neurons.

Prozac is not without its problems, however. Reports began to surface in 1990 that it can cause serious psychiatric reactions in a fraction of users (Grady 1990). In fact, there have been several claims that use of Prozac resulted in suicide or homicide (see the box). Some murder suspects are

For You to Consider...

Case History:
A Prozac Reaction

A 58-year-old man had suffered from severe depression for 13 years. Two of his previous episodes of depression had been successfully treated with the common antidepressant drug imipramine. He did not respond to the drug after being admitted to the hospital during a third episode. Prozac treatment was started. Only three days after beginning the Prozac administration, the patient developed suicidal thoughts and tried to hang himself with a rope. Four days after stopping the Prozac treatment, suicidal thoughts abated and the patient was successfully treated with electroconvulsive therapy (Masand et al. 1991).

claiming as their defense that mental disturbances induced by Prozac use were responsible for their violent acts. One report described six patients who experienced intense preoccupation with suicide only after beginning treatment with Prozac (Masand et al. 1991).

Obviously, such reports are very worrisome. However, at this time, it is not clear if the problems are truly related to the drug (*Medical Letter* 1991b; Teicher et al. 1990). It is possible that they occur because the populations using the drug tend to be emotionally unstable or because this popular drug is prescribed by physicians who are not trained to do so. The FDA is closely scrutinizing reports and will determine the fate of Prozac (*Medical Letter* 1990).

Other drugs that have recently been approved for treatment of major depression include bupropion (Wellbutrin) and trazodone (Desyrel). Still more drugs are being investigated as antidepressant agents, and new compounds almost certainly will be released for marketing in the near future (*Medical Letter* 1991b).

In general, therapy for the severely depressed population does not have an impressive success rate. While good pharmacological and psychological techniques do exist, they are often misused by clinicians due to inexperience and a lack of understanding of the disease process involved. Consequently:

1. Inappropriate drugs are given (e.g., frequently bipolar mood disorder is misdiagnosed as schizophrenia and drugs that worsen depression, such as tranquilizers, are prescribed)
2. Antidepressants are administered incorrectly (e.g., not given long enough or the dose is too low) or avoided altogether due to their side effects
3. Inappropriate combinations of pharmacotherapy and psychotherapy are employed.

Some clinicians estimate that, if optimal treatment were rendered, 70% to 80% of the patients suffering severe depression would experience substantial relief (Brotman et al. 1987).

ANTIMANICS Lithium is an alkali metal that has been found to be effective in treating the manic phase of manic-depressive disorders (also called *bipolar depressive disorders*). Lithium is a mood-stabilizing drug in these patients and is somewhat unique in that it causes no psychoactivity in normal subjects (i.e., it is neither a sedative nor a euphoriant). The lithium ion has no known biological role. It mimics some of the biological properties of both extracellular sodium and intracellular potassium. In a biological system, lithium appears to act more like sodium than other ions. Passage through the blood-brain barrier is slow, but lithium does enter the neurons of the brain. Lithium appears to affect the release of norepinephrine, dopamine, and serotonin, although it is not clear which if any of these effects accounts for its mood-stabilizing properties.

When dosage is maintained in a therapeutic range, lithium has few side effects; however, it has a low therapeutic index and can become extremely toxic at plasma levels only twice that of its therapeutic range. Thus, patients chronically using lithium should routinely have their blood levels checked to be sure the amount of the drug is not excessive (*Medical Letter* 1991b). Common complaints of side effects from lithium use include nausea, fatigue, tremors, thirst, excessive urination, and weight gain.

DRUG ABUSE AND PSYCHIATRIC DISORDERS: WHAT'S THE ASSOCIATION?

Recent elucidation of underlying causes for psychiatric disorders has led to dramatic improvement in the rate of successful treatment. Interestingly, this knowledge has also provided significant insight into factors that relate to the causes and treatment of drug abuse.

Because mental disorders appear to be due to inappropriate functioning of the neurotransmitters in the brain, it is not surprising that drugs of abuse, which substantially alter transmitter activity, can induce conditions that mimic various forms of mental illness. This association between drug abuse and mental illness (see box) has consequences of clinical relevance (Brady et al. 1990).

1. Individuals who already have a tendency toward certain mental disorders are more likely to experience abrupt expressions of the disorders when abusing these CNS-active drugs.

2. Sometimes patients with significant mental illnesses may try to self-medicate the problem with drugs of abuse. For example, an estimated 30% of those who routinely consume cocaine are trying to self-medicate depression. Interestingly, cocaine affects catecholamines and serotonin in a manner similar to traditionally used antidepressants. The significance of this fact is that, if the mental disorder is properly attended to, the motivation for abusing the drug disappears and the abuse problem may be eliminated.

3. Because of the association between drug abuse and mental illness, it is sometimes possible to use psychotherapeutic agents to treat drug abuse–related problems and vice versa. Thus, cocaine withdrawal is effectively treated with desipramine, a commonly used antidepressant; amphetamine-induced psychosis is controlled by administering the antipsychotic haloperidol; cocaine-induced

For You to Consider...

Case Histories:
Clinical Relevance of Association between Drug Abuse and Mental Illness

A. Effect of Drugs of Abuse on Underlying Mental Disorders

Pete was receiving antipsychotic medication for his psychiatric disorder. During this time, he began to believe that his coworkers were persecuting him and attempting to sabotage his work. Because of these delusions, Pete lost his job. When the dose of his medication was increased, the symptoms disappeared. However, the higher dose made Pete feel lethargic, bored, and unmotivated. To compensate for these side effects, Pete began drinking with the guys at the corner bar; he claimed alcohol helped him to relax and relieve the boredom. He eventually began using cocaine, which helped to increase his energy and confidence levels. Two weeks after starting regular cocaine use, Pete felt that the neighbors were spying on him and reporting his activities to the police. He ended up barricading himself in his friend's home. He was removed and placed in a hospital for treatment (Liberman 1988).

B. Self-Medication of Depression with Alcohol

An 80-year-old woman was repeatedly hospitalized over a period of 12 years for depression and alcoholism. Her psychiatric problems began immediately following the death of her husband. Each hospitalization was preceded by withdrawal, isolation, increased drinking, problems sleeping, and diminished appetite. After more than a decade of depression and self-medication with alcohol, she began to suffer brain deterioration because of liver damage caused by her drinking (Reiser et al. 1987).

---

anxiety and panic can be alleviated by giving a sedative such as a benzodiazepine.

4. Drugs of abuse can be used to create animal models of different types of mental illnesses; for example, studies in which high doses of cocaine or amphetamine are given to laboratory animals have demonstrated a great deal about the mechanisms involved in psychosis, such as schizophrenia.

Think About It...

1. A potentially dangerous psychotic patient refuses to take his drug because it causes unpleasant side effects, such as hand tremors and facial grimacing. Should the patient be forced to take the drug to control his psychotic behavior?
2. The pharmaceutical industry is very interested in developing drugs that either stimulate or block dopamine receptors in the brain. Why?
3. Imagine that you are a psychiatrist trying to treat a patient diagnosed with severe monopolar depressive disorder. You are trying to explain to her spouse (a) why the mental illness has made the patient so unresponsive and (b) what to expect from the antidepressant treatment. What would you say?
4. Critics have claimed that the relatively new and extremely popular antidepressant Prozac is dangerous. There are reports that use has caused patients with depressive disorders to attempt suicide. Most psychiatrists believe it is a very useful antidepressant; however, sentiment among the media and general public is that Prozac should be removed from the market. If you were the director of the FDA, how would you handle this problem?

K E Y   T E R M S

psychiatric disorder

affective disorders

bipolar disorders

endogenous depression

monopolar (unipolar) depression

cyclothymia

dysthymia

psychotherapy

reactive depression

anxiolytic

panic attack

extrapyramidal side effects

catatonia

akathisia

tardive dyskinesia

S U M M A R Y

1. Abuse of psychoactive drugs can cause mental conditions that closely mimic those of psychiatric disorders. Intense use of the stimulants amphetamine and cocaine or the hallucinogen PCP can cause psychotic symptoms like schizophrenia. Use of CNS depressants such as barbiturates, benzodiazepines, or alcohol can cause severe depression and suicide. Stimulants such as cocaine and amphetamines can also cause an elevated mood, like the manic phase of bipolar mood disorders.

2. Psychotic disorders are characterized by a lack of contact with reality. The thought processes are distorted and can include delusions and hallucinations, resulting in inappropriate and even dangerous behavior. The impaired mental state usually interferes with normal activity and personal relationships.

3. There are four principal types of affective disorders: (a) Bipolar mood disorder is characterized by a state of elevated mood and energy, often including periods of hallucinations and a loss of contact with reality; these patients frequently also go through a depressed state. (b) Major monopolar depressive disorder is characterized by diminished interest or pleasure in normal

activities, sleep disturbances, decreased appetite, fatigue, and a desire to commit suicide. (c) Cyclothymia consists of numerous mood fluctuations that persist for more than two years but are not as severe as bipolar disorders. (d) Dysthymia is the mildest form of depressive disorder; it persists for at least two years, does not include extreme mood fluctuations, and usually does not require drug treatment.

4. Drugs of abuse that cause psychiatric conditions that resemble mental disorders alter transmitter systems in the brain. Apparently, these same transmitters appear to be altered (either increased or decreased in activity) in mental illnesses. The transmitters most likely involved include dopamine, serotonin, and norepinephrine. Because of their effect on these transmitter systems, intense treatments in laboratory animals with drugs of abuse are sometimes used as models of psychiatric disorders.

5. Psychotherapeutic drugs help to reestablish the balance of transmitter activity that is apparently disrupted with mental disorders.

6. CNS depressants are used to treat anxiety and panic. During these mental states, some of the

brain's activities appear to be heightened; CNS depressants help to tone down this activity and cause the brain's transmitter systems to return to normal functioning. The drugs used to treat depression include the tricyclic antidepressants, MAO inhibitors, and newer drugs such as Prozac. These agents appear to exert their effects by increasing the activity of norepinephrine or serotonin transmitter systems. Lithium carbonate is the principal agent used to treat mania-related affective disorders. It appears to stabilize transmitter activity, but its mechanism of action is not known. Finally, all of the antipsychotic drugs used to treat conditions such as schizophrenia block dopamine receptors in the limbic system. This suggests that enhanced dopamine activity contributes to the development of these mental disorders.

7. Psychotherapeutic drugs used in the treatment of mental disorders have significant side effects. CNS depressants can cause lethargy and drowsiness and when used chronically may lead to dependence. The MAO inhibitors can dangerously interact with tyramine in food and with other sympathomimetic drugs. The tricyclic antidepressants have

substantial anticholinergic effects that can be very annoying. Prozac is being evaluated for causing increased suicide tendencies, and lithium carbonate can cause many side effects, including neurological problems such as dizziness, restlessness, and seizures.

8. Because the dopamine transmitter system plays a vital function in regulating mood and neurological activity, it is not surprising that alterations in the activity of this transmitter can cause motor problems and mental disorders and account for drug side effects.

Thus, in Parkinson's disease, there is a deficiency of dopamine in the extrapyramidal brain regions; in schizophrenia and following cocaine use, there is too much dopamine activity in the limbic regions of the brain. Antipsychotic drugs are used to treat schizophrenia and cocaine overdoses because they block limbic dopamine activity.

9. Depressive disorders are particularly difficult to treat properly. Often, depressive episodes are part of another mental disorder, such as

schizophrenia, which makes treatment complicated. Also, there are several types of depression that appear to be caused by different mechanisms; thus, a different treatment may be necessary for each type. Some clinicians mistakenly try to treat depressive disorders when they are untrained to diagnose the problem and are unfamiliar with the drugs and their side effects. Finally, psychotherapy and pharmacotherapy are not always used together in an effective manner.

R E F E R E N C E S

American Psychiatric Association. *Diagnostic and Statistical Manual of Mental Disorders*. 3rd ed., rev. Washington, D.C.: APA, 1987.

Andreason, N., and Black, D. *Introductory Textbook of Psychiatry*. Washington, D.C.: American Psychiatric Press, 1991.

Baldessarini, R. *Drugs and the Treatment of Psychiatric Disorders*, edited by A. Gilman, T. Rall, A. Nies, and P. Taylor. New York: Pergamon, 1990.

Beahrs, J. *Limits of Scientific Psychiatry: The Role of Uncertainty in Mental Health*. New York: Brunner/Mazel, 1986.

Bond, W. "Anxiety Disorders and Psychopharmacologic Therapies." *Facts and Comparisons, Drug Newsletter* 10 (1991): 9–11.

Brady, K., R. Anton, J. Ballenger, B. Lydiard, B. Adinoff, and J. Selander. "Cocaine Abuse among Schizophrenic Patients." *American Journal of Psychiatry* 147 (1990): 1164

Brotman, A., W. Falk, and A. Gelenberg.

"Pharmacological Treatment of Acute Depressive Subtypes." In *Psychopharmacology: The Third Generation of Progress*, edited by H. Meltzer. New York: Raven, 1987.

Grady, D. "Wonder Drug." *American Health*, October 1990, 60–65.

Grinspoon, L., ed. "Dysthymia and Other Mood Disorders." *The Harvard Mental Health Letter* 7 (May 1991): 1–3.

Holden, C. "Depression Research Advances, Treatment Lags." *Science* 233 (1986): 723–726.

Liberman, R. *Psychiatric Rehabilitation of Chronic Mental Patients*. Washington, D.C.: American Psychiatric Press, 1988.

Masand, P., S. Gupta, and M. Dewan. "Suicidal Ideation Related to Fluoxetine Treatment." *New England Journal of Medicine* 324 (1991): 420.

Medical Letter. "Fluoxetine (Prozac) Revisited." *The Medical Letter* 32 (7 September 1990): 83–85.

Medical Letter. *Drugs of Choice, Drugs for Psychiatric Disorders*. New Rochelle, NY: The Medical Letter Incorporated, 1991a.

Medical Letter. "Drugs for Psychiatric Disorders." *The Medical Letter* 33 (17 May 1991b): 43–46.

Reiser, S., H. Bursztajn, P. Appelbaum, and T. Gutheil. *Divided Staffs, Divided Selves: A Case Approach to Mental Health Ethics*. New York: Press Syndicate of the University of Cambridge, 1987.

Snyder, S. H. *Madness and the Brain*. New York: McGraw-Hill, 1974.

Stimmel, G. *Welcome Trends in Pharmacy*. New York: Health Education Technologies, December 1989.

Teicher, M., C. Glod, and J. Cole. "Emergence of Intense Suicidal Preoccupation during Fluoxetine Treatment." *American Journal of Psychiatry* 147 (1990): 207.

Drug Education, Prevention, and Treatment

CHAPTER OUTLINE

The Nature of Drug Addiction ▪ The American Problem ▪ Views on Addiction ▪ Levels of Addiction / **Drug Education** ▪ Using Education to Control Drug Use ▪ School-Based Drug Education Objectives ▪ A National Strategy for Drug Control / **Prevention** ▪ Prevention Models ▪ The Role of Social and Personal Development ▪ Alternatives to Drugs ▪ Nontraditional Prevention Methods / **Treatment** ▪ Beginnings and Goals ▪ Treatment Settings ▪ Treatment Methods ▪ Evaluating Program Effectiveness

LEARNING OBJECTIVES

On completing this chapter, you will be able to:

1. List and briefly explain the five different levels of drug addiction.
2. Explain how social influence relates to drug use.
3. List the seven types of users that drug education programs must be aware of.
4. Name the three categories of drug education programs, citing what each stresses.
5. Distinguish between primary, secondary, and tertiary prevention.

6. Cite the primary differences between the social science/ sociocultural model and the psychological model of drug use.
7. Explain the three assumptions that should be behind all primary prevention programs.
8. Cite what factors should be considered in evaluating the success of treatment programs for drug abuse.
9. Explain the differences among inhospital care, residential care, and day hospitals or intensive outpatient services.

10. List and discuss the differences between the six primary approaches to drug treatment.
11. Explain what the three states of consciousness—ergotropic, normal, and trophotropic— refer to.
12. Give a brief account of how either hypnosis or acupuncture can be used to treat drug abuse.

Source: Rhoda Sidney/Stock, Boston

DID YOU KNOW THAT . . .

- At various times in U.S. history, drug dependence has been considered a moral violation, a criminal act, and an illness.
- There are conflicting views of drug addiction; many people view it as a crime, while others view it as a disease.
- Social influence is a significant factor in drug use.
- Drug education actually began in the 1800s with the temperance movement.
- Some believe that drug abuse is widespread because we have an innate need to alter our consciousness.
- Generally, people who do not use psychoactive drugs have discovered other methods of altering their consciousness.
- Rehabilitation cannot succeed if it is not specifically tailored to the type of person and the type of drug user.
- The success of a treatment program for drug dependence cannot always be based on total abstinence because, in reality, this is rarely achieved.
- The primary approaches for treating drug abuse are medical, psychotherapeutic, social, behavioral, and innovative.
- Detoxification programs are aimed at reducing drug dependence to zero.
- Maintenance programs do not eliminate drug addiction; they merely stabilize it.
- Hypnosis and acupuncture are also being used by drug addicts as treatment methods.

The point has been made repeatedly throughout this book that people have always used drugs. Why? we may ask.

The reasons behind drug use are varied and complex, particularly in this contemporary age, when an assortment of drugs is readily accessible. Cultural values about drug use and abuse—that is, whether it's acceptable to use drugs, either licit or illicit, for treatment or recreation—are an integral part of the problem. Consider the role of the media, which reinforces the notion that some drug is available to "fix" whatever is wrong with you. Thus, we're told that it's okay to use drugs, at least for some purposes, and drugs are easy to get.

Given this context, what can be done to prevent drug abuse? Knowledge is certainly part of the answer. People must be informed about what drugs do and at what point using them becomes a problem. What's more, people must know how to identify that a problem exists and what can be done to resolve it.

In this chapter, our goal is to educate. We will begin by defining *addiction*, offering several views of its meaning and social impact. A discussion of drug education follows; education is considered as a tool in controlling drug abuse, particularly among youth. Drug prevention is examined in some detail; both traditional and nontraditional approaches are presented. The final topic is drug treatment—namely, alternative goals, settings, and methods. A review of the effectiveness of various approaches ends the chapter.

THE NATURE OF DRUG ADDICTION

THE AMERICAN PROBLEM

From the earliest days to the present, various types of drug dependence have plagued American society. At various times, drug dependence has been considered a moral violation, a criminal act, and an illness. Throughout history, the laws that have been passed in the United States have reflected the moral code of the times.

The history of drug addiction shows that, in the early days, alcoholism was rampant, and there were some pockets of opiate dependence. The Pilgrims and Puritans did not forbid drinking, only overindulgence. When the Revolutionary War ended in 1783, people continued to accept heavy drinking as a normal way of life, despite the belief that it was morally wrong to drink to excess. So many Americans were addicted to alcohol that Presidents Washington and Jefferson suggested that people switch from drinking distilled spirits to beer and wine to reduce the disruptive influence of alcoholism.

Other drug addictions developed, as well. From the early 1800s to the early 1900s, opiate and cocaine addiction grew; it was legal to smoke and use these drugs, and they were widely available. Patent medicines, tonics, and elixirs contained liberal amounts of opiates and cocaine as well as alcohol, which compounded the drug dependence.

Barbiturates were also available in the early 1900s. Even though some people became addicted, little attention was given to this problem because often supplies were obtained through medical channels. Amphetamine dependence was also managed medically. Barbiturates and amphetamines were not restricted by federal laws until 1965.

VIEWS ON ADDICTION

In 1964, the World Health Organization of the United Nations (WHO) defined **addiction** as "a state of periodic or chronic intoxication detrimental to the individual and society, which is characterized by an overwhelming desire to continue

For You to Consider...

Getting Straight

Recent statistics from the National Institute of Drug Abuse—the same data cited repeatedly by William Bennett and President Bush—show that the rate of illegal drug use peaked in the late 1970s (at about the same time the overall crime rate peaked) and has since continuously declined.

Survey data show that the demand for drugs of all kinds—legal and illegal—is at its lowest point in many years. Americans are drinking less, smoking less and using fewer illicit drugs. Every year since the middle '70s, researchers at the University of Michigan have measured the recent use of a wide variety of drugs in a national sample of high school seniors, the age group at greatest risk. For the most part, drug use by these teen-agers peaked in the late 1970s and has declined substantially since then. The percentage reporting using marijuana in the previous month in 1988 was 18, half the percentage reporting such use in 1979. Hard drugs, too, are down. PCP use has declined from a rate of 24 per thousand in 1979 to 3 per thousand in 1988. The use of cocaine, the drug featured in the president's proposals, declined by 50 percent between 1985 and 1988, from 6.7 percent of seniors to 3.4 percent. And heavy smokers of cigarettes are only half as plentiful today as 10 years ago.

Nor are these trends confined to teen-agers: the Michigan data show the same results for marijuana and cocaine use among those aged 19–22.

Other surveys confirm the move away from drugs in American society. The National Restaurant Association reports that alcohol consumption in restaurants dropped 17 percent between 1980 and 1987. During the same period beer consumption was down by 7 percent, wine consumption by 14, and distilled spirits by 23.

While law-enforcement and political groups portray an ever-worsening crisis (predictably suggesting that drug gangs are spreading the epidemic to the suburbs, to rural areas and to previously unaffected groups), the facts suggest that America's drug problem is being blown out of proportion, that our fear of drugs is generated more by drug fighters than drug users.

- *The reason that both drug use and crime have declined from their peaks early in the decade has more to do with the aging of the population than with government crime-control policies. The decline also reflects a major shift in attitudes toward drug use in the United States, as documented by the Michigan researchers* [emphasis added]. They report that the proportion of high-school seniors approving of marijuana use has declined by two-thirds since 1980, and the number thinking that marijuana carries little physical risk has been halved in the same period. These radical changes in attitude and behavior began well before—and thus could not have resulted from—the war on drugs or the current emphasis on lengthier prison terms.

Source: M. Gottfredson, and T. Hirschi, "Why We're Losing the War on Crime," *Washington Post,* 10 September 1989, 3.

---

taking the drug and to obtain it by any means" (WHO 1964, 9–10; see also Eddy et al. 1965, 721–733). Today, the WHO prefers the term *drug dependence*, which is indicative of changing views.

addiction
a condition consisting of periodic or chronic dependence on a drug or several drugs; an insatiable desire to use drugs contrary to legal and/or social prohibitions

There are conflicting views on the nature of drug addiction or dependence. The two most prevalent views are that drug uncontrolled dependence is a *crime* or a disease.

The U.S. Supreme Court ruled in 1962 that labeling drug dependence as a crime is unconstitutional. Like alcoholism, drug dependence is to be regarded as a disease rather than the result of moral weakness. The **disease model of drug dependence** has had a profound effect on most approaches to and treatments of drug dependence.

For You to Consider...

Could You Be an Addict?

by Margot Gilman

When we think of addicts we think of people who abuse drugs (including nicotine) or alcohol. And, to be sure, drug and alcohol abuse are the most pervasive addictions in our society. Recent research, however, reveals that addiction is a far more complicated phenomenon. According to Dr. Lawrence J. Hatterer, a clinical associate professor of psychiatry at Cornell University Medical School and the author of *The Pleasure Addicts* (Hatterer, 1980), a person can develop an overpowering need or addiction to just about any substance as well as to many behaviors. For example, a person can become addicted to gambling, to working, to playing, to eating chocolate, to running marathons, to buying clothes, even to having sex. All addictions are developed as ways to handle anxiety, conflict and stress, Dr. Hatterer says. And, if a behavior or substance makes you feel

good when you're down—if it helps you cope by providing a pleasurable "high"—it is potentially addicting, even if it's something as seemingly benign as eating ice cream first thing in the morning.

Unusual as that particular behavior may sound, addiction is not an isolated or insignificant problem: It is estimated that well over 30 percent of all Americans are addicts of some kind. Nor is addiction a sign of weak moral character, of lack of willpower or the result of other "personality" traits. It is a *disease*, Dr. Hatterer says, that some of us, for a host of physical and psychological reasons, are more vulnerable to than others.

Of course, just because you take or do something excessively doesn't by itself mean that you are addicted. (Even if you are addicted, that doesn't mean that you cannot be cured.) All addictions—whether to beer or baseball or candy or cocaine—share certain distinguishing characteristics: They provide a false sense of relief, cause us to build

up a tolerance and experience a withdrawal if the behavior or substance is removed. And, although no one would claim that an addiction to caffeine or ice cream in the morning is as dangerous and debilitating as an addiction to heroin, say, all addictions cause a person to lose control over his or her life and in that sense can be destructive.

The following test, designed by Dr. Hatterer, is *not* a way to diagnose whether you are in the early, middle or chronic stage of *addictive disease*. It is merely meant to help you understand addictive behavior better so you can recognize it in yourself or perhaps in people you know. If you answer "yes" to one half or more of the questions, however, you may have a problem and should seek immediate professional help. For a referral, contact your local mental health clinic (look in the Yellow Pages) or speak to your doctor.

The Addiction Test

1. I am a person of excesses. I can't regulate what I do for pleasure,

---

It assumes that the drug-dependent person is largely out of control and in need of help. He or she must be rehabilitated. However, law enforcement groups maintain that, in doing so, the addict should not be released from the responsibility of his or her criminal action to obtain drugs.

disease model of drug dependence
the view that drug dependence is an illness

Recall from Chapter 9 that most narcotic addicts exhibit antisocial behavior long before they start using drugs. They are poor or failing students and in trouble with the law. Eighty percent have preaddiction arrest records, and 40% have preaddiction convictions (Nurco 1979). Many have dropped out of middle or high school. They have never learned a vocational skill or completed the minimal educational levels to get a job so they could support themselves. Thus, they have removed themselves from being productive members of society. They are driven further into

Let's Get the Facts

Origins of the "Just Say No" Campaign

In January 1985, a group of children met at Peralta Year-Round School in Oakland, California, to discuss drugs and peer pressure with representatives of Oakland Parents in Action. Students viewed a film of Nancy Reagan's visit a year before. In the film, Reagan mentioned that one way to counter peer pressure to use drugs was to "Just Say No."

After viewing the film, discussions were held between the children and parents. One child asked if they could start a "Just Say No" club. Out of this discussion, the first such club was formed, and a national movement was started. There are now several hundred "Just Say No" clubs across the United States, sponsored by schools, civic organizations, and parent groups (Gelb 1984; U.S. Department of Education 1986).

Most members of "Just Say No" clubs are from 7 to 14 years old. The clubs teach that drug use is not normal and that a person has the right to decide not to bow to peer pressure and use drugs. This is based on the theory of "cognitive inoculation" (McGuire 1981), which is analogous to receiving an inoculation to protect you against disease. Similarly, teaching children to "say no" to drugs is supposed to protect them from peer pressure.

Through many activities, the clubs show students that they can have fun without using drugs. The primary emphasis remains that everyone has the right to say no to drugs.

courses, and the mass media are used extensively as mediums for educating the public about the negative consequences of drug abuse. Strategies vary enormously but can be placed into three general categories:

1. Those that focus and provide information
2. Those that stress values, beliefs, and attitudes
3. Those that emphasize the consequences of drug use (namely, warnings and scare tactics about drug abuse)

CONSIDERING THE AUDIENCE AND APPROACH
The audience for drug education is composed of users and nonusers. In analyzing the population of users, categories include (1) committed users, those who abuse drugs and have no interest in stopping; (2) former users; (3) nonproblem drug users, those who abuse drugs on occasion, mostly for recreation; and (4) problem users (Kinney 1991).

It is important for people involved in drug education to know about different types of users so that programs can cater to the specific needs of these groups. For committed users, drug education should aim to prevent or delay drug abuse. Former users should be given information that will reinforce their decision to quit abusing drugs. For nonproblem users, drug education programs should examine the abuse of drugs, reinforce the importance of how uncontrolled use leads to abuse, and educate on how to prevent use from escalating to abuse. Finally, for problem users, the goals should be to reduce use and change use patterns by presenting successful prevention strategies.

Professionals planning a drug education program have to decide on the type of audience they intend to pursue. A number of questions should be considered: To what type of audience should the drug information be targeted? Youths or adults? Peers or parents? Should information focus on knowledge, attitudes, or behavior? Should drug education emphasize and recommend abstinence or responsible use?

In most cases, it is appropriate for drug education to focus on knowledge, attitudes, and behavior. The three are clearly related. For instance, if the goal is to increase knowledge, should we assume that attitudes and behavior will change accordingly, or is knowledge about the harmful effects of drugs separate from attitudes and behavior? In other words, if you learn that smoking marijuana is a health hazard, equal to or more destructive than smoking cigarettes, does this knowledge change the satisfaction you derive from smoking marijuana with friends? Some would say yes. Unfortunately, many also would say no. In fact, knowledge about the harmful effects of certain types of drugs has very little effect on the personal attitudes and habits of most people. Proof of this is how many cigarette smokers are aware of the health risks involved with smoking but continue to smoke, day after day and year after year.

Drug education programs have to direct attention to a small range of behavioral objectives; they will not be effective if they address too many issues.

Finally, drug educators must decide if they will stress total abstinence or responsible use. Abstinence is radically different from responsible use. A program cannot advocate both. Consider the following: If a program decides to promote abstinence, it is certain to lose compulsive users and others not convinced that drug use (or even the use of a particular drug) is bad. If the program chooses to stress responsible use, it will lose people advocating abstinence, and, depending on the type of drug, others may or may not offer support. This decision is very complicated.

PROGRAM MODELS   Many alternatives and strategies are possible. There are a number of successful models for drug education programs:

The cognitive model stresses the dangers of drug abuse, often with scare tactics. An example is the television commercial produced by the Partnership's Campaign that shows frying an egg (Baumann and Waterston 1993 forthcoming). The effect intended with the graphic illustration is that, if you use drugs, your brain will become fried like the egg.

The information-based model stresses accurate, unbiased, and straight information on the use and effects of drugs. The model assumes that the audience is composed of rational people who can intelligently decide for themselves whether drug abuse is worth the physical and psychological risks involved.

Peer tutoring, teaching, and counseling employ peers or older youth to disseminate information on drug abuse. This includes using rehabilitated or recovering drug addicts and abusers as counselors; they

can identify with the audience and provide advice from "someone who's been there."

Social resistance training focuses largely on teaching how to resist peer pressure. Teachers and trainers in workshop settings teach students how to disagree, how to say no, how to be assertive without fear of reprisal, and how to respond effectively when drugs are offered in social settings.

SCHOOL-BASED DRUG EDUCATION OBJECTIVES

In an effort to educate students and make them aware of the dangers in using drugs, school-based drug education programs and objectives have been implemented in most American school curriculums. Specific objectives have been established for elementary, junior high, and senior high and college levels. These include:

Elementary Level

Drugs versus poisons
Effects of alcohol, tobacco, and marijuana on the body
Differences between candy and drugs
Drug overdoses
Dangers of experimentation
Saying no to peers using drugs
Reasons for taking drugs: curing illness; pleasure; escape; parental use; and ceremony

Junior High Level

How peer pressure works
How drugs affect the body, physiologically and psychologically
Attitudes toward drug use
Harmful effects of tobacco, alcohol, and marijuana on the body
Role of advertising in the use of drugs
Differences between wine, beer, and distilled liquors
Family drug use
Teen-age drug abuse and associated problems

Senior High and College Level

Responsible use of medications
How drugs affect the body and the mind
Legal versus illegal drugs
Drinking and driving
Drug effects on the fetus
Recreational drug use
Ways of coping with problems
Detecting problem drug users
Drug education, prevention, and treatment
Positive and negative role models
Criminal sanctions for various types of drug
   use

T h i n k   A b o u t   I t . . .

1. Of the three views on drug dependence—as a moral violation, a criminal act, and an illness—which do you most agree with? Give at least three reasons for your answer.
2. Interview two to four people, and evaluate their different views on drug use versus drug abuse. Report the differences and similarities.
3. Plan an effective drug education campaign for your school. What would you emphasize? Give specific details.

A NATIONAL STRATEGY FOR DRUG CONTROL

In September 1989, the White House published and distributed the *National Drug Control Strategy* ("Education" 1989) which represents an official, comprehensive, drug control approach taken by the president. Following are six excerpts from this publication. Each section ends with several comments and questions you may find worthy of further thought and discussion.

Excerpt 1

There are two ways to influence whether an individual decides to use drugs. One is to make him [or her] not to want to use them. Information and moral persuasion obviously help shape an individual's preferences, attitudes, and desires. The other approach is to make an individual fear the consequences and penalties that society will impose for drug use by making

it clear that the costs will outweigh whatever temporary benefits drugs can provide. . . . In short, young people and adults alike must be consistently confronted with the same message: drugs are wrong, they are harmful, and their use will bring certain consequences. (pp. 47–48)

Comments and Discussion Questions

1. We know that numerous drug abusers are fully aware of the health hazards and illegality of abusing drugs but nonetheless continue to do so. How does the statement above propose that we deal with such individuals?
2. Do you think that people who are dependent on a particular drug will come to realize that drug abuse is not worth the penalty it risks? Why or why not? Given that, would this national drug control strategy work?

Excerpt 2

When such schools [effective inner-city schools] teach that using drugs is wrong, students pay attention. (p. 50)

Comments and Discussion Questions

1. Inner-city school children and teen-agers often view school officials as not being a part of the same subculture. Further, peer groups tend to teach that "school officials represent and are a part of the adult world." Given this, can you propose a method to teach school children and teen-agers to believe school officials when they say that drug use is wrong? Develop a plan to tackle this problem.

Excerpt 3

Anne Arundel's drug policy [Anne Arundel County, Maryland, where a school system's strict drug policies have led to a dramatic drop in the use of drugs] is simple and straightforward. Any student caught selling or distributing drugs is immediately expelled. When a student is caught using or possessing drugs, the school notifies the police, calls his [or her] parents, and suspends him [or her] for one to five school days. (p. 50)

Comments and Discussion Questions

1. Drug use and drug peddling are a daily occurrence in an alarming number of schools. How would you deal with students selling drugs in such schools? Would you expel every offender? Isn't the punishment of expulsion or suspension what some drug-abusing students want? Also, there are laws mandating compulsory education up to age 16. What would you do with a 14-year-old drug pusher?

2. Drug abusers' parents are to be notified. How would you deal with a student who is from a dysfunctional family and never had responsible parents? What special needs do such students have?

Excerpt 4

The thirteen million students at our institutions of higher learning should know, just as all other students should know, that society will not tolerate the use of drugs. But too many colleges and universities have remained diffident when it comes to drugs. Most colleges pay lip service to the war on drugs, but only a handful have institution policies comparable to Anne Arundel County's. Rarely has a college president sent letters to all incoming freshmen saying "Drugs will not be tolerated on this campus." (p. 52)

Comments and Discussion Questions

1. Do you think your college or university only pays "lip service to the war on drugs"? How could your college or university be more effective in making students know that "society will not tolerate the use of drugs"? Develop a strategy that will make more students realize that drug abuse is deviant behavior and thus frowned upon by society.

2. How many drug-abusing college students are oblivious to the "war on drugs"? Why are some people not willing to support the laws against the use of illicit drugs?

3. What drug policy does your college or university have? Interview college officials responsible for student conduct to learn about your institution's drug policy.

Excerpt 5

Those adult professionals who enjoy positions of special trust, respect, and responsibility in the community must take a clear stand on drug use. The national organizations that represent doctors, lawyers, school teachers and college professors, sports figures, police, and other professionals should set firm, no-use policies, and should announce clear sanctions for violators. (p. 55)

Comments and Discussion Questions

1. If your professor spoke out against drug abuse, would drug-abusing students take heed? Would anyone in particular be able to influence these students?

2. Recall that, in Chapter 2, we reviewed drug use among certain professionals, namely, medical personnel and athletes. What kind of role models would these professionals be?

Excerpt 6

There are indications that all of the negative attention drugs have been getting in the media may be paying off. According to the University of Michigan's annual survey, the percentage of high school seniors who perceived a "great risk" in smoking marijuana rose from 35 to 77 percent between 1978 and 1988. More recently, between 1986 and 1988 the percentage who disapproved of using cocaine increased from 82 to 89 percent. (p. 55)

Comments and Discussion Questions

1. The results cited in the excerpt above are accurate, but, according to most social scientists, the reasons given are inaccurate. Refer to the box on page 425, and find out why. Why do you think fewer people are abusing drugs?

PREVENTION

Prevention pertains to avoiding and preventing substance abuse. It entails *intervention*, or stepping in and interfering with drug abuse. There are three types of prevention: primary, secondary, and tertiary. The differences among these types of prevention are summarized in Table 15-1.

TABLE 15-1 Differences among primary, secondary, and tertiary drug abuse and addiction prevention

Timing	Activities	Terminology
Before abuse	Education Information Alternatives Personal and social growth	Primary prevention
During early stages of abuse	Crisis intervention Early diagnosis Crisis monitoring Referral	Secondary prevention
During later stages of abuse	Treatment Institutionalization Maintenance Detoxification	Tertiary prevention

Source: J. D. Swisher, "Prevention Issues." In *Handbook on Drug Abuse*, edited by R. L. DuPont, A. Goldstein, and J. O'Donnell (Washington, D.C.: NIDA, 1979).

Primary prevention, defined as "persuasion against the abuse of a particular drug," seeks to avoid drug abuse. The "Just Say No" strategy discussed earlier is a case in point. The idea of primary prevention is complex and may include alternatives to drugs, personal and social growth strategies, mental health promotion, and individual motivation to reach a high level of functioning. Theoretically, this will prevent problems associated with drug abuse from occurring.

primary prevention
using persuasion to dissuade someone from use of a particular drug

Secondary prevention entails using immediate intervention once drug abuse has begun. Fines and incarceration are examples of secondary prevention measures for someone caught using marijuana. The goal of secondary prevention is to warn that continued drug abuse will lead to more serious consequences.

secondary prevention
using immediate intervention once drug use has begun

Tertiary prevention helps individuals to stop abusing drugs either immediately prior to addiction or in its early stages. Tertiary prevention is designed to help those who are already fairly dependent cease drug use.

tertiary prevention
helping an individual to stop using drugs either immediately, before, or in the early stages of addiction

PREVENTION MODELS

There are many models of drug abuse prevention. We will briefly discuss the three that are considered most important: (1) the neurochemical disorder model; (2) the social science or sociocultural model; and (3) the psychological model.

THE NEUROCHEMICAL DISORDER MODEL According to this model, drug abuse is explained as a neurochemical craving. For example, addiction to opiate narcotics results from a lack of endor-

For You to Consider...

Suggestions for Making Drug Education Programs More Effective

1. *Practice deliberate planning*—Begin by matching imagined needs with real needs. Make a thorough assessment of drug information needed and problems associated with drug use. Program content should be based on this careful assessment.

2. *Review the previous history*—Don't assume that people who have been exposed to previous educational campaigns have forgotten all of what they learned. Start by considering the amount and the kind of information people have already been exposed to. If they have experience with drug education, what was successful in previous campaigns?

3. *Establish links between the messages conveyed and learned and other aspects of students' life experiences*—Involve students, teachers, administrators, and even school janitors in the drug education program. Be aware that drug use comes from many sources and that students are involved in many relationships. The drug education program must involve parents and guardians as well as the wider community.

4. *Effectively promote programs*—The information you have to convey must reach important voters and decision makers in the community. The information has to be disseminated effectively to a wide audience.

5. *Allocate resources properly*—Be mindful that, unless drug use and abuse has become a community-wide burning issue, people will tend to be interested in the drug campaign initially but be quick to lose interest. If the drug education program is to take place in schools, for example, make certain that the amounts of curriculum time and staffing are adequate and can be sustained throughout the program's duration.

6. *Evaluate constantly*—Is the program effective for the target audience? Are the goals conveyed and understood by the target population? What are the positive and negative outcomes of the strategy employed? Interview staff members of the program as well as the members of the target audience. Are they satisfied? What suggestions do they have for improving the program? These are very important questions. Their answers will reveal if the drug education program is meeting its goals (U.S. Department of Education 1992).

---

phins (Leventhal 1988). Most of the neurochemical theories of opiate addiction state that a certain percentage of the population is born with a deficiency of endorphins in the brain. Consequently, these endorphin-deprived individuals feel emotional pain more than others and as a result crave substances such as heroin and morphine to diminish the pain.

THE SOCIAL SCIENCE OR SOCIOCULTURAL MODEL This model states that drug use is culturally ingrained in society, and if it is to be curtailed, policy makers must look at the culture's values and attitudes toward drug use. Consider alcohol consumption. According to this model, drinking should be viewed as a part of social ritual rather than as an activity by itself. For instance, at "happy hour," alcohol consumption is the central activity and a primary purpose for attending the event. The sociocultural model would be critical of this event and any other in which large amounts of alcohol are consumed, particularly when no food is offered. The model also condemns making alcohol consumption a regular part of meaningful events such as celebrations of job promotions, baptisms, barmitzvahs, weddings, and anniversaries. In short, the social science model proposes that, when alcohol is integrated with other social activities, drinking is promoted and considered acceptable.

THE PSYCHOLOGICAL MODEL   Approximately 10% of drug users are addicted to the drugs they consume. Studies show that alcohol abusers suffer more depression than nonabusers (Kennedy et al. 1987). Furthermore, psychologists identify **antisocial personalities** who display callous, cold, and dogmatic characteristics and **borderline personalities** who exhibit wide mood swings and have very intense emotional outbursts. These two types of personalities are likely to abuse drugs. According to this model, approaches to treating and preventing drug abuse must address the psychological state of the individual affected.

---

antisocial personalities
those characterized by callous, cold, and dogmatic traits

borderline personalities
those characterized by wide mood swings and intense emotional outbursts

---

THE ROLE OF SOCIAL AND PERSONAL DEVELOPMENT

In the past several years, most drug abuse prevention specialists have adopted the idea of emphasizing personal and social development as a method for preventing the harmful consequences of drug abuse. Three issues are primary:

1. Increased self-understanding and acceptance through activities such as values clarification, sensory awareness, and decision making
2. Improved interpersonal relations through activities such as communication training, peer counseling, and assertiveness training
3. Increased ability for meeting one's needs and accomplishing goals through social institutions such as the family, church, and community affiliations

Since 1989, the federal government has spent approximately $3 billion on funding new drug education and prevention programs under the Anti-Drug Abuse Acts of 1986 and 1988 ("Measuring" 1991, 5). Moreover, the U.S. federal government directs a diverse selection of programs that are useful in helping to prevent drug abuse. These programs range from treatment of delinquency to mental health activities to a wide range of activities developed by groups funded by the National Institute on Drug Abuse (NIDA). Drug information and referrals to social help agencies are several alternatives to drug abuse.

Presently, these programs do not have a major impact in primary prevention because of inconsistent funding, duplication of services, and recent cutbacks in federal spending.

The following assumptions should be behind all primary prevention programs (U.S. Department of Education 1992):

1. A reasonable goal for drug abuse prevention should be to educate people of all ages about responsible decision making regarding the use of all drugs.
2. Responsible decisions regarding personal use of drugs should result in fewer negative consequences for individuals.
3. The most effective approach to achieve the preceding goals would be a program that increases self-esteem, interpersonal skills, and participation in alternatives to drug use and involves parents.

Many local, state, and federal agencies have similar goals for dealing with other forms of problem behavior. What is needed is a unified, governmental effort that would result in funding of the development, implementation, and evaluation of a multidimensional prevention effort.

NIDA and several individual researchers have evaluated the multitude of drug abuse prevention programs in the United States. The general conclusions of these studies are:

1. Very few programs have demonstrated clear success or have been adequate in evaluating themselves.
2. The relationships among information about drugs, attitudes toward use, and actual uses of drugs are unclear in these programs.

Some factors that are key to developing successful programs include the following:

1. *Coordinating prevention at different levels*—Successful programs involve families, schools, and communities. In most cases, these efforts are not coordinated.

2. *Integrating ongoing activities of schools, families, and community organizations*—Superficial introduction of drug prevention strategies has limited effects. For instance, door-to-door distribution of literature to households, inclass presentations of the harmful effects of drugs, and posting banners and slogans warning of the consequences of drug abuse in communities are not successful methods. Instead, programs that are integrated into neighborhood clubs, organizations, and church activities are more likely to have a long-term impact on preventing drug use.

3. *Including personal autobiographical and social experience accounts of former drug abusers when distributing drug information*—Recipients of drug prevention information should be given real-life accounts of use, abuse, despair, and successful drug rehabilitation. Just getting drug information alone has little impact, either initially or over the long term.

Finally, when drug prevention programs are not well received, part of the reason may be the false impression on which these programs have been based. Many people still believe that only an abnormal minority abuses drugs. The truth is that all segments of the population use psychoactive drugs. Not everyone abuses what are considered illegal drugs; many people abuse legal drugs.

T h i n k   A b o u t   I t . . .

1. Table 15-1 cites differences among primary, secondary, and tertiary drug abuse and addiction. Redesign this table by listing the kind of prevention techniques you would use before abuse begins, during the early stages of abuse, and during the later stages of abuse.

2. Your younger sister or brother tells you that some of his or her friends have started abusing drugs. What preventive suggestions would you offer if your advice was sought?

3. How could you improve the suggestions for making drug education programs more effective (see the box on p. 434)?

ALTERNATIVES TO DRUGS

It has been suggested that people have an innate need to alter their conscious state. This belief is based on the observation that, as part of their normal play, preschoolers deliberately whirl themselves dizzy and even momentarily choke each other to lose consciousness (see Wilson and Wilson 1975, 26). Some young children progress to discovering and using chemicals (such as sniffing shoe polish or gasoline) to alter consciousness and learn to be very secretive about this behavior. They learn to be circumspect or come to feel guilty and repress the desire to alter consciousness when adults catch them in these activities.

If this desire to alter the state of consciousness is inherent in human beings, then the use of psychoactive drugs, legally or illegally, in adulthood is natural. Drug abuse is thus a logical continuation of a developmental sequence that goes back to early childhood (Carroll 1977; Weil 1972).

Other researchers argue that, even if there is an innate desire to alter consciousness, why do only some and not all people progress to abusing chemical substances? It appears that people who do not abuse psychoactive drugs have found positive alternatives to altering consciousness. They feel no need to take chemical substances for this purpose. Involvement in such activities as Boy Scouts and Girl Scouts, youth sports teams, music groups, and the YMCA and YWCA are examples of such alternatives.

This is known as the **alternatives approach.** Workers in the drug abuse field tend to agree on its effectiveness. They note that young exabusers

---

alternatives approach
one emphasizing the exploration of positive alternatives to drug abuse, based on replacing the pleasurable feelings gained from drug abuse with involvement in social and educational activities

of common illicit drugs are more likely to stop when they gain satisfaction from exploring positive alternatives rather than from a fear of consequent harm. The alternatives approach assumes the following (Cohen 1971):

1. People abuse drugs voluntarily to fill a need or basic drive.
2. Most people abuse drugs for negative reasons. They may be dealing with negative feelings or situations, such as relieving boredom, anxiety, depression, tension, or other unpleasant emotional and psychological states. They may be rebelling against authority, trying to escape feelings of loneliness or inadequacy, or trying to be accepted by peers. Peer pressure is extremely important as an inducing force.
3. Some people who abuse drugs believe the experience is positive. They may feel enhancement of sensual experiences or listening to music, achieve altered states of consciousness, or simply experience a sense of adventure. Some people may want to ex-plore their own consciousness and reasons for being.

Whether the reasons for drug use are positive or negative, the effects sought can be achieved through alternative, nondrug means. Such means are preferable to drug use and more constructive because the person is not relying on a psychoactive substance for satisfaction; rather, he or she is finding satisfaction based on personal achievements. Ideally, this should lead to a lifetime of self-satisfaction.

Table 15-2 lists various types of experiences, the motives for such experiences, the probable drugs of abuse that are associated, and alternatives to these drugs. As shown in the table, any constructive activity can be considered an alternative to drug abuse. For example, you can see that a young person who needs an outlet for increased physical energy might respond better to dance and movement training or a project in preventive medicine than work on ecological projects.

In a large alternatives program in Idaho, the following activities were planned during one

TABLE 15-2 Experiences, motives, and possible alternatives for a drug abuser

Experience	Corresponding Motives	Drugs Abused	Possible Alternatives
Physical	Desire for physical well-being: physical relaxation, relief from sickness, desire for more energy	Alcohol, sedative-hypnotics, stimulants, marijuana	Athletics, dance, exercise, hiking, diet, carpentry, outdoor work, swimming, hatha yoga
Sensory	Desire to magnify sensorium: sound, touch, taste, need for sensual/sexual stimulation	Hallucinogens, marijuana, alcohol	Sensory awareness training, sky diving, experiencing sensory beauty of nature, scuba diving
Emotional	Relief from psychological pain: attempt to resolve personal problems, relief from bad mood, escape from anxiety, desire for emotional insight, liberation of feeling and emotional relaxation	Narcotics, alcohol, barbiturates, sedative-hypnotics	Competent individual counseling, well-run group therapy, instruction in psychology of personal development

(continued)

TABLE 15-2   Experiences, motives, and possible alternatives for a drug abuser *(continued)*

Experience	Corresponding Motives	Drugs Abused	Possible Alternatives
Interpersonal	To gain peer acceptance, break through interpersonal barriers, "communicate"; defiance of authority figures	Any, especially alcohol, marijuana	Expertly managed sensitivity and encounter groups, well-run group therapy, instruction in social customs, confidence training, emphasis on assisting others—for example, YMCA or YWCA volunteer
Social	To promote social change, find identifiable subculture, tune out intolerable environmental conditions—for example, poverty	Marijuana, psychedelics	Social service community action in positive social change; helping the poor, aged, infirm, young; tutoring handicapped; ecology action; YMCA or YWCA Big Brother/Sister programs
Political	To promote political change (out of desperation with the social-political order) and to identify with antiestablish-ment subgroup	Marijuana, psychedelics	Political service, lobbying for nonpartisan projects—for example, Common Cause; field work with politicians and public officials
Intellectual	To escape boredom, out of intellectual curiosity, to solve cognitive problems, gain new understanding in the world of ideas, research one's own awareness	Stimulants, sometimes psychedelics	Intellectual excitement through reading, debate, and discussion; creative games and puzzles; self-hypnosis; training in concentration
Creative-aesthetic	To improve creative performance, enhance enjoyment of art already produced—for example, music; enjoy imaginative mental productions	Marijuana, stimulants, psychedelics	Nongraded instruction in producing and/or appreciating art, music, drama, and creative hobbies
Philosophical	To discover meaningful values, find meaning in life, help establish personal identity, organize a belief structure	Psychedelics, marijuana, stimulants	Discussions, seminars, courses on ethics, the nature of reality, relevant philosophical literature; explorations of value systems
Spiritual-mystical	To transcend orthodox religion, develop spiritual insights, reach higher levels of consciousness, augment yogic practices, take a spiritual shortcut	Psychedelics, marijuana	Exposure to nonchemical methods of spiritual development; study of world religions, mysticism, meditation, yogic techniques

Source: A. Y. Cohen, *Alternatives to Drug Abuse: Steps Toward Prevention*, NIDA Research Monograph no. 14 (Washington, D.C.: NIDA, 1973).

month: arts and crafts, karate, reforestation, back-packing, a Humane Society dog show, horseback riding, artwork for posters for various programs, astrology, camping, and volunteering in a local hospital. In southeastern Ohio, teen-agers from nine area high schools researched the history of coal mining and the canal in a three-county area. Publication of their report, which they produced themselves as part of the Youth Alternatives Program, was funded by a grant from the National Endowment for the Humanities. The students were justifiably proud of a job well done and clearly got a good deal of pleasure from it as well as learning some local history.

Another example is part-time job placement. This is extremely important as one of the alternative approaches. When a first- or second-year high school student is employed on a part-time basis and begins to earn money, the probability of drug abuse is lessened because less recreation time is available. Further, the extra income helps build feelings of self-worth and confidence.

Most communities offer a range of youth activities through various organizations. The problem is that the young people who readily participate in these organizations are often those who are already at low risk of becoming drug abusers. In short, they are more likely to have developed self-confidence and self-esteem, which is a factor in their not abusing drugs. Traditional organizations have few ways of reaching out to the high-risk youth who need their help. This is the irony of the alternatives approach: Much of what's needed is already in place, but it's not reaching those who need it the most. An effective drug abuse prevention program requires a leader who has community commitment to back him or her and the organizational skills to get high-risk young people involved.

NONTRADITIONAL PREVENTION METHODS

Information about non-Western methods for preventing drug abuse is important and necessary for comprehensive coverage of this topic. Various systems of mind control have been used for thousands

of years in other cultures to find peace and inner contentment, without using chemicals.

Many people are not aware that all of us have the ability to modify our conscious state of mind. Sleeping, daydreaming, meditation, anesthesia, and psychoses are examples of altered states of consciousness. The human brain is capable of processing millions of pieces (or bits) of information each minute, yet much of this processing is relegated to the unconscious. Under the influence of stress, drugs, and internal and external psychological factors, the input may be modified and the brain's interpretation may be changed. This is called *altering the conscious state*. Levels of stimulation above or below the normal range can cause such modifications and may be useful for preventing or treating drug abuse.

Examples of ways whereby states of consciousness can be altered include:

1. *Reducing sensory input*—Certain procedures or substances are able to reduce stimulation or motor activity, such as solitary confinement, floating on warm water in a darkened chamber, extreme muscle relaxation, biofeedback inducing an increase in alpha or theta brain wave rhythms, meditation, and use of some depressant drugs.

2. *Increasing sensory input*—Other procedures or substances increase sensory input, including religious ceremonies (revival meetings), long periods of tension (truck driving, flying, or sentry duty, video games, long-distance running), and hallucinogen and stimulant drugs.

3. *Modifying body chemistry*—Such modification influences input and interpretation. Causes include dehydration, fever, sleep deprivation, anesthesia, modification of acid-base balance in the blood (for example, by hyperventilation), hypoglycemia, and drugs such as hallucinogens, depressants, and stimulants.

Think About It...

1. Imagine that you are a moderator between two groups. One group believes that addiction results from a neurochemical disorder, while the second group believes that addiction is better explained socioculturally and psychologically.

How would you reconcile the differences and produce a unified perspective?

2. What alternatives to drugs would you suggest to an older-adolescent group of former addicts?

TREATMENT

BEGINNINGS AND GOALS

As stated earlier, drug abuse is considered an illness. More specifically, it may be viewed as either a medical or psychological problem. The medical model views drug abuse as a biological condition that is largely uncontrollable. The user is perceived as "sick" and thus irrational about continued drug use. The psychological perspective is that drug abuse is a disease and that treatment is the method for curing the disease.

In 1966, the federal government passed the Narcotic Addict Rehabilitation Act (NARA), which established national rules for admission to treatment and rehabilitation at federal centers. Addicts were given the opportunity to have their sentences reduced or charges dismissed if they would go for treatment.

In June 1971, the first drug treatment program, the Special Action Office for Drug Abuse Prevention (SAODAP), was established. One of the roles of this office was to provide additional support for efforts to control the availability of illicit drugs. The need for drug prevention programs had become critical. For instance, widespread use of heroin and other drugs by American servicepeople in Vietnam prompted President Nixon to direct the Secretary of Defense to reduce penalties for drug use, such that it would no longer be a court-martial offense. In 1972, the Drug Abuse Office and Treatment Act provided financial backing for treatment programs.

The goal of any treatment program is to stop the abuser from taking drugs. An integral step is stabilizing the abuser's personal life and helping him or her to feel like a productive member of society.

Over the past 20 years or more that active treatment programs have been in existence, it has been difficult to determine their effectiveness. Part of the problem has been that their goals are unclear. Should the goal be to get the drug abuser completely off drugs? Should the goal be to get the exabuser to hold a job? How long should a person be off drugs for the treatment to be deemed a success?

There are no easy answers. If someone gets off one drug completely, he or she must not abuse other drugs as substitutes. If the criteria is to hold a job, once the job is found, the drug abuser may slide back into old habits. And if an abuser is off drugs for a few years, there is still the possibility of regression. Any of these scenarios thwarts successful treatment outcomes.

A range of possible benefits and adverse effects can be attributed to treatment programs. To evaluate a given program's success, a variety of measuring devices should be employed. To base the evaluation solely on success or failure rates is not productive in that it ignores how these measures are achieved.

The success of a treatment program should be based on many factors. Namely, consider whether the individual has been able to accomplish the following:

Abstinence from using illegal drugs
Abstinence from using all addicting drugs
Achieving stabilization on a maintenance
    drug such as methadone
Holding down a job
Decrease in criminal conduct
The ability to support a family
Improved physical and mental health
Accomplishing any or all of these could indicate partial success (DeLong 1972;
    U.S. Department of Health and Human Services 1991).

TREATMENT SETTINGS

A number of treatment settings are used for alleviating or eliminating addiction. The level of treatment provided at these types of facilities is based on the severity of addiction and physiological and psychological symptoms.

1. *Inhospital programs*—Intense treatment is provided within an acute care hospital program. *Acute*

care refers to serious or critical care. In these settings, drug dependent patients are continually observed and given numerous diagnostic tests, efficiently stabilized, medically supervised and made aware of their particular problem, and provided with information about drug addiction through intensive counseling.

2. *Residential care*—These programs focus on education and therapy, which leads to rehabilitation. This type of care is provided 24 hours per day. While addicted patients are supervised by fewer medically trained staff members than in inhospital care programs, more counselors and mental health personnel are available. Other varieties of residential care include: (a) community hospital-based programs; (b) free-standing facilities in nonhospital settings; (c) therapeutic communities, which involve intense interaction and often confrontational dialogue in groups with other addicts (see later in the chapter); (d) "halfway houses," or transition settings between 24-hour-a-day programs and independent living; and (e) detoxification centers, where short-term stay units are usually maintained by charity organizations and provide necessary shelter, clothing, food, and medical needs.

3. *Day hospitals and intensive outpatient services*—Care is usually provided three or four hours per day for patients who need additional structure while living independently. Self-help groups, seminars, and individual and group therapy are some of the programs found in day hospitals or intensive outpatient services.

Treatment settings also can be selective or nonselective. *Selective* programs screen prospective clients and accept only those whom they judge are likely to benefit. *Nonselective* programs accept nearly all people with drug dependence problems who apply or who are sent there, except for psychotics and violent types.

Finally, treatment settings are either voluntary or involuntary. Practically all drug treatment involves some degree of coercion, if only from family or employer. However, *involuntary* usually refers to a legal requirement or a criteria for holding onto a job or staying out of jail. In either case,

the addict is required to enter some form of treatment and remain in it for some time, usually until he or she can demonstrate progress.

We will discuss the following major treatment approaches: (1) medical, (2) psychological and psychotherapeutic, (3) social, (4) behavioral, and (5) innovative. We will also consider the effectiveness of some of these treatments.

MEDICAL TREATMENTS   There are a variety of medical approaches to drug treatment.

Detoxification and Abstinence Programs. When isolated from other treatment methods, detoxification does not have a high long-term success rate. One positive aspect is that, even if addicts don't stay off drugs, their habit is often reduced, thus lessening the need to financially support drug use. For many addicts, this is a step toward rehabilitation.

The goals and procedures of detoxification programs vary greatly. They may be residential—where the patient lives in a hospital, clinic, or therapeutic community—or ambulatory, where the addict is treated on an outpatient basis with professional help and sometimes methadone or other support drugs. Some outpatient settings require daily attendance and vary according to one-on-one or group therapy sessions.

Interestingly, many heroin detoxification programs do not use drugs for support. Some use methadone maintenance and a variety of drug backups, such as sedatives.

Other abstinence programs treat drug dependence by reducing intake to zero and simultaneously giving the addict mental and psychological assistance during withdrawal. Opiate addicts can be helped through the withdrawal period in 5 to 10 days. This approach is usually not used for alcohol or barbiturate dependencies because withdrawal from heavy depressant dependence can be life threatening. Instead, these addicts are stabilized on a long-acting depressant and withdrawn gradually.

Maintenance Programs. Maintenance programs are based on the principle that past treatment programs have not been successful, so "incurable" addicts should be able to register and receive drugs, such as narcotics, under supervision. Proponents of these programs contend that many addicts are forced into a life of crime to support their habits but would become law-abiding and useful citizens if they received narcotics (usually a less euphoric type like methadone) legally. Moreover, it's argued, the illicit narcotics trade would be eliminated due to the loss of these customers. Opponents of maintenance programs say that there are sufficient treatment programs to cure many addicts and that providing addicts with substitute narcotics is not solving the basic problem causing drug dependence.

The concept of maintenance on a **noneuphoric opiate** is now widely accepted in the United States as one way help treat drug abusers.

---

noneuphoric opiate

a drug or drugs used in maintenance programs that satisfies the craving but does not produce the euphoric effect; e.g., methadone

---

Morphine Maintenance. After the Harrison Narcotics Act was passed in 1914, between 200,000 and 300,000 opiate addicts were no longer able to obtain drugs legally except through physicians. After 1918, more than 40 morphine maintenance clinics opened. However, public opinion was against maintenance because it was perceived as an approval of narcotic use, and the last clinic closed in 1923. The narcotics division of the federal government maintained a very tough attitude toward physicians who advocated maintenance and prescribed opiates for their patients. By 1938, approximately 25,000 doctors had been arrested for dispensing narcotics, and of these, approximately 5,000 went to jail (DeLong 1972).

Methadone Maintenance. Vincent Dole and Marie Nyswander were the first doctors to use the synthetic narcotic methadone in a rehabilitation program with heroin addicts in the mid-1960s. As of 1987, an estimated 70,000 to 75,000 addicts were on methadone maintenance. The drug is used to alleviate narcotic craving and to prevent the occurrence of withdrawal symptoms. The advantages of methadone over other forms of maintenance therapy are:

1. It can be administered orally.
2. It acts in the body for 24 to 36 hours, compared to heroin's action of 4 to 8 hours.
3. It causes no serious side effects at maintenance doses.
4. At sufficient dose levels, methadone will almost completely block the effects of heroin.
5. When taken orally, it does not produce substantial euphoric effects.

Disadvantages of methadone maintenance include:

1. The person taking it may develop dependence.
2. It will not prevent the addict from taking other drugs that may interfere with treatment and rehabilitation. To guard against the use of other drugs, some clinics require urine samples periodically during treatment.

Once stabilized on methadone, the addict faces a crucial period of adjustment. Once devoted to maintaining a heroin habit, 24 hours a day, 365 days a year, the addict must be transformed into a self-supporting, socially acceptable person. Methadone maintenance establishes the potential for such a change, but it is the person's motivation and capabilities that determine the success of the rehabilitation effort. A range of medical, psychiatric, social, and vocational services are usually available during this phase of treatment.

Many criticisms have been levied against the use of methadone, especially from proponents of therapeutic communities like Synanon, Narco, Daytop Village, Odyssey House, and others. Some critics have said that giving methadone to a heroin addict is like switching an alcoholic from bourbon to wine.

Methadone is not the ideal solution by any means. Former heroin addicts who had large habits may have to be maintained indefinitely on methadone. They are likely to relapse to heroin use if detoxified from methadone. They may never be rehabilitated in the conventional sense because their backgrounds are such that they never had a so-called normal life to begin with. To create normalcy for these people may be too much to expect.

Overall, maintenance programs provide a steady amount of a noneuphoric drug that satisfies the craving, prevents withdrawal, and eliminates the constant concern for money in order to support the habit. For a certain percentage of addicts, maintenance programs eliminate or severely curtail the amount of crime committed for supporting the drug habit.

On the other hand, detoxification from methadone is possible for methadone maintenance patients who were not addicted to heroin for a long period and who did not have an extensive background of criminal activity. Detoxification is not an automatic process in methadone maintenance. Of those who completed one detoxification program, as many as 35% were narcotic free and doing well up to six years later (Sells 1979).

Use of the nonopiate drug clonidine may help those who wish to stop taking methadone. Clonidine suppresses the signs and symptoms of opiate withdrawal and reduces the anxiety and irritability experienced by patients during the difficult withdrawal step (Gold et al. 1980).

The new long-acting methadone analog levo-alpha-acetylmethadol (LAAM) need only be taken three times a week and is being used experimentally in some programs. Initially, addicts participate daily in intensive counseling. Later in the program, they come in for the maintenance drug and follow-up treatment less frequently. Addicts may be treated with daily methadone first to increase the probability that they will at least attend counseling sessions and then be switched to LAAM when they reach an appropriate point in the program. Currently, LAAM is an investigational drug and has not been approved by the Food and Drug Administration (FDA) for general clinical use.

Heroin Maintenance. Great Britain set up heroin clinics to treat addicts in the early 1970s, citing both humanitarian and economic reasons. It was argued that prescription heroin for addicts would save lives, eliminate illicit narcotics dealing, and clean up the crime associated with the addict's need for money to buy heroin.

At the beginning, problems resulted due to lax controls, and heroin from the program was being sold on the "street." Eventually, better controls were established. Also, methadone began to be used in many clinics to treat heroin abuse. It was estimated that there were less than 6,000 opiate addicts in Great Britain in 1975 (Trebach 1982), with no appreciable increase by 1980.

Some have advocated the legal use of heroin in comparable maintenance programs in the United States. It is highly unlikely that this will be implemented, however, because methadone does not produce the euphoria and has other advantages over heroin. What's more, heroin use in the United States has an unsavory history.

Opiate Antagonists. Recall from Chapter 5 that an *antagonist* is a compound that suppresses the actions of a drug. Narcotic antagonists have properties that make them important tools in the clinical treatment of narcotic drug dependence. For instance, they counteract the central nervous system depressant effects in opioid drug overdoses.

Antagonists were developed as a byproduct of research in analgesics. Scientists were interested in dissociating the dependence-producing properties and necessary pain-relieving properties of substances that could replace morphine. This led to the development of nalorphine, the first specific opiate antagonist. Its short duration of action and frequent unpleasant side effects limited its clinical usefulness, but its properties stimulated further research on this class of drugs (Archer 1981).

Cyclazocine was the next important antagonist developed. It has a longer duration of action than nalorphine; however, it also induces some unpleasant side effects, such as sedation, visual distortions, and racing thoughts. Tolerance to the side effects develops if the dose is increased gradually over several weeks. Because of these psychotomimetic side effects, cyclazocine is not used much today.

Naloxone is a pure antagonist without analgesic properties. It does not have the unpleasant side effects that nalorphine and cyclazocine have, but it has a shorter duration of action and is less active if taken orally than desired for narcotic antagonist treatment programs. Nevertheless, it is valuable in treating toxic or near-lethal doses of narcotics. (It is five to eight times more antagonistic than nalorphine.) This drug blocks narcotics from binding the opiate receptors in the brain, thus relieving depression of breathing and heartbeat.

Naltrexone is a chemical modification of naloxone that was synthesized to find a longer-acting, more potent antagonist. It has low toxicity with few side effects, and a single dose provides an effective opiate blockade for up to 72 hours. Taking naltrexone three times a week is sufficient to maintain a fairly high level of opioid blockade. In 1971, Congress mandated a large-scale increase in research on narcotic antagonistic drugs. Naltrexone seems to be the best antagonistic developed at this point. It has been used widely in experimental narcotic antagonist treatment programs (Archer 1981).

Clinical tests with heroin addicts in treatment have shown that addicts placed on naltrexone will try heroin or methadone once or twice, early in treatment, and then stop. Addicts on placebos, on the other hand, continued to use illicit methadone or heroin sporadically. The naltrexone group also reported significantly less craving for heroin than the placebo group (Hopkins 1973).

Naltrexone is not a complete treatment (Ginzburg 1986). It is best suited to adolescent heroin users with relatively short drug experience, recently paroled prisoners who have been abstinent while incarcerated, and persons who have been on methadone maintenance and wish to get off but are afraid of relapsing to heroin. Unless some means of enforcing compliance can be established, such as requiring urine samples, or unless the person is highly motivated, narcotic antagonist treatment programs do not work well. Frankly, the narcotic antagonist drug does nothing positive for the user. It simply blocks the effects of heroin or methadone if the person takes these drugs up to three days after his or her last dose of naltrexone (Renault 1981).

As mentioned in Chapter 8, clonidine (Catapres) is useful in treating opiate-dependent persons during the difficult withdrawal stages (Ginzburg 1986). Studies thus far show the value of this drug for withdrawal from heroin, morphine, codeine, and methadone. Clonidine is not addictive and does not cause euphoria, but it does block cravings for drugs. It also makes the person feel better compared to the depression experienced by addicts using other methods of withdrawal.

PSYCHOLOGICAL AND PSYCHOTHERAPEUTIC APPROACHES Psychological approaches are rooted in the premise that certain types of personalities are more prone to addiction. Namely, why do approximately 10% of all drug users become addicted? Recent research indicates that drug-dependent persons are more likely to experience depression, which may be a factor (Kennedy et al. 1987).

Psychotherapeutic approaches assume that drug abusers are more likely to display antisocial personality disorders—such as coldness, aloofness, and adherence to dogmatic opinions—and that they are immature, dependent, and have difficulty in forming intimate social relationships. The general belief is that drug abuse is a symptom of deeper personality conflicts.

Within the last 20 years, psychological approaches have lost popularity. Critics charge that their success rates are low and that therapy is very time consuming and expensive, generally involving weekly hour-long sessions with a therapist over many years.

SOCIAL APPROACHES Social interactions and pressures clearly play a very important role in explaining drug use. Social approaches emphasize the lack of positive role models, peer influence, depressed economic conditions, and malfunctioning families as the root of drug abuse. Prevention strategies include providing positive role models, using peer intervention, improving economic conditions by increasing employment opportunities, and family counseling. Social workers are identified as the primary professionals when social approaches are implemented.

Alcoholics Anonymous (AA). Founded in the mid-1930s, AA is now an international organ-

For You to Consider...

AA's Twelve Steps for Recovery

1. We admitted we were powerless over alcohol—that our lives had become unmanageable.
2. Came to believe that a Power greater than ourselves could restore us to sanity.
3. Made a decision to turn our will and our lives over to the care of God *as we understood Him.*
4. Made a searching and fearless moral inventory of ourselves.
5. Admitted to God, to ourselves, and to another human being the exact nature of our wrongs.
6. Were entirely ready to have God remove all these defects of character.
7. Humbly asked Him to remove our shortcomings.
8. Made a list of all persons we had harmed, and became willing to make amends to them all.
9. Made direct amends to such people wherever possible, except when to do so would injure them or others.
10. Continued to take personal inventory and when we were wrong promptly admitted it.
11. Sought through prayer and meditation to improve our conscious contact with God *as we understood Him,* praying only for knowledge of His will for us and the power to carry that out.
12. Having had a spiritual awakening as the result of these steps, we tried to carry this message to alcoholics, and to practice these principles in all our affairs.

Source: Alcoholics Anonymous World Services, Inc., *Alcoholics Anonymous: The Story of How Many Thousands of Men and Women Have Recovered from Alcoholism,* 3rd ed. (New York: AA, 1976), 59–60.

Permission to reprint this material does not mean that AA has reviewed or approved the contents of this chapter, nor that AA agrees with the views expressed herein. AA is a program of recovery from alcoholism—use of the Twelve Steps in connection with programs and activities which are patterned after AA, but which address other problems, does not imply otherwise.

ization. The desire to stop drinking is the sole criterion required to join. The original founders of AA were strongly influenced by a religious movement known as the Oxford Groups and the psychoanalyst Carl Jung. The "Twelve Steps for Recovery" espoused by AA are cited in the adjacent box.

Today, this self-help group has many professional and nonprofessional members with drinking problems. (*Self-help groups* are defined as groups not employing professionals to run the group.) The strength of AA's program as a treatment method lies in its loose organizational structure and strong interpersonal relationships. In fact, AA's success was so renowned that it led to the establishment of NA, Narcotics Anonymous, to help other drug abusers help themselves.

How successful is the AA program? This is a difficult assessment, for three reasons:

1. AA insists on anonymity; it does not reveal names of members.
2. Membership is strictly voluntary. Those who want to join become members when they vow to give up drinking. Controlled studies are impossible.
3. Members are a homogeneous group. They tend to be middle class and socially conservative.

It appears that real problem drinkers rarely belong to AA, which may in part be responsible for the group's high success rate. Members are not typically hard-core alcohol addicts. Regardless, AA has been and continues to be a very important method for treating many recovering alcoholics.

Therapeutic Communities. Also known as **self-regulating communities,** therapeutic communities (TCs) operate on the premise that drug use is a symptom of an underlying character disorder or emotional immaturity (Klein and Miller

self-regulating communities
programs that advocate a complete change in lifestyle, such as complete abstinence from drugs, elimination of deviant behavior, and development of employable skills

1986). The main goal of TCs is a complete change in lifestyle: abstinence from drugs, elimination of criminal behavior, and development of employable skills, self-reliance, and personal honesty.

The first therapeutic community for drug addicts was Synanon, which was aimed at psychiatric patients. It was founded in Santa Monica, California, in 1958. Synanon was started by Charles E. Dederich, a former alcoholic, to treat alcoholics and was later expanded to include drug addicts. When drug addicts came into the program, the alcoholics left because they felt associating with addicts was degrading.

Many branches of Synanon were founded based on the same philosophy, for example, Daytop Village and Phoenix House. They have been used as models for a number of other programs, with modifications based on the circumstances in each community. TCs have had a major impact on drug abuse treatment.

As of 1990, there were over 400 residential therapeutic communities serving drug abusers, criminal offenders, and other socially dislocated persons. These programs are quite diverse, ranging in size from 35 to 500 beds, and they serve a variety of clients.

The TC program includes encounter group therapy, educational programs, job assignments within the community, and in the later stages, conventional jobs outside the community. The primary staff are former drug addicts who have been rehabilitated in TC programs. Most TCs use self-government and group pressures, instead of relying on a professional, therapeutic personnel.

The philosophy behind TCs is that only ex-addicts can truly understand and deal effectively with addicts. Some TCs also employ professionals with training in vocational guidance, education, medicine, and mental health who are paid or who may donate their services. Residents of the traditional TC stay at least 15 months before they return to the community. Several TCs have been experimenting with shorter resident times, ranging from 2 to 9 months, based on individual client needs and progress.

The rate of success in TCs is higher if the patient remains in the program more than 90 days. Findings indicate that narcotic addicts who were treated with either a therapeutic community approach or methadone maintenance had about a 25% chance of relapsing to daily narcotic use if they remained in treatment for more than 90 days (Bassin 1970). Relapse back to drug use was much higher when the length of stay was less than 90 days.

Most people who apply are admitted to TCs. Only obviously psychotic or violent individuals are rejected. Some people leave without completing the program for a variety of reasons:

1. They may not be ready to deal with the complete change in lifestyle demanded by the TC.
2. They may progress to a certain point and become bored or frustrated with the TC.
3. They may relapse and return to the TC at some later point.

Treatment should not be looked upon as a complete failure if the person relapses. Estimates of readmission to a TC or another form of treatment range from 30% to 60% (De Leon and Rosenthal 1979).

Family Therapy. Family therapy is based on the belief that drug abuse stems from family problems. When a drug user is involved in counseling with a family therapist, the entire family is brought in during sessions. Sometimes, even extended family members—such as uncles, aunts, and grandparents—are included. The strengths of the family system are also used to develop coping skills and teach tolerance.

BEHAVIORAL APPROACHES Behavioral approaches consist of operant or instrumental conditioning, counterconditioning (sensitization), biofeedback therapy, and contingency management techniques, as well as several alternative methods.

Operant or Instrumental Conditioning. This approach assumes that all behavior results from its consequences, or the rewards received when proper (acceptable) behavior is demonstrated. With regard to drug use and abuse, the belief is that the behavior is learned through **reinforcement**. The same type of conditioning that is believed to have caused the drug problem is also used to treat it. This involves rewarding appropriate behavior to change behavior.

---

reinforcement
any behavior that strengthens the likelihood that a behavior will be repeated

---

The addictive process is shaped by conditioned responses. Drugs shape behavior by their direct, pleasant effects (positive reinforcement, which produces primary psychological dependence) or by relieving withdrawal (negative reinforcement, which produces secondary psychological dependence). It has been observed that former addicts who were free of drugs often developed tearing and yawning (opiate withdrawal signs) when they discussed drugs in group therapy. Other research has shown that conditioned withdrawal responses can be produced in animals and in humans.

These conditioned withdrawal responses are thought to be caused in part by pairing pharmacological withdrawal with environmental cues. Eventually, the environmental stimuli, such as talking about drugs or showing pictures of drugs, could elicit a conditioned withdrawal. This would explain the reactions of former addicts (i.e., yawning or forming tears) when talking about drugs or when returning to the environment in which they had previously used drugs.

Not only do addicts develop drug craving during conditioned withdrawal, but they show actual physical signs of sickness. Some react to conditioning cues from the injection procedure alone and may even experience withdrawal relief when told they are getting an opiate, although they are actually getting a placebo. These people are sometimes called "needle freaks." When they find out the substance is a placebo, it no longer works.

Treatment methods have been developed based on our knowledge of conditioning in drug dependence (O'Brien and Ng 1979). Patients are taught how to alter the rewards derived from drug use. Often, the patient is taught how to replace or substitute drug use for behavior that elicits satisfaction or pleasure. Substituting a chemical "high" with the high experienced from intense physical exercise, such as long-distance running, is an example. Another behavioral method involves identifying and modifying conditions that create the craving for a particular drug.

Short-term goals involve eliminating or negating the reinforcing effects of drugs. Long-term goals center on eliminating drug use as an integral part of the patient's lifestyle and *reintegrating* the patient, returning him or her to a social situation where drugs are no longer an option. Such behavioral approaches have become very popular methods of treatment in the last five years.

Contingency Management Techniques. These techniques, based on operant or instrumental conditioning (discussed above), attempt to control behavior through a system of rewards, or schedules of reinforcement. One of the best known of these techniques is the *token economy system*, which has been used successfully to treat prisoners and mental patients. Through this system, the rewards and punishments in the addict's environment are identified and then manipulated to redirect his or her response. For example, subjects gain points if they perform certain tasks that are beneficial to the treatment program, such as participation in group therapy and educational programs, doing a project that benefits the group, or making a special contribution to the group. The accumulated points can be used to "buy" an early release or to get special privileges or other rewards. Addicts in such programs show greatly increased participation in therapeutic and educational activities (Pickens and Thompson 1984). They also report other socially desirable behaviors, such as improved communication and decreased hostility.

In an outpatient methadone program, it was found that "take-home" doses of methadone served as desired reinforcers. Attendance at counseling sessions increased markedly when take-home privileges were made contingent on attendance. In other programs, rewards are given if the participants' urine tests are negative for illicit drugs.

Contingency management techniques are most appropriate for structured treatment programs, such as methadone maintenance and inpatient settings. Comparisons of success rates with other techniques must still be made.

Counterconditioning (Sensitization). Counterconditioning procedures involve imagining scenes during therapy. As the patient develops a craving for drugs, he or she is asked to visualize, as clearly as possible, each link in the chain of events leading to drug taking. The patient is then supposed to imagine becoming severely ill, in vivid terms, due to taking the drug. When the patient focuses on avoiding drugs, he or she is told to imagine pleasant scenes.

This method has been used in several experimental programs but not on a large scale. It is best suited for a motivated, cooperative patient who is doing well in a therapeutic community or narcotic antagonist program.

Biofeedback Relaxation Therapy. Biofeedback is used to help drug addicts by stressing that the mind has the ability to control the urge or desire to ingest drugs. Therapeutic use of biofeedback is based on two distinct models: the learning theory model and the relaxation model.

In the learning theory model, the person learns to control a physiological process, such as blood pressure, with an appropriate monitoring device to let him or her know when the blood pressure is changing in the desired direction—usually down. The biofeedback is directed at general muscular or cortical relaxation, with the idea that, when in a stressful situation, the patient will use what he or she has learned.

One positive aspect of using biofeedback therapy in a treatment package is that it shifts the responsibility of "cure" from doctor to patient. The patient must become involved and actively work toward his or her own health, which should help maintain success over the long term.

Biofeedback-assisted relaxation procedures have been used as part of therapeutic approaches with alcoholics and methadone-maintenance addicts. Some patients report that they feel biofeedback has helped them. However, carefully controlled studies of addicts going through withdrawal, using muscular relaxation techniques and alpha EEG training, have not demonstrated suc-

cess. Unfortunately, for many of the people who had great expectations, the various types of biofeedback methods have not proven better than general relaxation procedures (Ray et al. 1979).

Alternative Behavioral Approaches. Alternative approaches consist of substituting chemically induced states of euphoria with natural "highs" brought on by altered states of consciousness.

Understanding Consciousness. Experimental psychiatrists, neurophysiologists, psychologists, and physicians are always investigating the mind. Roland Fischer is one of the researchers who has probed the ability and powers of the conscious and subconscious mind. Figure 15-1 shows his representation of the varieties of conscious states, with which he explains some abilities of the mind (Fischer 1971).

Notice in the figure that there are three major conscious states: ergotropic, normal, and trophotropic. The one in the middle, the normal waking state of mind, focuses on stimuli in normal life. This state of the conscious mind (called the *"I" portion*) is active during the daily routine. The state on the right, trophotropic, represents the lowered sensory input into the brain that occurs as a person relaxes; conversely, the state on the left, ergotropic, represents increased sensory input from activity, or a removal of filters to sensory input. The change in alertness may be measured by the types of brain wave and their intensity, as may be noted on the small semicircle in the center of the diagram.

The term **ergotropic** refers to the arousal state (shown on the left in Figure 15-1) and means "inciting activity." It is characterized by increased activity of the sympathetic nervous system and an activated psychic state. During the ergotropic state, more than normal amounts of sensory input are coming into the brain. As one moves from the *aroused* to the *hyperaroused* and finally to the *ecstatic* stage, the level of stimuli coming into the brain

ergotropic
refers to the arousal state of consciousness

VARIETIES OF CONSCIOUS STATE

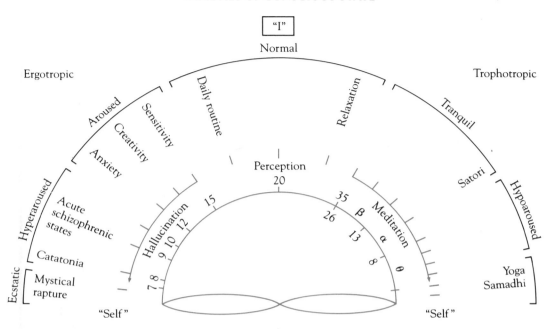

FIGURE 15-1 Fischer's map of varieties of conscious states, shown on a continuum of conscious arousal: *normal* waking consciousness ("I", middle); increased, or *ergotropic*, arousal (left); and decreased, or *trophotropic*, arousal (right). At either extreme is a state of transcendence in which the absolute "Self" is discovered; this is normally achieved only by mystics and advanced practitioners of meditation. *Source:* From R. Fischer, "A Cartography of the Ecstatic and Meditative States," *Science* 174 (26): 897–904. Copyright 1971 by the American Association for the Advancement of Science. Reprinted by permission.

increases, so the person's nervous system gets more excited and aroused.

This is very much like removing filters in the brain, which is probably one of the best ways to explain the increased activity. Initially, sensitivity and creativity are enhanced (aroused stage); the individual may feel inspired or have new ideas and feelings. With more stimulation, anxiety may follow (still aroused stage); the individual may now feel driven. Increased levels of stimulation may be difficult to handle, leading to psychological and physical problems. If the hyperaroused stage persists, schizophrenia or hallucinations may result, as normal processing of input fails; the person may become **catatonic.** In the ecstatic stage, **mystical rapture** is achieved. Few people are able to reach this most intense level of information processing without becoming catatonic or damaging their conscious minds. Those who can are considered

catatonic
refers to a state of arousal characterized by trancelike consciousness; sensory input is literally jammed and the body is rigidly fixed

mystical rapture
an ultimate state of consciousness similar to hallucination

to be mystics, who may be capable of visions and transcendental experiences. Some claim that they can reach this mystical stage with hallucinogenic drugs like LSD, psilocybin, and mescaline.

As the brain evolves, the sensory detection organs in and on the exterior of the body send in so much nerve impulse information that much of the information processing is delegated to the subconscious. This is a necessary function. As Aldous

Huxley concluded, "The function of the brain is to protect us from being overwhelmed . . . by this mass of largely useless and irrelevant knowledge, by shutting out most . . . and leaving only that . . . special selection which is likely to be practically useful" (1954).

At the other extreme is the **trophotropic** stage, during which less sensory input enters the brain (see Figure 15-1). As the brain filters out or blocks input into the conscious mind, the individual first reaches a feeling of tranquility, or deep relaxation. Some people who meditate reach a deep state of tranquility called *satori*, after the Zen Buddhist tradition (see section "Meditation," following). The *hypoaroused* stage is achieved when sensory input has been shut out until the arousal level is very low. The highest level of the hypoaroused stage, the *yoga samadhi* stage, is the ultimate in lowered input from the senses. It takes many years to achieve the mind and body control that characterize this stage, at which the person is in complete union with the Self, or the Absolute.

---

trophotropic

a state of consciousness in which there is decreased sensitivity to external stimuli and sedation

---

Note that this stage of complete union with the Self occurs at two points—mystical rapture and yoga samadhi. There is a loop, resembling the mathematical symbol for infinity, between these extremes of the ergotropic and trophotropic states. Fischer (1971) and others believe it is possible to move from samadhi into ecstasy and vice versa. This means that an experienced meditator may spontaneously move into total ecstasy, and the person in mystical rapture may spontaneously move into total calm and peace.

One final note: Fischer's interesting map of inner space is hypothetical. It should not be interpreted as a literal representation of data obtained on the human brain.

Meditation. Some of the most intriguing research about the brain is being done on the state of the mind during **meditation.** In certain countries, like India, people have long histories of being able to achieve certain goals through meditation. The word *yoga* is derived from the Sanskrit word for *union,* or *yoking,* meaning "the process of discipline by which a person attains union with the Absolute." In a sense, it refers to the use of the mind to control itself and the body.

---

meditation

a state of consciousness in which there is a constant level of awareness focusing on one object; e.g., Yoga and Zen Buddhism

---

Meditation involves brain wave activity centered on ponderous, contemplative, and reflective thought. An individual who meditates is able to decrease oxygen consumption within a matter of minutes as much as 20%, a level usually reached only after four to five hours of sleep in the nonmeditator. However, meditation is physiologically different from sleep, based on the EEG pattern and rate of decline of oxygen consumption (although some people do fall asleep during meditation) (Pagano et al. 1976). Along with the decreased metabolic rate and changes in EEG, there is also a marked decrease in blood lactate. Lactate is produced by metabolism of skeletal muscle, and the decrease is probably due to the reduced activity of the sympathetic nervous system during meditation. Heartrate and respiration are also slowed.

Herbert Benson (1977) has dubbed this sequence of changes "the relaxation response." He was interested in applying nondrug means to treat hypertensive patients and bring down their blood pressure. With the assistance of Maharishi Mahesh Yogi and volunteers from Transcendental Meditation (TM), a Westernized form of yoga, he worked out a clinical approach he had used to treat hypertension (Benson 1977).

The four basic conditions to elicit a relaxation response are:

1. A passive attitude (probably the most important condition)
2. A quiet environment
3. An object to dwell on, such as a word or sound repetition

4. A comfortable position, such as sitting, in which the person is not as likely to fall asleep during the 20-minute session as if he or she lies down

Benson recommends using the word *one* to concentrate on or a simple prayer from your own religious tradition. The relaxation response is elicited twice daily for 10 to 20 minutes each time. Benson and his coworkers recommend that the procedure works best on an empty stomach. The relaxation response is a most useful way of reducing the effects of stress on the body and mind.

The Natural Mind Approach. Some people who take drugs eventually look for other methods of maintaining the valuable parts of the drug experience. These people may learn to value the meditation "high" and abandon drugs. Long-term drug users sometimes credit their drug experiences with having given them a taste of their potential, even though continued use has diminished the novelty of drug use. Once these individuals become established in careers, they claim to have grown out of chemically induced altered states of consciousness. As Weil (1972) put it, "One does not see any long-time meditators give up meditation to become acid heads."

Although chemical "highs" are effective means of altering the state of consciousness, they interfere with the most worthwhile states of altered consciousness because they reinforce the illusion that highs come from external, material agents rather than from within your own nervous system.

Some people have difficulty using meditation as an alternative to drugs because, in order to be effective, meditation takes practice and concentration; the effects of drugs are immediate. Nevertheless, it is within everyone's potential to meditate.

INNOVATIVE TREATMENTS Hypnosis and acupuncture are two innovative methods of treating drug use and abuse. While the two approaches are unconventional, they remain options of choice.

Hypnosis. This procedure has been used to link drug-taking behavior to negative consequences such as nausea, anxiety, and so on. It has also been used to produce imagery of a previous "good trip," or happy drug experience. Advan-

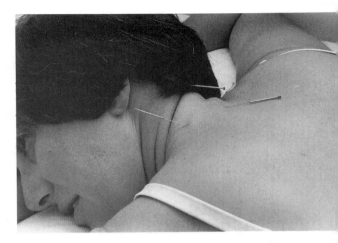

Acupuncture has been reported to temporarily relieve cravings for, and withdrawal symptoms from, narcotic drugs. *Source:* Judy S. Gelles/Stock, Boston

tages of such an approach are that they are free, under the subject's control, and not against the law. Subjects can be taught to hypnotize themselves, thus giving them further control when they feel the temptation to use drugs. Hypnosis can also be used to help achieve relaxation, similarly to biofeedback. At present, there is too little evidence to claim that hypnosis is an effective treatment program for drug abuse.

Acupuncture. The medical use of needles has been practiced in China for 3,000 years or more and is still used there for various anesthetic purposes. Speculation about the effectiveness of acupuncture abounds. It is possible that acupuncture prompts the release of endorphins, the natural opiates of the body.

In 1972, acupuncture was used in Hong Kong on opium addicts having neurosurgery; they claimed they felt relief from withdrawal symptoms, although the acupuncture was intended only as an anesthetic. Later, a combination of acupuncture and electrical stimulation was used on heroin and opium addicts (O'Brien and Ng 1979). Fine acupuncture needles were placed subcutaneously in the outer ear and connected to an electrical stimulator for about 30 minutes. The investigators reported that symptoms of tearing, runny nose, aching bones, cramps, and irritability

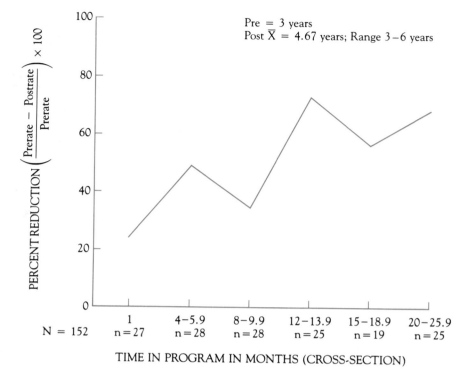

FIGURE 15-2 Reduction in the arrest rate of dropouts from therapeutic communities (age at program entry is 19 years and older). Note that, the longer the length of treatment (time in program), the greater the reduction in arrest rate. *Source:* De Leon and Rosenthal 1979.

FIGURE 15-3 Pre- and posttreatment arrest rates for therapeutic community dropouts and graduates. Note the dramatic decreases in arrest rates for both groups during and posttreatment. *Source:* De Leon and Rosenthal 1979.

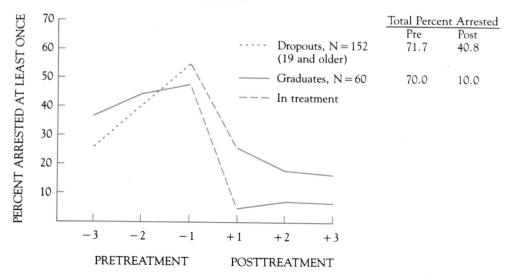

usually disappeared after about 10 to 15 minutes. While under stimulation, the patients' craving for the narcotic drug ceased, and they began to feel more relaxed.

Following this study, other researchers in the United States and abroad have given acupuncture treatments to addicts, with variation in the numbers of needles and types of needle stimulation (e.g., manual, with heating, or with electricity). Encouraging results have been reported. Recently, studies at Lincoln Hospital in the Bronx, New York, have shown acupuncture to be effective. Michael Smith, director of Lincoln Hospital, says that there has been a "60 percent success rate at keeping hard-core addicts straight for a solid three months—high compared with other programs" (Findlay et al. 1991).

EVALUATING PROGRAM EFFECTIVENESS

When federal funds became available to treat drug addiction in the late 1960s, four major treatment modalities evolved: methadone maintenance, therapeutic communities, outpatient drug-free programs, and short-term detoxification. These are the treatment modalities most frequently compared. Criteria for comparison include later use of narcotics and other drugs, arrest record or criminality, employment record, and follow-up treatment required.

Evaluating the success rate of a program depends on the criteria selected. "Graduates" of TCs, or those who complete the community's residential treatment program, are just a small proportion (10% to 15%) of all admissions. Five to ten years after "graduation," these former addicts have stable lifestyles, are employed, are not using opiates,

and are not engaging in criminal activity. Less improvement is shown by the majority who drop out of TC programs before completion, and as might be expected, the extent of improvement is directly correlated to the length of residence in the TC (see Figures 15-2 and 15-3). The greatest proportion of dropouts leave during the first 30 days of residence; the rate declines rapidly thereafter. This is fairly typical of other drug abuse treatment programs as well (De Leon and Rosenthal 1979).

Methadone maintenance programs operate on an outpatient basis and are combined with a rehabilitation-oriented therapy program (U.S. Department of Health and Human Services 1991). Drug-free programs, where patients are not allowed to use any drugs, are outpatient, intended primarily for nonopiate users (Akers 1992). They range from highly demanding, socialization-oriented programs, like daytime TCs, to relaxed programs that offer "rap" sessions and support on request. There is an even higher dropout rate from drug-free programs than from TCs.

As described earlier, detoxification programs are usually short term, not over 21 days, and may be inpatient or outpatient, depending on the drug and degree of dependence. Their primary goal is to eliminate physiological dependence.

Considering the variability in treatment approaches and the selection of patients, we can say that methadone maintenance, therapeutic communities, and drug-free programs have approximately the same success rates, whereas opiate antagonist and detoxification-only programs have appreciably lower success rates (Sells 1979; Akers 1992). Finally, other research by Simpson and Sells (1981) shows that detoxification-only programs were no more effective than not receiving any treatment.

K E Y   T E R M S

addiction
disease model of drug dependence
social influence
primary prevention
secondary prevention
tertiary prevention

antisocial personalities
borderline personalities
alternatives approach
noneuphoric opiate
self-regulating communities
reinforcement

ergotropic
catatonic
mystical rapture
trophotropic
meditation

S U M M A R Y

1. The four levels of addiction identified by Doweiko (1990) are: Level 0—total abstinence; Level 1—rare social use; Level 2—heavy social use; Level 3—early addiction; and Level 4—mature or late addiction.

2. Social influence relates to drug use because it involves the ability to inspire, motivate, or convince others to go along and share drug use.

3. Drug education programs must be aware of the following types of drug abusers: (a) committed abusers; (b) abusers who have no interest in stopping; (c) former abusers; (d) nonproblem abusers; (e) occasional abusers; (f) recreational abusers; and (g) problem abusers.

4. Drug education programs can be placed into three categories: (1) those that provide information; (2) those that stress values, beliefs, and attitudes; and (3) those that focus on the consequences of drug abuse.

5. The three different types of prevention are primary, secondary, and tertiary prevention. *Primary prevention* refers to using persuasion with regard to drug abuse. *Secondary prevention* entails using immediate intervention, such as fines and incarceration for drug

violations. *Tertiary prevention* is used to help individuals stop abusing drugs either immediately before or in the early stages of addiction.

6. The social science model states that drug use is a cultural phenomenon and an outgrowth of values and attitudes. The psychological model views drug abuse as an outgrowth of personality structure. For example, psychologists identify antisocial and borderline personalities, whereas social scientists look at drinking patterns, peer influence, and malfunctioning families as the causes of persistent drug use and abuse.

7. Primary prevention programs should be based on three assumptions: (a) A reasonable goal should be to educate people of all ages regarding the abuse of all drugs; (b) responsible decisions regarding personal abuse should result in fewer negative consequences for individuals; and (c) successful programs should increase self-esteem, interpersonal skills, and participation in alternatives to drug abuse and involve parents and the community.

8. The success of treatment programs should be based on any

one or more of the following behaviors by patients: (a) abstinence from illegal drugs; (b) abstinence from all addicting drugs; (c) stabilization on a maintenance drug; (d) holding down a job; (e) decrease in criminal activity; (f) ability to support a family; and (g) improved physical and mental health.

9. Inhospital programs stress intense treatment within an acute care hospital program. Residential care programs focus on education and therapy on a 24-hour-per-day basis. Day hospitals or intensive outpatient services provide therapy sessions three or four hours per day while patients live independently.

10. Five drug treatments include medical, psychological and psychotherapeutic, social behavioral, and innovative treatment methods. Medical treatment methods include (a) detoxification and abstinence programs; (b) maintenance programs; (c) morphine maintenance programs; (d) methadone and LAAM maintenance programs; (e) heroin maintenance programs; and (f) opiate antagonist programs. Psychological methods look for individualistic explanations, while

social approaches emphasize the lack of positive role models, peer influence, and the effects of economic deprivation. Behavioral approaches are based on the belief that drug abuse is learned and can be unlearned. Alternative behavioral approaches stress the importance of natural states of consciousness and how to reach relaxed levels of consciousness. Finally, innovative treatment methods, those outside the five types already discussed above, include hypnosis and acupuncture.

11. The three major states of consciousness are the ergotropic, normal, and trophotropic states. The *ergotropic* state is characterized by increasing levels of sensory input; it may be divided into aroused, hyperaroused, and ecstatic stages. As input increases, enhanced sensitivity and creativity may be followed by anxiety; if levels of input are not controlled, dysfunction may result, including hallucinations, schizophrenia, and catatonia. The *normal* state of consciousness refers to the spectrum of routine activity to relaxation; perceptual awareness characterizes this state. The *trophotropic* state is characterized by decreasing levels of sensory input; it may be divided into tranquil and hypoaroused stages.

12. Hypnosis is used for conditioning the drug user to link drug-taking behavior to negative consequences, such as nausea, anxiety, and so on. Acupuncture is used as a method of relieving heroin and opium withdrawal symptoms, primarily the craving for these two drugs.

R E F E R E N C E S

Akers, R. L. *Drugs, Alcohol, and Society: Social Structure, Process, and Policy.* Belmont, CA: Wadsworth, 1992.

Alcoholics Anonymous World Services, Inc. *Alcoholics Anonymous: The Story of How Many Thousands of Men and Women Have Recovered from Alcoholism.* 3rd ed. New York: AA, 1976.

Archer, S. "Historical Perspective on the Chemistry and Development of Naltrexone." In *Narcotic Analgonists: Naltrexone Pharmaco-Chemistry and Sustained-Release Preparations,* edited by R. E. Willette and G. Barnett. NIDA Research Monograph no. 28. Washington, D.C.: NIDA, 1981.

Bassin, A. "Daytop Village." In *Readings in Social Psychology Today.* Del Mar, CA: CRM Books, 1970.

Baumann, J., and A. Waterston. "Advertising the 'War on Drugs': Images from America's Television." *Drug Use in America: Social, Cultural and Political Perspectives,* edited by P. J. Venturelli. Boston, MA: Jones and Bartlett, 1993 (forthcoming).

Benson, H. "Systemic Hypertension and the Relaxation Response." *New England Journal of Medicine* 296 (1977): 1152–1156.

Carroll, E. "Notes on the Epidemology of Inhalants." In *Review of Inhalants,* edited by C. W. Sharp and M. L. Brehm. NIDA Research Monograph no. 15. Washington, D.C.: NIDA, 1977.

Cohen, A. Y. *Alternatives to Drug Abuse: Steps Toward Prevention.* NIDA Research Monograph no. 14. Washington, D.C.: NIDA, 1973.

Cohen, A. Y. "The Journey Beyond Trips: Alternatives to Drugs." *Journal of Psychedelic Drugs* 3, no. 2 (Spring 1971): 7–14.

De Leon, G., and M. S. Rosenthal. "Therapeutic Communities." In *Handbook on Drug Abuse,* edited by R. L. DuPont, A. Goldstein, and J. O'Donnell. Washington, D.C.: NIDA, 1979.

DeLong, J. V. "Treatment and Rehabilitation." In *Dealing with Drug Abuse: A Report to the Ford Foundation.* New York: Praeger, 1972.

Doweiko, H. E. *Concepts of Chemical Dependency.* Pacific Grove, CA: Brooks/Cole, 1990.

Eddy, N. B., H. Halbach, H. Isbell, and M. H. Seevers. "Drug Dependence: Its Significance and Characteristics." *Bulletin of the World Health Organization* 32 (May 1965): 721–733.

"Education, Community Action and the Workplace." In *National Drug Control Strategy.* Washington, D.C.: Government Printing Office, September 1989.

Findlay, S., D. Podolsky, and J. Silberner. "Wonder Cures from the Fringe." *U.S. News and World Report,* 23 September 1991.

Fischer, R. "A Cartography of the Ecstatic and Meditative States." *Science* 174 (1971): 897–904.

Gelb, L. N. *Just Say No.* Washington, D.C.: NIDA, 1984.

Gilman, M. "Could You Be an Addict? Special Health Report: The Crisis of Addiction—Women and Cocaine." *McCall's,* November 1986, 105.

Ginzburg, H. M. *Naltrexone: Its Chemical Utility.* Rockville, MD: NIDA, 1986.

Gold, M. S., A. C. Pottash, D. R. Sweeney, and H. D. Kleber. "Opiate Withdrawal Using Clonidine." *Journal of the American Medical Association* 243 (1980): 343–346.

Gottfredson, M., and T. Hirschi. "Why We're Losing the War on Crime." *Washington Post,* 10 September 1989, 3.

Hatterer, L. J. *The Pleasure Addicts.* New York: Barnes, 1989.

Hopkins, H. C. "Getting a Handle on Methadone." *FDA Consumer,* September 1973, 43–47.

Huxley, A. *The Doors of Perception.* New York: Harper & Brothers, 1954.

Kennedy, B., M. Konstantareas, and S. Homatidis. "A Behavior Profile of Polydrug Abusers." *Journal of Youth and Adolescence* 16 (1987): 115–127.

Kinney, J. *Clinical Manual of Substance Abuse.* St. Louis, MO: Mosby, 1991.

Klein, J. M., and S. I. Miller. "Three Approaches to the Treatment of Drug Addiction." *Hospital and Community Psychiatry* 37 (1986): 1083–1085.

Leventhal, C. F. *Messenger of Paradise: Opiates and the Brain.* New York: Anchor/Doubleday, 1988.

McGuire, W. "Theoretical Foundations of Campaign." In *Public Communication Campaign,* edited by R. Rice and W. Paisley Nadelmann. Beverly Hills, CA: Sage, 1981.

"Measuring the Impact of Drug Prevention Programs." *Prevention Newsline* 4, no. 4 (Summer 1991): 3–4.

Nurco, D. N. "Etiological Aspects of Drug Abuse." In *Handbook on Drug Abuse,* edited by A. Goldstein, R. L. Dupont, and J. O'Donnell. Washington, D.C.: NIDA, 1979.

O'Brien, C. P., and L. K. Y. Ng. "Innovative Treatments for Drug Addiction." In *Handbook on Drug Abuse,* edited by A. Goldstein, R. L. Dupont, and J. O'Donnell. Washington, D.C.: NIDA, 1979.

Pagano, R. R., R. M. Rose, R. M. Stivers, and S. Warrenburg. "Sleep During Transcendental Meditation." *Science* 191 (1976): 308–310.

Pickens, R. W., and T. Thompson. "Behavioral Treatment of Drug Dependence." In *Behavioral Intervention Techniques in Drug Dependence Treatment,* edited by M. L. Stitzer, J. Grabowski, and J. E. Henningfield. Rockville, MD: NIDA, 1984.

Ray, W. J., J. M. Raczynski, T. Rogers, and W. H. Kimball. *Evaluation of Clinical Biofeedback.* New York: Plenum, 1979.

Renault, P. F. "Historical Perspective on the Chemistry and Development of Naltrexone." In *Narcotic Analgonists: Naltrexone Pharmaco-Chemistry and Sustained-Release Preparations,* edited by R. E. Willette and G. Barnett. NIDA Research Monograph no. 28. Washington, D.C.: NIDA, 1981.

Sells, S. B. "Treatment Effectiveness." In *Handbook on Drug Abuse,* edited by A. Goldstein, R. L. DuPont, and J. O'Donnell. Washington, D.C.: NIDA, 1979.

Simpson, D. D., and S. B. Sells. *Highlights of the DARP Follow-Up Research on the Evaluation of Drug Abuse Treatment Effectiveness.* Washington, D.C.: NIDA, 1981.

Swisher, J. D. "Prevention Issues." In *Handbook on Drug Abuse,* edited by R. L. DuPont, A. Goldstein, and J. O'Donnell. Washington, D.C.: NIDA, 1979.

Trebach, A. S. *The Heroin Solution.* New Haven, CT: Yale University Press, 1982.

U.S. Department of Education. *Learning to Live Drug Free: A Curriculum Model for Prevention.* Rockville, MD: NCADI, 1992.

U.S. Department of Education. *What Works: Schools Without Drugs.* Washington, D.C.: U.S. Department of Education, 1986.

U.S. Department of Health and Human Services. *Drug Abuse and Drug Abuse Research.* Third Triennial Report to Congress from the Secretary. Department of Health and Human Services Publication no. 91-1704. Washington, D.C.: Government Printing Office, 1991.

Weil, A. *The Natural Mind.* Boston, MA: Houghton Mifflin, 1972.

Wickler, A. *Theories on Drug Research.* NIDA Research Monograph no. 30. Rockville, MD: NIDA, 1980.

Wilson, M., and S. Wilson, eds. *Drugs in American Life.* New York: H. W. Wilson, 1975.

World Health Organization. "Expert Committee on Addiction-Producing Drugs." *World Health Organization Technical Report* 273 (1964): 9–10.

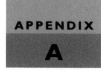

Chemical Structures

A-1: TRANSMITTERS

$$CH_3-C(=O)-O-CH_2-CH_2-N^+-(CH_3)_3$$

Acetylcholine

$$HOOC-CH_2-CH_2-CH_2-NH_2$$

Gamma aminobutyric
acid (GABA)

L-Dopa

Dopamine

Norepinephrine

Epinephrine

5-Hydroxytryptamine
(serotonin)

A-2: HORMONES

FEMALE HORMONES

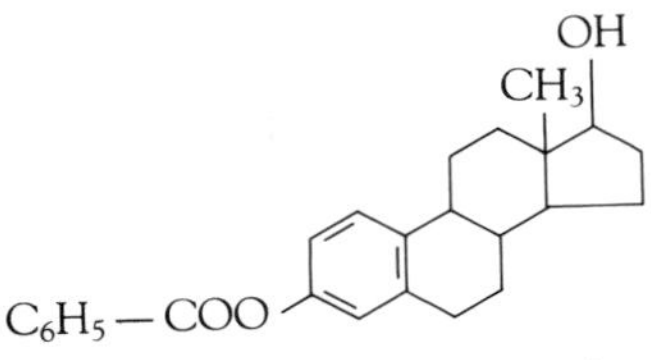

Estradiol (Estrogen)

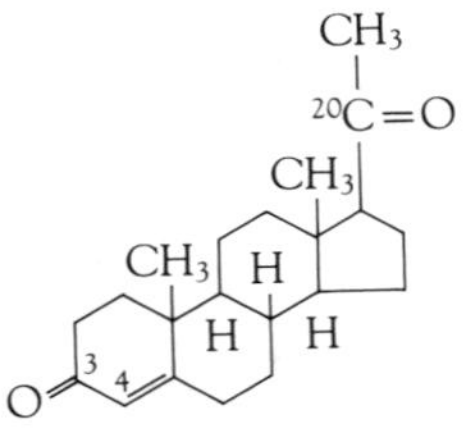

Progesterone

MALE HORMONE (ANABOLIC STEROID)

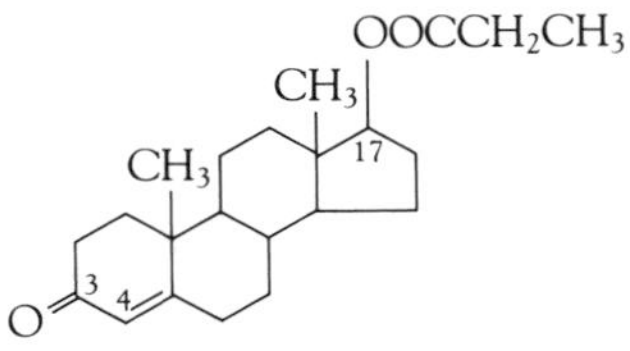

Testosterone

CORTICOSTEROID

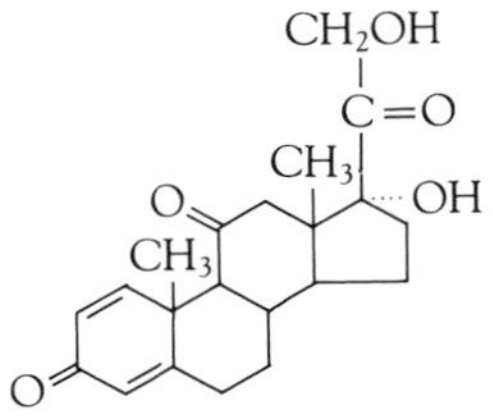

Prednisone

A-3: DEPRESSANTS

BENZODIAZEPINES

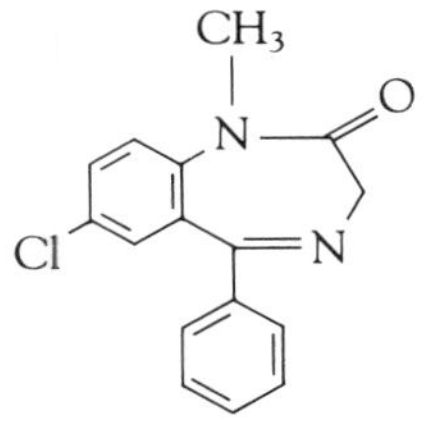

Diazepam (Valium®)

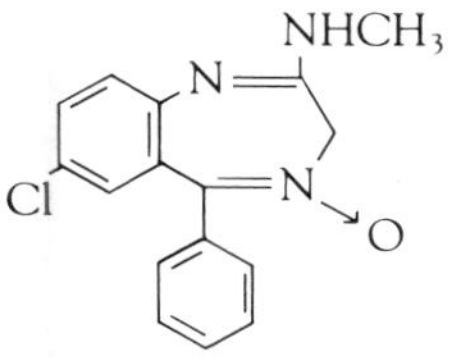

Chlordiazepoxide (Librium®)

BARBITURATE TYPES

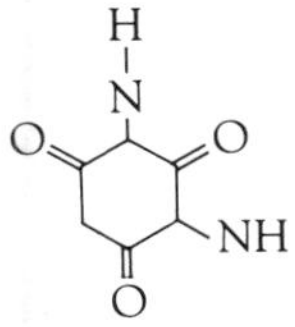

Barbituric acid

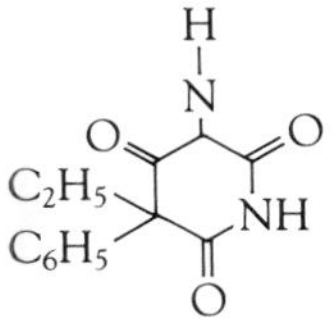

Phenobarbital

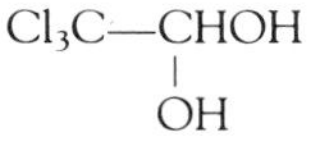

$$Cl_3C-CHOH$$
$$\quad\quad\quad |$$
$$\quad\quad\quad OH$$

Chloral hydrate

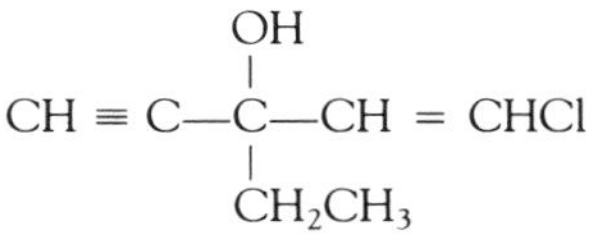

$$CH \equiv C - \overset{\overset{\displaystyle OH}{|}}{\underset{\underset{\displaystyle CH_2CH_3}{|}}{C}} - CH = CHCl$$

Ethchlorvynol

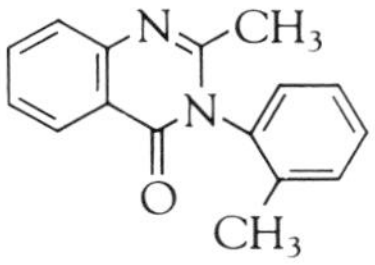

Methaqualone

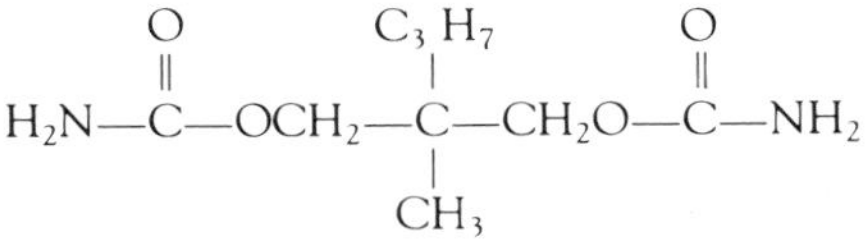

$$H_2N-\overset{\overset{\displaystyle O}{\|}}{C}-OCH_2-\overset{\overset{\displaystyle C_3H_7}{|}}{\underset{\underset{\displaystyle CH_3}{|}}{C}}-CH_2O-\overset{\overset{\displaystyle O}{\|}}{C}-NH_2$$

Meprobamate

ANTIHISTAMINE

$$\begin{array}{c} C_6H_5 \\ \\ C_6H_5 \end{array} CHOCH_2CH_2N \begin{array}{c} CH_3 \\ \\ CH_3 \end{array}$$

Diphenhydramine

A-4: NARCOTICS

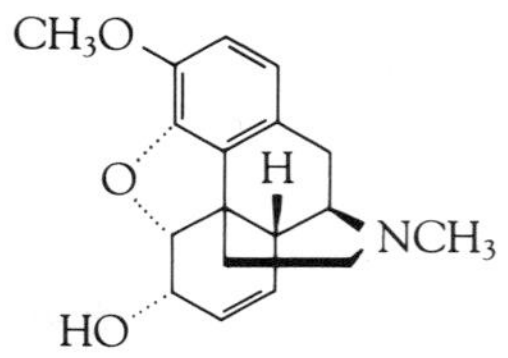

Codeine

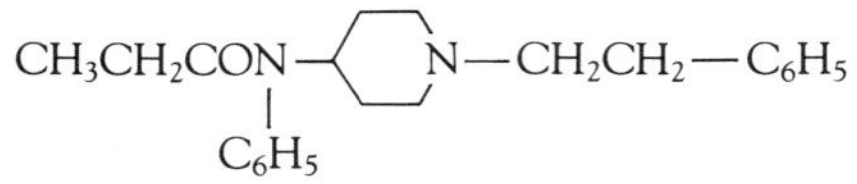

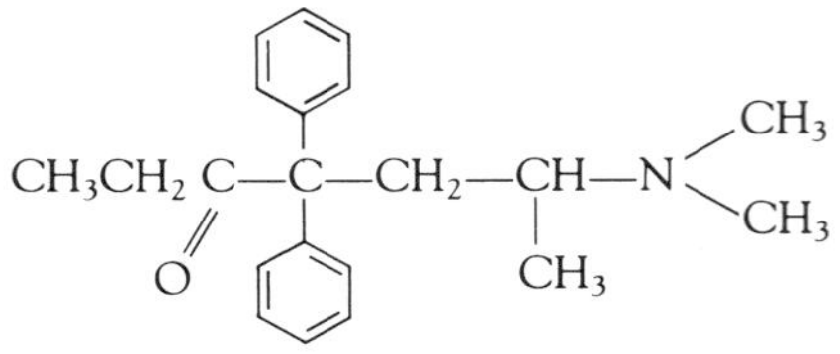

Methadone

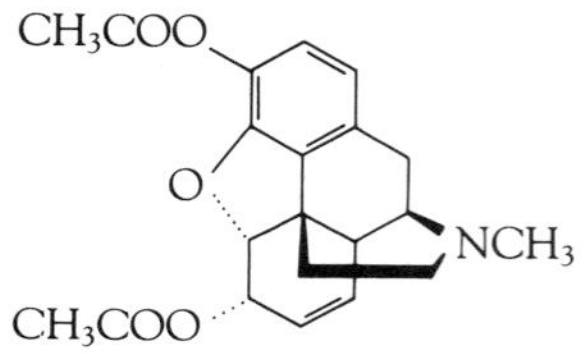

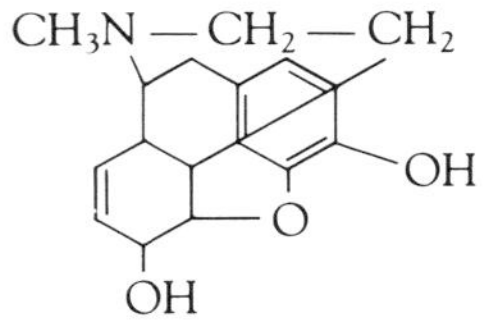

Fentanyl

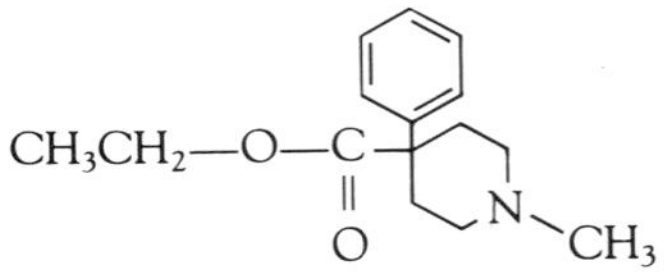

Morphine

Heroin

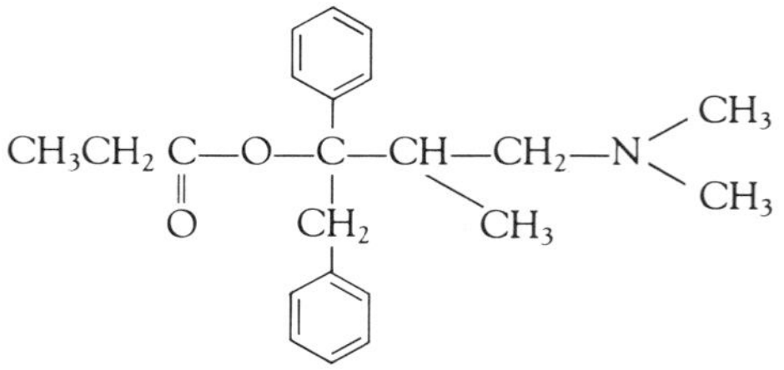

Propoxyphene

Meperidine

A-5: ANALGESICS

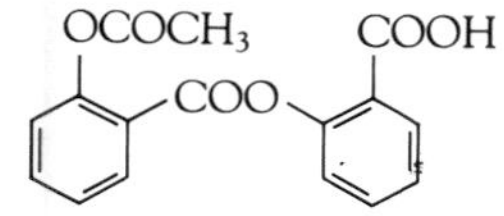

OCOCH$_3$ COOH

COO

Aspirin (acetylsalicylic acid)

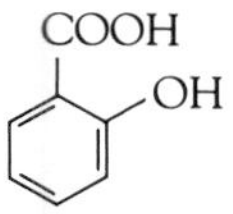

CH$_3$CONH—〈 〉—OH

Acetaminophen

COOH

OH

Salicylic acid

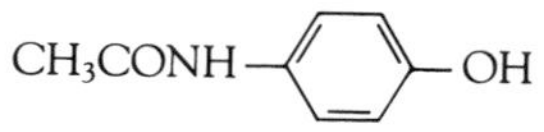

$(CH_3)_2CHCH_2$—〈 〉—$\overset{CH_3}{\underset{}{CHCOOH}}$

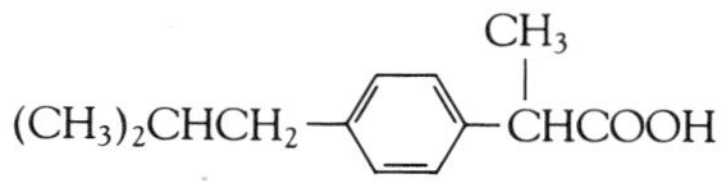

Ibuprofen (NSAIDS)

A-6: STIMULANTS AND SYMPATHOMIMETICS

AMPHETAMINE TYPES

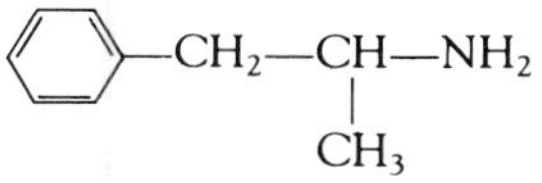

—CH$_2$—CH—NH$_2$
       |
      CH$_3$

Amphetamine

CH$_2$〈O O〉—CH$_2$ CH—NH$_2$
                    |
                   CH$_3$

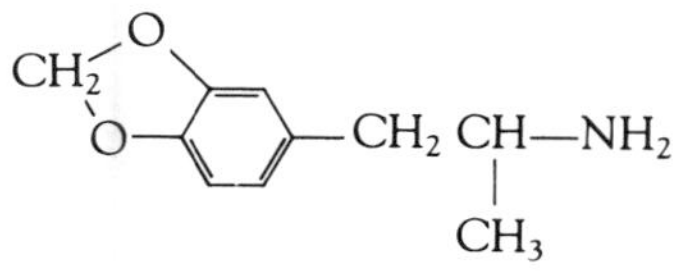

MDA
3, 4-Methylenedioxyamphetamine

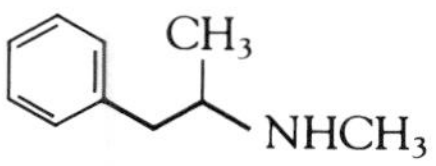

CH$_3$

NHCH$_3$

Methamphetamine

C
|
H
|
C=O
|
OCH$_3$

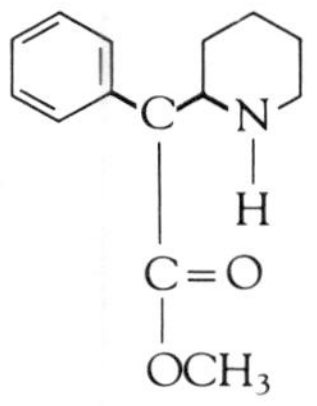

Methylphenidate

XANTHINES

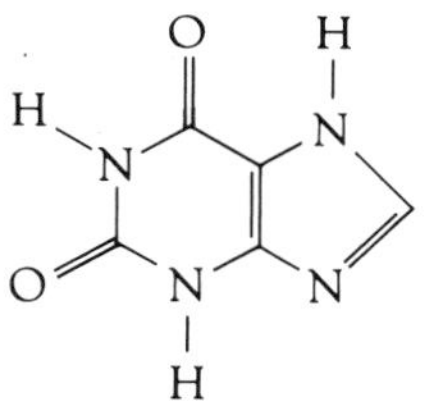

Xanthine

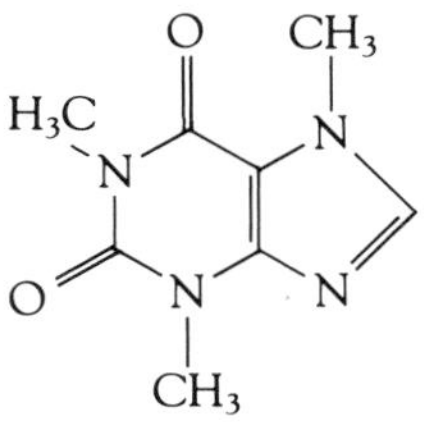

Caffeine

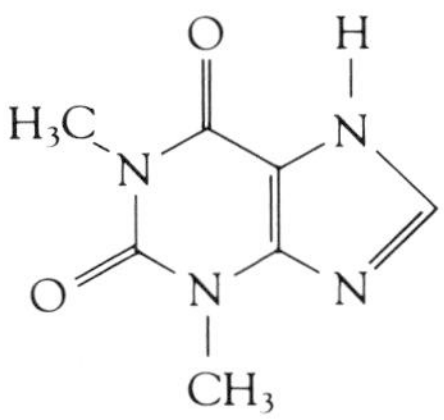

Theophylline

STIMULANTS AND SYMPATHOMIMETICS *(continued)*

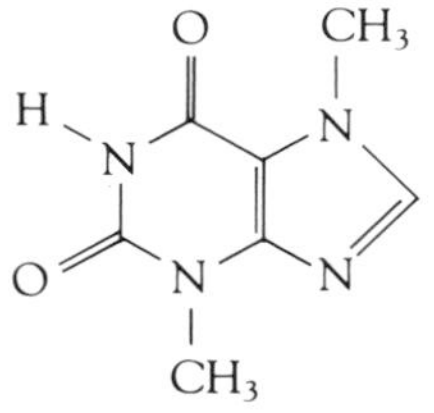

Theobromine

Phenylpropanolamine

DECONGESTANTS

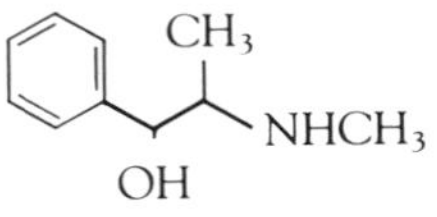

Ephedrine

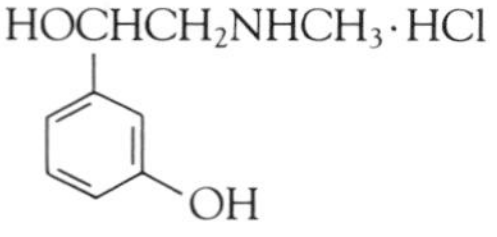

Phenylephrine

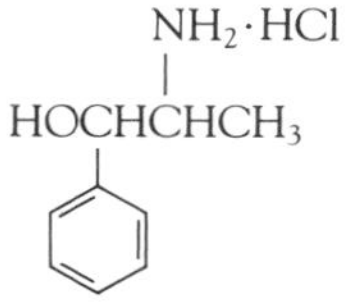

OTHERS

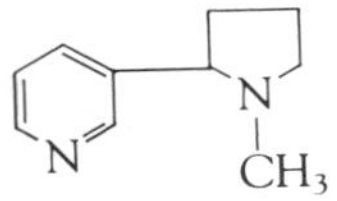

Nicotine

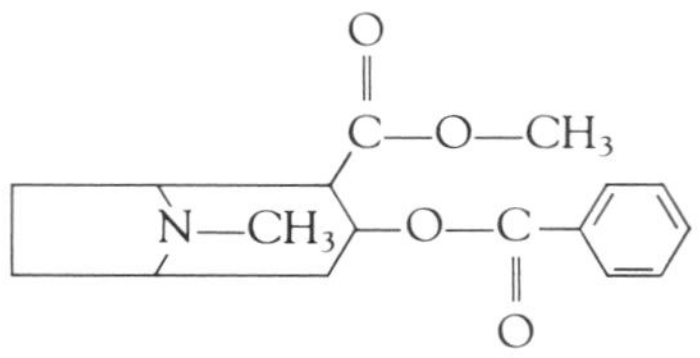

Cocaine

A-7: HALLUCINOGENS
LSD TYPES

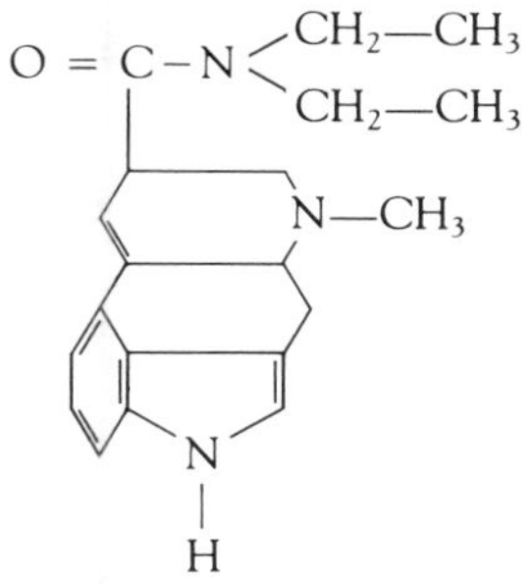

d-lysergic acid diethylamide (LSD)

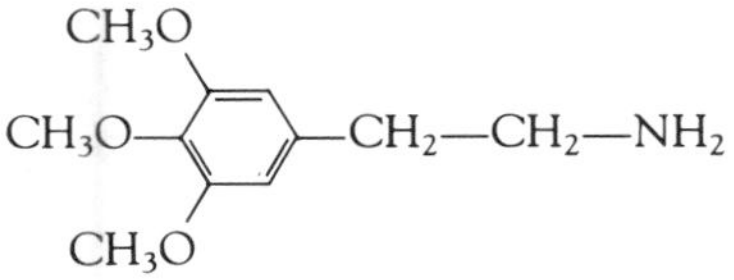

Mescaline
3, 4, 5-Trimethoxyphenethylamine

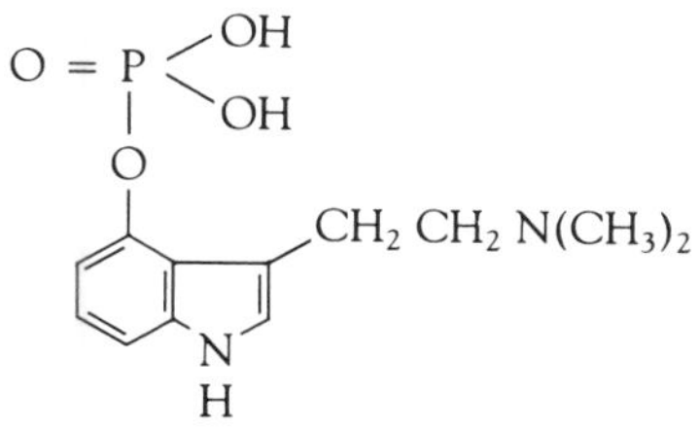

Psilocybin

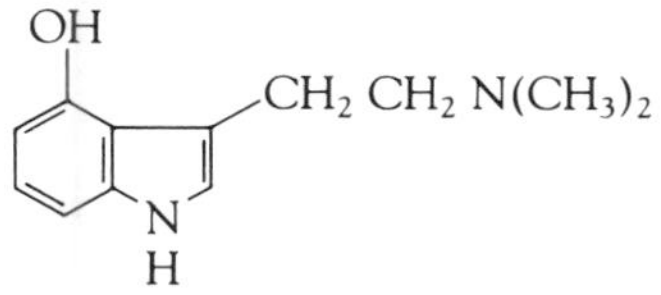

Psilocin

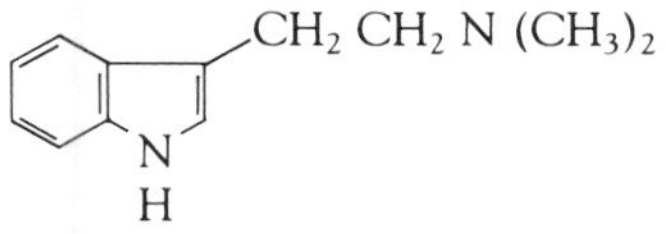

N, N-dimethyltryptamine (DMT)

AMPHETAMINE TYPE

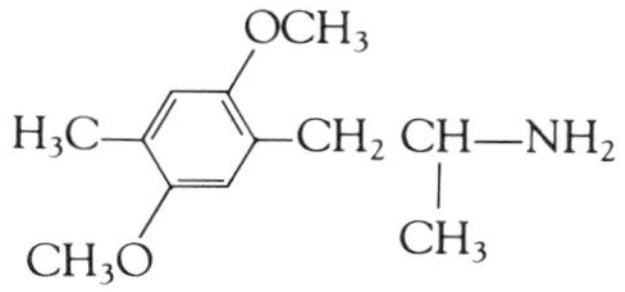

DOM (STP)
2,5-Dimethoxy-4-
methylamphetamine

(See also MDA in section A-6.)

ANTICHOLINERGIC TYPES

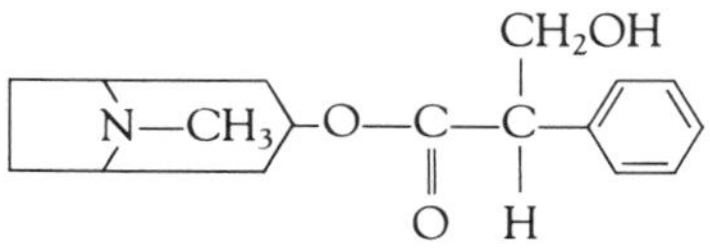

Atropine (dl-hyoscyamine)

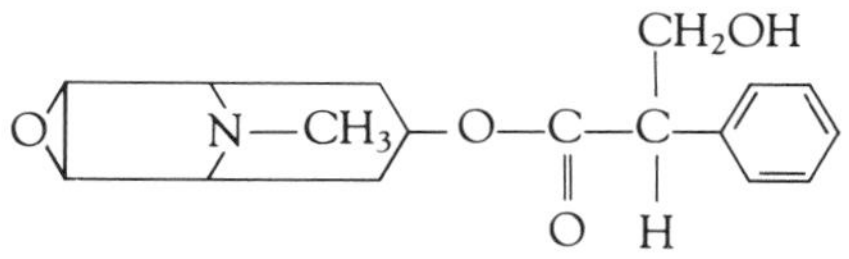

Scopolamine (l-hyoscine)

OTHERS

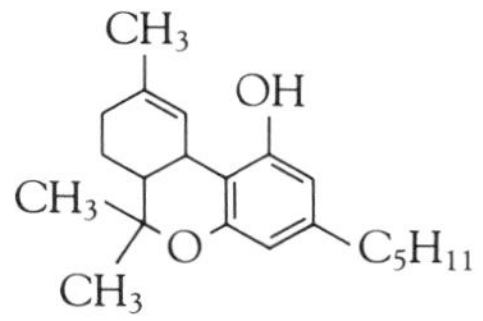

Δ^9—THC (Marijuana)

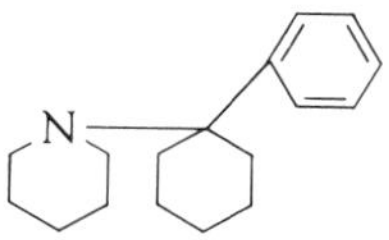

Phencyclidine

A-8: PSYCHOTHERAPEUTIC DRUGS

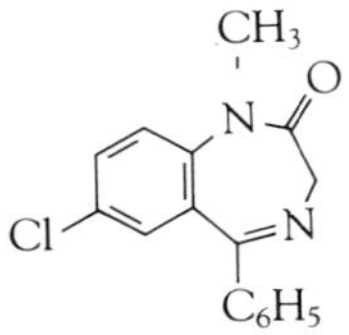

Diazepam (Valium)

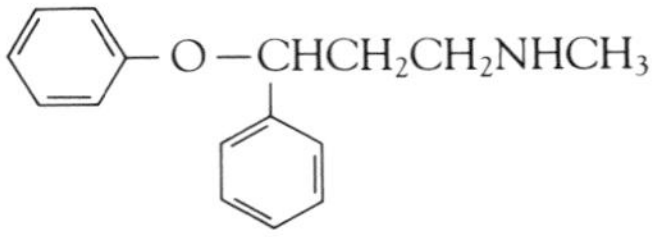

Fluoxetine (Prozac)

$$C_6H_5CH_2NCH_2C \equiv CH$$

Pargyline (MAO inhibitor)
(Eutonyl)

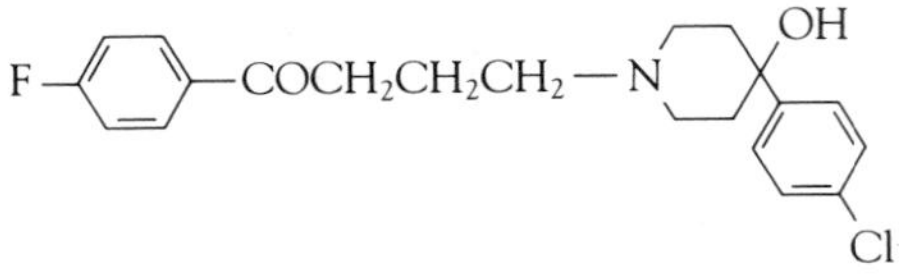

Haloperidol (Haldol)
(antipsychotic)

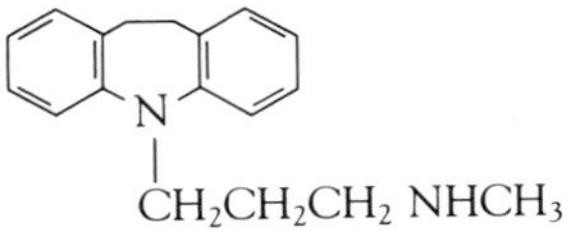

Desipramine (tricyclic antidepressant)
(Norpramin)

Schedule Classifications of Common Drugs of Abuse

Note: The active component is in nonitalicized type.

SCHEDULE I

Narcotics
*Acetyl-alphamethyl*fentanyl
*Alpha-methyl*fentanyl
Codeine *methylbromide*
Etorphine
Heroin
*Para-fluoro*fentanyl

Stimulants
MDA
MDMA ("Ecstasy")

Hallucinogens
LSD
Marijuana
Mescaline
Peyote
Phencyclidine (PCP) analogs
Psilocybin
Tetrathydocannabinol

Depressants
Methaqualone (Quaalude)

SCHEDULE II

Narcotics
Alfentanyl
Codeine (pure)
Fentanyl (Sublimaze)
Hydrocodone
Methadone
Morphine
Opium extracts
Oxycodone
Raw opium
Sufentanil

Stimulants
Amphetamine
Coca leaves or derivative (e.g., cocaine)
Methamphetamine
Methylphenidate (Ritalin)

Hallucinogens
Phencyclidine (PCP)

Depressants
Secobarbital (Seconal)

SCHEDULE III

Narcotics
Low doses of codeine
Low doses of morphine

Narcotic Antagonists
Nalorphine

Stimulants
Benzphetamine
Mazindol (Sanorex)

Depressants
Glutethimide (Doriden)
Methyprylon (Noludar)

Steroids
Anabolic steroids
Methyl testosterone
Testosterone *proprionate*

SCHEDULE IV

Narcotics
Dextropropoxyphene (Darvon)

Depressants (benzodiazepines)
Alprazolam (Xanax)
Chlordiazepoxide (Librium)
Clonazepam (Klonopin)
Clorazepate (Tranxene)

Cloxazolam
Diazepam (Valium)
Flunitrazepam
Flurazepam (Dalmane)
Lorazepam (Ativan)
Medazolam
Oxazepam (Serax)
Temazepam (Restoril)

Depressants (barbituratelike)
Ethchlorvynol
Phenobarbital

SCHEDULE V

Narcotics
Very low doses of codeine (e.g., cough
  medicine)

Common Drug Interactions

Interacting Drugs	Effect Produced	Comments
Acetaminophen with:		
Alcohol	Liver damage	Most likely in alcoholics
Alcohol with:		
all CNS depressants	Increased CNS depression	Suppresses respiration; may be fatal
barbiturates		
benzodiazepines		
narcotics		
antihistamines		
other drugs metabolized by liver	Altered metabolism	Either increases or decreases effects
Antacids with:		
digoxin	Decreased absorption	Decreases effect
fluoride	Decreased absorption	Decreases effect
iron	Decreased absorption	Decreases effect
dilantin	Decreased absorption	Decreases effect
salicylates	Increased excretion	Decreases effect
tetracycline	Decreased absorption	Decreases effect
Anticoagulants with:		
aspirin	Increased anticlotting effects	Danger of hemorrhage
nonsteroidal antiinflammatory	Increased anticlotting effects	Danger of hemorrhage
Antidepressants with:		
alcohol	Decreased metabolism	Increases toxicity of both
lithium	Not known	Increases tremor
sympathomimetics	Stimulated norepinephrine effects	Hypertension and heart arrhythmia
Contraceptives (oral) with:		
alcohol	Decreased metabolism	Increases contraceptive effect
antidepressants	Decreased metabolism	Increases contraceptive effect
barbiturates	Increased metabolism	Decreases contraceptive effect
caffeine	Decreased metabolism	Increases caffeine effect
penicillins	Decreased absorption	Decreases contraceptive effect
tetracycline	Decreased absorption	Decreases contraceptive effect
steroids	Not known	Increases steroid toxicity
tobacco	Increased metabolism	Decreases contraceptive effect

Interacting Drugs	Effect Produced	Comments
Insulin with:		
anabolic steroids	Not known	Increases insulin effects
salicylates	Not known	Increases insulin effects
tobacco, smoking	Decreased absorption	Decreases insulin effects
Marijuana with:		
antidepressants	Increased effects	Tachycardia
Narcotics with:		
CNS depressants	Increased effects	Serious CNS depression; impaired breathing
tranquilizers	Not known	Increases narcotic toxicity
Salicylates (aspirin) with:		
alcohol	Increased effects	Increases bleeding
steroids	Not known	Decreases salicylate effect
some antihypertensive drugs	Inhibition of prostaglandins	Elevates blood pressure
Sympathomimetics with:		
digitalis	Increased effects	Heart arrhythmia
insulin	Not known	Decreases insulin effect
MAO inhibitors	Increased release of norepinephrine	Severe hypertension
Tetracycline with:		
alcohol	Increased metabolism	Decreases tetracycline effect
anticoagulants	Not known	Increases bleeding
calcium	Decreased absorption	Decreases tetracycline effect
iron	Decreased absorption	Decreases tetracycline effect
lithium	Decreased absorption	Decreases tetracycline effect
zinc	Decreased absorption	Decreases tetracycline effect
Tryptophan with:		
MAO inhibitors	Not known	Increases toxicity of MAO inhibitors

Source: Adapted with permission from The Medical Letter, *Handbook of Adverse Drug Interactions*, New Rochelle, NY: The Medical Letter, 1990.

First Aid in Drug Abuse–Related Emergencies

Diagnosing the seriousness of a drug overdose or withdrawal and determining what first-aid treatment is appropriate is risky for a person without medical training. A wrong decision can mean the difference between saving a life and causing permanent damage (e.g., impaired brain function) or even death. When in doubt, call a poison control center or the nearest emergency medical service for advice. Hospitals that receive any form of federal funding are forbidden by law to refuse to treat drug abuse cases and to report the identity of adult drug abuse cases to legal authorities. Laws regarding treatment of minors without parental consent vary from state to state. A good recommendation is to call, regardless of the law.

Diagnosis in a drug emergency is made difficult by several factors. The identity of the drug, the dosage, and the purity are often not known. The patient may have taken more than one drug, either deliberately (like cocaine and heroin) or accidentally, without realizing the potentiation effect (like Darvon and alcohol). The person may not be having difficulty with the abused drug itself but from a concurrent injury (such as a concussion) or from a serious infection from nonsterile injection techniques (common with the "needle habits"). The person might not be suffering from a drug effect at all but rather withdrawal from benzodiazepines, alcohol, barbiturates, or narcotics. Or he or she might have a medical condition, such as epilepsy, diabetic coma, or acute schizophrenia. Check for a Medic Alert necklace or bracelet. There

may be medical information in the person's wallet or purse as well as needed identification.

The following signs and symptoms are intended only as a guide to first aid when a drug abuse problem is suspected. These guidelines are not intended as a substitute for professional diagnosis and treatment.

DIFFERENTIAL DIAGNOSIS
GENERAL APPEARANCE

Behavioral symptoms of drug intoxication are usually nonspecific and thus do not provide much help. Hallucinogens, amphetamines, phencyclidine, cocaine, and marijuana all can cause acute panic or paranoid reactions. Amphetamines and cocaine can induce paranoid delusions and aggressive behavior. The person intoxicated with alcohol or barbiturates may be aggressive; aggression is very rare in opiate intoxication. The person who is "high" on phencyclidine (PCP) has a characteristic blank stare and is catatonic; he or she does not usually become psychotic and aggressive until "coming down." Restlessness or agitation suggests the use of amphetamines or LSD or withdrawal from barbiturates or heroin. A quiet, withdrawn appearance suggests the use of barbiturates, heroin, or hallucinogens or "crashing" from

The section on "Differential Diagnosis" (pp. 4 based on Bourne 1976.

phetamines. The speech of the barbiturate user is often thick and slurred, somewhat like that of the drunk; the heroin user's speech may be slow, but his or her diction remains intact.

CONVULSIONS Convulsions are not useful for identifying the type of drug that might be involved. Convulsive seizures can occur if the person (1) has taken toxic doses of codeine, propoxyphene (Darvon), methaqualone, amphetamines, cocaine, strychnine, or LSD; (2) has taken an overdose of depressant (the brain has been deprived of oxygen); (3) is experiencing withdrawal from sedative-hypnotics or alcohol; or (4) already suffers from some other cause of seizures, such as epilepsy.

BREATHING Opiates, barbiturates, alcohol, benzodiazepines, and other sedatives are respiratory depressants, and it is the depressant action that puts the patient in immediate danger. Doing mouth-to-mouth resuscitation or, if necessary, cardiopulmonary resuscitation (CPR) until an ambulance arrives can save the victim from incurring severe brain damage or death.

Narcotics can cause pulmonary edema (fluid in the lungs), which might be characterized by a wheezing or whistling sound as the person breathes. This is another indication that no time should be lost in taking the person to an emergency medical facility.

A reddened, ulcerated nose suggests use of cocaine, volatile substances, or relatively pure marijuana. A runny nose (rhinorrhea) is an early sign of heroin withdrawal.

The odor of some depressants may be detected on the victim's breath. Examples include alcohol, ether, paraldehyde, ethchlorvynol (Placidyl), and volatile substances (see Chapter 11).

EYES The size of the pupils and how they respond to light may be valuable information about drug ingestion, if modifying factors are considered. (For example, if the person has fallen and suffered a concussion, the size and response of the pupils will not tell anything about the drug that may be involved.) Pinpoint pupils (miosis) in dim light suggests the use of heroin or another opioid. If both pupils are dilated (mydriasis) and responsive to changes in light intensity, the patient could be in opioid withdrawal or intoxicated with LSD, the tryptamines (like DMT), mescaline, or morning glory seeds. Dilated and sluggishly reactive pupils suggest the use of glutethimide (Doriden) or high doses of amphetamine. Both pupils dilated but nonresponsive to light changes suggests ingestion of high doses of anticholinergic drugs (see Figure D-1).

Reddened, irritated appearance of the whites of the eyes (conjunctival injection) is characteristic of marijuana use. Side-to-side eye movements (lateral nystagmus) suggests use of PCP or barbiturates or barbiturate withdrawal. An exaggerated blink reflex commonly indicates barbiturate withdrawal.

SKIN If a person has taken enough of a drug to be having a bad reaction or is experiencing a type of withdrawal, he or she will perspire. This nonspecific stress response is not really helpful, however, because it only indicates that the person's body is under stress. Dry, flushed skin suggests use of an anticholinergic drug, such as jimsonweed, or a preparation containing atropine or scopolamine (see Chapter 11). Gooseflesh occurs with an LSD reaction or during withdrawal from narcotics. Needle "tracks" usually mean narcotics but can signal the use of amphetamines or cocaine.

PULSE Tachycardia (a rapid heartbeat) is a nonspecific stress response found in most acute drug reactions. A fast, irregular pulse suggests amphetamine, cocaine, or volatile substance abuse. (Blood pressure may be dangerously elevated after taking amphetamines or cocaine, but most people don't carry a sphygmomanometer around to check!) A fast pulse rate is not dangerous unless the person has a cardiac condition. Cardiac arrhythmias occur with use of volatile substances and large doses of codeine, propoxyphene (Darvon), methaqualone, amphetamines, cocaine, methylphenidate (Ritalin), and alcohol. The condition can be life threatening and requires medical attention as soon as possible. If the heart stops, CPR can save the person's life.

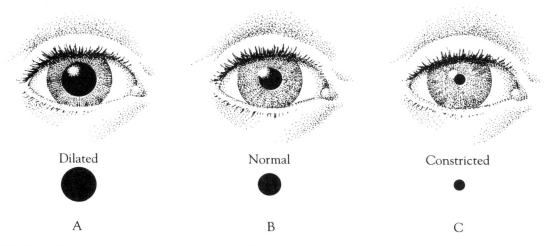

FIGURE D-1 Pupil reactions to various drugs: (A) Dilation of pupils (mydriasis) may be caused by amphetamines, LSD, mescaline, psilocybin, DMT, MDA, and the anticholinergics, such as scopolamine and atropine. The anticholinergics cause the pupil to remain fixed even when light strikes it. Mydriasis also occurs during withdrawal from narcotics. (B) Normal pupil seen in average light. Marijuana, barbiturates, and PCP would usually leave the pupil like this. (C) Constricted pupils (miosis) that are not responsive to dim light are characteristic of the opiates, such as heroin.

TEMPERATURE Elevated body temperature may be present after LSD ingestion or amphetamine and cocaine administration or during withdrawal from narcotics or barbiturates. It may also be caused by an infection if the person has a "needle habit."

FIRST AID FOR CRISES INVOLVING COMMONLY ABUSED DRUGS

As most drug users know, not all overdoses are medical emergencies. A good rule of thumb for the person trying to assess whether an emergency exists or not is: If the dose was taken more than two hours before you appeared on the scene and the user is still conscious and coherent, there is probably no great cause for alarm. No action may be necessary, other than emotional support and having someone reliable stay with the user until the effects of the drug have worn off.

The section on first aid (pp. 471–476) is based on McDonnell et al. 1977.

Some hallucinogens give fairly long "trips" (12 to 18 hours), depending on the dosage. Because the user's sense of time is distorted, it may seem much longer to him or her. Reassurance and a supportive atmosphere are essential at this time. The person having a "bad trip" is at real risk of committing suicide, either intentionally or unintentionally because he or she cannot discriminate between illusion and reality. Comforting physical contact, such as holding the patient's hand, is probably more useful than words.

Typical effects of commonly abused drugs and withdrawal symptoms are summarized in Tables D-1 and D-2, respectively. Professional treatments for more serious drug intoxications and withdrawals are discussed in the appropriate chapters.

Giving another drug to counteract the original drug the person has taken should **never** be done except by medical personnel. Do not force coffee tea, milk, or other liquids on an unconscious semiconscious patient; he or she may chok them and/or inhale them into the lungs. F same reasons, do not make an unconscio conscious, or convulsing person vomit

TABLE D-1   Typical effects of acute drug intoxication

Drug	Psychological Effects	Physical Effects
Amphetamines	Confused; disoriented; agitated; irritable; aggressive; may hallucinate and be paranoid at high doses	Sweating; irregular pulse; hyperactivity; cardiac arrhythmia
Anticholinergics	Disoriented; no distortion of space and time; visual hallucinations	Decreased salivation; mydriasis; dry, flushed skin
Barbiturates	May be disoriented; loss of inhibitions; euphoria	Nystagmus; coma at high dose; respiratory depression
LSD type	Disoriented; anxious; emotionally labile; hypersuggestible; delusions	Gooseflesh; mydriasis; stress reaction symptoms
Marijuana	Oriented; space, time distortion; mild anxiety to panic	Reddening of whites of eyes
Narcotics	Oriented; normal; quietly euphoric	Miosis; drowsy, nodding
Phencyclidine (PCP)	Disoriented; excited; confused; feelings of isolation, apathy; may become acutely psychotic	Blank stare; catatonic; nystagmus; impaired motor coordination; stress reaction symptoms
Volatile substances	Disoriented; confused; may be delirious	Impaired motor coordination; cardiac arrhythmia

TABLE D-2   Early "crashing" and withdrawal symptoms

Drug	Psychological Effects	Physical Effects
Amphetamines	Sleepy; lethargic; depressed	Hungry; muscles ache
Alcohol and barbiturates	Confused; disoriented; extreme restlessness; delirium	Tremors; insomnia; fever; nystagmus; exaggerated blink reflex with barbiturates; severe convulsions; cardiovascular collapse
Narcotics	Restless; agitated	Runny nose; teary eyes; mydriasis and pupils responsive to light; gooseflesh; low back pain

propriate to induce vomiting, give the patient syrup of ipecac (available in 1 oz. bottles for first-aid kits). The ipecac may be used safely a second time if vomiting has not occurred within 15 to 20 minutes. Use of a salt solution to cause vomiting can be more dangerous than not inducing vomiting at all, especially in children. If activated charcoal is available in a first-aid kit, it can be given after vomiting ceases. It will adsorb many toxic substances and, if used in recommended amounts,

will do no harm. The old "home remedies"—such as a mixture of burnt toast, strong tea, and milk of magnesia—are generally useless.

ALCOHOL

Alcohol overdose is not usually a medical emergency, unless the heartbeat is irregular or the person is in a coma. The two immediate causes of death are from cardiac arrhythmia ("holiday heart") and respiratory depression. If the person is seriously uncoordinated and possibly has also taken a depressant, such as barbiturates or benzodiazepines (Valium) or a narcotic (Darvon), the risk of respiratory failure is serious enough that a physician should be consulted. Otherwise, keep the person warm, and assist him or her to a bathroom to vomit as necessary. Do not let this person drive.

If methyl alcohol (wood alcohol) poisoning is suspected, induce vomiting, and get medical attention as rapidly as possible. The most common sources of wood alcohol are canned heat and cooking fuels. If the victim is isolated and a long distance from medical help, have him or her drink regular (ethyl) alcohol after he or she finishes vomiting. The liver will preferentially oxidize the grain alcohol, and this may be enough to save the victim's vision or life. Isopropyl ("rubbing") alcohol is not as toxic as methyl alcohol. It will cause severe gastrointestinal symptoms, such as nausea, vomiting, and diarrhea.

Withdrawal from alcohol dependence has a mortality rate of up to 25% when untreated. To withdraw safely, the alcoholic needs medical treatment, usually in a hospital, for 10 to 21 days. The initial symptoms are severe muscle tremors, nausea, weakness, and anxiety. The alcoholic in withdrawal will be actively seeking alcohol or, as a substitute, other depressants like barbiturates or benzodiazepines.

AMPHETAMINES

Amphetamine overdose can be fairly serious. If the person has *just taken* an oral dose, induce vomiting. If he or she is already showing signs of overstimulation, do not induce vomiting because this can send the person into convulsions. If he or she is having chest pains, has an irregular pulse, or has a history of heart trouble, get him or her to an emergency room immediately. Otherwise, this person should be kept as calm and quiet as possible. A bad amphetamine trip is not as responsive to talking down as a bad hallucinogen trip. Amphetamines induce paranoia, fear, and sometimes a temporary psychosis. Occasionally, there is long-term anxiety or even paranoia, which responds to psychotherapy.

The person crashing after amphetamines may be extremely depressed and perhaps suicidal. However, the physical symptoms are not usually a serious threat because there is only moderate physical dependence.

BARBITURATES

Barbiturate overdose can be very serious, depending on the dosage and whether it was combined with alcohol. Alcohol potentiates the depressant effect. If the drug was taken recently, induce vomiting. Try to keep the patient awake and moving. If the person is conscious, get him or her to drink strong coffee or tea. If he or she lapses into unconsciousness, call for medical help. Be ready to use mouth-to-mouth resuscitation (or cardiovascular resuscitation if no pulse can be detected) to prevent brain damage or death.

Withdrawal from a barbiturate or other sedative-hypnotic drug dependency can be extremely dangerous because of the risk of convulsions and death. It definitely requires medical treatment. Symptoms are similar to those of withdrawal from alcohol.

COCAINE

Cocaine can be extremely toxic in high doses, but sometimes, even low doses can cause severe, life-threatening responses. The cocaine epidemic of the 1980s has proven repeatedly how dangerous this stimulant can be.

The CNS effects of cocaine are similar to those caused by amphetamines and include agitation, excitation, and paranoia with visual and auditory hallucinations or uncontrolled violent behavior within 24 hours of administration. If doses are great enough or a user is particularly sensitive, seizures can occur. This effect is in part due to the local anesthetic action of cocaine. A common toxic sign that occurs in chronic cocaine users is the "cocaine bugs" that seem to be crawling o and under the surface of the skin. The cardiov cular system is particularly sensitive to co Even modest doses or intranasal use of have caused fatal cardiovascular response adults with normal cardiovascular func effects can consist of heart attack, stroke, and vascular spasms.

DEPRESSANTS

Depressant overdose can be very serious (see Chapter 6). People who overdose with depressants often are reaching out for help in a dangerous way. Depressant withdrawal is more dangerous than withdrawal from heroin, and it requires specific medical treatment due to depression of respiratory and cardiovascular systems.

Abuse of benzodiazepines, such as Valium and Librium, is fairly common. An overdose is not as dangerous as with barbiturates, unless the person has taken another central nervous system depressant like alcohol. If a dose larger than the maximum recommended was taken within the past hour or so, get the person to vomit. Keep him or her warm, watch for respiratory depression, and consult a physician.

HALLUCINOGENS

Overdose with hallucinogens, such as LSD or mescaline, is rarely fatal by itself. The main problem is the suggestibility of the person, causing him or her to misinterpret the surroundings and become frightened and respond in a dangerous manner. Quiet surroundings and reassurance are usually the best treatment; use the person's suggestible state to convince him or her that everything will be all right. A bad trip can be aborted with an antianxiety drug, like Valium, but this usually just makes the medical personnel feel better, not the patient. An occasional LSD user or user of other hallucinogens will develop chronic anxiety or even a true psychosis that persists for months afterwards. These conditions typically can be alleviated with tranquilizers or psychotherapy.

"Flashback" reactions are a return of the subjective sensations in the absence of the drug. They most commonly result from LSD but can occur from morning glory seeds, marijuana, and other hallucinogens. Treatment consists of reassurance that the condition will go away. If anxiety persists, a physician may prescribe a sedative.

MARIJUANA

Marijuana intoxication is rarely serious. An overdose of marijuana or hashish puts the user to sleep. Hashish or hash oil may trigger hallucinations and panic reactions, requiring reassurance and quiet surroundings to let the drug effects wear off. Do not let the user drive.

NARCOTICS

Narcotic overdose is usually serious. If the person has taken another depressant—such as a barbiturate, benzodiazepine, or alcohol—that is still in his or her system, he or she is in greater danger of respiratory failure and death from the combination than from a simple overdose of heroin.

If the person is unconscious, check his or her airway, breathing, and pulse. Arrange for medical assistance, and be ready to do mouth-to-mouth resuscitation or, if necessary, cardiopulmonary resuscitation. Narcotic antagonists, such as naloxone, can be injected by a physician to reverse the respiratory depression. The patient should not leave the hospital until the staff is certain he or she is out of danger; some narcotics, such as methadone, have a longer duration of action, and the patient may lapse into another coma as the naloxone wears off if the narcotic is still present in the body.

Withdrawal from heroin or other opioids can be quite unpleasant, but it does not require treatment with the urgency that withdrawal from the alcohol-barbiturate type of dependence does.

PHENCYCLIDINE (PCP)

Phencyclidine was originally developed as an anesthetic. Low doses make the user feel numb; increasing doses produce anesthesia; and large doses can cause coma, respiratory depression, convulsions, and death. The physical signs are like those of a stress reaction: sweating, flushing, and a rapid pulse. The blank-stare appearance and the tendency to remain in whatever position the person is placed (catatonia) appear to be effects unique to PCP abusers. Pupil size remains normal, and the presence of side-to-side eye movements (lateral nystagmus) plus poor muscular coordination help distinguish PCP intoxication from stimulant and LSD abuse (Lerner and Burns 1978).

Simple, uncomplicated PCP trips are handled like trips from other hallucinogen drugs, except that it is not helpful to try to talk the person down. PCP is more likely to cause severe psychotic reactions than other hallucinogens. The person who goes into a coma should be taken to a hospital immediately. (The medical management of PCP overdose is described in Chapter 11.)

STIMULANTS

Stimulants, in general, can be life threatening, especially to those with weak hearts or other serious medical complications. Stimulant overdose can cause tremors, convulsions, hallucinations, paranoia, or simple hyperactivity (see Amphetamines). Large doses of amphetamines and methylphenidate (Ritalin) can cause cardiac arrhythmia.

VOLATILE SUBSTANCES

Volatile substances can be dangerous. Some cause death from cardiac arrhythmia; most can cause respiratory failure.

Remove the source of vapor, and check the victim's airway, breathing, and pulse. Do cardiopulmonary resuscitation if there is no pulse or mouth-to-mouth resuscitation if the heart is still going but the victim is not breathing on his or her own. Less serious intoxication can be treated simply by removing the source of vapor. Most abused volatile substances are not metabolized but are removed from the body by exhalation comparatively quickly. Once the user's confusion and disorientation clears, there is little risk of relapse into coma unless he or she has taken something else, as well.

FIRST AID FOR TREATING WITHDRAWAL

Withdrawal symptoms from drugs that induce physical dependence and crashing from high doses of drugs that induce psychological dependence may need first aid followed by medical assistance. Withdrawal and crashing symptoms are usually the opposite of the effects of the drug in question. Withdrawal from depressants—such as alcohol, barbiturates, benzodiazepines, and narcotics—causes symptoms of tremors, runny nose, teary eyes, cramps, irritability, depression, hallucinations, and risk of convulsions. Not all patients will have the full range of symptoms with great severity. It depends on the individual, the dosage, and which depressant was used. A heavy dependence on alcohol and barbiturates requires specific medical treatment for the best chance of survival. Often alcoholics do not realize they are physically dependent. They have not accepted the fact that they are alcoholics and will try to prove that they can "take it or leave it."

Benzodiazepine dependency is in some ways more insidious because dependent persons may have been taking the drug as prescribed by a physician. When they are away from home and the prescription runs out, they are in trouble because they had no idea they were physically dependent.

Crashing from stimulants like amphetamines and cocaine leads to marked exhaustion and depression. The person may be suicidal. The only treatment usually necessary is supportive care, reassurance, and rest.

Specific first-aid measures for withdrawal from the various drugs are covered in previous sections under the appropriate category heading.

MOUTH-TO-MOUTH RESUSCITATION AND CARDIOPULMONARY RESUSCITATION TECHNIQUES

Mouth-to-mouth and CPR are important life-saving techniques that should be learned and practiced under professional supervision. Instruction is generally available through local chapters of the Red Cross or the American Heart Association. Sometimes the local police, fire department, or hospital sponsors classes. The resuscitation methods quite simple once you learn what to do and technique is appropriate. The Red Cross mends that people get training in cardiopulmonary resuscitation and learn how to activate the local emergency medical services (EMS) system by telephoning 911, 0, or the local EMS number.

Before beginning mouth-to-mouth resuscitation, check to see if the person is conscious by speaking to him or her or tapping his or her shoulder; do not shake the person if there is any chance of head, neck, or back injury. If the person is unconscious, try to attract someone else's attention quickly, so he or she can get help while you check for breathing.

Roll the unconscious person over on his or her back (assuming no neck or back injury). Check the airway to verify that nothing is preventing the person from breathing (like a swallowed tongue or slipped dentures). First, tip the head back until the chin points up; one way to do this is to apply pressure with one hand on the person's forehead while gently lifting the back of the neck with the other. As you are lifting, put your ear close to the person's mouth, and watch his or her chest. If he or she is breathing, you will see the chest rise and fall and feel the expired air on your face. Keep checking for about five seconds.

There is no time to be lost. If the person does not appear to be breathing after you have tipped his or her head, give four quick, full breaths by mouth to mouth (or mouth to nose if you cannot get a good seal on the mouth). After giving four quick breaths without pausing, check the carotid pulse and check for breathing again for at least five but not more than ten seconds. The carotid pulse is checked by locating the Adam's apple and sliding your fingers into the groove at the side of the neck nearby. You should feel the pulsation of the carotid artery if the heart is beating. The Red Cross calls this *A Quick Check*, which helps remind you of *A*irway, four *Quick* breaths, and *Check* for breathing and pulse.

If the victim is still not breathing but has a pulse, continue with mouth-to-mouth resuscitation until he or she starts breathing independently, someone else can take over, emergency medical personnel arrive, or you cannot continue any longer. Breaths should be given once every five seconds. Stop every few minutes for five seconds to check again for pulse and breathing.

If the person is not breathing and has no detectable pulse, he or she needs cardiopulmonary resuscitation (CPR) and emergency medical service. If you are not trained to give CPR, it is still worthwhile to try mouth-to-mouth resuscitation. There is a chance that the heart may be beating weakly, and your breathing for the victim may keep him or her alive. Continue making quick scans for someone to get help or someone who knows CPR. Breathe air into the victim about once per five seconds, and check for a pulse and breathing every few minutes, until it is clear the person is dead. (Actually, only a physician or other authorized person can declare a person legally dead.)

IDENTIFICATION OF DRUG ABUSERS

One of the first things to do before or during an emergency is identify the person with a drug problem. The Pharmaceutical Manufacturers Association has developed a list of the signs and symptoms associated with drug abuse of various types.

The following is a list of changes or symptoms commonly seen in abusers:

1. Abrupt changes in attendance at school or work, quality of work, and discipline
2. Unusual flare-ups or outbursts of temper
3. Deterioration of physical appearance
4. Secretive behavior about personal possessions, such as a backpack or the contents of a locker
5. Wearing sunglasses when no one else is
6. Wearing long-sleeved garments in hot weather
7. Association with known drug abusers
8. Unusual borrowing of money from relatives or associates
9. Stealing items that can be readily pawned or sold
10. Withdrawal socially and from responsibility
11. Changed frequency of going to basement, storage room, closet, or bathroom

The following are lists of some of the changes or symptoms specifically related to particular drugs.

Depressants

1. May seem intoxicated but no alcohol odor on breath
2. Staggering or stumbling movements
3. Falling asleep in class (even if interested in subject) or at work
4. Lost interest in former activities

Hallucinogens

1. Often appears to be daydreaming or in a trancelike state
2. May touch objects and examine everyday things carefully for long periods
3. Body image and senses may be distorted, causing panic

Marijuana

1. Odor of burned marijuana on clothes
2. Whites of eyes may appear irritated
3. May behave more quietly than previously

Narcotics

1. May have raw, red nostrils if sniffing and needle tracks if "shooting up"
2. Lethargic, drowsy behavior when high; purposive when obtaining money or locating source of drug

3. Needs money to support habit, moreso than for other drugs

Phencyclidine (PCP)

1. Dazed, blank-stare expression, side-to-side eye movements
2. Poor physical coordination as if drunk but no odor of alcohol
3. Sweating, flushed skin and excess salivation

Stimulants

1. Pupils may be dilated
2. Excessive activity, irritability, nervousness, and aggression
3. Mouth and nose dry, bad breath, lick lips frequently
4. Thin; goes for long periods without eating or sleeping
5. May have needle tracks if "shooting up"

Volatile Substances

1. Odor of substance on clothes, breath
2. Runny nose
3. Irritation and ulcerations around mouth
4. Watery eyes
5. Poor muscular coordination, drowsiness

R E F E R E N C E S

Bourne, P. G., ed. *Acute Drug Emergencies: A Treatment Manual.* New York: Academic, 1976.

Lerner, S. E., and R. S. Burns. "Phencyclidine Use Among Youth: History, Epidemiology, and Acute and Chronic Intoxica-

tion." In *Phencyclidine (PCP) Abuse: An Appraisal,* edited by R. C. Petersen and R. C. Stillman. NIDA Research Monograph no. 21. Washington, D.C.: NIDA, 1978.

McDonnell, R. F., Jr., E. Dupree, and G. Parcel. "Poisoning and Toxic Reactions." In *First Aid in Emergency Care,* edited by G. S. Parcel. St. Louis, MO: C. V. Mosby, 1977.

Glossary

acute immediate or short-term effects after taking a single drug dose

addiction a condition consisting of periodic or chronic dependence on a drug or several drugs; an insatiable desire to use drugs contrary to legal and/or social prohibitions

adulterated contaminating substances are mixed in to dilute the drugs

affective disorders mood swings that, when extreme, can interfere with normal behavior

agonistic a type of substance that activates a receptor

akathisia a syndrome characterized by motor restlessness and an inability to remain sitting associated with a feeling of muscle quivering

alcoholic a person who is addicted to alcohol

altered perceptions changes in the interpretation of stimuli, as resulting from marijuana use

alternatives approach one emphasizing the exploration of positive alternatives to drug abuse, based on replacing the pleasurable feelings gained from drug abuse with involvement in social and educational activities

amnesiac causing the loss of memory

amotivational syndrome personality change due to drug use; characterized by apathy, a lack of interest in pursuing and accomplishing goals, and an overall lack of ambition

anabolic chemicals able to convert nutrients into tissue mass

anabolic steroids compounds chemically like the steroids that stimulate production of tissue mass

analgesic related to drugs that block pain without causing unconsciousness

analogs drugs with similar structures

anesthesia a state characterized by loss of sensation or consciousness

anesthetic a drug that blocks sensitivity to pain

angina pectoris severe chest pain and feelings of suffocation associated with diminished blood supply to the heart

anorexiants drugs that suppress the activity of the brain's appetite center, causing reduced food intake

antagonistic a type of substance that blocks a receptor

anticholinergic antagonizing the activity of acetylcholine receptors

antipyretic drugs that relieve fevers

antisocial personalities those characterized by callous, cold, and dogmatic traits

antitussives drugs that block the coughing reflex

anxiolytics drugs that relieve anxiety

aphrodisiac a substance that stimulates or intensifies sexual desire

axon an extension of the neuronal cell body along which electrochemical signals travel

behavioral stereotypy meaningless repetition of a single activity

biological half-life the time required for the body to eliminate and/or metabolize half of a drug dose

biotransformation the process of changing the chemical properties of a drug, usually by metabolism

bipolar disorders exaggerated and debilitating mood swings, consisting of both severe manic and depressive episodes; also called manic-depressive disorder

blood-brain barrier selective filtering between the cerebral blood vessels and the brain

borderline personalities those characterized by wide mood swings and intense emotional outbursts

bradykinin an endogenous peptide that initiates pain

caffeinism symptoms caused by taking high chronic doses of caffeine

Cannabis sativa the hemp plant marijuana

carcinogenic able to cause cancer

catatonia a state of physical rigidity with stuporous periods

catatonic refers to a state of arousal characterized by trancelike consciousness; sensory input is literally jammed and the body is rigidly fixed

catecholamines a class of biochemical compounds, including the transmitters norepinephrine, epinephrine, and dopamine

chronic long-term effects, usually after taking multiple drug doses

chronic stage Jellinek's (1952) third stage of alcohol addiction

cirrhosis scarring of the liver and destruction of fibrous tissues; results from alcohol abuse

CNS (central nervous system) one of the major divisions of the nervous system, composed of the brain and spinal cord

cocaine babies children exposed to cocaine while in the womb

congeners nonalcoholic substances found in alcoholic beverages

"crack" already processed and inexpensive "free-based" cocaine, ready for smoking

crucial stage Jellinek's (1952) second stage of alcohol addiction

cumulative effect the build-up of a drug in the body after multiple doses taken at short intervals

cyclothymia high to low mood swings with chronic, mild mood instability; the patient usually remains functional

DEA the Drug Enforcement Administration, the principal federal agency responsible for enforcing drug abuse regulations

delirium tremens (DTs) a condition that affects chronic abusers of alcohol during alcohol withdrawal; characterized by agitation, hallucinations, and involuntary body tremors

dendrites short branches of neurons that receive transmitter signals

"designer" drugs illicit drugs that are chemically modified so they are not considered illegal but that retain abusive properties

detoxification elimination of a toxic substance, such as a drug, and its effects

"die hards" slang term for drug users who strongly resist quitting

disease model of drug dependence the view that drug dependence is an illness

disinhibition the loss of conditioned reflexes due to depression of inhibitory centers of the brain

distillation the process used when fermented mixtures of cereal grains or fruits are heated in a still

diuretic a drug or substance that increases the production of urine

dopamine system the transmitter system believed to mediate the rewarding aspects of most drugs of abuse

drugs any substances that modify biological, psychological, or social behavior

dysphoric characterized by unpleasant mental effects; the opposite of euphoric

dysthymia a mild, chronic depressive disorder, causing persistent unhappiness

electrolytes charged molecules—such as sodium, potassium, calcium, bicarbonate, and chloride—that dissolve in body fluids

emphysema a common type of lung disease

endogenous depression extreme depression that can occur spontaneously in the absence of a specific stimulus

endorphins neurotransmitters that have narcoticlike effects

enteral refers to drugs taken orally

enzyme induction an increase in the metabolic capacity of an enzyme system

"equal-opportunity" affliction refers to the fact that drug abuse is found among all races, religions, and social levels

ergotism poisoning by toxic substances from the ergot fungus *Claviceps purpurea*

ergotropic refers to the arousal state of consciousness

ethanol the consumable type of alcohol that is the psychoactive ingredient in alcoholic beverages; often called grain alcohol

ethylene glycol alcohol used as antifreeze

expectorants substances that stimulate mucus secretion and diminish mucus viscosity

extrapyramidal side effects   effects caused by drugs that interfere with functioning of the extrapyramidal motor system, including tremors, stooped posture, shuffling of feet, and unusual extreme facial grimacing and tongue protrusions

fermentation   the biochemical process in which yeast converts sugar into alcohol

fetal alcohol syndrome (FAS)   a condition affecting children born to alcohol-consuming mothers that is characterized by facial deformities, growth deficiency, and mental retardation

"flashback"   the recurrence of an earlier drug-induced sensory experience in the absence of the drug

fortified wines   wines with a higher than usual concentration of alcohol

"freebasing"   the conversion of cocaine to an alkaline form so it can be smoked

gastritis   inflammation or irritation of the gut

"gateway" drugs   drugs whose use leads to the use of other drugs; alcohol, cigarettes, and marijuana are considered "gateway" drugs

glaucoma   an eye disease manifested by increased intraocular pressure

hallucinogens   substances that alter sensory processing in the brain, causing perceptual disturbances, changes in thought processing, and depersonalization

haptene   a chemical that is viewed as foreign by the body and eliminated by an allergic response

homeostasis   maintenance of internal stability; often biochemical in nature

hormones   regulatory chemicals released by endocrine systems

hyperkinesis   excessive movement

hyperpyrexia   elevated body temperature

hypnotics   CNS depressants used to induce drowsiness and encourage sleep

hypoxia   a state of oxygen deficiency

iatrogenic   illness caused by the treatment

"ice"   a smokable form of methamphetamine

interdiction   the policy of cutting off or destroying supplies of illicit drugs

isopropyl alcohol   rubbing alcohol, sometimes used as an anesthetic

keratin layer   the outermost protective layer of the skin

keratolytics   caustic agents that cause the keratin skin layer to peel

"mainlining"   intravenous injection of a drug of abuse

margin of safety   the range in dose between the amount of drug necessary to cause a therapeutic effect and a toxic effect

Marinol   FDA approved THC in capsule form (dronabinol)

master status   the overriding status in the eyes of others that identifies an individual, e.g. doctor, lawyer, alcoholic, HIV positive

meditation   a state of consciousness in which there is a constant level of awareness focusing on one object; e.g., Yoga and Zen Buddhism

mental set   the collection of psychological and environmental factors that influence an individual's response to drugs

metabolism   chemical alteration of drugs by body processes

metabolites   the chemical products of metabolism

methyl alcohol   wood alcohol, or methanol

monopolar (unipolar) depression   an extreme mood swing that includes depression but no manic phase

the "munchies"   hunger experienced while under the effects of marijuana

muscarinic   a receptor type activated by ACh; usually inhibitory

mutagenic   able to cause mutation (alter genes)

mydriasis   pupil dilation

mystical rapture   an ultimate state of consciousness similar to hallucination

narcolepsy   a condition causing spontaneous and uncontrolled sleeping episodes

neurons   the principal cells in nervous systems; conduct electrochemical impulses and release neurotransmitters

neurotransmitters   biochemical messengers, which cause the impulse from one neuron to be transferred to the next

Nicotiana tabacum   the tobacco primary plant species cultivated on the American continent

nicotine   the main active ingredient in tobacco

nicotinic   a receptor type activated by ACh; usually excitatory

NIDA   the National Institute on Drug Abuse, the principal federal agency responsible for directing drug abuse–related research

nociceptors   receptors that are activated by painful sensations

noneuphoric opiate   a drug or drugs used in maintenance programs that satisfies the craving but does not produce the euphoric effect; e.g., methadone

operant pain   that due to learned behavior

opioid   relating to the drugs that are derived from opium

pain threshold   the minimum amount of pain necessary to cause pain

pain tolerance   the maximum amount of pain that can be tolerated

pain tract   the system of neurons that transmit the pain message to the thalamus in the brain

panic attack   an episode of intense fear or discomfort accompanied by physiological symptoms such as dizziness, increased heartrate, shortness of breath, and shaking

paradoxical   an unexpected effect

parenteral   refers to drugs taken by other than oral means

patent medicines   unregulated proprietary medicines often associated with fraudulent therapy

patterns of behavior   consistent and related behaviors that occur together, such as marijuana use and euphoria, alcohol abuse and intoxication

peristaltic   wavelike contraction of muscles

pharmacokinetics   the study of factors that influence the distribution and concentration of drugs in the body

phocomelia   a birth defect; impaired development of the arms or legs or both

physical dependence   the result of physiological changes or adaptations that occur in response to the frequent presence of a drug

placebo effects   effects caused by suggestion and psychological factors, not the pharmacological activity of a drug

plateau effect   the maximum drug effect, regardless of dose

potency   the amount of drug necessary to cause an effect

primary deviance   deviant behavior with which the perpetrator does not identify

primary groups   close-knit groups that share a high amount of intimacy, spontaneity, and emotional bonding

primary prevention   using persuasion to dissuade someone from use of a particular drug

prodromal stage   Jellinek's (1952) term for early addiction to alcohol, the first stage

progestins   compounds similar to the female hormone progesterone

prostaglandins   endogenous chemicals that, when released, contribute to pain and inflammatory responses

psychedelic   substances that expand or heighten perception and consciousness

psychiatric disorder   inappropriate behavior due to abnormal transmission, processing, or responding by the brain to sensory input

psychoactive   drugs that affect mood or alter the state of consciousness

psychological dependence   dependence that results because a drug produces pleasant mental effects

psychotherapy   treatment of psychiatric disorders primarily based on verbal (counseling) or nonverbal communication

psychotogenic   substances that initiate psychotic behavior

psychotomimetic   substances that cause psychoticlike symptoms

reactive depression   depression that occurs in response to unpleasant or stressful stimuli

rebound effect   a form of withdrawal; paradoxical effects that occur when a drug has been eliminated from the body

receptor   a special region in a membrane that is activated by natural substances or drugs to alter cell function

reflexes   automatic responses to stimuli that do not require brain processing

reinforcement   any behavior that strengthens the likelihood that a behavior will be repeated

reinforcement theory   a theory that asserts that alcohol use results from positive "stroking," leading to satisfying feelings

REM sleep   the restive phase of sleep associated with dreaming

respondent pain   that caused by physical factors

retrospective interpretation   the social psychological process of redefining a person's reputation within a particular group

reverse tolerance   an enhanced response to a given drug dose; opposite of tolerance

"run"   intense use of a stimulant, consisting of multiple administrations over a period of days

secondary deviance   type of deviant behavior that develops when the perpetrator views himself or herself as deviant

secondary groups   groups that share more distant and segmented relationships

secondary prevention   using immediate intervention once drug use has begun

second-hand smoke   the smoke from burning tobacco that pollutes the air and is breathed by smokers and nonsmokers alike

sedatives   CNS depressants used to relieve anxiety, fear, and apprehension

self-regulating communities   programs that advocate a complete change in lifestyle, such as complete abstinence from drugs, elimination of deviant behavior, and development of employable skills

"sidestream" smoke   smoke released into the air directly from the lighted tip of a cigarette

sinsemilla   one of the most potent types of marijuana available; means "without seeds"

smokeless tobacco   two types of tobacco: chewing and snuff tobacco

snuff   powdered or finely cut tobacco leaves that are not chewed but instead placed between the lip or cheek and gum

social influence   the ability to inspire, motivate, or convince others to go along with or share in novel behavior

social learning theory   a theory that asserts that alcohol use and later abuse result from early socialization experiences

social substance   refers to when alcohol is not perceived as a drug

socialization   the process by which individuals learn and internalize the attitudes, values, and behaviors needed to become participating members of conventional society

somatic pain   that associated with musculoskeletal structures, including bones, voluntary muscles, skin, and teeth

"speed"   an injectable methamphetamine used by drug addicts

"speedball"   a combination of amphetamine or cocaine with an opioid narcotic, often heroin

status   refers to individual popularity and social position in the eyes of others

sudden infant death syndrome (SIDS)   unexpected and unexplainable death that occurs while infants are sleeping

switching policy   an FDA policy allowing the change of suitable prescription drugs to OTC status

sympathomimetic   agents that mimic the effects of norepinephrine or epinephrine

symptomatic   drugs that relieve symptoms but not causes of medical problems

synapse   a minute gap between the neuron and target cell across which neurotransmitters travel

synergism   the ability of one drug to enhance the effect of another; potentiation

synesthesia   a subjective sensation or image of a sense other than the one being stimulated, such as an auditory sensation caused by a visual stimulus

tachycardia   rapid beating of the heart

tardive dyskinesia   a syndrome characterized by involuntary movement of tongue, lips, and jaw

teratogenic   something that causes physical defects in the fetus

tertiary prevention   helping an individual to stop using drugs either immediately, before, or in the early stages of addiction

thalidomide   a sedative drug that, when used during pregnancy, can cause severe developmental damage to the fetus

therapeutic index   the toxic dose divided by the therapeutic dose; used to calculate margin of safety

threshold   the minimum drug dose necessary to cause an effect

tolerance   changes causing decreased response to a set dose of a drug

toxicity   the capacity of a drug to do damage or cause adverse effects in the body

trophotropic   a state of consciousness in which there is decreased sensitivity to external stimuli and sedation

"uppers"   a slang term for CNS stimulants

vasculature   relating to the blood vessels

visceral pain   that associated with internal organs, involuntary muscles, and blood vessels

volatile   readily evaporated at low temperatures

withdrawal   unpleasant effects that occur when use of a drug is stopped

Index